Basic Maths

Basic Maths

Ewart Smith

First published 1996 by
MACMILLAN PRESS LTD
Houndmills, Basingstoke, Hampshire RG21 6XS
and London
Companies and representatives
throughout the world

ISBN 0–333–63397–0

A catalogue record for this book is available
from the British Library.

10 9 8 7 6 5 4 3 2 1
05 04 03 02 01 00 99 98 97 96

Technical drawings and cartoons by Stewart Miller
Typeset by Wearset, Boldon, Tyne and Wear
Printed in Great Britain by Unwin Brothers Ltd,
The Gresham Press, Old Woking, Surrey
A member of the Martins Printing Group

Acknowledgements
The author and publishers acknowledge, with thanks, the following illustration sources: BMW p. 38; The Boeing Company p. 181; London Electricity p. 96; Ordnance Survey, with the permission of the Controller of Her Majesty's Stationery Office, © Crown Copyright pp. 175, 177; Thomson Tour Operations Limited pp. 81 and 85.

Every effort has been made to trace copyright holders, but if any have been inadvertently overlooked the publishers will be pleased to make the necessary arrangements at the first opportunity.

CONTENTS

Preface

This easily readable book aims to present the concepts of basic mathematics in a simple and appealing way. Much use is made of real life, everyday situations in a book that is suitable for students of all ages.

The theory needed is presented clearly and concisely, followed by carefully worked examples that show how the theory applies to real-life situations. Each chapter contains plenty of carefully graded exercises, multiple-choice exercises and a self assessment test. The book concludes with a collection of investigations, puzzles and problems. These provide challenges across a broad range of basic mathematics and should add to the satisfaction of coming to terms with the basic concepts.

All answers are included.

Ewart Smith
January 1996

All of you need to use a calculator accurately. In the early part of the book there are many places where you are asked to do the number work without using a calculator. This you should try to do. However, from Chapter 5 onwards, no clear instruction is given whether or not a calculator should be used. This is because so much depends on the individual. You must choose, but remember that the more practice you have in working things out in your head or using paper and pencil methods, the more able you will be in dealing with numbers. Always remember, whether you are using a calculator or not, you should estimate the answer and satisfy yourself that it is sensible.

CHAPTER 1
Whole numbers

Numbers in words and figures

EXERCISE 1a

Write the following numbers in figures.

1 Seventy-two

2 Three hundred and eight

3 Seven hundred and thirty-seven

4 Five thousand six hundred

5 Four thousand seven hundred and six

6 Sixteen thousand and fifty

7 Two hundred thousand

8 Eight hundred and fifty thousand six hundred

9 Two million five hundred thousand

10 Five million fourteen thousand and sixty

Write the following numbers in words.

11 87 **12** 370 **13** 592 **14** 6700

15 4439 **16** 47 000 **17** 50 750 **18** 675 000

19 420 350 **20** 65 000 000

In questions 21 to 25 write, in figures, the number referred to in each sentence.

21 This coach will seat forty-four passengers.

22 Prince Plastics is to create twelve hundred new jobs.

23 Kingston Hospital has five hundred and twenty-seven beds.

24 Last year, British Airtours carried twenty-seven thousand three hundred and seventeen passengers.

25 The number of new cars sold in the first three months of this year was two hundred and forty-eight thousand, five hundred and fifty-four.

How numbers are used

Whole numbers are often used as a shorthand for a group of words. For example, instead of saying 'I want the bus that goes from North Finchley to Victoria', I would be more likely to say 'I want a number 82 bus.'

Similarly, at a sporting event it is often easier to draw a friend's attention to a particular player by referring to the number on his or her back rather than by using the player's name.

Think of cases that describe things by using numbers, for example
- the rooms in your college/school
- a seat at a concert
- a business invoice
- a cheque from a bank – what do the different numbers on a cheque mean? Is every unused cheque different?

Symbols in the media

Live-in Manager for
Residential Home
£16K p.a.

This is part of an advertisement for a job as the manager in an old people's home. The letter K after the number stands for the number of thousands. This advertisement is offering the job for a salary of £16 000 a year.

If the word circa or its abbreviation 'c' appears in front of the figure, it means that the salary is in the region of the figure given.

For example, circa £18K means 'about eighteen thousand pounds – it may be a little more or it may be a little less'.

Property advertisements sometimes use the letter 'm' after a number. In the above advertisement the price being asked is £5 million, i.e. £5 000 000.

National finance is concerned with much larger numbers; for example, 'The government expect a deficit next year in the region of £54bn.' 'bn' means billion. In the mass media a billion is a thousand million, so £54bn is a short way of writing £54 000 000 000.

EXERCISE 1b

QUESTION

Write in figures (a) £50K (b) £3m (c) £2bn.

ANSWER

(a) £50K = £50 thousand (1 thousand is written as 1 with 3 zeros after it, i.e. 1 000)
= £50 000

(b) £3m = £3 million (1 million is written as 1 with 6 zeros after it, i.e. 1 000 000)
= £3 000 000

(c) £2bn = £2 billion (1 billion is written as 1 with 9 zeros after it, i.e. 1 000 000 000)
= £2 000 000 000

1

INDUSTRY	
Financial Controller	£28k + car
Management Accountant	£23k + car
Finalist/N/Qual.	£20k
Cost Accountant	£15k
Assistant Accountant	£13k

Use the newspaper cutting shown here to write, in figures, the yearly pay offered for the job of
(a) cost accountant
(b) assistant accountant
(c) management accountant
(d) financial controller.

2 The budget for Prestley School next year has been set at £13m. Write this number in figures.

3 Court Mcpherson has just announced plans for a £15m expansion at their Fulton plant. Write the number in figures.

4 Exports for the last quarter amounted to £896bn. Write this number in figures.

5 Write in words
(a) the year 1995
(b) the number 1995.

Place value

A figure's place in a number is important. It tells us what that figure is worth. In the number 864, the 4 means 4 'ones' or 'units', the 6 means 6 'tens' and the 8 means 8 'hundreds'. We can write a number by putting each figure under a place heading. For example:

	Thousands	Hundreds	Tens	Units
3267 can be arranged	3	2	6	7
and 2049 can be arranged	2		4	9

(There are no hundreds, so we can leave the hundreds column blank.)

EXERCISE 1c

Write down, in figures, the numbers given below.

	Hundreds of thousands	Tens of thousands	Thousands	Hundreds	Tens	Units
1			3	9	2	4
2			5		7	2
3			4			5
4					8	
5		5	6			
6		4		7		6
7	4	8		3		9

In the number 3592 the 5 stands for 5 hundreds, and the 9 stands for 9 tens.

8 What does the 7 stand for in the number 5743? What does the 4 stand for?

9 What does the 6 stand for in the number 63 495? What does the 3 stand for?

10 What does the 3 stand for in the number 123 762? What does the 1 stand for?

11 What does the 4 stand for in the number 458 762? What does the 8 stand for?

12 What does the 5 stand for in the number 73 522 289? What does the 7 stand for?

The largest and smallest numbers of a set

Look at the 3-figure numbers 352, 325, 253, 235, 532 and 523.

The largest of these numbers must start with the largest possible figure, i.e. the largest number must be either 532 or 523. The numbers 532 and 523 have the same first figure.

The larger of them is the number with the larger second figure, i.e. 532.

The largest of the six given numbers is therefore 532.

Similarly, the smallest of these numbers must start with the smallest possible figure, i.e. it must be either 253 or 235.

The smaller of these two numbers is the number with the smaller second figure, i.e. 235.

The smallest of the six given numbers is therefore 235.

NOTE: Any 4-figure number is larger than every 3-figure number, e.g. 1005 is larger than 998. Similarly, any 5-figure number is larger than every 4-figure number, and so on.

EXERCISE 1d

1 From the numbers 732, 476, 539, 843 and 666 select (a) the largest number (b) the smallest number.

2 From the numbers 463, 475, 442, 484 and 462 select (a) the smallest number (b) the largest number.

3 From the numbers 848, 874, 999, 435 and 839 select (a) the largest number (b) the smallest number (c) the largest number but one.

4 From the numbers 3301, 867, 352, 1042 and 794 select (a) the smallest number (b) the smallest number but one (c) the largest number.

5 From the numbers 2904, 973, 1015, 3156 and 538 select (a) the smallest number but one (b) the largest number but one.

6 Put the following numbers in order of size, smallest first.

(a) 152, 78, 362, 289 (b) 172, 94, 325, 533

(c) 672, 627, 762, 767 (d) 1567, 988, 756, 2009, 777

7 Put the following numbers in order of size, largest first.

(a) 532, 744, 384, 423 (b) 78, 974, 1643, 264

(c) 476, 467, 564, 576 (d) 707, 745, 709, 742

Addition

In the next exercise you are asked to attempt some questions without using a calculator. If at all possible, follow this instruction, even if it takes you longer. The happier you are working with numbers without a calculator the more confident you will become. If this is not possible then use a calculator.

EXERCISE 1e

QUESTION
Use a calculator to find 562 + 73 + 284.

ANSWER
(Press the buttons in the following order.)
AC 5 6 2 + 7 3 + 2 8 4 =
The display shows 919.
$\therefore$ 562 + 73 + 284 = 919.

Use a calculator to find

1 47 + 53 **2** 182 + 93

3 372 + 59 **4** 413 + 267

5 1031 + 54 **6** 2317 + 767

7 482 + 95 **8** 317 + 2493

9 4185 + 267 + 44 **10** 3216 + 4728 + 7298

QUESTION
Find, without using a calculator, (a) 427 + 16 + 1523 (b) 2815 + 493 + 745 + 66.

ANSWER
(a) (To add 427, 16 and 1523 put them one beneath the other so that all the units figures are lined up, all the tens figures are lined up, and so on.)

427	(First step: 3 + 6 + 7 = 16 Put 6 down and carry 1 to the tens column)
16	(Second step: 1 + 2 + 1 + 2 = 6)
+1523	(Third step: 5 + 4 = 9)
1966 (carry 1)	(Fourth step: bring down the 1)

(b) (2815 + 493 + 745 + 66 is set out.)

2815	(First step: 6 + 5 + 3 + 5 = 19 Put 9 down, carry 1 to the tens column)
493	(Second step: 1 + 6 + 4 + 9 + 1 = 21 Put 1 down, carry 2 to the hundreds column)
745	(Third step: 2 + 7 + 4 + 8 = 21 Put 1 down, carry 2 to the thousands column)
+ 66	(Fourth step: 2 + 2 = 4 Write 4 in the thousands column)
4119	
2 2 1	

Do not use a calculator for questions 11 to 29.

Find

11 362 + 25 + 412 **12** 546 + 316 + 132 **13** 447 + 1743 + 457 **14** 735 + 973 + 2375 **15** 635 + 354 + 2967

(each set out in a column)

16 456 + 75 + 142 **17** 342 + 2173 + 98

18 675 + 8003 + 777 **19** 536 + 253 + 932

20 362 + 7445 + 1234 + 2233 **21** 7241 + 884 + 2773 + 5134 **22** 4261 + 3725 + 6357 + 1877 **23** 7437 + 8836 + 4273 + 2165 **24** 5634 + 1635 + 3326 + 6644

(each set out in a column)

25 643 + 854 + 98 + 3226

26 3354 + 567 + 1723 + 65

27 7674 + 2154 + 863 + 1834

28 352 + 6478 + 12 234 + 8746

29 33 445 + 1795 + 8744 + 5009

Now check your answers by using a calculator.

Subtraction

EXERCISE 1f

QUESTION
Find, without using a calculator, (a) 278 − 46
(b) 258 − 169.

ANSWER
(a) (To subtract 46 from 278 set 46 beneath 278, with the units' digits lined up.)

278	(First step: 8 − 6 = 2)
− 46	(Second step: 7 − 4 = 3)
232	(Third step: 2 − 0 = 2)

(b) (Similarly for 258 − 169.)

258	(First step: 8 − 9, cannot. Change the 5 tens to 4 tens and 10 units, 18 − 9 = 9)
−169	(Second step: 4 − 6, cannot. Change the 2 hundreds into 1 hundred and 10 tens; then 14 − 6 = 8)
89	(Third step: 1 − 1 is 0, which it is unnecessary to write)

If you use a different method from this and usually get the correct answer then stay with your method.

Find, without using a calculator,

1 67 − 52 **2** 85 − 54 **3** 79 − 57 **4** 645 − 532 **5** 415 − 197

6 814 − 276 **7** 725 − 589 **8** 5934 − 2155 **9** 4231 − 3117 **10** 8261 − 3287

(each set out in a column)

11 345 − 166 **12** 827 − 339 **13** 1084 − 738

14 4365 − 2784 **15** 1775 − 639

16 Subtract 67 from 285 **17** Subtract 175 from 497

18 Subtract 285 from 829

QUESTION
Use a calculator to find 7264 − 2938.

ANSWER
(Press the buttons in the following order.)
AC 7 2 6 4 − 2 9 3 8 =
The display shows 4326
∴ 7264 − 2938 = 4326

Use a calculator to find

19 943 − 537 **20** 692 − 384 **21** 1436 − 738

22 5663 − 845 **23** 8292 − 7215 **24** 2047 − 1482

25 5574 − 1004 **26** 1642 − 666

Problems involving addition and subtraction

EXERCISE 1g

QUESTION
At a conference, one of the speakers was more boring than usual. Of the 224 delegates, 39 fell asleep, 82 retired to the bar and 68 read their newspapers instead. How many delegates were still listening to the speech?

ANSWER
Number not listening to the speech = number asleep + number in the bar + number reading their newspapers
= 39 + 82 + 68
= 189
Number still listening = number of delegates − number not listening
= 224 − 189
= 35
∴ Number still listening to the speech was 35

1 Kerry wants 90 breadrolls for refreshments after a match. She goes to buy them from the local baker. He can only supply her with 67. How many short is she?

2 In a council election Mr Bullen received 1264 votes, Mr Watton 983, Mrs Deare 163 and Mr Furnell 547 votes. How many people voted?

3 Nina was born in 1977. Which birthday will she celebrate (a) in the year 1998 (b) in the year 2042?

4 In a parliamentary election the votes cast were as follows: Joe Stuart 7684, Warren Evans 24 537, Tim Hearse 17 943 and Nita Nesburn 4359. In addition there were 184 spoilt voting papers and 5793 registered voters failed to vote. What is the size of the electorate?

5 At the beginning of a week a main dealer has a stock of 22 new cars and 46 secondhand cars.

(a) How many cars do they have altogether?

(b) During the week they sell 6 new cars and 8 secondhand cars. They take in 4 cars in part exchange, but do not take delivery of any new cars. How many cars do they have at the end of the week?

QUESTION
The crowd at Highbury stadium for a Premier Division game on one Saturday last season was 38 867. On the following Saturday there were 3876 fewer spectators. What was the attendance for the second game?

ANSWER
Number in attendance on the second Saturday is the difference between 38 867 and 3876,
i.e. 38 867 − 3876 = 34 991

6 For one meeting the attendance at Cheltenham racecourse was 27 564. At the following meeting it was 25 246. Find the decrease in attendance.

7 Graham's Insurance Services have 117 fewer staff now than this time last year. It is expected that there will be a further reduction of 53 staff by this time next year. If there are 1336 employees now, find (a) the number of staff employed this time last year (b) the number expected to be employed this time next year.

QUESTION
In the local golf club there are 17 more women than men. If there are 155 members altogether, how many of each sex are there?

ANSWER
Of the 155 members 17 are definitely women.
This leaves 155 − 17 = 138 members unaccounted for.
These 138 members must be equally divided between men and women, i.e. there must be 138 ÷ 2 = 69 of each.
The membership is therefore made up of 69 men and 69 + 17, i.e. 86 women.

8 The employees in a tax office are made up of 314 men, 645 women and 107 young people. 796 of the workforce are paid a weekly wage and the remainder are paid an annual salary. How many employees are paid a salary?

Multiplication by 10, 100, 1000, etc.

When we multiply by 10, the number of units becomes the number of tens, the number of tens becomes the number of hundreds, and so on.

For example, $367 \times 10 = 3670$ and $7629 \times 10 = 76\,290$.
Similarly, $85 \times 100 = 8500$ and $794 \times 100 = 79\,400$.

Multiplication by other numbers

To multiply two single-digit numbers together you should know thoroughly your tables from 2×2 up to 10×10. You should try very hard to learn these tables, (copies of which are given on the inside back cover) but if this proves too difficult then you will have to use a calculator.

EXERCISE 1h

Find

1 352×10 **2** 70×100 **3** 123×100

4 $56\,700 \times 10$ **5** 710×100 **6** 43×1000

7 70×1000 **8** 520×1000 **9** $397 \times 10\,000$

10 $590 \times 100\,000$

QUESTION
Find 37×4.

ANSWER

```
  37    (First step: 4×7 = 28, 8 down, carry 2 tens)
×  4    (Second step: 4 × 3 = 12, add 2, to give
         14)
 148
  2
```

---

11 82×5 **12** 76×3 **13** 78×7

14 83×9 **15** 67×8

QUESTION
Find 285×36.

ANSWER

```
   285   (First step: 5 × 6 = 30, 0 down carry 3 to
          the tens column)
×   36   (Second step: 8 × 6 = 48, 48 + 3 = 51, 1
          down carry 5 hundreds)
  1710   (Third step: 2 × 6 = 12, 12 + 5 = 17)
   53
  8550   (Fourth step: We wish to multiply 285
  21      by 30, which is the same as 2850 × 3)
 -----
 10260   (Fifth step: find the total)
  1
```

(It is much easier to multiply using a calculator, but you will become far more confident with figures if you can do it this way.)

---

16 325×34 **17** 653×76 **18** 832×82

19 973×51 **20** 742×29

QUESTION
Use a calculator to find 732×186.

ANSWER
(Press the buttons as follows.)
AC 7 3 2 × 1 8 6 =
This display shows 136 152

$\therefore 732 \times 186 = 136\,152$

Use a calculator to find

21 89×173 **22** 542×67 **23** 481×39

24 154×27 **25** 643×214 **26** 777×354

27 639×184 **28** 567×765

Division by 10, 100, 1000, etc.

When we divide by 10, the number of tens becomes the number of units, the number of hundreds becomes the number of tens, and so on.

For example, $620 \div 10 = 62$ and $7800 \div 100 = 78$.

Division by a single digit

Work out $492 \div 3$.

```
   164     (First step: 3 into 4 goes once with 1 over)
3)4¹9¹2    (Second step: 3 into 19 goes 6 times with 1
            over)
           (Third step: 3 into 12 goes 4 times with no
            remainder)
```

Division by a two-figure number

Find $1628 \div 44$.

```
     37    (First step: 4 into 16 goes 4 times)
44)1628    (Second step: 44 × 4 = 176, which is too
   132      big. Try 3 times: 44 × 3 = 132, which is
            less than 162)
    308    (Third step: subtract, and bring down the
            next figure (8))
    308    (Fourth step: 4 into 30 goes 7
            times. 44 × 7 = 308)
```

Division with remainders

What if there are remainders? What is 273 ÷ 5?

```
   54
5)273   (The answer is 54, remainder 3)
  25
  23
  20
   3
```

What is 776 ÷ 28?

```
    27
28)776   (First step: 28 is almost 30, 30 goes into 77
   56     twice, 28 × 2 = 56)
   216   (Second step: subtract, to give 21; bring
          down the 6.)
   196   (Third step: Try 7; 28 × 7 = 196)
    20   (Fourth step: subtract)
```

The answer is 27, remainder 20.

EXERCISE 1i

Find

1 8300 ÷ 10	**2** 3620 ÷ 10	**3** 790 000 ÷ 100
4 920 000 ÷ 1000	**5** 44 000 ÷ 100	**6** 536 ÷ 4
7 795 ÷ 5	**8** 1071 ÷ 7	**9** 1032 ÷ 8
10 1470 ÷ 6	**11** 5049 ÷ 9	**12** 1377 ÷ 17
13 1904 ÷ 34	**14** 2496 ÷ 26	**15** 3285 ÷ 45
16 1288 ÷ 23	**17** 1064 ÷ 19	**18** 1332 ÷ 37
19 5936 ÷ 53	**20** 6678 ÷ 59	**21** 600 ÷ 23
22 897 ÷ 34	**23** 3625 ÷ 45	**24** 3026 ÷ 63
25 6781 ÷ 51	**26** 1867 ÷ 35	**27** 4634 ÷ 74
28 9738 ÷ 67	**29** 6437 ÷ 48	**30** 8844 ÷ 39

Problems involving multiplication and division

EXERCISE 1j

QUESTION

A circular running track is 400 m long.

(a) Linford runs in a race that is fifteen times round the track. How long is the race?

(b) How many laps of the track must be covered to run 10 000 m?

ANSWER

(a) Length of race

= distance covered in one lap × number of laps

= 400 m × 15

= 6000 m

(b) Number of laps

$$= \frac{\text{length of race}}{\text{distance covered in one lap}}$$

$$= \frac{10\,000 \text{ m}}{400 \text{ m}}$$

= 25

i.e. a 10 000 m race requires 25 laps of the track.

1 A farmer packs eggs on trays. Each tray has 6 rows and there are 8 eggs to a row. The trays are packed in boxes. Each box contains 6 trays. How many eggs are there (a) on one tray (b) in one box (c) on a lorry carrying 56 boxes?

2 A bus company operates 14 fifty-seater coaches, 12 forty-five-seater coaches and 6 twenty-four-seater coaches. How many seats does the coach company have available at any one time?

3 Tom Carney plays soccer and estimates that he runs about 8 miles during a match. If he plays twice a week for a 35-week season, about how far, in total, does he run during all the season's matches?

4 A farmer bought 30 tons of fertiliser at £40 per ton. The government paid him a subsidy of £12 per ton. How much did the fertiliser actually cost him?

You need the information given in the following table to do questions 5 to 7. The table shows the populations, in millions, of India, China and the United States of America in recent times.

Year	India	China	USA
1971	551	852	208
1981	675	1008	230
1991	844	1116	253

5 Write, in figures, the population of (a) India in 1981 (b) China in 1991.

6 In 1971, how many more people lived in China than (a) in India (b) in the USA?

7 Which country shows, and by how much, the greatest increase in population from 1971 to 1991?

The next worked example and questions 8 to 10 refer to the information given in the following table, which shows the minimum numbers of staff required to run kitchens in hospitals of various sizes providing meals for long-stay patients.

Hospital size	Minimum number of kitchen staff
Under 100 beds	1 staff per 15 persons fed
100 to 300 beds	1 staff per 25 persons fed
300 to 700 beds	1 staff per 35 persons fed
700 to 1000 beds	1 staff per 40 persons fed
Over 1000 beds	1 staff per 45 persons fed

(If any number of staff works out as a fraction that fraction must be increased to the next whole number.)

QUESTION

The Lady Diana Hospital has 1120 long-stay beds and has 768 staff. It employs 39 kitchen staff. (a) Does it meet the minimum requirements? (b) If not, how many more kitchen staff does it need to employ?

ANSWER

(a) Number of persons to be fed

= number of patients + number of staff

= 1120 + 768

= 1888

Since the number of beds is over 1000, the minimum number of kitchen staff is 1 per 45 persons fed.

That is, $\frac{1888}{45} = 41.95\ldots$

= 42 to the next whole number

The hospital employs 39 kitchen staff but should employ 42, i.e. it does *not* meet the minimum requirements.

(b) Number of extra staff required to meet the minimum requirements = 42 − 39 = 3, i.e. three extra staff are required.

8 Cornfield Hospital has 163 long-stay patients and 112 staff. (a) How many persons are there to feed? (b) What is the minimum number of kitchen staff required?

9 St Theodore's Hospital has 534 long-stay patients and employs 318 staff. How many kitchen staff must it employ?

10 Princetown Hospital employs 435 staff to look after 623 long-stay patients. It advertises for 3 kitchen staff in addition to the 29 it already has.

Does it satisfy the minimum regulations (a) before it makes the 3 new appointments (b) after it has made the 3 appointments?

11 The table shows the present known world oil reserves by region.

Area	Reserves in thousand million barrels
North America	40
Latin America	120
Europe (except former Soviet Union)	10
Africa	60
Middle East	660
Former Soviet Union	60
Asia (except former Soviet Union) and Australasia	50

(a) Which area has (i) the greatest (ii) the smallest, amount of the world's reserves of oil?

(b) Are the reserves in the Middle East more than the rest of the world put together?

(c) How many barrels of oil reserves are there estimated to be in Europe? Write your answers in figures.

(d) What do the total known world oil reserves amount to?

12 Fifty-three-seater coaches are available to carry tourists from an airport to the city centre. How many coaches are needed to transport 1278 tourists? How many spare seats will there be on the last coach, assuming that all the others are full?

13 When a cruise ship arrives in Naples, passengers can opt either to go on an organised tour or to make their own arrangements. When bookings close the numbers for tours are: Tour A 187, Tour B 324, Tour C 97 and Tour D 152. The coaches for all tours are 47-seaters.

(a) How many coaches do they need altogether?

(b) How many additional passengers could they have taken on tours without increasing the number of coaches?

(c) The fares for the tours are: Tour A, £12; Tour B, £15; Tour C, £25 and Tour D, £35. Find the total receipts for the passengers booked on these tours.

(d) By how much would the receipts have been increased if all the available seats had been taken on all the coaches?

Mixed operations

The order in which you work out mixed operations, which sometimes include brackets, is important.

First step. Work out the brackets.

Second step. Next do the division and multiplication. (Which of these two you do first does not really matter; for example, $12 \div 3 \times 4 = 4 \times 4 = 16$ and $12 \times 4 \div 3 = 48 \div 3 = 16$.)

Third step. Complete the addition and subtraction. (Once again, which of the two comes first does not matter.)
(Remember that $1 - 2 + 3$ means 'take away' 2 only, not take away 2 and 3. You may find it better to add together the + numbers first,
i.e. $1 - 2 + 3 = 1 + 3 - 2 = 4 - 2 = 2$.)

$9 + 5 \times 4 - 3 = 9 + 20 - 3$ (Multiplication first)
$= 29 - 3$ (Addition next)
$= 26$ (Subtraction last)

$46 - 3 \times 7 + 8 = 46 - 21 + 8$ (Multiplication first)
$= 25 + 8$ (Subtraction next)
$= 33$ (Addition last)

If you wish to keep the order: addition before subtraction, then:

$46 - 21 + 8 = 54 - 21$
$= 33$

$18 \div (2 \times 3) = 18 \div 6$ (Brackets first)
$= 3$ (Then division)

Remember to work out the brackets first, then deal with multiplication and division, and finally addition and subtraction.

NOTE: Not all calculators use the same logic system. When you have a new calculator you should read the instructions carefully to see that you are using it correctly. Use it to do some simple calculations that can be checked by pencil-and-paper methods.

EXERCISE 1k

Find

1 $9 \times 8 - 7 \times 4$ **2** $12 \div 3 + 5 \times 6$

3 $24 \div 3 + 5 \times 6 - 12$ **4** $(5 + 7) \div (4 \times 5 - 8)$

5 $5 \times 8 \div 10 - 2$ **6** $(13 - 7 + 8) \div 7 + 4 \times 8$

7 $(15 \div 3 + 15) + 20 \div 2$ **8** $48 \div 3 \div 4 - 3$

9 $(7 \times 3 + 12 \div 4) \div 4$ **10** $(24 \div 4 + 6 \times 4) \times 2 \div 5$

11 $8 - 3 \times 4 + 30 \div 5$ **12** $5 \div 2 \div 3 \div 4 \times 48$

EXERCISE 1l

Find the approximate value of

1 37×91 **2** 104×78 **3** 493×67 **4** 376×49

5 $887 \div 48$ **6** $4982 \div 831$ **7** $6745 \div 93$ **8** $9335 \div 721$

EXERCISE 1m: Mixed exercise in addition, subtraction, multiplication and division

1 The Feathers Hotel has 12 double rooms and 7 single rooms. How many guests can it sleep?

2 There are 21 young people in a group and there are three more girls than boys. (a) How many boys are there? (b) How many girls are there?

3 There are twelve no. 8 screws in a packet. (a) How many screws are there in 6 packets? (b) Sid needs 60 screws. How many packets should he buy?

4 In a darts match Simon threw treble 8, double 12 and 3. What was his total score?

5 Nine coaches are hired to transport supporters to an away match. Each coach holds forty-five passengers. All the coaches are full. How many supporters are there altogether?

6 A keyboard operator can type 70 words a minute. She has to type a manuscript of 60 000 words. How many minutes should it take?

7 The table shows the number of lunches served by a restaurant one week earlier in the year.

Sun	Mon	Tue	Wed	Thur	Fri	Sat	Total for week
83	34	60	59			77	448

(a) How many lunches were served in total on Thursday and Friday?

(b) If 15 fewer lunches were served on Thursday than on Friday, how many were served on Friday?

8 A bookseller buys 56 packets of a new cookbook, each packet containing 24 books. He stores them on shelves, at the rate of 42 books to a shelf. How many shelves does he use?

9 A lorry operator owns fourteen 20 tonne lorries, six 15 tonne lorries and thirty-eight 10 tonne lorries. How many journeys have to be made to remove 28 500 tonnes of hardcore, assuming that all the lorries make the same number of journeys?

10 In my street the houses are numbered from 1 to 31.
(a) How many houses have odd numbers?
(b) How many houses have even numbers?

11 Christopher Columbus is said to have discovered America in the fifteenth century. What are the first two figures of the year in which America was discovered?

The sum of the four figures in the year is 16, and when the units figure is subtracted from the tens figure the answer is 7. In which year did Columbus discover America?

Rounding numbers

ENGLAND v. SCOTLAND

65 000 tickets already sold

Frequently it is useful to round numbers. For example, a newspaper headline like this one giving the number of spectators attending a sporting occasion has more impact if it is given to the nearest thousand rather than as an exact figure.

Consider the number 468. To the nearest 10, this is 470.
We write this 468 = 470 to the nearest 10

On the other hand, the number 563 is 560 to the nearest 10.
We write this 563 = 560 to the nearest 10

In the case of 385, which is exactly halfway between 380 and 390, the rule to give it to the nearest 10 is to round up,
i.e. 385 = 390 to the nearest 10

Suppose a newspaper reported that 5000 people had died in an earthquake. This means that the largest number they believe had died was 5499 (5500 would round up to 6000) and the smallest number of deaths was 4500 (4499 would round down to 4000)

EXERCISE 1n

In questions 1 to 8 write each number correct to (a) the nearest 10 (b) the nearest 100 (c) the nearest 1000

1 1795 **2** 7893 **3** 7354 **4** 8888

5 21 635 **6** 35 729 **7** 9286 **8** 36 667

QUESTION

Round the numbers given in the following sentences to the nearest 100:
(a) The population of Chesham is 642.
(b) Boston Youth Club has 279 members.
(c) Express Motors has 850 second-hand cars in stock.
(d) There are 1856 seats in St George's Hall.
(e) At Raine Rovers' last home game there were 4827 spectators.

ANSWER

(a) 642 rounds to 600.
(b) 279 rounds to 300.
(c) 850 rounds to 900. (850 is halfway between 800 and 900. It is the custom to round halfway figures up.)
(d) 1856 rounds to 1900.
(e) 4827 rounds to 4800.

9 Last Saturday the total number of customers at Kingsley's department store was 5835. Give this number correct to: (a) the nearest 10 (b) the nearest 100.

10 The area of the hall at a leisure centre is 29 653 square feet.

(a) What is the place value of (i) the 9 (ii) the 6?

(b) Give the area of the hall correct to (i) the nearest hundred square feet (ii) the nearest thousand square feet.

11 In an air disaster 253 people died.

(a) The first news item after the crash gave this figure correct to the nearest 100. What figure did they give?

(b) In a later news bulletin the figure was given correct to the nearest 10. What figure was given in the later bulletin?

12 Last year Mitsushoni produced 1 876 439 television sets. Give this figure correct to (a) the nearest thousand (b) the nearest hundred thousand.

Greatest and least values

Suppose the personnel manager reported that 300 people had applied for jobs at his factory. If this figure was correct to the nearest 100, what is the greatest number of applicants possible? What is the least number?

If 350 people applied then this would have been rounded up to 400, whereas if 349 applied this would have been rounded down to 300.

Similarly, 250 would be rounded up to 300 but 249 would be rounded down to 200.

Hence the largest possible number of applicants was 349 and the smallest possible number was 250.

EXERCISE 1p

QUESTION

Correct to the nearest 100, there were 9300 students at a concert. What was (a) the largest number (b) the smallest number, that could have been present?

ANSWER

(a) 9349 is the largest whole number that gives 9300 when corrected to the nearest 100. Therefore 9349 is the largest number that could have been present.

(b) 9250 is the smallest whole number that gives 9300 when corrected to the nearest 100. Therefore 9250 is the smallest number that could have been present.

1 What is the smallest whole number that, when rounded to the nearest 100, will give (a) 500 (b) 1300 (c) 1800 (d) 57 400?

2 What is the largest whole number that, when rounded to the nearest 100, will give (a) 500 (b) 1900 (c) 4400 (d) 13 900?

3 What is the smallest whole number that

(a) when rounded to the nearest 10, gives 210

(b) when rounded to the nearest 100, gives 1600

(c) when rounded to the nearest 100, gives 33 000

(d) when rounded to the nearest 1000, gives 49 000?

4 What is the largest whole number that

(a) when rounded to the nearest 100, gives 200

(b) when rounded to the nearest 10, gives 1650

(c) when rounded to the nearest 100, gives 83 000

(d) when rounded to the nearest 1000, gives 47 000?

5 Correct to the nearest thousand, 45 000 attended a concert.

(a) What is the largest number that could have been present?

(b) What is the smallest number that could have been present?

6 The population of Romania is given as 23 000 000 correct to the nearest million.

(a) What is the largest possible population?

(b) What is the smallest possible population?

7 An aircraft engine needs a full service after 10 000 hours' flying time. If this figure is correct to the nearest thousand hours, what is (a) the shortest (b) the longest time, that the engine should be used before servicing?

8 At a demonstration the organisers claimed that 100 000 people attended, while the police stated that the figure was nearer 55 000. Both claims were correct – it all depends on how the rounding is done. Explain the apparent contradiction.

Calculators

There are several different kinds of calculators. If you buy a new one you are advised to buy a **scientific calculator** with **memory** and **brackets** keys. Some keys, such as 0 1 2 3 4 5 6 7 8 9; the basic function keys + − × ÷ and the = and . are the same on all calculators. Other keys can vary from one calculator to another. When you have bought a calculator, it is important that you understand how to use it quickly and easily. If there is anything you don't understand or feel you are doing incorrectly then you must check with your instruction booklet. The calculator used for calculations in this book was a Casio Scientific Calculator fx-10F.

Keys that clear the calculator

Some calculators have only one *clear* key. To clear the last entry, you press this key once, while to clear the whole calculator you press it a second time. It is more than likely that your calculator has two clear keys. The **AC** (all cleared) key puts the calculator on or clears it completely, while the **C** key clears the last entry but does not clear the memory.

Correcting mistakes

When you use a calculator you must take great care. This includes asking yourself at each stage 'Is my answer reasonable?' If you make a mistake it is probably better to start again.

However, if you do enter a wrong number, it is possible to use the **C** key to remove the error.

For instance, to work out 157 − 93 Mike pressed **AC** **1** **5** **7** **−** **9** **7** and realised his mistake straight away. He pressed **C** followed by **9** **3** **=** This cleared his mistake, entered the new number and gave **64** in the display, which was the correct answer.

Sometimes you can press the wrong 'operation' key, that is you might press **×** instead of **+**, or **÷** instead of **−** Such a mistake can be corrected easily by pressing the correct key next.

For example, to find 84 ÷ 79 Lena pressed **AC** **8** **4** **−** She stopped here realising that she had pressed **−** instead of **÷** The mistake was corrected by pressing **÷** next and then **7** **9** The display showed **1.06329...** , which is the correct answer.

Apart from making a mistake when you enter a number, for example keying in 5964 instead of 5694, or 899 instead of 889, or pressing the wrong operation key, take care always to press the **=** key last. Although you may find that this is sometimes unnecessary, it will never do any harm. It is better to press it when it is not really needed than it is to forget to do so when it is. Finally, take care that you write down the number from the display correctly when you transfer it to your paper.

Check these calculations using your calculator:

(a) 634 + 1219 − 816.
Press **AC** **6** **3** **4** **+** **1** **2** **1** **9** **−** **8** **1** **6** **=**
The display shows **1037**

(b) 72 × 46.
Press **AC** **7** **2** **×** **4** **6** **=**
The display shows **3312**

(c) 59 × 23 + 421.
Press **AC** **5** **9** **×** **2** **3** **+** **4** **2** **1**
The display shows **1778** which is correct.
The calculator will multiply 59 by 23 before adding 421. Check that your calculator does this. If it does not then refer to your instruction booklet.

Always be aware of what you need to do on **your** calculator when you are following a key sequence in a textbook.

Most calculators have an 8- or 10-digit display. You will not usually need all the digits.

Rounding the answer in the display is almost always necessary. Every time you round a number you should state what you have done. For example, say that you have rounded the number to the nearest 10 or the nearest 100.

What about the order?

Try finding 3 + 4 × 5 on your calculator: press **AC** **3** **+** **4** **×** **5** **=** If your display shows **23** then the answer is correct and your calculator gives priority to multiplication by finding 4 × 5 before it adds 3.

Maybe your display shows 35. This means that 3 and 4 have been added together and their total multiplied by 5. This is incorrect. On a calculator that does this you must change the order. In this example the order needs to be changed to:
press **AC** **4** **×** **5** **+** **3** **=**
The display shows **23** which is correct.

Now work out 23 + 15 × 18 − 4 × 37.
Press **AC** **2** **3** **+** **1** **5** **×** **1** **8** **−** **4** **×** **3** **7** **=**
The display should show **145**

Also try
AC **1** **5** **×** **1** **8** **−** **4** **×** **3** **7** **+** **2** **3** **=**

Remember that it does not matter in which order you add and subtract numbers; for example, 23 + 270 − 148 is the same as 270 − 148 + 23.

Checking calculations

Often we use rounded numbers to check calculations.

Suppose Denise wishes to find the weight of 769 packets of bolts, each of which weighs 347 grams. Using a calculator, she finds that 769 × 347 is 266 843. Is this answer reasonable?

To the nearest 100, 769 is 800
and 347 is 300

Without using a calculator, 800 × 300 = 240 000. This is a six-figure number that is reasonably close to the six-figure number 266 843, and so confirms that Denise's answer is about right.

If she had got a number that was close to 2400 or 2 400 000 then she would know that she had made a mistake and would need to start again.

EXERCISE 1q

1 Given below are the calculations needed to find the areas, in square feet, of four rectangular buildings

(a) 86 ft × 48 ft (b) 67 ft × 24 ft
(c) 77 ft × 48 ft (d) 977 ft × 87 ft

By giving each number correct to the nearest ten, estimate the ground area of each building in square feet.

2 (a) Use a calculator to find the exact answers for the calculations given in question 1.

(b) Do the answers you got in question 1 help to confirm the answers you got in part (a)?

3 By giving each number correct to the nearest 100, estimate the area of four rectangular plots of land whose dimensions are given as

(a) 798 m by 547 m (b) 374 m by 285 m
(c) 1287 m by 646 m (d) 8975 m by 633 m
(area of rectangle = length × breadth)

4 Check your answers to question 3 by using a calculator to find the exact answers.

5 By giving each number correct to the nearest 100 estimate the value of

(a) $\dfrac{723 \times 977}{693}$ (b) $\dfrac{446 \times 864}{376}$

(c) $\dfrac{1187 \times 654}{837}$ (d) $\dfrac{5447 \times 8519}{4475}$

Multiple-choice questions 1

In questions 1 to 5 several alternative answers are given. Write down the letter that corresponds to the correct answer.

1 A salary of £28K a year is

A £2800 **B** £28 000 **C** £280 000 **D** £28 000 000

2 The lampstandards in my street are placed at 50 metre intervals along one side and are numbered consecutively, from 127 at one end of the street to 159 at the other end. The length of my street from one end to the other is

A 1500 m **B** 1650 m **C** 1550 m **D** 1600 m

3 Teri lives 1 mile from work and goes home for lunch every day. From 1 September to the end of the year she worked 5 days a week for 17 weeks, without missing a day. The total distance she cycled back and forth to work was

A 34 miles **B** 68 miles **C** 156 miles **D** 340 miles

4 On his first turn in a darts match Len scored 19, double 6 and treble 14. His total score was

A 39 **B** 73 **C** 45 **D** 67

5 By giving each number correct to the nearest 100 the estimated value of $\dfrac{9349 \times 793}{627}$ is found to be

A 12 000 **B** 1200 **C** 9000 **D** 10 000

6 The number of customers passing through the door of Bettashop last week was 26 928. Which of the following statements are true and which are false?

A Correct to the nearest 100 the number of customers was 26 900

B Correct to the nearest 100 the number of customers was 27 000

C Correct to the nearest 10 the number of customers was 26 930

D Correct to the nearest 1000 the number of customers was 26 000

7 The largest number of components ever produced in a day at Microcorp Electronics is 86 000, correct to the nearest 100. Which of the following statements are true and which are false?

A The largest number that could have been produced that day was 86 499

B The smallest number that could have been produced that day was 85 500

C The largest number that could have been produced that day was 86 049

D The smallest number that could have been produced that day was 85 950

8 The following statements have been made:
Statement 1. Victor earns £18 700 a year which is less than his sister, Vicki, who earns about £21K a year.
Statement 2. Capital expenditure of £2bn is less than research and development costs of £200m.
How are the two statements best described?

A True, True **B** True, False
C False, True **D** False, False

9 The Barrett family set out on a 2500 mile trip from home to Moscow via Vienna and Bucharest. The most they wanted to travel in a day was 320 miles. On the first day they drove 287 miles, on the second day 315 miles, on the third day 292 miles and on the fourth day 189 miles. The following two statements have been made:
Statement 1. They still had at least 6 days driving left.
Statement 2. There was more than 1500 miles driving still to do.
How are these two statements best described?

A True, True **B** True, False
C False, True **D** False, False

Self-assessment test 1

1 Write as a number (a) £65K (b) £5bn.

2 The table shows the number of washing machines a factory warehouse took into stock each day on a particular week, together with the number of machines dispatched to distributors.

	Mon	Tues	Wed	Thur	Fri
Number produced and added to stock	372	392	405	386	307
Number dispatched to distributors	406	418	397	482	114

(a) How many washing machines were (i) produced and added to stock on Wednesday
(ii) dispatched to distributors on Thursday?

(b) At the start of the week there were 294 machines in stock. How many machines were there in stock when the factory closed for the weekend?

3

In a knockout competition there are 8 teams, with 15 players plus 2 substitutes for each team. How many players are involved in the competition?

4 For the Rugby League Cup Final at Wembley there were 72 854 spectators. Write this number correct to the nearest (a) 100 (b) 1000 (c) 10

5 Correct to the nearest thousand pounds, Ken's annual pay is £16 000. Find (a) the largest amount (b) the smallest amount, that he could be earning.

6 A pallet of building blocks consists of six layers with 27 blocks in each layer. How many pallets of blocks must be ordered for a building that is estimated to require 120 000 blocks?

7 In a school with 846 pupils the estimate is that each pupil will use 16 exercise books during the course of the year. At the beginning of the year there are 2873 exercise books in stock, and during the year they receive two deliveries, one for 6500 books and the other for 6000 books. How many books do they estimate will be in stock at the end of the year? Give your answer correct to the nearest 100.

8 A train pulls into a station carrying 783 passengers.

(a) What is the least number of carriages on the train if each carriage has 92 seats and every passenger has a seat?

(b) If 347 passengers get off and 138 get on, how many passengers are there on the train as it pulls away from the station?

(c) As the train pulls out, how many spare seats are there?

CHAPTER 2

Numbers and number patterns

Odd and even numbers

The whole numbers 1, 2, 3, 4, 5, 6, . . . are divided into two types – even numbers and odd numbers. If a whole number can be divided exactly by 2 then that whole number is an *even number*, otherwise it is an *odd number*. The even numbers are 2, 4, 6, 8, 10, . . .
and the odd numbers are 1, 3, 5, 7, 9, . . .

Multiples of numbers

$5 = 1 \times 5, \quad 15 = 3 \times 5 \quad \text{and} \quad 30 = 6 \times 5$
i.e. 5, 15 and 30 are *multiples* of 5.

Similarly, 4, 20 and 24 are multiples of 4.

Factors

$6 = 1 \times 6$ and $6 = 2 \times 3$,
so 1, 2, 3 and 6 are all *factors* of 6

Similarly, $12 = 1 \times 12, \quad 12 = 2 \times 6 \quad \text{and} \quad 12 = 3 \times 4$,
so 1, 2, 3, 4, 6 and 12 are all factors of 12.

A calculator makes it easy to find out whether or not any number is a factor of another number.
For example, pressing the buttons AC 2 4 7 ÷ 1 9 = gives 13 in the display.
This shows that 19 divides into 247 exactly, i.e. 19 is a factor of 247 (and so is 13).
However, pressing the buttons AC 1 8 6 ÷ 7 does not give a whole number, so 7 is not a factor of 186.

EXERCISE 2a

QUESTION
Which of the numbers 5, 7, 10, 12, 14, 15, 18 are
(a) odd (b) even (c) multiples of 5
(d) multiples of 6?

ANSWER
(a) 5, 7 and 15 are odd numbers.

(b) 10, 12, 14 and 18 are even numbers.

(c) 5, 10 and 15 are multiples of 5.

(d) 12 and 18 are multiples of 6.

---

1 Which of the numbers 7, 9, 10, 15, 21, 24, 28, 33, 36 are
 (a) even numbers
 (b) multiples of 4
 (c) multiples of 6?

2 Write down all the multiples of 7 between 20 and 40.

3 Write down all the multiples of 5 between 24 and 42.

4 (a) Is 42 a multiple of 6?
 (b) Is 44 a multiple of 5?
 (c) Is 72 a multiple of 9?

QUESTION
List the factors of 24.

ANSWER
The factors of 24 are 1, 2, 3, 4, 6, 8, 12, 24.

---

5 List the factors of (a) 12 (b) 15 (c) 36 (d) 60.

6 (a) Is 3 a factor of 15?
 (b) Is 5 a factor of 35?
 (c) Is 6 a factor of 30?

7 Write down the factors of 84 that are odd.

8 Write down the factors of 56 that are even.

9 Find a number smaller than 30 that is a multiple of 6 and 9.

10 Find a number between 80 and 90 that is a multiple of 6 and 7.

Prime numbers

A whole number bigger than 1, that has no factors other than itself and 1, is called a *prime number*.
(Note that 1 is not a prime number.)

The first 9 prime numbers are 2, 3, 5, 7, 11, 13, 17, 19 and 23.

Rectangular numbers

Numbers that are not prime can be represented using dots arranged in a rectangle (or a square, which is a special type of rectangle) with at least two lines of dots. Such numbers are called *rectangular numbers*.

For example, 12 is a rectangular number. 12 dots can be arranged as follows:

Square numbers

The whole numbers 1, 4, 9, 16, 25, ... are called *square numbers*. They can be represented by dots arranged in squares:

Square numbers can be expressed as the square of smaller whole numbers:

e.g. $4 = 2 \times 2 = 2^2$, $16 = 4 \times 4 = 4^2$ and $81 = 9 \times 9 = 9^2$.

Triangular numbers

The numbers 1, 3, 6, 10, 15, ... are called *triangular numbers*. They can be represented by dots in the form of triangles:

1 3 6 10 15

Cube numbers

The numbers 1, 8, 27, 64, ... are called *cube numbers* because they can be expressed as the cubes of smaller whole numbers,
e.g. $8 = 2 \times 2 \times 2 = 2^3$ and $27 = 3 \times 3 \times 3 = 3^3$.

Square roots and cube roots

Because $9 = 3 \times 3$ we say that the *square root* of 9 is 3. We write this $\sqrt{9} = 3$.

To find the square root of 225 on a calculator press

AC **2** **2** **5** **√** **=**

The display shows 15, so $\sqrt{225} = 15$.

Because $64 = 4 \times 4 \times 4$, the *cube root* of 64 is 4. We write this $\sqrt[3]{64} = 4$.

To find the cube root of 343 using a calculator, press

AC **3** **4** **3** **$x^{\frac{1}{y}}$** **3** **=**

The display reads 7, so $\sqrt[3]{343} = 7$.

The square roots and cube roots of some numbers are not whole numbers. These are dealt with later in the book.

EXERCISE 2b

1 Draw as many different rectangular patterns as you can for the number 24.

2 Which of the numbers 15, 16, 17, 18, 19, 20 are
(a) rectangular numbers
(b) non-rectangular numbers?

3 Which of the numbers 6, 8, 9, 13, 15, 17, 18, 19 are prime?

4 Which of the following numbers are prime numbers: 29, 30, 31, 32, 45, 47, 55, 67?

5 What are the next three prime numbers after 35?

QUESTION
Find (a) the square of 8 (b) the square root of 36
(c) the cube of 7.

ANSWER
(a) The square of 8 is 8×8 i.e. 64.

(b) Since $36 = 6 \times 6$ the square root of 36 is 6.

(c) The cube is 7 is $7 \times 7 \times 7$ i.e. 343.

---

6 Find the square of (a) 5 (b) 7 (c) 11.

7 16 and 25 are square numbers. Write down the next 3 square numbers.

8 Which of the numbers 75, 81, 90, 95, 100, 130 and 145 are square numbers?

9 Find the next cube number after 125.

10 Which of the numbers 10, 16, 27, 48, 64, 75, 100 and 125 are cube numbers?

11 Find the cube of (a) 5 (b) 6 (c) 8 (d) 9.

12 The square root of a number is 8. What is the number?

13 The cube of a number is 125. What is the number?

14 Can you write down a number between 60 and 70 that is the square of one number and the cube of another number?

15 Find two consecutive whole numbers whose squares differ by 13.

16 Find two consecutive whole numbers whose squares add up to 41.

17 Look at the numbers 7, 8, 9, 15, 16, 17, 18.

(a) Which number is (i) the largest prime number (ii) a factor of 60 (iii) a square number?

(b) Can you find two numbers that add together to give a prime number? (There is more than one correct answer.)

(c) Which two numbers have a sum that is a cube number?

18 Sid thinks of a number that is prime, is 4 more than a cube number and is 5 less than a square number. What number is Sid thinking of?

Directed numbers

We are all familiar with temperatures on TV weather charts. In the summer, for this country, they are always positive but in the winter they are sometimes negative i.e. below zero.

Negative numbers are used to describe situations; thus, if my bank balance is described as −£50 it means that I am £50 in debt; a temperature of −6 °C means 6 degrees below zero and an increase in weight of −2 kg means a loss of 2 kg.

EXERCISE 2c

QUESTION

The diagram shows a ladder fixed to a harbour wall. Draw a sketch to show the position of the surface if the water level
(a) rises 2 feet (b) falls 4 feet.

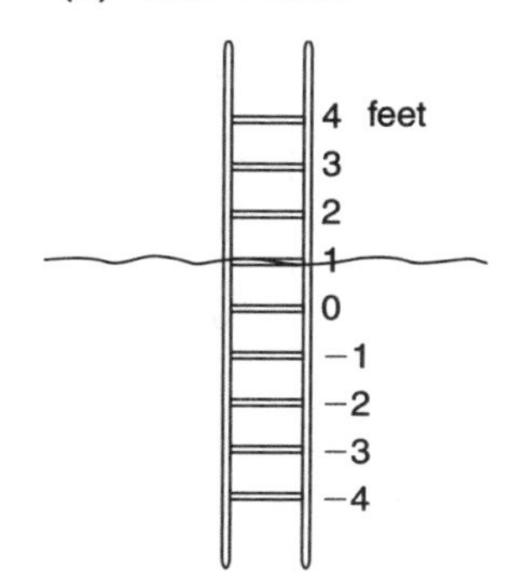

ANSWER

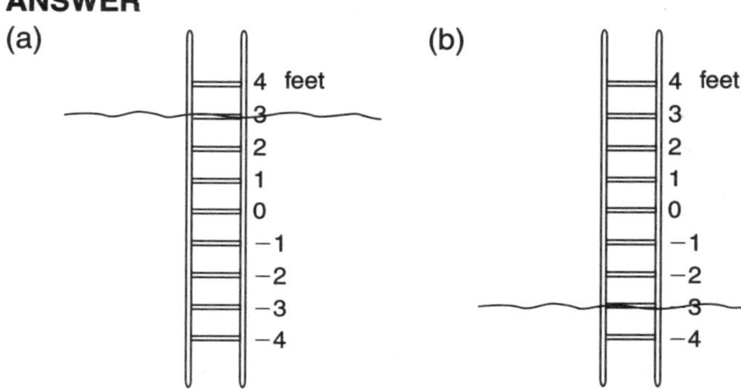

This shows a rise of 2 ft. This shows a fall of 4 ft.

1 Peg is standing halfway up the stairs. If +3 means 'go up 3 stairs', what is meant by (a) −2 (b) −5 (c) +2?

2 If +2 means that I have put on 2 kg, what does −5 mean?

3 If +5 means I am 5 m above the water line, what does −3 mean?

4 I am painting the house. If +1 means that I am 1 m above the level of the guttering, what does (a) +2 (b) −6 mean?

5 The water level in the local river is described as +1 if it is 1 metre above normal and −1 if it is 1 metre below normal. What can you say about the water level if it is described as (a) −3 (b) +4 (c) 0?

6 The amount of money in Wayne's bank account is described as +100 if he has a credit of £100 and −100 if he is £100 in debt. What is the state of his finances if his account is described as (a) +250 (b) −75 (c) 0?

7 What is the temperature on the thermometer shown below?

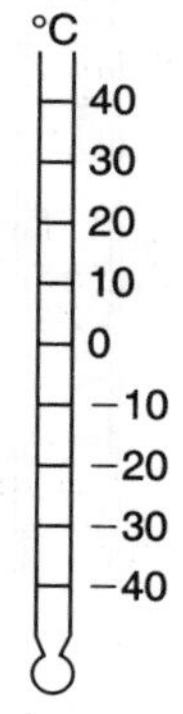

8 What would the reading on the thermometer be if the temperature rose by
(a) 12 °C
(b) 15 °C
(c) 20 °C
(d) 22 °C
(e) 40 °C?

9 Which is warmer
(a) 5 °C or −10 °C
(b) −4 °C or −5 °C
(c) −2 °C or 2 °C?

10 Which is colder
(a) −15 °C or −20 °C
(b) −8 °C or −9 °C
(c) −4 °C or 3 °C?

11 The midday temperatures at Estergrad during one week were

Sun	Mon	Tue	Wed	Thur	Fri	Sat
−2 °C	−4 °C	−1 °C	5 °C	6 °C	−3 °C	0 °C

Which day had (a) the highest midday temperature
(b) the second lowest midday temperature
(c) the third highest midday temperature?

12 How many degrees has the temperature risen or fallen if

(a) it was 3 °C and it is now −7 °C

(b) it was −3 °C and it is now −5 °C?

(c) it was −5 °C and it is now 4 °C

(d) it was 5 °C and it is now 8 °C?

The number line

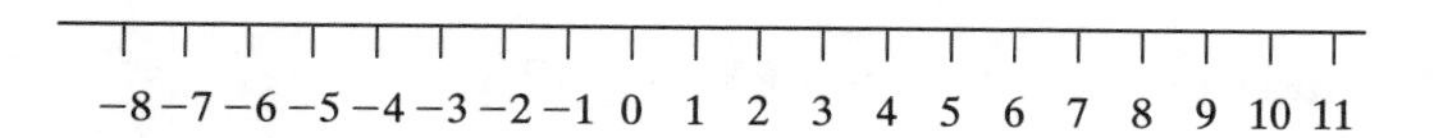

We can mark positive and negative numbers on a *number line*. Positive numbers are marked to the right of zero and negative numbers to the left of zero.

On the number line 2 is to the right of −1. We say that 2 is greater than −1 and use the symbol > to mean 'is greater than', i.e. $2 > -1$.

Similarly, $-2 > -3$ since −2 is to the right of −3 on the number line
and $3 > -4$.

On the other hand, −3 is to the left of −1 on the number line, so −3 is less than −1.

Using the symbol < to mean 'is less than' we have $-3 < -1$.

EXERCISE 2d

In questions 1 to 10 write either > or < between the two numbers.

1 −4 3	**2** −5 −4	**3** −4 −2
4 0 −6	**5** 6 −2	**6** −3 −5
7 −10 −4	**8** 6 −3	**9** −2 0
10 −4 −5	**11** 10 −6	**12** −8 −12

Adding and subtracting directed numbers

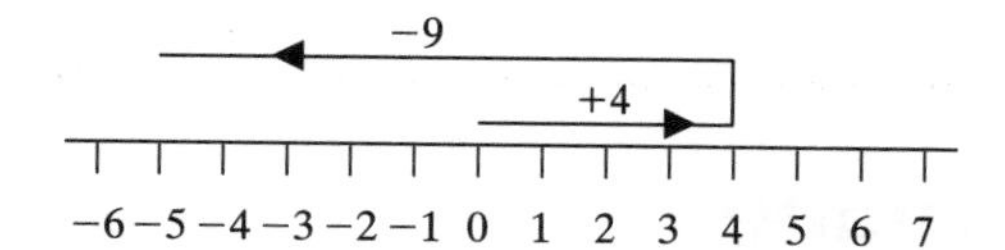

To find 4 − 9 we start at zero, move 4 steps to the right followed by 9 steps to the left.

We are now at −5,
so $4 - 9 = -5$

Adding a negative number is the same as taking away a positive number,
e.g. $+(-5) = -(+5) = -5$
and taking away a negative number is the same as adding a positive number,
e.g. $-(-10) = +10$

EXERCISE 2e

−13 −12 −11 −10 −9 −8 −7 −6 −5 −4 −3 −2 −1 0 1 2 3 4 5 6 7 8 9 10 11 12 13

QUESTION
Find (a) $3-5$ (b) $5+(-2)$ (c) $-5-(-8)$

ANSWER
(a) $3-5=-2$

(b) $5+(-2)=5-2$
$=3$

(c) $-5-(-8)=-5+8$
$=3$

Find, using the number line if it helps

1 $6-10$ **2** $4-11$ **3** $12-13$

4 $16-24$ **5** $6-(-7)$ **6** $-1+(-6)$

7 $-5+(-5)$ **8** $-4-(-4)$

QUESTION
Find $3+(-4)-(-3)$

ANSWER
$3+(-4)-(-3)=3-4+3$
$=2$

Find

9 $3+(-2)+(-1)$ **10** $(-2)+(-2)+(-2)$

11 $5-(-3)+(-2)$ **12** $-3-(-4)+(-2)$

13 $6-(-5)+(-2)$ **14** $8-(-3)-(-4)$

QUESTION
Find $3-(8-3)$.

ANSWER
$3-(8-3)=3-5$
$=-2$

Find

15 $5-(4-3)$ **16** $8-(7-3)$

17 $-4-(5-8)$ **18** $4+(9-11)$

19 $(2-7)-8$ **20** $(4-9)-(5-2)$

21 It is necessary to keep the temperature of a storage shed at 15 °C. Temperatures above 15 °C are recorded as positive and temperatures below 15 °C as negative, for example a recorded temperature of −3 means that the temperature has fallen to 12 °C.

(a) Find the recorded temperature if the actual temperature is (i) 18 °C (ii) 13 °C (iii) 0 °C (iv) 8 °C.

(b) Find the actual temperature if the recorded temperature is (i) +3 (ii) −4 (iii) −10 (iv) 0.

22 In a quiz Waldo scores 5 points for a correct answer and has 3 points deducted for an incorrect answer. The table shows his answers to 12 questions.

Question	1	2	3	4	5	6	7	8	9	10	11	12
Answer	✓	✗	✗	✗	✓	✗	✓	✓	✓	✗	✓	✗

What was his score after answering (a) 4 questions (b) 8 questions (c) all the questions?

23

The scoring system in a radio quiz is 3 points for a correct answer and −1 for an incorrect answer. The table shows the answers given by four contestants:

Question	1	2	3	4	5	6	7	8	9	10
Mr Eaves	✓	✓	✗	✗	✗	✓	✓	✓	✓	✗
Ms Waite	✗	✗	✗	✓	✓	✓	✓	✓	✗	✗
Mrs Peake	✓	✓	✓	✓	✗	✓	✓	✓	✗	✓
Mr Gould	✗	✗	✗	✗	✗	✓	✓	✓	✓	✗

(a) Who was leading after each person had answered (i) 4 questions (ii) 8 questions?

(b) Who won? How many points did the winner have?

(c) What was the name of the runner-up?

(d) How many more points did the person who won have than the person who came last?

(e) Suppose Tim Gardner also attempts these questions. (i) What is the highest number of points he can score? (ii) What is the lowest score he can get?

Multiplication of directed numbers

3×2 means $2 + 2 + 2 = 6$
and $3 \times (-2)$ means $(-2) + (-2) + (-2) = -6$
Since order does not matter when we multiply
$3 \times (-2) = (-2) \times 3 = -6$
and $2 \times (-3) = (-3) \times 2 = -6$

EXERCISE 2f

QUESTION
Find (a) $4 \times (-3)$ (b) $(-3) \times 4$ (c) $(-3) \times (-4)$

ANSWER
(a) $4 \times (-3) = -12$
(b) $(-3) \times 4 = -12$
(c) $(-3) \times (-4) = 12$

Find

1 $5 \times (-3)$ **2** $3 \times (-5)$ **3** $(-5) \times 4$

4 $7 \times (-5)$ **5** $(+2) \times (-7)$ **6** $(-3) \times (+6)$

7 $(-8) \times 1$ **8** $(+4) \times (-5)$

Dividing a negative number by a positive number

Since $3 \times 4 = 12$, $12 \div 4 = 3$
Similarly since $(-3) \times 4 = -12$, $-12 \div 4 = -3$

EXERCISE 2g

QUESTION
Find (a) $-12 \div 6$ (b) $-12 \div (+2)$

ANSWER
(a) $-12 \div 6 = -2$ (b) $-12 \div (+2) = -6$

Find

1 $(-8) \div 4$ **2** $(-8) \div 2$

3 $-12 \div 4$ **4** $(-18) \div 6$

Negative numbers using a calculator

To get a negative number in the display of a calculator, key in the number followed by the +/- button.

EXERCISE 2h

QUESTION
Use a calculator to find (a) $5 + (-10)$ (b) $5 - (-10)$
(c) $-5 + (-10)$ (d) $-5 - (-10)$

ANSWER
(a) Press AC 5 + 1 0 +/- =
The display shows -5, so $5 + (-10) = -5$.

(b) Press AC 5 − 1 0 +/- =
which gives $5 - (-10) = 15$

(c) Press AC 5 +/- + 1 0 +/- =
which gives $-5 + (-10) = -15$

(d) Press AC 5 +/- − 1 0 +/- =
which gives $-5 - (-10) = 5$

Use a calculator to find

1 $-3 + (-4)$ **2** $3 - (-4)$ **3** $6 + (-7)$

4 $-6 - (-7)$ **5** $-6 + 7$ **6** $-5 - (-7)$

7 $4 + (-8)$ **8** $4 - (-8)$

QUESTION
Use a calculator to find (a) $3 \times (-5)$ (b) $(-3) \times (-5)$
(c) $12 \div (-3)$ (d) $(-8) \div (-4)$

ANSWER
(a) AC 3 × 5 +/- = Answer -15
(b) AC 3 +/- × 5 +/- = Answer 15
(c) AC 1 2 ÷ 3 +/- = Answer -4
(d) AC 8 +/- ÷ 4 +/- = Answer 2

Use a calculator to find

9 $6 \times (-3)$ **10** $(-6) \times (-3)$

11 $(-6) \div 3$ **12** $6 \div (-3)$

13 $(-12) \div (-3)$ **14** $4 \times (-7)$

15 $(-3) \times (-6)$

16 $(-15) \div 3$

17 $-2 + 3 \times (-4)$

18 $2 - 3 \times (-4)$

19 $2 + (-3) \times (-4)$

20 $(-2) \times 3 + 4$

21 $2 \times (-3) + 4$

22 $2 \times (-3) - (-4)$

23 $(-2) \times (-3) - 4$

24 $4 \div (-2) - 3$

25 Find two numbers that multiply together to give -18. How many ways can you find of doing this?

26 Find two numbers that divide to give an answer of -3. How many ways can you find of doing this?

Number patterns

Earlier in this chapter we looked at both triangular and square numbers. Each sequence of numbers forms a pattern from which it is possible to find other numbers in the sequence.

The first 5 square numbers are 1, 4, 9, 16, 25. The next 3 are 36, 49 and 64. We get these numbers by squaring, in order, the natural numbers 1, 2, 3, 4, 5, 6, 7, 8.

The 10th number in the sequence is 10×10, i.e. 100, and the 15th number in the sequence is 15×15, i.e. 225.

Similarly the first 5 triangular numbers are 1, 3, 6, 10, 15. We get triangular numbers by starting with 1 then adding the natural numbers in order, i.e. first we add 2, then 3, then 4, and so on. The next four numbers in this sequence are 21, 28, 36, 45.

The *n*th term in a pattern

If a set of numbers forms a pattern it is possible to express each number in terms of its position. For example, in the pattern 2, 4, 6, 8, 10, ... each number is twice the number that gives its position. The 3rd number is 2×3, i.e. 6, and the 5th number is 2×5, i.e. 10.

If we continued the pattern then the 10th number would be 2×10, i.e. 20, and the 16th number would be 2×16, i.e. 32.

In general terms the value of the nth term, written T_n, is $2n$, i.e. $T_n = 2n$.

Similarly, for the pattern 9, 13, 17, 21, 25 the numbers go up 4 at a time and we can see that $T_n = 4n + 5$.

EXERCISE 2i

QUESTION

Write down the next two numbers in the sequence
(a) 5, 6, 8, 11 (b) 9, 4, −1, −6.

ANSWER

(a) The sequence starts with 5, then adds the numbers 1, 2, 3, ...
The next two terms are therefore 11 + 4, i.e. 15, and 15 + 5, i.e. 20.

(b) The sequence starts with 9 and subtracts 5 each time.
The next two terms are −6 −5, i.e. −11, and −11 −5, i.e. −16.

Find the next three numbers in each pattern:

1 1, 2, 3, 4, ...

2 4, 6, 8, 10, ...

3 20, 27, 34, 41, ...

4 1, 2, 4, 8, ...

5 1, 3, 5, 7, ...

6 10, 15, 20, 25, ...

7 0, 2, 6, 12, ...

8 18, 15, 12, 9, ...

9 19, 15, 11, 7, ...

10 20, 19, 17, 14, ...

11 10, 3, −4, −11, ...

12 2, 6, 18, 54, ...

QUESTION

Write down the next two numbers in the sequence
(a) 1, 8, 27, 64, ... (b) 0, 3, 8, 15, ...

ANSWER

(a) The numbers in the sequence 1, 8, 27, 64 are the cubes of the numbers 1, 2, 3, 4.
The next two numbers are therefore $5 \times 5 \times 5 = 125$ and $6 \times 6 \times 6 = 216$.

(b) The numbers in the sequence 0, 3, 8, 15 are found by squaring the natural numbers 1, 2, 3, 4, and taking 1 away. The next two numbers are therefore $5 \times 5 - 1 = 24$ and $6 \times 6 - 1 = 35$.

Find the next two numbers in the sequence

13 25, 36, 49, 64, ...

14 1, 8, 27, 64, 125, 216, ...

15 $1 \times 2, 2 \times 3, 3 \times 4, 4 \times 5, \ldots$

16 $2 \times 2 - 1, 3 \times 3 - 2, 4 \times 4 - 3, 5 \times 5 - 4, \ldots$

17 3, 5, 9, 17, ...

18 1, 2, 6, 24, 120, ...

19 (a) Check that the first three lines of this pattern are correct:

$1 \times 1 + 2 \times 2 = 3 \times 3 - 2 \times 2$
$2 \times 2 + 3 \times 3 = 7 \times 7 - 6 \times 6$
$3 \times 3 + 4 \times 4 = 13 \times 13 - 12 \times 12$

(b) Write down the next three lines.

20 (a) Use a calculator to work out the pattern

$1 \times 9 + 2 =$
$12 \times 9 + 3 =$
$123 \times 9 + 4 =$
$1234 \times 9 + 5 =$
$12345 \times 9 + 6 =$

(b) Without using a calculator write down the value of (i) $123456 \times 9 + 7$ (ii) $1234567 \times 9 + 8$.

QUESTION

Find an expression for the *n*th term of the number pattern (a) 2, 5, 8, 11, 14, ... (b) 6, 11, 16, 21, ... In each case use your expression to find the 9th term.

ANSWER

(a) We see that the terms go up 3 at a time. If we think that each term is 3 times its position, then we have the pattern 3, 6, 9, 12, ... Comparing this with the given pattern each number is 1 too large.

$\therefore T_n = 3n - 1$ (Check that this gives all the terms in the pattern)

Hence $T_9 = 3 \times 9 - 1 = 27 - 1 = 26$

(b) Similarly, the numbers in the pattern 6, 11, 16, 21, ... go up 5 at a time. Going up in 5s gives 5, 10, 15, 20, ...

It follows that for the given numbers $T_n = 5n + 1$ and $T_9 = 45 + 1 = 46$

In questions 21 to 26 write down the *n*th term of the pattern and use it to find the 12th term.

21 4, 8, 12, 16, 20, ...

22 5, 7, 9, 11, 13, ...

23 3, 8, 13, 18, 23, ...

24 8, 11, 14, 17, 20, ...

25 6, 13, 20, 27, 34, ...

26 5, 15, 25, 35, 45, ...

Multiple-choice questions 2

In questions 1 to 5 several possible answers are given. Write down the letter that corresponds to the correct answer.

1 The next prime number after 50 is

A 51 **B** 53 **C** 57 **D** 59

2 The rectangular number 24 is to be represented by dots. The number of different ways in which this can be done is

A 2 **B** 3 **C** 4 **D** 5

3 The temperature at 6 a.m. was −6 °C. By 1 p.m. it had gone up by 9 °C. The temperature at 1 p.m. was

A 15 °C **B** −15 °C **C** 3 °C **D** 9 °C

4 The value of $5 - (-3) \times 4$ is

A 12 **B** 4 **C** −7 **D** 17

5 The expression for the *n*th term of the pattern 7, 11, 15, 19 is

A $6n + 1$ **B** $n + 6$
C $4n + 3$ **D** $2n + 5$

6 Which of these statements are true and which are false?

A No even number is prime.

B Some odd numbers are prime.

C 13, 17, 19 and 21 are prime.

D The next prime number after 40 is 43.

7 The following statements have been made:
Statement 1: No number other than 1 is both a square number and a cube number.
Statement 2: The smallest number greater than 1 that is both a square number and a cube number is 64.
How are these two statements best described?

A True, True **B** True, False
C False, True **D** False, False

Self-assessment test 2

1 (a) Find all the factors of 48.

(b) Which of these factors are (i) even numbers (ii) prime numbers?

2 (a) Find the next prime number after 47.

(b) Write three multiples of 6 that are less than 25.

(c) What is the next triangular number after 28?

3 The amount of money in a bank account is described as $+10$ if it is £10 above £200 and as -10 if it is £10 below £200. How much money is in the account if it is described as (a) $+100$ (b) -150 (c) -250?

4 Which is the warmer (a) -9 °C or -15 °C (b) 0 °C or -3 °C?

5 Find (a) $5 \times (-4)$ (b) $1 - (-4) + 10$ (c) $(-3) \times 2 + 8$ (d) $-14 \div 7$

6 Write down the next three numbers in each of the following sequences:

(a) 5, 8, 11, 14, ... (b) 9, 18, 27, 36, ...
(c) 8, -13, 18, -23, ... (d) 1, 1, 2, 3, 5, 8, 13, ...

7 Give the next two lines of each number pattern:

(a)
$9 \times 11 = 99$
$9 \times 22 = 198$
$9 \times 33 = 297$
$9 \times 44 = 396$

(b)
$1 \times 8 + 1 = 9$
$12 \times 8 + 2 = 98$
$123 \times 8 + 3 = 987$
$1234 \times 8 + 4 = 9876$

8 (a) For the pattern 9, 15, 21, 27, ... write down an expression for the nth term

(b) Hence find, for this pattern, the number that is (i) the 8th term (ii) the 15th term.

CHAPTER 3

Fractions

The meaning of a fraction

If $\frac{3}{4}$ of the CDs on a market stall are secondhand then three out of every four are secondhand.

The bottom number in a fraction is called the *denominator* and gives the fraction its name. It tells us of the number of equal-sized parts into which the whole has been divided.

The top number in a fraction is called the *numerator* and states how many of the equal parts are being considered.

For example, $\frac{5}{8}$ of a cake means that the cake has been divided into 8 equal-sized parts and 5 of these are being considered:

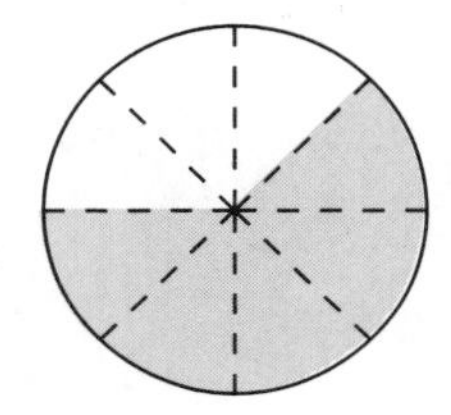

$\frac{5}{8}$ of this cake is shaded.

EXERCISE 3a

QUESTION
The shading shows that part of a bar of chocolate that has been eaten. What fraction is this?

ANSWER
(The rectangle is divided into 12 equal parts and 7 are shaded.)
$\frac{7}{12}$ of this rectangle is shaded, so $\frac{7}{12}$ of the bar of chocolate has been eaten.

In questions 1 to 6, write down the fraction of the whole shape that is shaded.

1

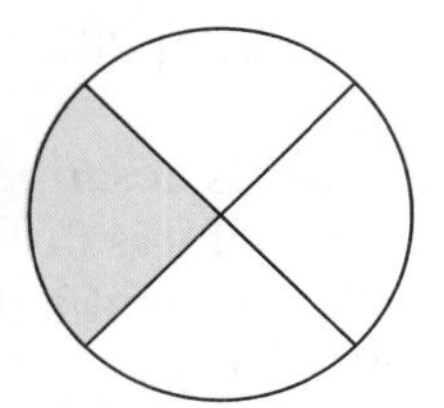

The shading represents a portion of a pizza.

2

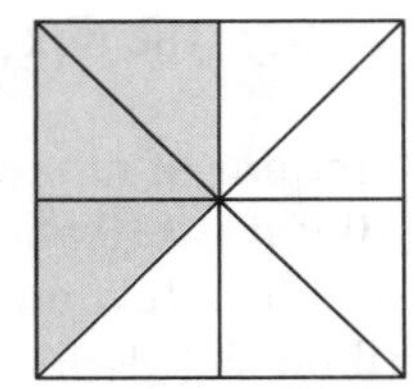

The shading represents that part of the lower tier of a wedding cake that was used at the reception.

3

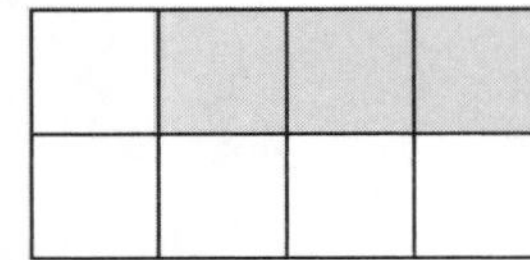

Part of a bar of chocolate is shaded.

4

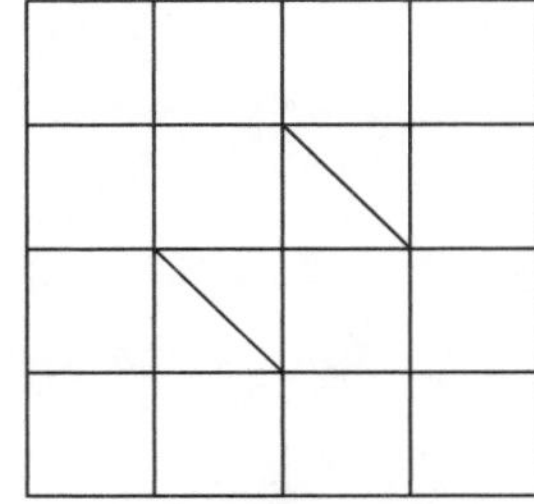

A floor design using tiles.

5

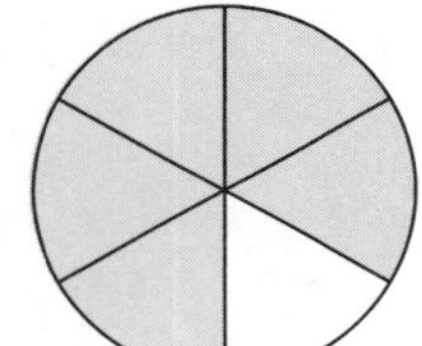

A fruit cake.

6

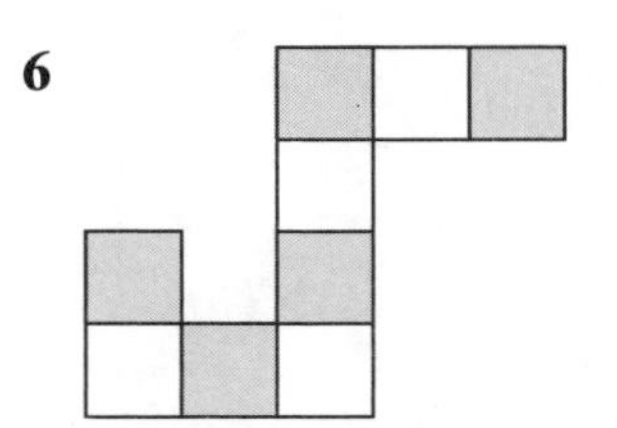

A design with paving stones in a garden.

7 For each fraction draw a shape like one of those in questions 1 to 6 and use it to shade the given fraction of the whole.

(a) $\frac{1}{2}$ of a rectangular field

(b) $\frac{7}{8}$ of a circular flower bed

(c) $\frac{11}{12}$ of a bar of chocolate with twelve pieces

(d) $\frac{5}{16}$ of a square tile

Equivalent fractions

Suppose a rectangular sheet of plywood is divided up in three different ways:

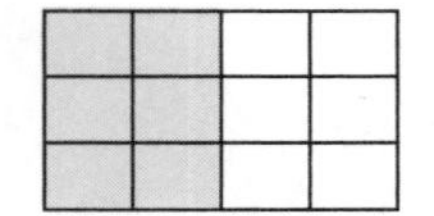

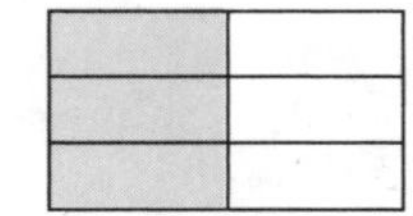

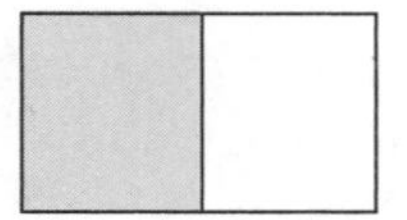

It is clear that there is the same amount of shading in all three diagrams,

so $\frac{6}{12} = \frac{3}{6} = \frac{1}{2}$

and $\frac{6}{12} = \frac{1 \times 6}{2 \times 6} = \frac{1}{2}$

Writing $\frac{6}{12}$ as $\frac{1}{2}$ is called *reducing* the fraction to its lowest terms or *simplifying* the fraction. Dividing the top and the bottom by 6 is called *cancelling*

i.e. $\frac{6}{12} = \frac{6 \div 6}{12 \div 6} = \frac{1}{2}$

Similarly, $\frac{14}{49} = \frac{14 \div 7}{49 \div 7} = \frac{2}{7}$

i.e. we have divided the top and the bottom by 7.

When a fraction has been simplified to give the smallest possible numerator (top) and denominator (bottom), the fraction is said to be expressed *in its lowest terms*.

Equivalent fractions, i.e. fractions with the same value, are found by multiplying (or dividing) the top and the bottom of the fraction by the same number.

For example, $\frac{12}{20} = \frac{12 \div 4}{20 \div 4} = \frac{3}{5} = \frac{3 \times 5}{5 \times 5} = \frac{15}{25}$

EXERCISE 3b

QUESTION
Show, by glazing a rectangular window in three different ways, that $\frac{8}{12} = \frac{4}{6} = \frac{2}{3}$

ANSWER

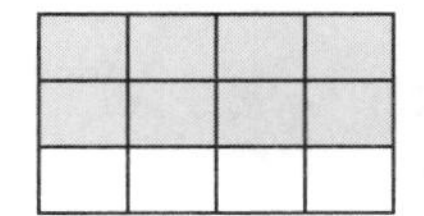
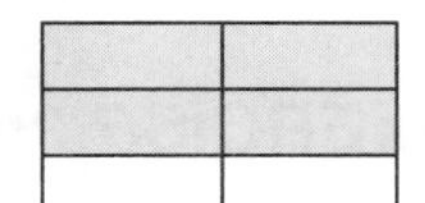
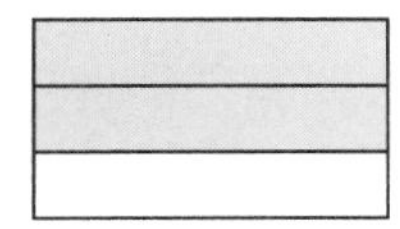

In the first diagram the window is divided into 12 identical rectangles. Eight of them, which are shown shaded, cover two-thirds of the window.

In the second diagram the window is divided into 6 identical rectangles. Four of them (shown shaded) cover two-thirds of the window.

In the third diagram the window is divided into 3 identical pieces. Two of them (shown shaded) cover two-thirds of the window.

In all three cases the shading covers two-thirds of the window, i.e. $\frac{8}{12} = \frac{4}{6} = \frac{2}{3}$.

1 (a) Draw diagrams like the one in the worked example to represent $\frac{9}{12}$ of the area of a rectangular table-top and $\frac{3}{4}$ of the area of the same table-top.

(b) Is it true that $\frac{9}{12} = \frac{3}{4}$?

(c) Write another fraction that simplifies to $\frac{3}{4}$.

2 Reduce the following fractions to fractions in their lowest terms: (a) $\frac{3}{15}$ (b) $\frac{14}{28}$ (c) $\frac{27}{36}$ (d) $\frac{13}{39}$ (e) $\frac{56}{72}$ (f) $\frac{96}{144}$

QUESTION
Give three fractions that are equivalent to $\frac{3}{5}$.

ANSWER

$\frac{3}{5} = \frac{3 \times 2}{5 \times 2} = \frac{6}{10}$

$\frac{3}{5} = \frac{3 \times 3}{5 \times 3} = \frac{9}{15}$

$\frac{3}{5} = \frac{3 \times 4}{5 \times 4} = \frac{12}{20}$

3 Copy and complete

(a) $\frac{3}{5} = \frac{3 \times 5}{5 \times 5} =$ (b) $\frac{4}{7} = \frac{4 \times 4}{7 \times 4} =$

(c) $\frac{5}{9} = \frac{5 \times 6}{9 \times 6} =$

4 Give a fraction that is equivalent to
(a) $\frac{2}{3}$ (b) $\frac{2}{7}$ (c) $\frac{5}{11}$ (d) $\frac{4}{5}$

5 Complete the following statements

(a) $\frac{2}{5} = \frac{\quad}{10} = \frac{\quad}{15}$ (b) $\frac{1}{4} = \frac{8}{\quad} = \frac{\quad}{24}$

(c) $\frac{1}{2} = \frac{\quad}{18} = \frac{21}{\quad}$ (d) $\frac{5}{6} = \frac{\quad}{36} = \frac{25}{\quad}$

6 Give three fractions that are equivalent to
(a) $\frac{3}{4}$ (b) $\frac{5}{7}$ (c) $\frac{7}{11}$

7 Give (a) $\frac{1}{2}$ in sixteenths (b) $\frac{3}{4}$ in twentieths
(c) $\frac{3}{5}$ in tenths (d) $\frac{1}{4}$ in hundredths

8 Change into twentieths $\frac{1}{4}$, $\frac{3}{10}$, $\frac{1}{2}$, $\frac{3}{5}$, $\frac{4}{5}$

Comparing the size of two fractions

To decide which of two fractions is the larger, express each fraction over the same denominator.

$\frac{2}{3} = \frac{14}{21}$ and $\frac{5}{7} = \frac{15}{21}$

so $\frac{5}{7}$ is bigger than $\frac{2}{3}$

Similarly, $\frac{5}{6} = \frac{15}{18}$ and $\frac{8}{9} = \frac{16}{18}$

i.e. $\frac{8}{9}$ is bigger than $\frac{5}{6}$

EXERCISE 3c

1 Which fraction is the larger?
(a) $\frac{4}{9}$ or $\frac{7}{12}$ (b) $\frac{2}{3}$ or $\frac{3}{4}$ (c) $\frac{5}{9}$ or $\frac{7}{12}$
(d) $\frac{11}{20}$ or $\frac{5}{8}$ (e) $\frac{8}{9}$ or $\frac{6}{7}$

QUESTION
Which is the larger, $\frac{5}{6}$ of the trees in a wood or $\frac{4}{5}$ of the trees in the wood?

ANSWER
$\frac{5}{6} = \frac{5 \times 5}{6 \times 5} = \frac{25}{30}$ and $\frac{4}{5} = \frac{4 \times 6}{5 \times 6} = \frac{24}{30}$

Since $\frac{25}{30}$ is bigger than $\frac{24}{25}$, $\frac{5}{6}$ of the trees in the wood is larger than $\frac{4}{5}$ of them.

2 Which is the larger:
(a) $\frac{1}{2}$ of a loaf of bread or $\frac{5}{12}$ of a loaf of bread?
(b) $\frac{7}{12}$ of a kilogram or $\frac{5}{8}$ of a kilogram?

3 Which is the smaller,
(a) $\frac{3}{8}$ of a mile or $\frac{5}{12}$ of a mile?
(b) $\frac{5}{7}$ of the passengers in an aircraft or $\frac{8}{9}$ of the passengers in the aircraft?

4 Some students each choose a potato from a bag and weigh it. The weights of the potatoes are $\frac{11}{16}$ lb, $\frac{9}{16}$ lb, $\frac{7}{16}$ lb and $\frac{13}{16}$ lb. Arrange these weights in order of size with the smallest first.

5 Another group of students do the same thing. The weights of their potatoes are $\frac{5}{8}$ lb, $\frac{9}{16}$ lb, $\frac{1}{2}$ lb, $\frac{3}{4}$ lb and $\frac{13}{16}$ lb. Arrange these weights in order of size with the largest first. (Express each fraction in sixteenths.)

6 The members of a committee are asked to read a report. After half an hour the fraction that each person has read is: Joe $\frac{4}{5}$, Vera $\frac{7}{10}$, Mandy $\frac{17}{20}$ and Nick $\frac{3}{4}$. Express each fraction in twentieths. Who has read
(a) the greatest fraction of the report
(b) the smallest fraction of the report?

7 The lengths of four nails are $\frac{5}{7}$ inch, $\frac{1}{2}$ inch, $\frac{3}{4}$ inch and $\frac{5}{14}$ inch. Arrange them in order of size with the smallest first.

Whole numbers, mixed numbers and improper fractions

Whole numbers can be expressed as fractions

e.g. $5 = \dfrac{5}{1} = \dfrac{5 \times 3}{1 \times 3} = \dfrac{15}{3}$

Conversely $\dfrac{24}{6} = \dfrac{24 \div 6}{6 \div 6} = \dfrac{4}{1} = 4$

Fractions that are less than 1 are called *proper fractions*,

e.g. $\frac{1}{2}$, $\frac{7}{8}$, $\frac{3}{16}$

$1\frac{3}{4}$, $2\frac{1}{2}$, $10\frac{3}{5}$ are examples of *mixed numbers*.

Fractions where the top (numerator) is larger than the bottom (denominator) are called *improper fractions*; e.g. $\frac{12}{5}$, $\frac{27}{11}$ and $\frac{13}{7}$.

We can think of 1 as four quarters, so we can write $1\frac{1}{4}$ as $\frac{4}{4} + \frac{1}{4} = \frac{5}{4}$.

When we write $1\frac{1}{4}$ as $\frac{5}{4}$ we are changing a mixed number into an improper fraction.

Similarly $2\frac{3}{4} = \frac{8}{4} + \frac{3}{4} = \frac{11}{4}$ and conversely $\frac{19}{8} = \frac{16}{8} + \frac{3}{8} = 2\frac{3}{8}$

EXERCISE 3d

1 Consider the following fractions:
$\frac{12}{5}$, $\frac{4}{5}$, $3\frac{2}{7}$, $\frac{36}{6}$, $5\frac{9}{11}$, $\frac{9}{10}$, $51\frac{1}{4}$, $\frac{123}{33}$, $\frac{5}{9}$, $\frac{39}{13}$
Which of these (a) are improper fractions (b) simplify to a whole number (c) are mixed numbers (d) are proper fractions?

2 Express as an improper fraction
(a) $5\frac{1}{3}$ (b) $4\frac{3}{4}$ (c) $7\frac{5}{6}$ (d) $3\frac{4}{7}$ (e) $8\frac{3}{5}$

3 Express as a mixed number
(a) $\frac{15}{4}$ (b) $\frac{12}{5}$ (c) $\frac{34}{7}$ (d) $\frac{15}{8}$ (e) $\frac{29}{4}$

Expressing one quantity as a fraction of another

Suppose Jo goes out in the evening on four evenings a week. There are seven evenings in a week, so the fraction of the evenings in a week that Jo goes out is $\frac{4}{7}$.

Similarly, if we have 60p in change, the fraction of £1 we have in change is $\frac{60}{100} = \frac{3}{5}$, i.e. 60p is £$\frac{3}{5}$.

To express one quantity as a fraction of another, first express both quantities in the same unit and then put the first quantity over the second quantity.

EXERCISE 3e

QUESTION

Write 5 pairs of shoes as a fraction of 20 pairs of shoes.

ANSWER

$$\frac{5}{20} = \frac{1}{4}$$

so 5 pairs of shoes is $\frac{1}{4}$ of 20 pairs of shoes.

1 What fraction of £1 is
(a) 50p (b) 25p (c) 80p (d) 65p?

2 What fraction of one hour is (a) 30 minutes
(b) 45 minutes (c) 25 minutes (d) 6 minutes?

3 Last April it rained on 12 days. On what fraction of the days in April (a) did it rain (b) did it not rain?

4 A youth club has 96 members, 60 of whom are girls. What fraction are girls?

5 Jogwear plc advertised for machine operators. They had 304 applications and took on 57 operators. What fraction of those that applied succeeded?

6 A doctor prescribed a course of 84 tablets, to be given at the rate of 3 per day. What fraction of the total tablets was to be taken
(a) each day (b) each week?

7 Danilo saves £3.50 a week towards buying a radio costing £42. What fraction has he saved after 8 weeks?

8 Sandy has £130. She spends £65 on clothes and £52 on food. What fraction does she (a) spend on food
(b) have left?

9 Don painted 15 m^2 of the walls of the lounge. The total area of the walls is 36 m^2. What fraction of the walls (a) did he paint (b) remains to be painted?

10 In a town band $\frac{3}{20}$ of the players are men, $\frac{1}{5}$ women, $\frac{7}{20}$ girls and the rest boys. What fraction of the band is
(a) boys (b) not girls?

Fractions of a quantity

To find a fraction of a quantity, multiply that quantity by the numerator and divide by the denominator.
For example, $\frac{2}{3}$ of 36 = 36 × 2 ÷ 3 = 72 ÷ 3 = 24
('of' means 'multiply by')

EXERCISE 3f

QUESTION

Three-eighths of the boys in my class play soccer. There are 32 boys in my class. How many of these
(a) play soccer (b) do not play soccer?

ANSWER

(a) Number of boys that play soccer $= \frac{3}{8} \times 32$
$= \frac{3}{\cancel{8}_1} \times \frac{\cancel{32}^4}{1}$
$= 12$

(b) Number of boys that do not play soccer $= 32 - 12$
$= 20$

1 Cheryl had £60 and spent $\frac{5}{12}$ of it. (a) How much did she spend? (b) How much did she have left?

2 Betty bought a 3 kg bag of flour. She lost $\frac{1}{10}$ of it through a hole in the side. (a) How many grams did she lose? (b) How many grams did she have left? (1 kg = 1000 g.)

3

Shavi bought an 8 litre can of engine oil. He poured $\frac{3}{8}$ of it into his engine. (a) How many litres of oil did Shavi put into his engine? (b) How many litres remained?

4 During the month of September Corey spent $\frac{2}{3}$ of the days at his workplace, $\frac{2}{15}$ of them working on the house and the remainder going away for daytrips.
(a) How many days are there in September?
(b) How many days did Corey spend working on the house?
(c) How many daytrips did he make?

5 A man left $\frac{3}{8}$ of his money to his wife and $\frac{1}{2}$ of the remainder to his brother. If he left £240 000, how much did his brother get?

Adding fractions

If we add 3 cars to 2 cars we have 5 cars.
Similarly, if we add three sixths to two sixths we have five sixths

i.e. $\frac{3}{6} + \frac{2}{6} = \frac{5}{6}$

In each case the bottom number (denominator) is nothing more than the name of the item we are considering.

To add fractions they must have the same denominators.

For example, $\frac{2}{9} + \frac{5}{9} = \frac{7}{9}$

and
$$\begin{aligned}\tfrac{4}{5} + \tfrac{3}{10} &= \tfrac{8}{10} + \tfrac{3}{10}\\ &= \tfrac{11}{10}\\ &= \tfrac{10}{10} + \tfrac{1}{10}\\ &= 1\tfrac{1}{10}\end{aligned}$$

To get the same denominator you must look for the lowest common multiple (LCM) of the numbers on the bottom, i.e. the smallest number that the denominators will go into. For example, to express $\frac{2}{3}$, $\frac{3}{4}$ and $\frac{4}{5}$ with the same denominator, the smallest number 3, 4 and 5 will go into is 60.

Then $\frac{2}{3} = \frac{2 \times 20}{3 \times 20} = \frac{40}{60}$

$\frac{3}{4} = \frac{3 \times 15}{4 \times 15} = \frac{45}{60}$

and $\frac{4}{5} = \frac{4 \times 12}{5 \times 12} = \frac{48}{60}$

so that
$$\begin{aligned}\frac{2}{3} + \frac{3}{4} + \frac{4}{5} &= \frac{40}{60} + \frac{45}{60} + \frac{48}{60}\\ &= \tfrac{133}{60}\\ &= \tfrac{120}{60} + \tfrac{13}{60}\\ &= 2 + \tfrac{13}{60}\\ &= 2\tfrac{13}{60}\end{aligned}$$

Similarly, for the fractions $\frac{2}{3} + \frac{5}{6} + \frac{7}{12}$ we must express the fractions in twelfths:

$$\begin{aligned}\frac{2}{3} + \frac{5}{6} + \frac{7}{12} &= \frac{2 \times 4}{3 \times 4} + \frac{5 \times 2}{6 \times 2} + \frac{7}{12}\\ &= \tfrac{8}{12} + \tfrac{10}{12} + \tfrac{7}{12}\\ &= \tfrac{25}{12}\\ &= \tfrac{24}{12} + \tfrac{1}{12}\\ &= 2\tfrac{1}{12}\end{aligned}$$

EXERCISE 3g

Find

1 $\frac{2}{7} + \frac{3}{7}$ **2** $\frac{4}{15} + \frac{7}{15}$ **3** $\frac{1}{8} + \frac{5}{8}$

4 $\frac{2}{5} + \frac{3}{5} + \frac{4}{5}$ **5** $\frac{1}{3} + \frac{1}{12}$ **6** $\frac{2}{3} + \frac{3}{5}$

7 $\frac{5}{6} + \frac{4}{9}$ **8** $\frac{2}{11} + \frac{5}{9}$ **9** $\frac{11}{12} + \frac{1}{6} + \frac{1}{3}$

10 $\frac{4}{15} + \frac{3}{5} + \frac{7}{10}$ **11** $\frac{7}{18} + \frac{5}{6} + \frac{2}{3}$ **12** $\frac{7}{8} + \frac{1}{3} + \frac{7}{9}$

Adding mixed numbers

When you add mixed numbers add the whole numbers first, then the fractional parts.

EXERCISE 3h

QUESTION
Find $3\frac{1}{2} + 5\frac{7}{8}$.

ANSWER
$$\begin{aligned}3\tfrac{1}{2} + 5\tfrac{7}{8} &= 3 + 5 + \tfrac{1}{2} + \tfrac{7}{8}\\ &= 8 + \tfrac{4}{8} + \tfrac{7}{8} \quad \text{(8 is the LCM of 2 and 8)}\\ &= 8 + \tfrac{11}{8}\\ &= 8 + \tfrac{8}{8} + \tfrac{3}{8}\\ &= 8 + 1 + \tfrac{3}{8}\\ &= 9\tfrac{3}{8}\end{aligned}$$

Find

1 $4\frac{3}{4} + 1\frac{7}{8}$ **2** $5\frac{1}{3} + 2\frac{1}{6}$ **3** $9\frac{1}{3} + 4\frac{5}{6}$

4 $12\frac{1}{2} + 5\frac{3}{7}$ **5** $3\frac{11}{12} + 1\frac{1}{4}$ **6** $3\frac{7}{12} + 3\frac{5}{8}$

7 $10\frac{3}{8} + 4\frac{7}{16}$ **8** $7\frac{9}{16} + 2\frac{1}{2}$

QUESTION
Find $7\frac{3}{10} + 2\frac{5}{8} + 3\frac{1}{2}$.

ANSWER

$$7\frac{3}{10} + 2\frac{5}{8} + 3\frac{1}{2} = 7 + 2 + 3 + \frac{3}{10} + \frac{5}{8} + \frac{1}{2}$$
$$= 12 + \frac{12}{40} + \frac{25}{40} + \frac{20}{40} \quad \text{(40 is the LCM of 10, 8 and 2)}$$
$$= 12 + \frac{12 + 25 + 20}{40}$$
$$= 12 + \frac{57}{40}$$
$$= 12 + \frac{40}{40} + \frac{17}{40}$$
$$= 12 + 1 + \frac{17}{40}$$
$$= 13\frac{17}{40}$$

Find

9 $5\frac{1}{3} + 3\frac{3}{4} + 7\frac{2}{5}$ **10** $5\frac{1}{5} + 3\frac{7}{20} + 5\frac{3}{4}$

11 $3\frac{1}{2} + 2\frac{1}{4} + 1\frac{1}{8}$ **12** $7\frac{3}{10} + 2\frac{5}{8} + 3\frac{1}{2}$

13 $3\frac{1}{7} + 1\frac{9}{14} + 2\frac{1}{2}$ **14** $4\frac{2}{7} + 2\frac{4}{9} + 4\frac{5}{14}$

Subtracting fractions

If we have 5 plates and remove 1 plate we have 4 plates left.
Similarly, if we have five eighths of a cake and take away one eighth of the cake we have four eighths of the cake left

i.e. $\frac{5}{8} - \frac{1}{8} = \frac{4}{8}$

Similarly $\frac{2}{3} - \frac{5}{9} = \frac{6}{9} - \frac{5}{9} = \frac{1}{9}$

and $\frac{11}{12} - \frac{1}{4} - \frac{2}{3} = \frac{11}{12} - \frac{1 \times 3}{4 \times 3} - \frac{2 \times 4}{3 \times 4}$

$$= \frac{11}{12} - \frac{3}{12} - \frac{8}{12}$$

$$= \frac{0}{12} = 0 \quad (11 - 3 - 8 = 0)$$

EXERCISE 3i

Find

1 $\frac{7}{9} - \frac{4}{9}$ **2** $\frac{1}{3} - \frac{1}{4}$ **3** $\frac{3}{4} - \frac{2}{3}$

4 $\frac{11}{12} - \frac{5}{6}$ **5** $\frac{3}{5} - \frac{7}{20}$ **6** $\frac{5}{6} - \frac{11}{18}$

7 $\frac{4}{5} - \frac{5}{7}$ **8** $\frac{34}{35} - \frac{5}{7}$ **9** $\frac{19}{20} - \frac{2}{5} - \frac{1}{4}$

10 $\frac{3}{4} - \frac{1}{3} - \frac{2}{5}$ **11** $\frac{4}{9} + \frac{2}{3} - \frac{11}{12}$ **12** $\frac{5}{6} - \frac{5}{12} + \frac{1}{2}$

Subtracting mixed numbers

Once again consider the whole numbers first, then the fractional parts.

EXERCISE 3j

QUESTION
Find $4\frac{2}{3} - 3\frac{1}{4}$.

ANSWER

$$4\frac{2}{3} - 3\frac{1}{4} = (4 - 3) + (\frac{2}{3} - \frac{1}{4})$$
$$= 1 + (\frac{8}{12} - \frac{3}{12}) \quad \text{(LCM of 3 and 4 is 12)}$$
$$= 1 + \frac{5}{12}$$
$$= 1\frac{5}{12}$$

Find

1 $2\frac{3}{4} - 1\frac{1}{2}$ **2** $3\frac{2}{3} - 2\frac{1}{2}$

3 $5\frac{3}{4} - 2\frac{3}{8}$ **4** $7\frac{1}{2} - 3\frac{1}{3}$

5 $9\frac{3}{4} - 7\frac{5}{8}$ **6** $5\frac{7}{8} - 4\frac{3}{5}$

7 $4\frac{5}{6} - 1\frac{2}{3}$ **8** $12\frac{11}{16} - 7\frac{1}{2}$

QUESTION
Find $5\frac{1}{2} - 2\frac{2}{3}$.

ANSWER

$$5\frac{1}{2} - 2\frac{2}{3} = (5 - 2) + \frac{1}{2} - \frac{2}{3}$$
$$= 3 + \frac{3}{6} - \frac{4}{6} \quad \text{(We can't find } \frac{3}{6} - \frac{4}{6}\text{)}$$
$$= 2 + 1 + \frac{3}{6} - \frac{4}{6}$$
$$= 2 + \frac{6}{6} + \frac{3}{6} - \frac{4}{6}$$
$$= 2 + \frac{5}{6}$$
$$= 2\frac{5}{6}$$

Find

9 $7\frac{1}{2} - 3\frac{2}{3}$ **10** $9\frac{7}{12} - 3\frac{3}{4}$

11 $6\frac{1}{4} - 1\frac{5}{8}$ **12** $10\frac{3}{8} - 7\frac{3}{4}$

13 $5\frac{1}{8} - 2\frac{1}{2}$ **14** $8\frac{5}{8} - 3\frac{5}{6}$

15 $10\frac{5}{8} - 7\frac{3}{4}$ **16** $3\frac{1}{8} - 2\frac{2}{3}$

Combined adding and subtracting of fractions

EXERCISE 3k

QUESTION

Find $6\frac{1}{6} - 2\frac{2}{3} + 1\frac{4}{9}$.

ANSWER

$$\begin{aligned}
6\tfrac{1}{6} - 2\tfrac{2}{3} + 1\tfrac{4}{9} &= 6 - 2 + 1 + \tfrac{1}{6} - \tfrac{2}{3} + \tfrac{4}{9} \\
&= 5 + \tfrac{3}{18} - \tfrac{12}{18} + \tfrac{8}{18} \\
&= 5 + \tfrac{11}{18} - \tfrac{12}{18} \\
&= 4 + 1 + \tfrac{11}{18} - \tfrac{12}{18} \\
&= 4 + \tfrac{18}{18} + \tfrac{11}{18} - \tfrac{12}{18} \\
&= 4 + \tfrac{29}{18} - \tfrac{12}{18} \\
&= 4 + \tfrac{17}{18} \\
&= 4\tfrac{17}{18}
\end{aligned}$$

Find

1 $3\frac{1}{4} + 4\frac{1}{3} - 5\frac{1}{6}$ **2** $5\frac{1}{4} - 1\frac{2}{3} - 3\frac{1}{2}$ **3** $7\frac{3}{4} - 3\frac{5}{8} + 1\frac{2}{3}$

4 $5\frac{2}{5} + 4\frac{5}{6} - 6\frac{3}{4}$ **5** $6\frac{3}{4} + \frac{7}{12} - 3\frac{9}{16}$ **6** $4\frac{7}{12} - 3\frac{5}{8} + 1\frac{2}{3}$

7 $5\frac{1}{2} - 2\frac{2}{3} - 1\frac{1}{5}$ **8** $12\frac{6}{7} - 5\frac{1}{3} - 1\frac{1}{4}$

Problems that involve adding and subtracting fractions

Real-life problems often arise where we need to work in fractions.

EXERCISE 3l

QUESTION

In a class of students, $\frac{1}{2}$ of the students come by bus, $\frac{2}{5}$ come by car and the remainder walk. (a) What fraction of the students walk to college? (b) What fraction do not come by car?

ANSWER

(a) Fraction of students that do not walk to college

= fraction that come by bus + fraction that come by car

$= \frac{1}{2} + \frac{2}{5}$

$= \frac{5}{10} + \frac{4}{10}$ (expressing each fraction in tenths)

$= \frac{9}{10}$

Fraction that walk = 1 − fraction that do not walk

$= 1 - \frac{9}{10}$

$= \frac{10}{10} - \frac{9}{10}$

$= \frac{1}{10}$

i.e. $\frac{1}{10}$ of the students walk to college.

(b) Fraction that come by car is $\frac{2}{5}$

∴ fraction that do not come by car is $1 - \frac{2}{5}$

$= \frac{5}{5} - \frac{2}{5}$

$= \frac{3}{5}$

i.e. $\frac{3}{5}$ of the students do not come by car.

1 At a pop festival, $\frac{2}{3}$ of the groups were all male, $\frac{1}{5}$ of the groups had one female and the rest had more than one female. What fraction of the groups (a) were not all male (b) had more than one female?

2 An airline allows each passenger to take 66 pounds of luggage. Maxine has one case weighing $27\frac{5}{8}$ lb and another weighing $12\frac{1}{4}$ lb. How many pounds is she under the limit?

3 A petrol storage tank is $\frac{3}{4}$ full. After a certain quantity of petrol is drawn off it is $\frac{3}{5}$ full. What fraction of a full tank is drawn off?

4 A reel of rope is $42\frac{1}{2}$ yards long. Lengths of rope $5\frac{1}{4}$ yd, $6\frac{5}{8}$ yd and $12\frac{5}{8}$ yd are cut from it. How much rope is left on the reel?

Multiplying fractions

Two fractions are multiplied together by multiplying their numerators (tops) and multiplying their denominators (bottoms).

Suppose the records show that $\frac{3}{5}$ of Derek Johnson's farmland is devoted to growing cereals and $\frac{7}{8}$ of his cereal crop is maize. To find the fraction of his land used to grow maize we must multiply $\frac{7}{8}$ by $\frac{3}{5}$,

i.e. $\dfrac{7}{8} \times \dfrac{3}{5} = \dfrac{21}{40}$

Hence $\frac{21}{40}$ of Derek's land is used to grow maize.

When a mixed number is multiplied by a fraction it must first be changed into an improper fraction.

For example, $\frac{3}{4} \times 2\frac{2}{3} = \frac{\cancel{3}^1}{\cancel{4}_1} \times \frac{\cancel{8}^2}{\cancel{3}_1} = \frac{2}{1} = 2$

and $5\frac{1}{3} \times 2\frac{3}{4} = \frac{\cancel{16}^4}{3} \times \frac{11}{\cancel{4}_1} = \frac{44}{3} = 14\frac{2}{3}$

EXERCISE 3m

QUESTION
Find $\frac{5}{7} \times \frac{2}{3}$

ANSWER

$$\frac{5}{7} \times \frac{2}{3} = \frac{5 \times 2}{7 \times 3} = \frac{10}{21}$$

Find

1 $\frac{3}{5} \times \frac{2}{7}$ **2** $\frac{5}{11} \times \frac{2}{3}$ **3** $\frac{3}{4} \times \frac{5}{7}$ **4** $\frac{7}{12} \times \frac{7}{5}$

QUESTION
Find (a) $\frac{5}{12} \times \frac{4}{15}$ (b) $\frac{7}{20} \times \frac{5}{14} \times \frac{8}{9}$

ANSWER
(a) $\frac{\cancel{5}^1}{\cancel{12}_3} \times \frac{\cancel{4}^1}{\cancel{15}_3} = \frac{1}{9}$

(b) $\frac{\cancel{7}^1}{\cancel{20}_{\cancel{4}_1}} \times \frac{\cancel{5}^1}{\cancel{14}_{\cancel{2}_1}} \times \frac{\cancel{8}^{\cancel{2}^1}}{9} = \frac{1}{9}$

Find

5 $\frac{5}{8} \times \frac{3}{10}$ **6** $\frac{3}{5} \times \frac{4}{9}$ **7** $\frac{20}{21} \times \frac{7}{4}$

8 $\frac{5}{9} \times \frac{3}{20}$ **9** $\frac{7}{12} \times \frac{9}{28} \times \frac{4}{5}$ **10** $\frac{5}{9} \times \frac{12}{25} \times \frac{5}{7}$

11 $\frac{11}{18} \times \frac{21}{44} \times \frac{9}{14}$ **12** $\frac{4}{7} \times \frac{14}{27} \times \frac{9}{28}$

Multiplying fractions that involve improper fractions

To multiply mixed numbers first write them as improper fractions.

EXERCISE 3n

QUESTION
Find $4\frac{1}{4} \times 2\frac{1}{2}$

ANSWER

$$\begin{aligned} 4\tfrac{1}{4} \times 2\tfrac{1}{2} &= \frac{17}{4} \times \frac{5}{2} \\ &= \frac{85}{8} \\ &= \frac{80}{8} + \frac{5}{8} \\ &= 10 + \frac{5}{8} \\ &= 10\tfrac{5}{8} \end{aligned}$$

Find

1 $4\frac{1}{2} \times \frac{4}{9}$ **2** $1\frac{2}{5} \times 2\frac{1}{2}$ **3** $5\frac{1}{3} \times 1\frac{3}{8}$ **4** $3\frac{1}{5} \times 1\frac{3}{4}$

QUESTION
Find $3\frac{3}{7} \times 1\frac{5}{12} \times 4\frac{2}{3}$.

ANSWER

$$\begin{aligned} 3\tfrac{3}{7} \times 1\tfrac{5}{12} \times 4\tfrac{2}{3} &= \frac{\cancel{24}^2}{\cancel{7}_1} \times \frac{17}{\cancel{12}_1} \times \frac{\cancel{14}^2}{3} \\ &= \frac{68}{3} \\ &= \frac{66}{3} + \frac{2}{3} \\ &= 22 + \frac{2}{3} \\ &= 22\tfrac{2}{3} \end{aligned}$$

Find

5 $\frac{4}{7}$ of $4\frac{3}{8}$ **6** $2\frac{5}{8} \times \frac{3}{7} \times 2\frac{2}{5}$

7 $3\frac{1}{6} \times 1\frac{5}{7} \times 5\frac{1}{4}$ **8** $3\frac{3}{7} \times 1\frac{5}{9} \times 2\frac{1}{8}$

Reciprocals

If, when two numbers are multiplied together, the answer is 1 then each number is called the *reciprocal* of the other.

For example, $3 \times \frac{1}{3} = 1$, so the reciprocal of 3 is $\frac{1}{3}$ and the reciprocal of $\frac{1}{3}$ is 3.
Similarly, since $\frac{4}{5} \times \frac{5}{4} = 1$ the reciprocal of $\frac{4}{5}$ is $\frac{5}{4}$.

The reciprocal of a number is given when 1 is divided by that number. The result is the same as turning the original number upside down; for example, the reciprocal of $\frac{6}{7}$ is $\frac{7}{6}$ and the reciprocal of $\frac{3}{13}$ is $\frac{13}{3}$, i.e. $4\frac{1}{3}$.

EXERCISE 3p

Find the reciprocal of

1 $\frac{3}{5}$ **2** $\frac{7}{9}$ **3** $\frac{11}{5}$

4 $2\frac{1}{5}$ **5** $3\frac{4}{7}$ **6** $3\frac{5}{12}$

Dividing by a fraction

George wants to use some $\frac{1}{8}$ inch metal washers to raise the height of his gate by $\frac{3}{4}$ inch. How many does he need? This means that he needs to know how many eighths there are in $\frac{3}{4}$.

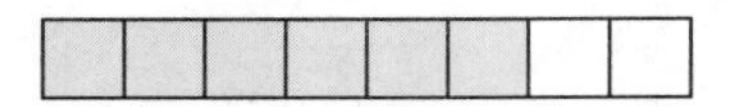

The rectangle has been divided into 8 equal squares, so each square represents $\frac{1}{8}$ of the whole.
$\frac{3}{4}$ of the rectangle has been shaded.
There are six eighths in $\frac{3}{4}$

$$\frac{3}{4} \div \frac{1}{8} = 6$$

George therefore needs 6 washers to fill the gap.

To divide by a fraction multiply by its reciprocal, i.e. by the fraction turned upside down.
For example, $\frac{2}{3} \div \frac{1}{4} = \frac{2}{3} \times \frac{4}{1} = \frac{8}{3} = 2\frac{2}{3}$
and $6\frac{4}{9} \div 1\frac{1}{3} = \frac{58}{9} \div \frac{4}{3} = \frac{\cancel{58}^{29}}{\cancel{9}_{3}} \times \frac{\cancel{3}^{1}}{\cancel{4}_{2}} = \frac{29}{6} = 4\frac{5}{6}$

EXERCISE 3q

QUESTION
Find $5 \div \frac{2}{3}$.

ANSWER
$5 \div \frac{2}{3} = 5 \times \frac{3}{2}$
$= \frac{15}{2}$
$= 7\frac{1}{2}$

Find

1 $4 \div \frac{1}{2}$ **2** $6 \div \frac{1}{3}$ **3** $5 \div \frac{3}{5}$ **4** $3\frac{1}{5} \div \frac{4}{7}$

QUESTION
Find $3\frac{1}{4} \div 1\frac{1}{6}$.

ANSWER
$3\frac{1}{4} \div 1\frac{1}{6} = \frac{13}{4} \div \frac{7}{6}$
$= \frac{13}{\cancel{4}_{2}} \times \frac{\cancel{6}^{3}}{7}$
$= \frac{39}{14}$
$= \frac{28}{14} + \frac{11}{14}$
$= 2 + \frac{11}{14}$
$= 2\frac{11}{14}$

Find

5 $4\frac{1}{2} \div 1\frac{1}{2}$ **6** $1\frac{1}{2} \div 1\frac{1}{5}$

7 $2\frac{1}{3} \div 1\frac{5}{9}$ **8** $4\frac{2}{5} \div 5\frac{1}{2}$

9 $6\frac{2}{5} \div 9\frac{3}{5}$ **10** $4\frac{1}{3} \div 9\frac{3}{4}$

11 $5\frac{1}{3} \div 1\frac{1}{7}$ **12** $4\frac{1}{7} \div 2\frac{5}{12}$

Solving problems that involve multiplying and dividing fractions

EXERCISE 3r

QUESTION
On a shopping trip Carole spent $\frac{3}{4}$ of her money on clothes and $\frac{1}{6}$ on compact discs. She had £12 left.

(a) How much did she start with?

(b) How much did she spend on clothes?

(c) How much did the CDs cost?

ANSWER
(a) Fraction of Carole's money that she spent $= \frac{3}{4} + \frac{1}{6}$
$= \frac{9}{12} + \frac{2}{12}$
$= \frac{11}{12}$

Fraction Carole had left $= 1 - \frac{11}{12}$
$= \frac{12}{12} - \frac{11}{12}$
$= \frac{1}{12}$

Since she had £12 left,
$\frac{1}{12}$ of the amount she started with is £12
i.e. the whole of the amount she started with is
£12 $\div \frac{1}{12}$
= £12 $\times \frac{12}{1}$
= £144

(b) Amount spent on clothes is $\frac{3}{4} \times$ £144
= £$\frac{3}{4} \times \frac{144}{1}$
= £108

(c) Cost of CDs is $\frac{1}{6} \times$ £144
= £$\frac{1}{6} \times \frac{144}{1}$
= £24

1 In a local election there were two candidates. Allan Buzzard got $\frac{5}{12}$ of the votes and Betty Austin got $\frac{1}{3}$. A total of 3000 people entitled to vote did not do so.
(a) What fraction of the electorate
(i) voted (ii) did not vote?
(b) How large is the electorate?
(c) How many votes did Betty Austin get?

2 My school is divided into the lower school, the middle school and the upper school. $\frac{1}{5}$ of the pupils are in the upper school, $\frac{1}{4}$ in the middle school and 396 in the lower school. (a) What fraction of the pupils are in the lower school? (b) How many pupils are there in the school?

3 In a business the total receipts for the year were used as follows: $\frac{2}{5}$ was spent on materials, $\frac{7}{20}$ on wages, $\frac{1}{10}$ on fixed overheads, $\frac{1}{20}$ on dividends and the remainder was put into the reserve fund. (a) What fraction of the income was placed in the reserve fund? (b) If £$\frac{1}{2}$ million was placed in the reserve fund how much was spent on (i) materials (ii) wages?

QUESTION
How many bottles of wine, each holding $\frac{7}{10}$ litre, can Sheila fill from a cask holding $10\frac{1}{2}$ litres?

ANSWER
(We need to know how many times $\frac{7}{10}$ will divide into $10\frac{1}{2}$.)
Number of bottles is $10\frac{1}{2} \div \frac{7}{10}$

$$= \frac{21}{2} \div \frac{7}{10}$$
$$= \frac{\cancel{21}^{3}}{\cancel{2}_{1}} \times \frac{\cancel{10}^{5}}{\cancel{7}_{1}}$$
$$= 15$$

i.e. 15 bottles, each holding $\frac{7}{10}$ litre, can be filled from a cask holding $10\frac{1}{2}$ litres.

---

4 How many jars of marmalade, each of which holds $\frac{1}{2}$ kg, can be filled from a drum of marmalade holding 25 kg?

5 How many $4\frac{1}{2}$ cm lengths of wire can be cut from a coil of wire that is 90 cm long?

6 It takes $3\frac{3}{4}$ minutes to read 50 lines of a novel. How long does it take to read (a) one line (b) 350 lines?

7 A doctor estimates that it takes him $3\frac{1}{2}$ minutes to see a patient in his surgery. (a) How many patients does he expect to see in his morning surgery, which lasts $1\frac{3}{4}$ hours? (b) Evening surgery is time-tabled to last $1\frac{1}{4}$ hours. Twenty patients attend to see him. Should he be able to see all of them in $1\frac{1}{4}$ hours?

8

A motorcyclist travels $313\frac{1}{2}$ metres in $8\frac{1}{4}$ seconds. How far does he travel in one second?

9 A furnisher retailer prices every piece of furniture she sells at one half more than it costs her. Find (a) the sale price of a bed that cost her £200 (b) the cost price of a dining suite that she sells for £540.

10 The firm of Krause & Amick publish local history books. For any given publication they estimate that the fixed costs are £2500 and in addition the cost of each book produced is £3.50. These books they sell to the retailer at £8 a copy.

(a) They decide to print 1500 copies and are surprised to sell $\frac{2}{3}$ of them in the first month. Have they got their money back?

(b) After one year all the books have been sold. How much profit have they made?

(c) The book retails at £12.50 and one local outlet takes $\frac{7}{10}$ of the books sold. The retailer's expenses work out at 50p a book. What profit does this retailer make? Does he make more profit than the publisher?

Combined operations

The questions in the next exercise are more difficult. Some of them mix adding or subtracting with multiplying or dividing.

EXERCISE 3s

QUESTION
Find $(2\frac{1}{2} - 1\frac{3}{8}) \div \frac{3}{4}$

ANSWER

$$(2\tfrac{1}{2} - 1\tfrac{3}{8}) \div \tfrac{3}{4} = (1 + \tfrac{1}{2} - \tfrac{3}{8}) \times \tfrac{4}{3} \quad \text{(Work the bracket out first)}$$
$$= (1 + \tfrac{4}{8} - \tfrac{3}{8}) \times \tfrac{4}{3}$$
$$= (1 + \tfrac{1}{8}) \times \tfrac{4}{3}$$
$$= 1\tfrac{1}{8} \times \tfrac{4}{3}$$
$$= \frac{\cancel{9}^{3}}{\cancel{8}_{2}} \times \frac{\cancel{4}^{1}}{\cancel{3}_{1}}$$
$$= \tfrac{3}{2}$$
$$= 1\tfrac{1}{2}$$

Find

1 $\frac{9}{10} \div \frac{3}{8} \div 3\frac{1}{5}$

2 $1\frac{2}{5} \times (\frac{2}{3} - \frac{1}{4}) + \frac{1}{4}$

3 $1\frac{17}{18} \div 1\frac{4}{5} \times 2\frac{7}{10}$

4 $1\frac{5}{16} \times 4\frac{4}{5} \div 1\frac{2}{5}$

5 $3\frac{2}{3} \div 1\frac{5}{9} \div 1\frac{5}{28}$

6 $3\frac{2}{3} \div (\frac{2}{3} + \frac{1}{15})$

7 $1\frac{5}{9} \div 1\frac{1}{7} \div 5\frac{1}{4}$

8 $3\frac{3}{7} \times 8\frac{1}{6} \div 11\frac{2}{3}$

9 $3\frac{1}{8} \times 2\frac{14}{15} + 7\frac{3}{8}$

Multiple-choice questions 3

In this exercise several alternative answers are given. Write down the letter that corresponds to the correct answer.

1 The largest of the fractions $\frac{5}{8}$, $\frac{3}{4}$, $\frac{13}{16}$ and $\frac{19}{32}$ is

A $\frac{3}{4}$ **B** $\frac{19}{32}$ **C** $\frac{13}{16}$ **D** $\frac{5}{8}$

2 If the fractions $\frac{1}{2}$, $\frac{2}{3}$, $\frac{13}{24}$, $\frac{7}{12}$ and $\frac{11}{24}$ are put in order of size with the smallest first, the second fraction is

A $\frac{1}{2}$ **B** $\frac{2}{3}$ **C** $\frac{13}{24}$ **D** $\frac{7}{12}$

3 The value of $4\frac{1}{3} - 2\frac{7}{8} + 1\frac{3}{4}$ is

A $3\frac{3}{8}$ **B** $3\frac{5}{24}$ **C** $3\frac{5}{12}$ **D** $3\frac{1}{2}$

4 The value of $\frac{2}{3} \times 1\frac{2}{7} \div 2\frac{1}{7}$ is

A $1\frac{41}{49}$ **B** $\frac{17}{21}$ **3** $\frac{5}{17}$ **D** $\frac{2}{5}$

Self-assessment test 3

1 Complete the following statement: $\frac{15}{20} = \frac{45}{20} = \frac{}{4} = \frac{12}{20}$

2 Which is the greater distance, $\frac{7}{12}$ of a mile or $\frac{11}{18}$ of a mile?

3 One hundred and twelve of the two hundred and fifty-six pages of a book have diagrams. What fraction of the pages
(a) have diagrams (b) do not have diagrams?

4 Find

(a) $5\frac{3}{4} + 2\frac{2}{3}$ (b) $6\frac{2}{3} - 3\frac{3}{4}$
(c) $7\frac{1}{4} - 3\frac{7}{8} + 4\frac{3}{5}$ (d) $5\frac{1}{4} \times 1\frac{7}{9}$
(e) $2\frac{1}{12} \div 4\frac{3}{8}$ (f) $2\frac{8}{9} \div (1\frac{5}{6} + \frac{1}{3})$

5 Last year, Len's motoring costs were divided into: repayment of the loan $\frac{5}{8}$, tax and insurance $\frac{1}{12}$, petrol $\frac{1}{4}$ and the remainder was for servicing and repairs which cost him £100. (a) What were his motoring costs? (b) How much did Len spend (i) on petrol (ii) repaying the loan?

CHAPTER 4

Decimals

Decimal notation

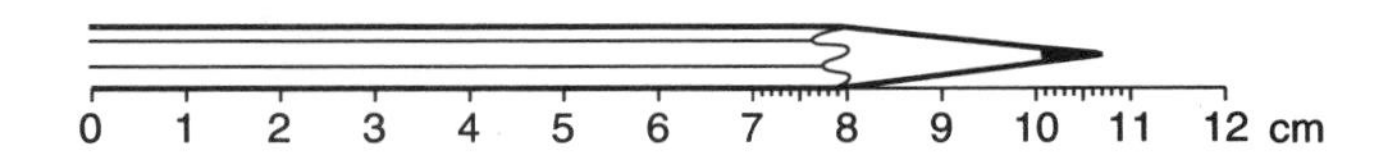

I measure my pencil on a ruler graduated in centimetres and tenths of a centimetre. The length of the pencil is 10 centimetres plus seven tenths, i.e. $\frac{7}{10}$, of a centimetre.

In decimal notation we write this as 10.7 cm.

When the part near the tip of the pencil is magnified ten times we can measure the length of the pencil more accurately.

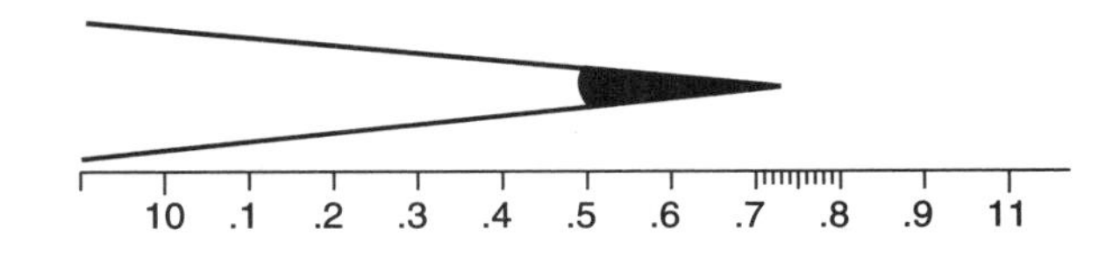

Through a magnifying glass let us assume that each tenth of a centimetre is divided into ten parts, i.e. into hundredths of a centimetre.

We can see that the length of the pencil is 10.7 centimetres plus three hundredths, i.e. $\frac{3}{100}$, of a centimetre.

In decimal notation we write this as 10.73 cm.

The dot is called the *decimal point*. We read this length as 'ten point seven three centimetres'.

We can set out the number 10.73 under headings:

Tens	Units		Tenths	Hundredths
1	0	.	7	3

EXERCISE 4a

QUESTION
Write as a decimal (a) $\frac{3}{10}$ (b) $\frac{7}{100}$.

ANSWER
(a) $\frac{3}{10} = 0.3$ (We put a 0 to the left of the decimal point to show that there are no units)

(b) $\frac{7}{100} = 0.07$ (There are no units, no tenths, but 7 hundredths)

1 Write as a decimal

(a) $\frac{7}{10}$ (b) $\frac{9}{100}$ (c) $\frac{17}{100}$ (d) $\frac{1}{1000}$

2 Write as a fraction with 100 as the denominator:

(a) 0.27 (b) 0.81 (c) 0.09 (d) 0.01

QUESTION
For the number 3.142, write down the place value of each figure.

ANSWER
3 represents 3 units
1 represents 1 tenth
4 represents 4 hundredths
2 represents 2 thousandths

3 Write down for each number the value of the 7:

(a) 4.67 (b) 3.792 (c) 7.504 (d) 3.872

4 Write down for each number the value of the smallest figure:

(a) 5.38 (b) 12.54 (c) 5.382 (d) 8.747

5 Write down for each of the following numbers (a) the number of tenths (b) the number of hundredths (c) the number of thousandths:

(i) 39.748 (ii) 421.947 (iii) 2.763

QUESTION
Give the number that follows as a decimal:

Units		Tenths	Hundredths	Thousands
5	.		2	7

ANSWER
There are no tenths, so we fill in with a 0.
The number is 5.027.

6 Write each number as a decimal:

	Hundreds	Tens	Units		Tenths	Hundredths	Thousandths
(a)		3	1	.	8	3	
(b)			9	.	2	5	
(c)	4	6		.	3	4	
(d)			6	.	5	4	3
(e)	3			.	2	1	9

7 Express each number in the form shown in the above table:

(a) 31.5 (b) 755.81 (c) 5.036
(d) 361.06 (e) 37.228

QUESTION
Write $\frac{3}{10} + \frac{9}{100} + \frac{2}{1000}$ as a decimal.

ANSWER
$\frac{3}{10} + \frac{9}{100} + \frac{2}{1000} = 0.392$

---

8 Write each group of fractions as a decimal:

(a) $\frac{3}{10} + \frac{5}{100}$ (b) $\frac{7}{10} + \frac{3}{100} + \frac{5}{1000}$
(c) $\frac{8}{10} + \frac{4}{1000}$ (d) $\frac{6}{100} + \frac{4}{1000}$

QUESTION
Write 0.925 as the sum of fractions whose denominators are 10, 100 and 1000.

ANSWER
$0.925 = \frac{9}{10} + \frac{2}{100} + \frac{5}{1000}$

---

9 Write each decimal as the sum of fractions with denominators 10, 100, 1000:

(a) 0.447 (b) 0.803 (c) 0.971 (d) 0.028

QUESTION
Express as a fraction in its lowest terms
(a) 0.8 (b) 0.104.

ANSWER
(a) 0.8 is 8 tenths $= \frac{8}{10}$
$= \frac{4}{5}$ (Dividing top and bottom by 2)

(b) 0.304 is $\frac{3}{10} + \frac{4}{1000} = \frac{300}{1000} + \frac{4}{1000}$
$= \frac{304}{1000}$
$= \frac{38}{125}$ (Dividing top and bottom by 8)

---

10 Give as a fraction in its lowest terms

(a) 0.6 (b) 0.48 (c) 0.64 (d) 0.177
(e) 0.875 (f) 0.125 (g) 0.444

QUESTION
Express as a decimal (a) five and four tenths
(b) seventeen and three hundredths
(c) fifteen and forty-three hundredths.

ANSWER
(a) five and four tenths $= 5 + \frac{4}{10} = 5.4$

(b) seventeen and three hundredths,
i.e. $17 + \frac{0}{10} + \frac{3}{100} = 17.03$

(c) fifteen and forty-three hundredths $= 15\frac{43}{100}$
$= 15 + \frac{40}{100} + \frac{3}{100}$
$= 15 + \frac{4}{10} + \frac{3}{100}$
$= 15.43$

---

11 Write as a decimal

(a) three and seven tenths
(b) four tenths and eight hundredths
(c) twelve and five hundredths
(d) $6\frac{1}{10}$ (e) $12\frac{37}{100}$ (f) $5\frac{7}{100}$ (g) $\frac{3}{10}$

QUESTION
The width of a ruler is being measured using another ruler marked in centimetres and tenths of a centimetre. Write its width in decimal notation.

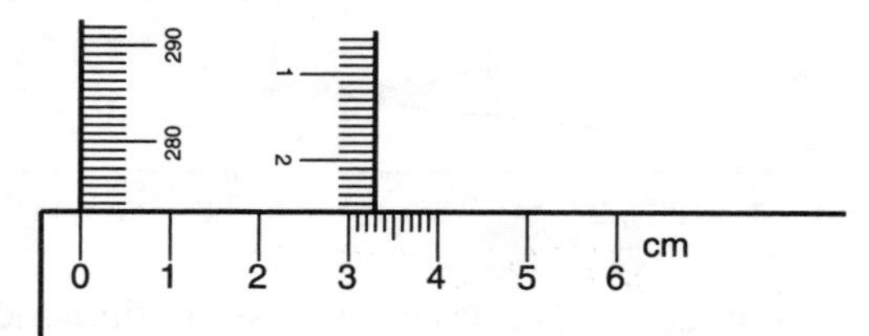

ANSWER
The width is 3 centimetres and three tenths,
i.e. $\frac{3}{10}$ of a centimetre.
In decimal notation we write this as 3.3 cm.

In questions 12 to 15 write the length of each object as a decimal.

12

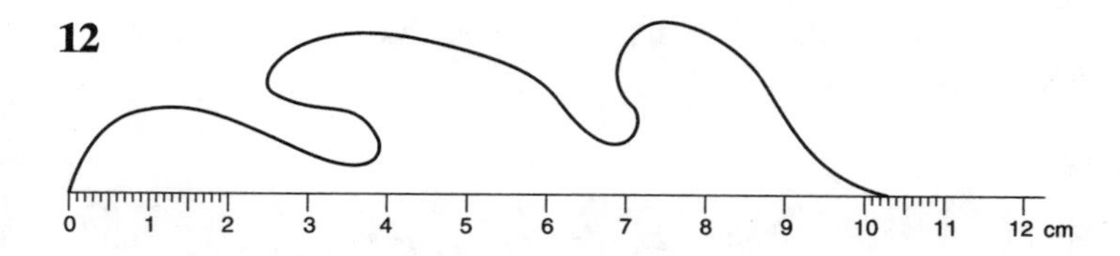

13

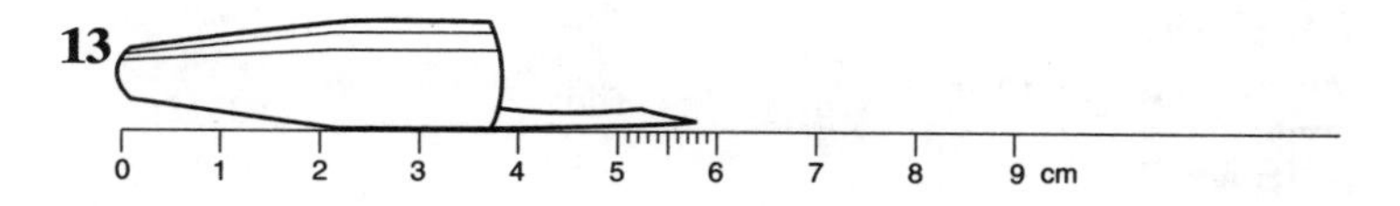

14

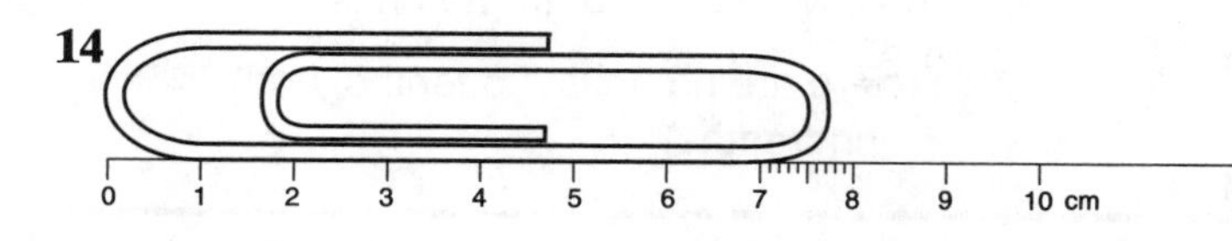

15

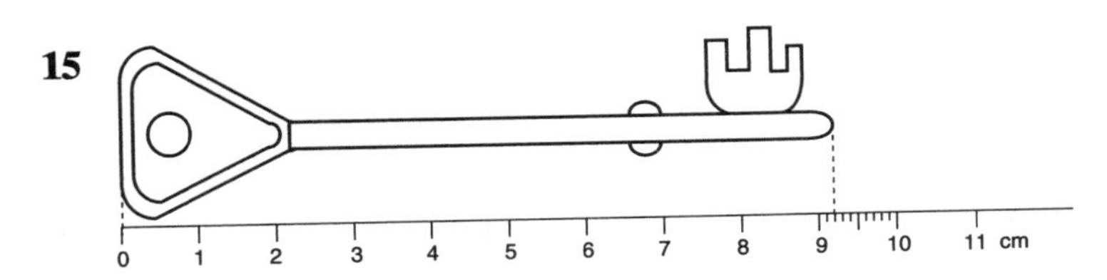

Fractions as decimals

To change a fraction into a decimal divide the top (the numerator) by the bottom (the denominator).

For example $\frac{4}{5} = 4 \div 5$ **4 ÷ 5 =**
$= 0.8$

$\frac{23}{50} = 23 \div 50$ **2 3 ÷ 5 0 =**
$= 0.46$

and $\frac{17}{32} = 17 \div 32$ **1 7 ÷ 3 2 =**
$= 0.531\ 25$

Some fractions do not give exact decimals. These are dealt with later.

EXERCISE 4b

Write each fraction as a decimal:

1 $\frac{2}{5}$ **2** $\frac{3}{8}$ **3** $\frac{3}{4}$ **4** $\frac{19}{25}$

5 $\frac{14}{25}$ **6** $\frac{63}{125}$ **7** $\frac{14}{25}$ **8** $\frac{9}{32}$

QUESTION
Change into a decimal (a) $5\frac{3}{8}$ (b) $7\frac{13}{40}$

ANSWER

(a) $\frac{3}{8} = 0.375$
$\therefore 5\frac{3}{8} = 5.375$

(b) $\frac{13}{40} = 0.325$
$\therefore 7\frac{13}{40} = 7.325$

Write each mixed number as a decimal:

9 $1\frac{1}{2}$ **10** $3\frac{1}{4}$ **11** $5\frac{4}{5}$ **12** $7\frac{11}{20}$

13 $4\frac{7}{25}$ **14** $13\frac{29}{40}$ **15** $6\frac{27}{32}$ **16** $24\frac{3}{16}$

Putting decimals in order of size

To decide which is the larger, 5.86 or 5.89:
First look at the number of units – they are the same.
Then look at the number of tenths – they are also the same.
Finally look at the number of hundredths – 9 is bigger than 6.
So 5.89 is larger than 5.86.

EXERCISE 4c

Decide which is the larger of these numbers:

1 7.38 or 7.83   **2** 9.2 or 5.9
3 3 or 2.98   **4** 2.587 or 2.584

Put these numbers in order of size, smallest first:

5 5.66, 4.92, 6.99   **6** 7.34, 7.43, 7.17

7 10.35, 3.92, 0.998   **8** 7.15, 7.005, 7.45, 7.05

9 21.48, 20.74, 21.39, 20.87

Put these numbers in order of size, largest first:

10 5.09, 8.33, 4.27   **11** 3.09, 3.11, 3.27

12 67.3, 50.37, 54.39   **13** 9.04, 9.44, 9.4, 9.444

14 10.62, 16.02, 12.60, 16.20

15 From the numbers 12.6, 9.57, 12.2, 12.55, 1.55 and 2.55 write down (a) the smallest number (b) the largest number.

Expressing a number to a given number of decimal places

Rounding off

If we find $\frac{4}{7}$ as a decimal using a calculator, the figures fill the display.
That is, $\frac{4}{7} = 4 \div 7 = 0.571\ 428\ 571 \ldots$
We do not always need all these figures, so we often give a number correct to the nearest tenth of a unit, to the nearest hundredth of a unit or in some other way.

Suppose we wish to give 9.3578 correct to the nearest tenth.

We have 9 units and 3 tenths.

Mark a dotted line after the tenths: 9.3¦578.

If the next figure after the dotted line is 5 or more, we add 1 to the number of tenths.

So 9.3¦578 = 9.4 correct to the nearest tenth.

However, if the figure after the dotted line is less than 5 then we leave the number of tenths as it is. For example, 5.4¦287 = 5.4 correct to the nearest tenth.

Decimal places

'Correct to 2 decimal places' means correct to the second figure after the decimal point. To do this look at the figure in the 3rd place after the point. If this figure is 5 or greater than 5 then the number in the 2nd place is increased by 1; otherwise, it is the figure there already.

For example, in the number 5.637 the figure in the 3rd place after the point is 7, so we increase the figure in the 2nd place to 4.

That is, 5.637 is 5.64 correct to 2 d.p. (d.p. is the shorthand way of writing decimal places). Similarly 35.062 is 35.1 correct to 1 d.p. and 35.06 correct to 2 d.p.

EXERCISE 4d

1 Give each number correct to the nearest whole number:

(a) 45.78 (b) 7.334 (c) 13.88 (d) 123.774
(e) 0.943

2 Give each number correct to 1 decimal place:

(a) 8.93 (b) 0.563 (c) 73.735 (d) 0.078
(e) 0.276

3 Give each number correct to 2 decimal places:

(a) 37.345 (b) 9.293 (c) 63.587
(d) 0.0843 (e) 0.342

4 Give each number correct to 3 decimal places:

(a) 2.5578 (b) 0.9475 (c) 14.6666
(d) 7.333 33 (e) 8.707 07

The diagrams show a magnification of a ruler graduated in centimetres. Give each of the following measurements correct to (a) 2 decimal places (b) 1 decimal place:

5

6

7

8

9 Raoul checked the weights of some bolts. The first five he weighed gave weights of 2.935 g, 2.947 g, 3.006 g, 2.983 g and 3.018 g.
Give each weight (a) correct to 1 decimal place (b) correct to the nearest hundredth of a gram.

10

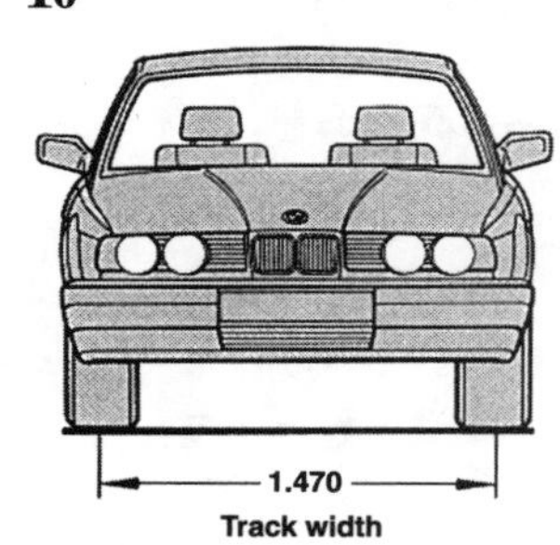

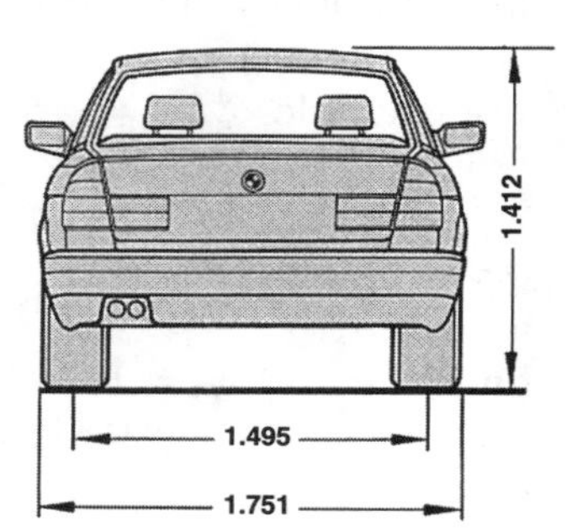

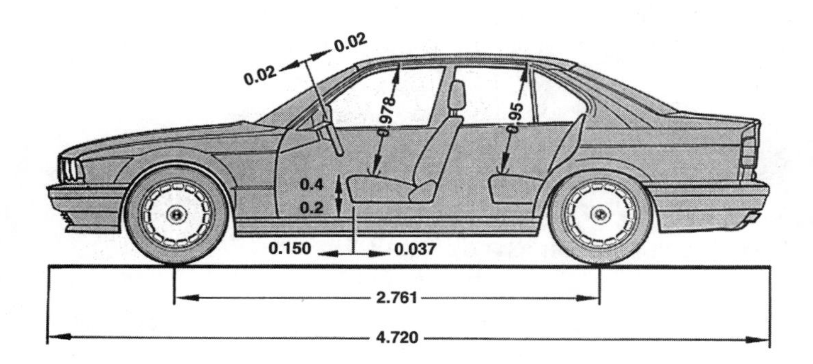

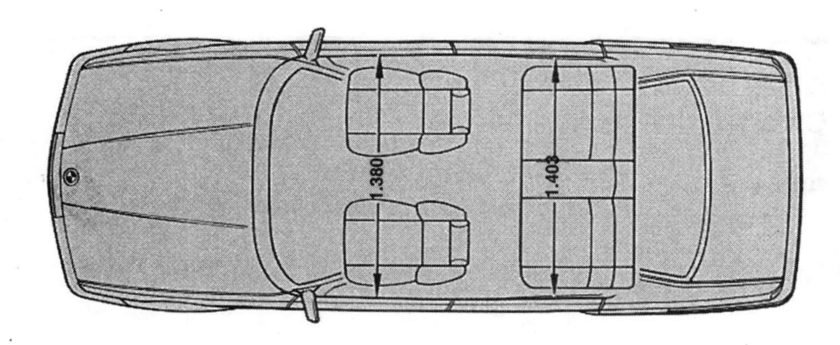

The sketch shows the lengths, in metres, for the various dimensions of a motorcar.

(a) What is the overall length correct to the nearest metre?

(b) What is the overall width, excluding the wing mirrors, correct to the nearest tenth of a metre?

(c) What is the height of the car correct to 2 d.p.?

(d) What is the rear track width correct to 1 d.p.?

(e) What is the front track width correct to 2 d.p.?

(f) What is the length of the wheelbase correct to the nearest centimetre?

(g) What is the difference between the width at shoulder level in the front seat and the width at shoulder level in the rear seat? Give your answer correct to 2 decimal places.

Significant figures

My height could be given as 1.84 m, or as 184 cm, or as 1840 mm.

Each of these measurements has the same degree of accuracy – it is given to the nearest centimetre. In each number the figure 1 has a different place value, even though it is the first figure each time. It is called the first significant figure. Similarly, 8 is the second significant figure and 4 is the third significant figure.

If you read any number from the left-hand side, without taking any notice of the position of the decimal point, the first significant figure is the first non-zero figure, the second significant figure is the next figure (whether it is a 0 or not) and so on for further significant figures.

For example, in the number 73.809, the first significant figure is 7, the second is 3, the third is 8, the fourth is 0 and the fifth is 9.

In many questions, particularly those involving length, area, volume and weight, you will often be asked to give your answer correct to 3 significant figures (3 s.f. for short).

To give a number correct to a certain number of significant figures the rule is: look at the next significant figure, if it is 5 or more than 5, round up; if it is less than 5 round down, i.e. leave the figure in the last place you require unchanged.

For example, 7.663 is 7.66 correct to 3 s.f.
(The 3rd figure is 6, while the 4th figure is 3. This is less than 5, so the 3rd figure stays unchanged at 6.)

Similarly, 3.057 07 is 3.06 correct to 3 s.f.
(The 3rd figure is 5, while the 4th figure is 7. This is more than 5, so the 3rd figures increases by 1 to 6.)

Combining these results with previous results, we say that the number 18.478 is

20 correct to the nearest 10
18 correct to the nearest whole number
18.5 correct to one decimal place (1 d.p.)
18.48 correct to 2 decimal places (2 d.p.)
18.5 correct to 3 significant figures (3 s.f.)
and 18 correct to 2 significant figures (2 s.f.)

Similarly,
0.057 84 is 0.1 correct to 1 decimal place
0.06 correct to 1 significant figure
0.058 correct to 2 significant figures
and 0.0578 correct to 3 significant figures

EXERCISE 4e

1 Give each number correct to 2 significant figures:

(a) 53.89 (b) 4.832 (c) 173.49 (d) 0.8365
(e) 3.008

2 Give each number correct to 3 significant figures:

(a) 527.6 (b) 0.8115 (c) 0.064 52
(d) 3527 (e) 9.8845

3 Give each number correct to 4 significant figures:

(a) 18.5555 (b) 5.0088 (c) 7.070 707
(d) 0.505 050 5 (e) 435.93

4 Give 47.096 28 correct to

(a) the nearest whole number (b) 2 d.p.
(c) 3 s.f. (d) 4 d.p. (e) 5 s.f.

5 Give 7.060 407 correct to

(a) 1 d.p. (b) 3 s.f. (c) 3 d.p.
(d) 2 d.p. (e) 4 s.f.

Adding decimals

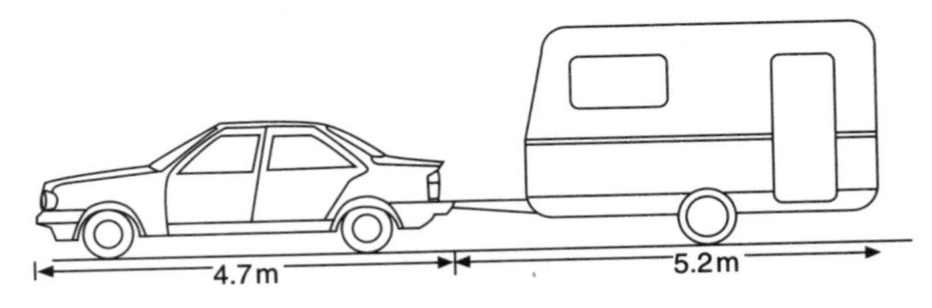

This car is 4.7 metres long and the caravan is 5.2 metres long.
4.7 metres means 4 metres and 7 tenths of a metre;
5.2 metres means 5 metres and 2 tenths of a metre.

If we add the whole metres we have 4 metres + 5 metres i.e. 9 metres and if we add the tenths of a metre we have 7 tenths + 2 tenths, i.e. 9 tenths.

The total length of the car and the caravan is therefore 9 metres and 9 tenths of a metre i.e. 9.9 metres.

This is easier to see if we set it out in columns:

Tens	Units		Tenths
	4	.	7
	5	.	2
	9	.	9

We can see that decimal numbers are added together in much the same way as whole numbers. The most important thing to remember is to put the decimal points for the different numbers in a vertical line. For example, we write 1.47 + 0.82 as

$$\begin{array}{r} 1.47 \\ +\underline{0.82} \\ 2.29 \end{array}$$ (The decimal points are in a vertical line)

We find 42.74 + 1.089 + 0.76 in a similar way:

$$\begin{array}{r} 42.740 \\ 1.089 \\ +\underline{\ 0.760} \\ 44.589 \end{array}$$ (Arrange the decimal points in a vertical line; also fill in any spaces with zeros so that each decimal has 3 digits after the decimal point)

EXERCISE 4f

Find, without using a calculator,

1 3.6 + 4.3 **2** 1.5 + 4.3 **3** 6.1 + 1.8

4 5.2 + 3.7 **5** 7.4 + 2.5 **6** 2.33 + 5.41

7 4.55 + 3.43 **8** 7.3 + 1.28 **9** 9.7 + 4.62

10 5.98 + 3.45 **11** 4.88 + 6.78 **12** 9.37 + 14.14

QUESTION

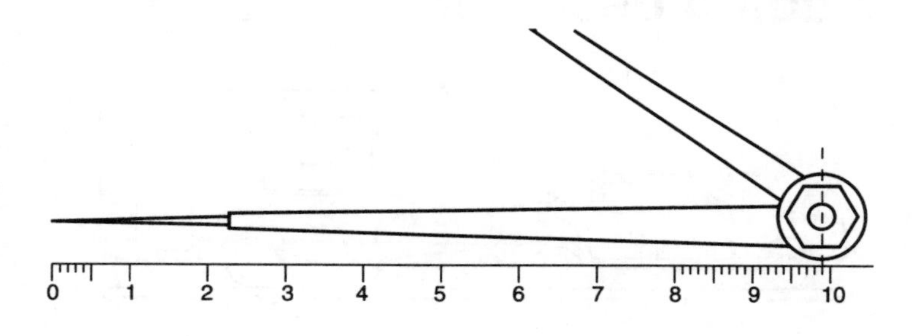

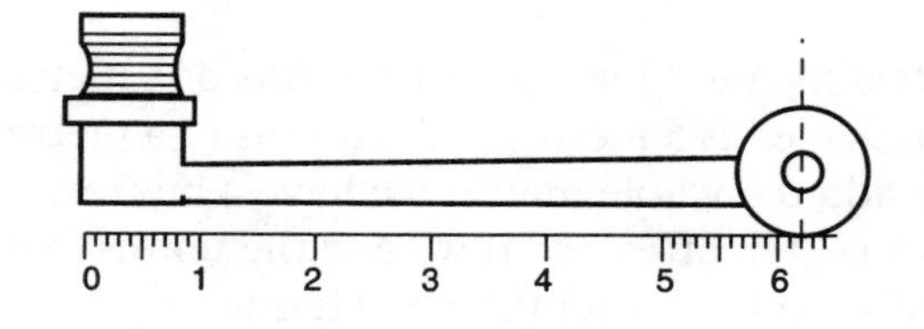

The sketch shows a pair of compasses. Find their total length when opened out.

ANSWER

The length of the long arm is 9.9 cm and the length of the short arm is 6.2 cm

$\therefore$ total length is 9.9 cm + 6.2 cm = 16.1 cm

$$\begin{array}{r} 9.9 \\ \underline{6.2} \\ 16.1 \end{array}$$

13

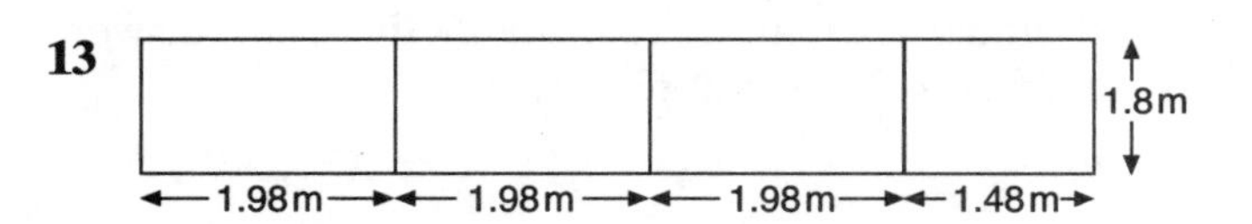

Find the total length of this fence.

14

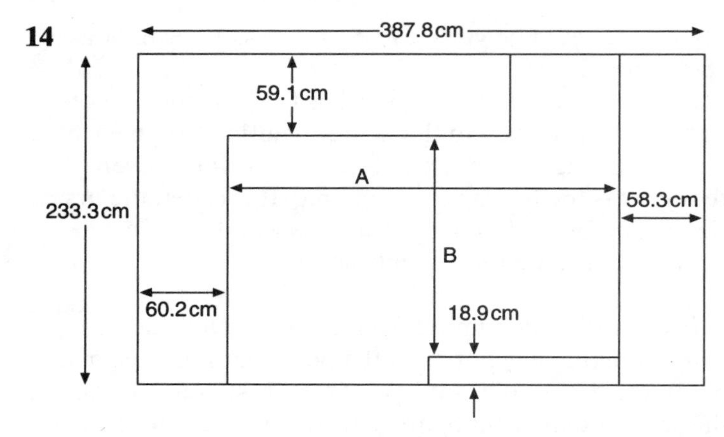

(a) This is a plan of Meg's kitchen. All the corners are right angles.
(i) Find the distance marked A
(ii) Find the distance marked B.

(b) Kitchen mats can be bought in lengths and widths that are exact multiples of 10 cm, for example 100 cm × 60 cm. What is the length and breadth of the largest mat that can be laid in this kitchen?

15

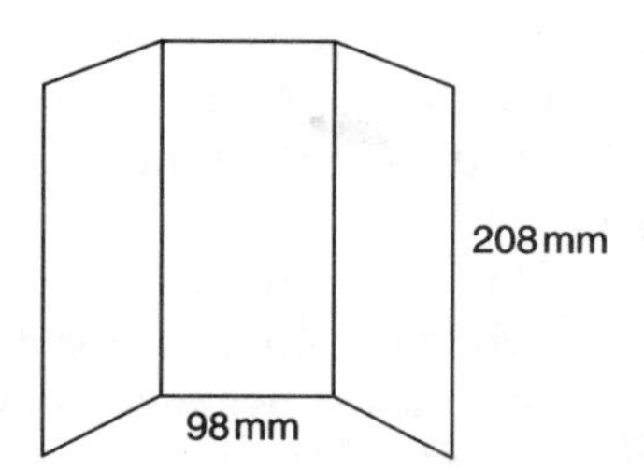

A concert programme is made by folding a single sheet of paper into three identical rectangles. Find the dimensions of the original sheet.

16

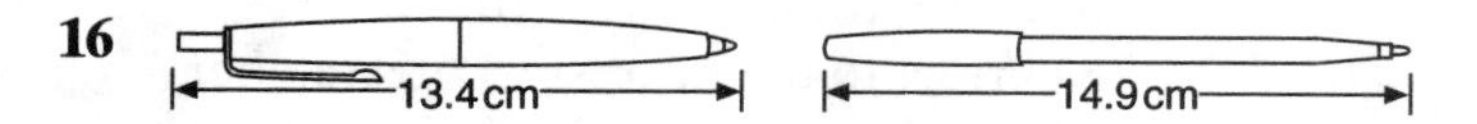

What is the total length of these two ballpoint pens if they are laid end to end?

Find, using a calculator if you wish:

17 62.3 + 15.895

18 5.837 + 12.64 + 34.883

19 7.372 + 0.779 + 3.72

20 6.22 + 9.471 + 0.708

21 6.92 + 27.668 + 5.931

22 76.009 + 0.926 + 3.741

23 13.43 + 8.2 + 124.08 + 5.98

24 2.142 + 36.085 + 50.92 + 845.2

Subtracting decimals

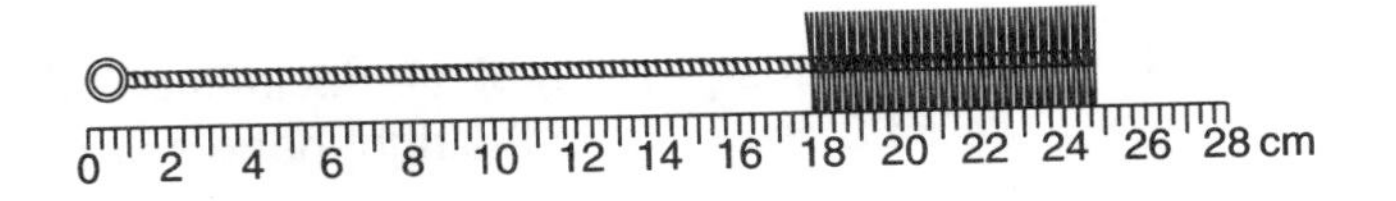

To find the length of the bristle area on this brush, we could count back on the scale from the position of the end of the bristle. However, it is easier to subtract the length of the handle from the overall length of the brush.

Length of bristle area is 24.4 cm − 17.8 cm = 6.8 cm.

EXERCISE 4g

QUESTION
Find 31.6 − 2.49.

ANSWER

```
 31.60     (Fill in the space with a zero)
  2.49
 29.11
```

Find

1 35.4 − 3

2 6.7 − 0.66

3 25.4 − 9.6

4 12.6 − 5.67

5 125.8 − 76.45

6 7 − 0.83

7 18.54 − 1.76

8 100 − 38.57

9 19.2 − 0.8092

10 46 − 3.097

QUESTION
The overall height of a new car is 127.25 cm and the ground clearance is 18.7 cm. How far is it vertically from the lowest point of the car (excluding the wheels!) to the highest point of the roof?

ANSWER
We need to find the difference between 127.25 and 18.7

```
  127.25
 − 18.70     (We write 18.7 as 18.70)
  108.55
```

The vertical distance from the lowest point of the car to the top of the roof is 108.55 cm.

11

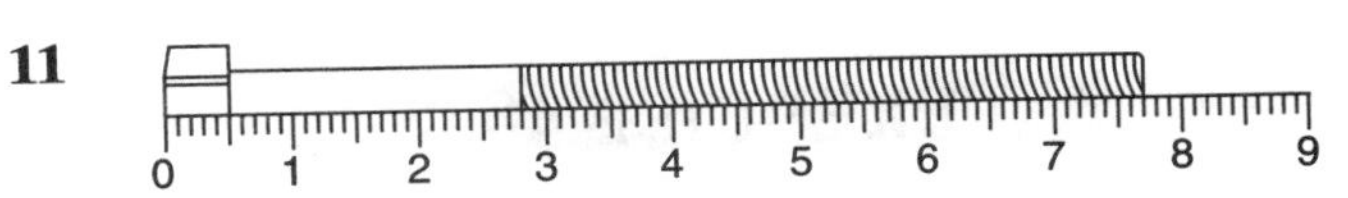

(a) How long is the threaded part of this bolt?

(b) What is the greatest distance this bolt could rest in a hole with the head above the hole?

12

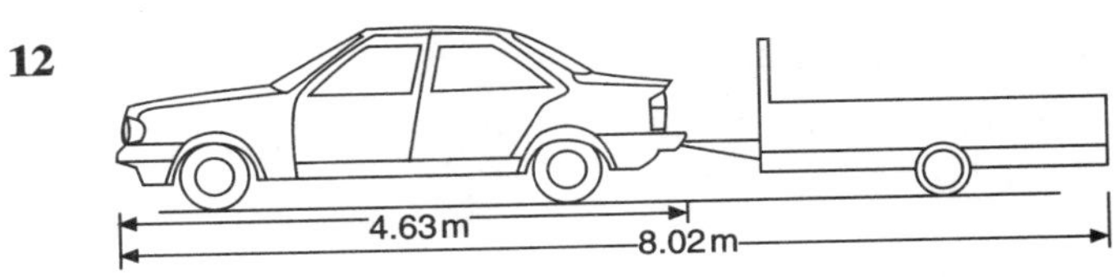

How long is the trailer?

13

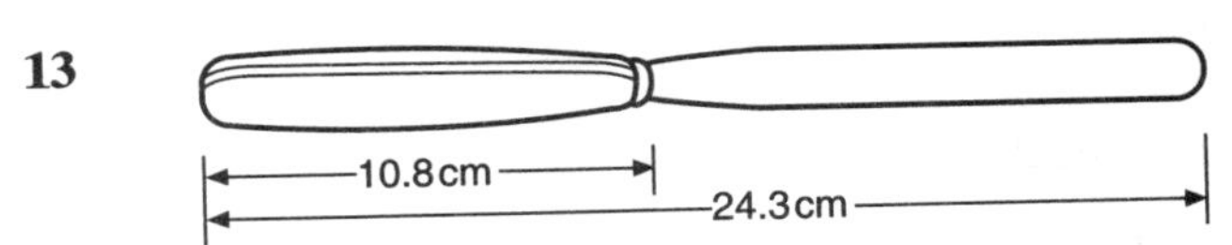

How long is the blade of this palette knife?

14

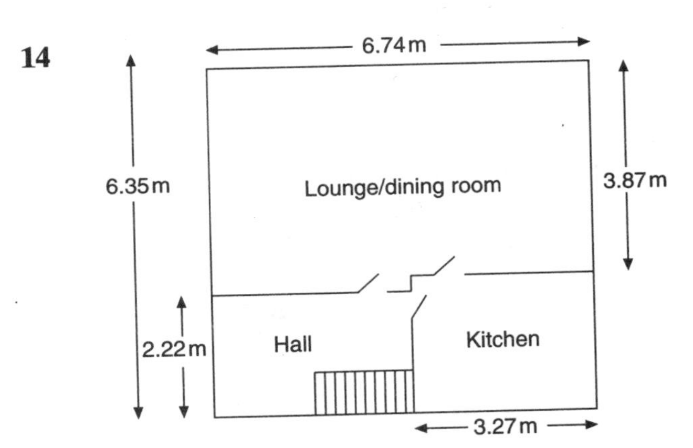

(a) How wide is the kitchen?

(b) How wide is the lounge at its widest part?

(c) How long is the hall?

Multiplication and division of decimals by 10, 100, 1000

To multiply by 10, 100 or 1000, we move the figures one, two or three places to the left;
for example, $9.27 \times 10 = 92.7$
$53.94 \times 100 = 5394$
$0.0724 \times 1000 = 72.4$

To divide by 10, 100 or 1000, we move the figures one, two or three places to the right;
for example, $5.7 \div 10 = 0.57$
$0.47 \div 100 = 0.0047$
$176.92 \div 1000 = 0.176\,92$

EXERCISE 4h

1 Multiply each number by 10:

(a) 4.34 (b) 1.985 (c) 67.43 (d) 0.7374
(e) 0.0088

2 Divide each number by 10:

(a) 56.8 (b) 17.445 (c) 4.69 (d) 0.723
(e) 0.008

3 Multiply each number by 100:

(a) 2.649 (b) 45.38 (c) 95.3 (d) 0.0445
(e) 0.6174

4 Divide each number by 100:

(a) 767.2 (b) 7.6 (c) 15.82 (d) 0.78
(e) 0.0437

Find

5 8.72×10 **6** $39.4 \div 10$ **7** $372 \div 1000$

8 0.044×1000 **9** 0.646×100 **10** $64.8 \div 100$

11 $0.92 \div 10$ **12** 0.034×100 **13** 1.2×30

14 $0.48 \div 40$ **15** 0.61×70 **16** $1.5 \div 50$

Multiplication of decimals

The multiplication of decimals is similar to the multiplication of whole numbers.

3.72×4 is written

```
   3.72
×     4
  14.88
```

(Count the number of places to the right of the decimal point in the first number (2) and add to it the number of places to the right of the decimal point in the second number (0). Count this number of places from the right-hand side of the final number to give the answer.)

Hence $3.72 \times 4 = 14.88$.

EXERCISE 4i

QUESTION
Find 5.78×4.3

ANSWER

```
   5.78
    4.3
  1 734
 23 120
 24.854
```

(2 d.p. + 1 d.p. gives 3 d.p.)

(To give the position of the decimal point, count 3 places from the right-hand side)

Find, without using a calculator,

1 6.35×6 **2** 5.87×7

3 3.84×8 **4** 8.31×4.2

5 25.7×9.2 **6** 9.06×3.14

7 2.27×4.7 **8** 0.76×3.86

9 0.45×0.83 **10** 7.45×3.6

QUESTION
Use a calculator to find (a) the exact value of 3.64×7.62
(b) its value correct to 3 s.f.

ANSWER
(a) $3.64 \times 7.62 = 27.7368$
(3 . 6 4 × 7 . 6 2 =)
(b) $27.7368 = 27.7$ (to 3 s.f.)

Use a calculator to find
(a) correct to 3 s.f. (b) correct to 2 d.p.

11 14.38×5.93 **12** 54.89×0.876 **13** 345×0.0538

14 70.16×0.293 **15** 5.64×3.45 **16** 450×0.0229

Division of a decimal by a single digit

We begin with questions that lead to exact answers, then move on to questions that do not.

EXERCISE 4j

QUESTION
Divide 2.08 by 8.

ANSWER
Using short division,

$$8\overline{)2.08}\quad = 0.26$$

i.e. $2.08 \div 8 = 0.26$

Find, without using a calculator:

1 $23.79 \div 3$ **2** $0.55 \div 5$

3 $1.96 \div 7$ **4** $13.56 \div 6$

5 $38.43 \div 9$ **6** $15 \div 4$

7 $0.944 \div 8$ **8** $43 \div 5$

9 $0.1512 \div 7$ **10** $35.55 \div 9$

11 $9.8 \div 8$ **12** $16.92 \div 3$

Sometimes the answer is not exact.

QUESTION
Use a calculator to find $5.79 \div 1.98$. Give your answer correct to 3 s.f.

ANSWER
$5.79 \div 1.98 = 2.92$ (correct to 3 s.f.)
(5 . 7 9 ÷ 1 . 9 8 =)

Use a calculator to find, correct to 3 s.f.:

13 $56.6 \div 17$ **14** $33.74 \div 3.3$

15 $0.8753 \div 0.68$ **16** $3.663 \div 3.58$

17 $4.963 \div 11$ **18** $6.74 \div 2.74$

19 $6943 \div 98.45$ **20** $3.756 \div 8.42$

Problems involving decimals

Many problems on weights and measures, and on money, require us to use the four rules applied to decimals.

EXERCISE 4k

QUESTION
A packet contains 22 nails, each of which is 3.35 centimetres long. How far will they stretch if they are laid end to end?

ANSWER
Distance the nails will stretch
= number of nails × the length of one nail
= 22 × 3.35 cm
= 73.7 cm
i.e. the nails in the packet, when laid end to end in a line, will stretch a distance of 73.7 cm.

1 There are 200 buttons in a box. Each button weighs 4.8 grams. What is the total weight of all the buttons in the box?

2 Wall tiles are 0.45 centimetres thick. How high is a pile of 24 of these tiles?

3 Millie worked $38\frac{1}{4}$ hours at an hourly rate of £6.24.
(a) Express $38\frac{1}{4}$ as a decimal.
(b) Find how much Millie earned.

4 An operator takes 0.85 minutes to solder a joint. How many minutes should this operator take to solder 250 such joints?

5 A bag contains 48 screws. The bag weighs 15.7 grams and each screw weighs 3.6 grams.
Find (a) the weight of the screws (b) the weight of the bag together with the screws.

6

A lorry weighs 2.88 tonnes. It is loaded with 30 boxes, each weighing 0.038 tonnes.
Find (a) the total weight of the boxes
(b) the total weight of the loaded lorry.

QUESTION
The total weight of 36 identical steel washers is 89.28 grams.
Find (a) the weight of one washer
(b) the weight of 136 similar washers.

ANSWER
(a) If the weight of 36 washers is 89.28 g
then the weight of 1 washer is $\frac{89.28}{36}$ g = 2.48 g
(b) Weight of 136 similar washers
= 136 × weight of one washer
= 136 × 2.48 g
= 337.28 g

7 Karen's car travelled 119.7 kilometres on 9.5 litres of petrol. How many kilometres per litre was this?

8 The instructions on a bag of weedkiller state that it should be used at the rate of 0.04 kilograms to the square metre. How many square metres should the contents of a 2 kilogram bag cover?

9 A bottle holds 0.7 litres of wine. How many glasses can be filled from this bottle if each glass holds 0.0875 litres?

10 From a 500 centimetre length of tape Andrew cuts off pieces 33.25 centimetres long.
(a) What is the greatest number of pieces he can cut off?
(b) How much is left over?

11 A jug holds 1.5 litres of milk. The capacity of a glass is 0.125 litres. How many times will the milk from the jug fill the glass?

12 Last week Norman earned £256.50 after working for 37.5 hours. How much was this per hour?

13 Tablets, each weighing 0.54 grams, are packed into foil strips each containing 24 tablets. Four foil strips are put into each box and 250 boxes are packed into a carton. What is the weight of tablets in the carton?

14 On average, each cow in a herd of 54 cows gives 17.8 litres of milk per day. How much milk should this herd give (a) per day (b) per week?
Give each answer correct to 3 s.f.

15 A machine in a factory counts screws into batches by weighing them. Each screw weighs 2.43 grams and the weight of screws in each batch is 145.8 grams. How many screws are there in a batch?

16 The pitch of the thread of a bolt is the distance a nut moves along the bolt for one complete turn of the nut. If a thread has a pitch of 1.26 mm, how far will the nut move along the bolt if it makes 20 full turns?

Estimating a result

A rectangular room is 4.375 metres long and 3.643 metres wide. Its area is found by multiplying these two distances together.
To find 4.375 × 3.643 using a calculator is very easy, but it is also easy to make a mistake by, for example, pressing a wrong button. It is only common sense to know roughly what answer you expect so that you can check that your calculator answer is reasonable.
If we correct each number to one significant figure then

4.375 × 3.643 is roughly 4 × 4 i.e. 16

The calculator value is 15.938 125, which compared with our estimated value is reasonable.

Most problems do not require this degree of accuracy. Correct to 2 d.p., this answer is 15.94 square metres and correct to 3 s.f. this answer is 15.9 square metres

EXERCISE 4I

QUESTION
Estimate the cost of 1860 books at £9.75 each. Use your calculator to find the actual cost.

ANSWER
Estimated cost is 2000 × £10 i.e. £20 000
Actual cost is 1860 × £9.75 i.e. £18 135

1 Estimate a travel agent's income from selling 587 package holidays at £496 each. Compare your estimate with the exact value obtained by using a calculator.

2 Estimate the cost of 9.38 metres of cloth at £7.58 a metre. Compare your estimate with the actual cost.

3 Estimate the weight of 2834 computer components if each component weighs 4.21 grams. Compare your estimate with the value you get using a calculator.

4 The area of a room is 36.44 square metres and it is 5.29 metres wide. (a) Estimate its length. (b) Use a calculator to find its length in metres, correct to 3 s.f.

5 Paul earns £228.93 for a 39-hour week. Estimate Paul's hourly rate and compare it with the value you get by using a calculator.

6 Pete has 6700 Greek drachmas when 100 drachmas is equivalent to £0.288. (a) Estimate the value of his drachmas in pounds. (b) Find the exact equivalent giving your answer correct to the nearest 10p.

7 A signpost in France indicates that it is 278 kilometres to Paris. If 1 kilometre is equivalent to 0.625 miles,
(a) estimate the distance to Paris in miles
(b) calculate the exact value giving your answer correct to the nearest mile.

Degrees of accuracy

If you measure the length of your kitchen it is probably sensible to give it, at best, correct to the nearest centimetre. It would be a very rough measurement if given correct to the nearest metre, and an attempt to give it correct to the nearest millimetre would be absurd. Depending on the reason for the measurement, one way would be to give it correct to the nearest 10 cm.

EXERCISE 4m

For each measurement write down the degree of accuracy you think is reasonable. There is no single correct answer.

1 The thickness of this book.

2 The depth of tread on a tyre.

3 The length of a hockey pitch.

4 The distance from Manchester to Southampton.

5 The distance from one Yorkshire village to the next one.

6 The weight of an aspirin tablet.

7 The amount of water you put in the kettle to make a pot of tea.

8 The area of a dairy farm.

9 The weight of a parcel you want to send by first-class letter post.

10 The number of people (a) in the doctor's surgery (b) at an international match (c) on a train.

Multiple-choice questions 4

In questions 1 to 5 several possible answers are given. Write down the letter that corresponds to the correct answer.

1 15.72 + 27.69 is

A 42.41 **B** 43.41 **C** 43.31 **D** 53.41

2 Correct to 2 decimal places, 4.0934 − 1.8751 is

A 2.21 **B** 2.2 **C** 2.20 **D** 2.22

3 Correct to 3 significant figures, 45.2 × 0.3907 is

A 17.6 **B** 17.7 **C** 17.65 **D** 17.66

4 Kim finds the area of the office notice board by multiplying its length by its width. She finds that the board has a width of 1.5 metres and an area of 5.25 square metres. The length of the notice board is

A 6.75 m **B** 3.75 m **C** 7.875 m **D** 3.5 m

5 The cost of a one unit telephone call is 4.2 pence. An important business call uses 452 units. The cost of this call, correct to the nearest penny, is

A £189.84 **B** £18.99
C £18.98 **D** none of these

6 Two cars are parked bumper to bumper in a multistorey carpark. One of the cars is 4227 mm long and the other one is 3897 mm long. Which of the following statements are true and which are false? Correct to three significant figures the cars' combined length is

A 8120 mm **B** 8.10 m
C 813 cm **D** 8.12 m

7 In France, Jean-Claude's car will travel 216 kilometres on 15 litres of petrol. He wants to make a journey of 500 miles in England and knows that 1 mile = 1.609 km. The following statements have been made:
Statement 1. Jean-Claude's car travels 14.4 kilometres on one litre of petrol.
Statement 2. The distance Jean-Claude intends travelling in England is about 310 km, so he will need about 22 litres of petrol.
How are these two statements best described?

A True, True **B** True, False
C False, True **D** False, False

Self-assessment test 4

1 Find the exact value of

(a) $5.044 + 23.761 + 463.09$
(b) 76.95×0.884
(c) $32.512 \div 51.2$
(d) $18.94 - 4.377 - 1.8$
(e) $5.7 \times 16.8 \div 7.98$

2 Give 53.0938 (a) correct to 3 s.f. (b) correct to 1 d.p. (c) correct to the nearest whole number.

3 Find correct to 3 s.f.

(a) 5.835×3.092 (b) $78.945 \div 42.35$

(c) $\dfrac{18.45 \times 8.342}{0.7593}$

4 Find correct to 3 significant figures

(a) $\dfrac{82.6 - 39.4}{9.32 \times 0.871}$ (b) $\dfrac{16.9 + 9.78}{24.2 - 13.64}$

5 A scraper for removing wallpaper is 23.3 cm long and its handle is 14.7 cm long. How long is the blade?

6 When a length of metal tubing is heated it expands in length by 0.00064 mm for each degree Celsius rise in temperature. How much will it increase in length if its temperature is raised from 19 °C to 78 °C? Give your answer correct to 3 s.f.

7 The sketch shows the ground floor plan of a three-bedroomed house. Use the information in it to answer the questions that follow. All dimensions are in metres. Ignore wall thicknesses.

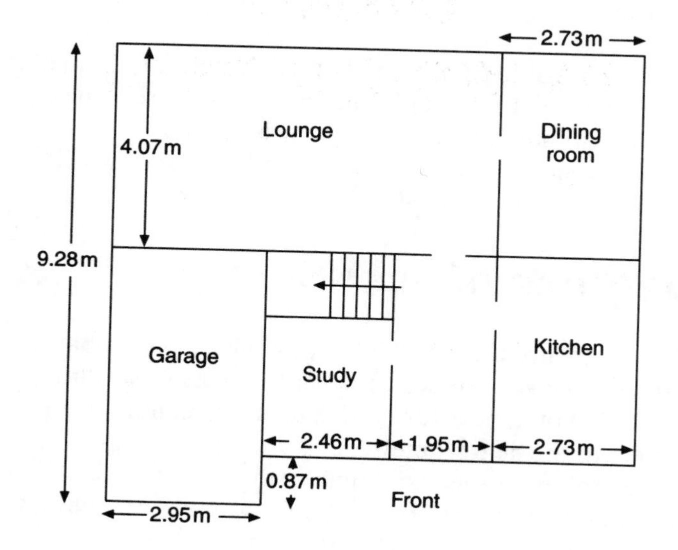

(a) How wide is the house when viewed from the front?

(b) How long is the lounge?

(c) What are the dimensions of (i) the garage (ii) the study, given that the stairs are 1 m wide?

(d) What is the area of the lounge? Give your answer in square metres,
(i) exactly (ii) correct to 3 significant figures
(iii) correct to 2 decimal places.
(Area of a rectangle = length × breadth.)

(e) A rectangular carpet, which has an area of 9.375 m^2, is laid in the dining room. If the carpet is 3.75 m long, how wide is it?

8 A room is 8.92 metres long and 6.21 metres wide.

(a) By rounding each measurement to the nearest whole number estimate the area of the room in square metres. (Area = length × width.)

(b) Use a calculator to find the exact area of the room. Give your answer correct to three significant figures.

CHAPTER 5

Basic measurement

Length

In the *metric system* the basic unit of length is the metre (m). Other units in everyday use are the centimetre (cm), the millimetre (mm) and the kilometre (km).

The relationships between these quantities are:

1 m = 100 cm

1 cm = 10 mm

and 1 km = 1000 m

To convert from the larger unit (say metres) to the smaller unit (say centimetres) we multiply by the conversion factor.

For example since 1 m = 100 cm
4 m = 4 × 100 cm = 400 cm

and since 1 cm = 10 mm
6.3 cm = 6.3 × 10 mm = 63 mm

To convert from the smaller unit (say metres) to the larger unit (say kilometres) we divide by the conversion factor.

For example since 1000 m = 1 km

4400 m = $\frac{4400}{1000}$ km, i.e. 4.4 km

and since 100 cm = 1 m

5800 cm = $\frac{5800}{100}$ m, i.e. 58 m

It is useful to remember that

'kilo' means 1000 times bigger

'centi' means $\frac{1}{100}$ part of

and 'milli' means $\frac{1}{1000}$ part of

The units of length used in the *imperial system* are: the inch (in), the foot (ft), the yard (yd) and the mile, where

1 ft = 12 in (often shown as 12")

1 yd = 3 ft (often shown as 3')

1 mile = 1760 yd

EXERCISE 5a

QUESTION

(a) How many millimetres are there in
(i) 8 cm (ii) 3.5 cm?

(b) How many centimetres are there in
(i) 7 m (ii) 4.6 m?

(c) How many metres are there in
(i) 3 km (ii) 5.57 km?

ANSWER

(a) Since 1 cm = 10 mm
(i) 8 cm = 8 × 10 mm = 80 mm
and (ii) 3.5 cm = 3.5 × 10 mm = 35 mm

(b) Since 1 m = 100 cm
(i) 7 m = 7 × 100 cm = 700 cm
and (ii) 4.6 m = 4.6 × 100 cm = 460 cm

(c) Since 1 km = 1000 m
(i) 3 km = 3 × 1000 m = 3000 m
and (ii) 5.57 km = 5.57 × 1000 m = 5570 m

---

1 Give the number of millimetres in

(a) 5 cm (b) 12 cm (c) 342 cm
(d) 8.2 cm (e) 13.5 cm (f) 0.8 cm

2 Give the number of centimetres in

(a) 8 m (b) 15 m (c) 433 m
(d) 5.9 m (e) 14.27 m (f) 0.74 m

3 Give the number of metres in

(a) 2 km (b) 11 km (c) 7.5 km
(d) 0.33 km (e) 1.49 km (f) 0.05 km

QUESTION

Give the number of centimetres in 1800 mm.

ANSWER

Since 10 mm = 1 cm
1800 mm = $\frac{1800}{10}$ cm = 180 cm

---

4 Give the number of centimetres in

(a) 50 mm (b) 250 mm (c) 8000 mm

5 Give the number of metres in

(a) 3500 cm (b) 90 000 cm (c) 452 cm

6 Give the number of kilometres in

(a) 10 000 m (b) 7500 m (c) 450 m

QUESTION

(a) The distance between two villages is 5.2 km. Express this distance in metres.

(b) The depth of a kitchen unit is 672 mm. What is this in centimetres?

(c) Kate measured the length of her garden and found it to be 8746 cm. How many metres is this?

ANSWER

(a) 1 km = 1000 m

5.2 km = 5.2 × 1000 m (Large unit to small unit so multiply by 1000)
= 5200 m

The distance between the villages is therefore 5200 m.

(b) 10 mm = 1 cm

672 mm = $\frac{672}{10}$ cm (Small unit to large unit so divide by 10)
= 67.2 cm

The kitchen unit is therefore 67.2 cm deep.

(c) 1 m = 100 cm

8746 cm = $\frac{8746}{100}$ m (Small unit to large unit so divide by 100)
= 87.46 m

Kate's garden is therefore 87.46 m long.

---

7 A table is 1.9 m long. How long is this in
(a) centimetres (b) millimetres?

8 A picture is 1.3 m long and 0.95 m wide.
(a) What is its length in centimetres?
(b) What is its width in millimetres?

9 A factory site is 1.67 km long and 650 metres wide.
Express (a) its length in metres
(b) its width in kilometres.

10 The Humber Bridge is the longest suspension bridge in the world. It is 1410 metres long.
How many kilometres is this?

QUESTION

Change (a) 5 feet into inches (b) 8 yards into feet
(c) $4\frac{1}{2}$ yards into inches.

ANSWER

(a) Since 1 ft = 12 in
5 ft = 5 × 12 in = 60 in

(b) Since 1 yd = 3 ft
8 yd = 8 × 3 ft = 24 ft

(c) Since 1 yd = 36 in
$4\frac{1}{2}$ yd = $\frac{9}{2}$ × 36 in = 162 in

---

11 How many inches are there in
(a) 9 ft (b) 15 ft (c) $3\frac{1}{2}$ ft (d) $4\frac{3}{4}$ ft?

12 How many feet are there in
(a) 4 yd (b) 12 yd (c) $6\frac{1}{3}$ yd (d) $8\frac{1}{4}$ yd?

13 How many inches are there in
(a) 2 yd (b) 9 yd (c) $5\frac{1}{2}$ yd (d) $8\frac{1}{4}$ yd?

14 If there are 1760 yards in a mile find
(a) 5 miles in yards (b) $3\frac{1}{4}$ miles in yards
(c) 12 320 yards in miles (d) 4 miles in feet

QUESTION

Penny lives in an old house. Downstairs the ceilings are 9 feet 3 inches high.

(a) How many inches is this?

(b) She measures the lounge and finds that it is 275 inches long and 182 inches wide. Give these dimensions in feet and inches.

ANSWER

(a) Since 1 ft = 12 in
9 ft = 9 × 12 in
= 108 in
9 ft 3 in = 108 in + 3 in
= 111 in

(b) 275 in = $\frac{275}{12}$ ft = 22.916 66 . . . ft

Now 22 ft = 22 × 12 in = 264 in
∴ 275 in = 264 in + 11 in
= 22 ft 11 in

Similarly, 182 in = $\frac{182}{12}$ ft = 15.1666 . . . ft

15 ft = 15 × 12 in
= 180 in
182 in = 180 in + 2 in
= 15 ft 2 in

---

15 The length of the Olympic marathon is 26 miles 385 yards. How many yards is this?

16 The oldest of the five English classics in the horseracing calendar is the St Leger. It takes place annually at Doncaster over a distance of 1 mile 6 furlongs and 127 yards. How many yards is this? (1 furlong = 220 yards.)

17 Arthur is checking the fencing around a large field. He counts the number of paces he takes and finds this to be 5280. If the length of each pace is $\frac{3}{4}$ yards find the distance he walks (a) in yards (b) in miles.

18 The Cutty Sark is 213 ft long, 36 ft in the beam and has a draught of 21 ft. Give each dimension (a) in yards (b) in inches.

Perimeter

The distance all round a shape is called its *perimeter*.

EXERCISE 5b

QUESTION
Find the perimeter of

(a) the square paving slab shown below;

(b) a field in the shape of a pentagon, details of which are shown in the sketch.

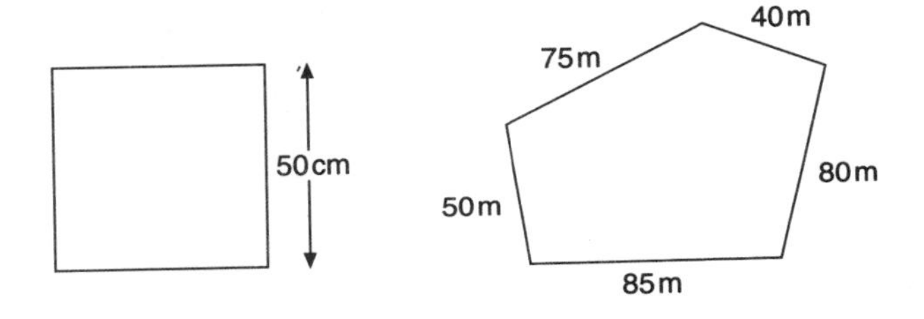

ANSWER

(a) The perimeter of the square slab is
50 cm + 50 cm + 50 cm + 50 cm = 200 cm.

(b) The perimeter of the field is
85 m + 50 m + 75 m + 40 m + 80 m = 330 m.

In questions 1 and 2 find the perimeter of each shape.

1 A square tile of side
(a) 30 cm (b) 16 cm (c) 145 mm.

2 A rectangular rug measuring
(a) 150 cm by 90 cm (b) 1.3 m by 0.95 m.

3 Find the perimeter of this room. (All the corners form right angles.)

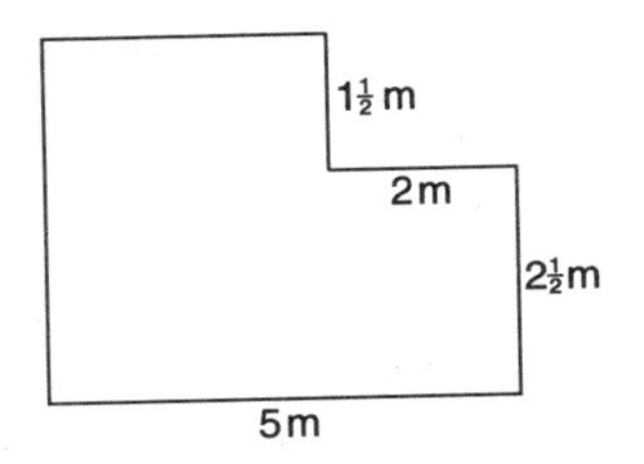

4 Find the perimeter of this field.

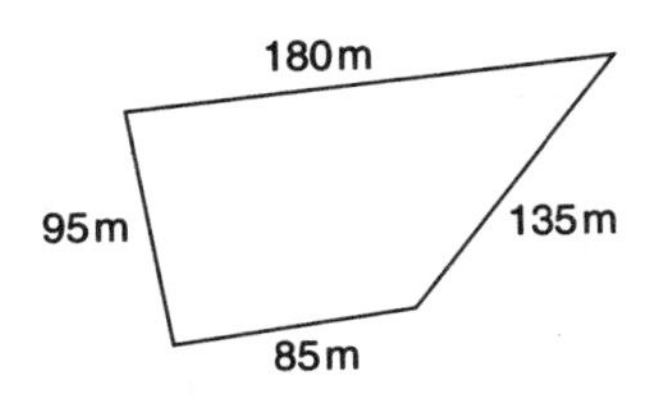

5 Find the perimeter of this cross-section of a metal bar. (All measurements are in inches.)

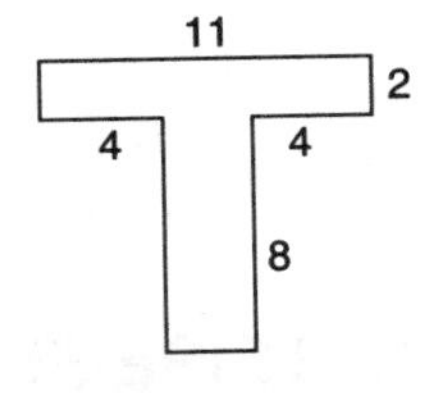

Area – by counting squares

The area of a shape is the amount of surface enclosed within its boundary. Area is measured in squares.

To compare areas we need to use the same size of square. In the *metric system*, for small areas we usually use a square of side 1 centimetre and for larger areas a square of side of 1 metre.

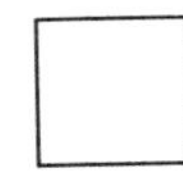

This square has a side of 1 cm. Its area is 1 square centimetre. We write this as 1 cm^2.

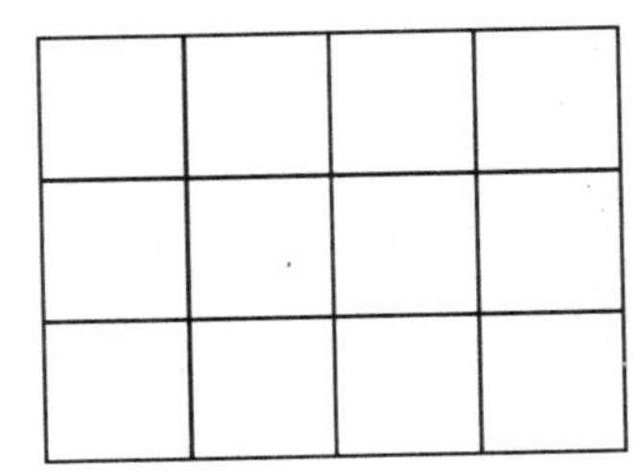

Some areas can be found exactly quite easily. For example, the area of this rectangle is 12 squares of side 1 cm, i.e. its area is 12 cm^2.

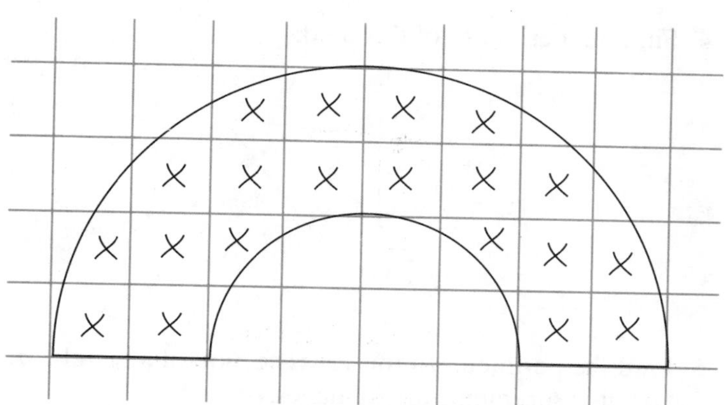

Other areas are more difficult to find exactly. For example, the area of this metal plate can be found approximately by counting squares. If half a square or more is within the shape it is counted, otherwise it is not. In this case the approximate area is 20 squares, i.e. 20 cm^2. (The squares that are counted are marked with an x.)

EXERCISE 5c

QUESTION

The diagram shows the outline of a Welsh reservoir. By counting squares find its area.

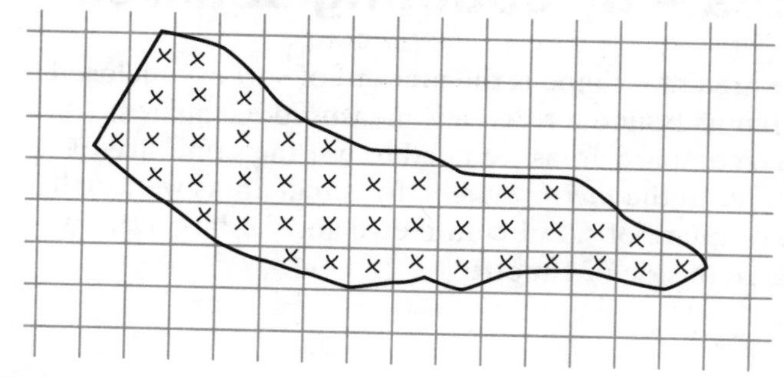

ANSWER

The area is 42 squares.

1 Count squares to find the area of each lake. Count a square if half of it or more is within its boundary, otherwise do not.

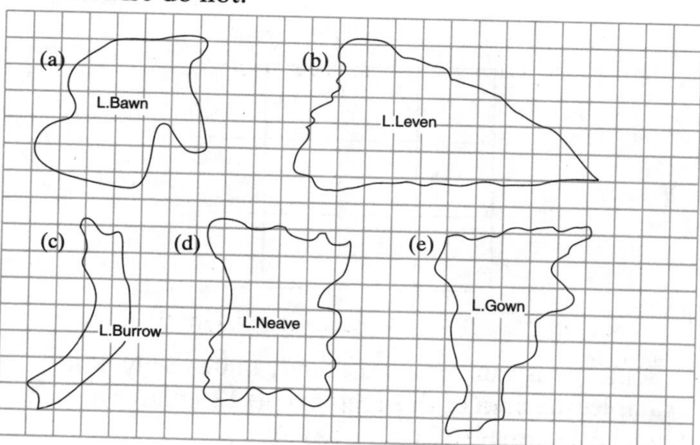

2 The diagrams show gaskets for four different carburettors. By counting squares find the area of each.

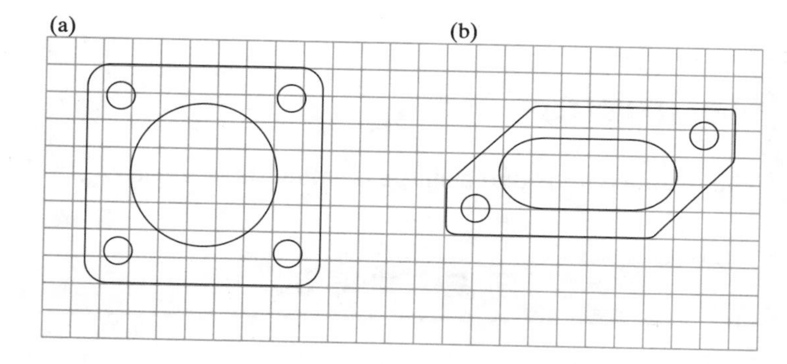

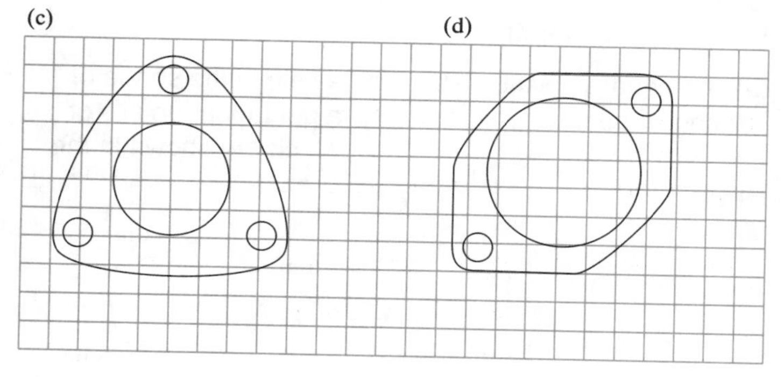

Units of area

The most common units of area in the *metric system* are the square metre (m^2), the square centimetre (cm^2), the square millimetre (mm^2) and the hectare (ha), where

$$1\text{ m}^2 = 100 \times 100\text{ cm}^2 = 10\,000\text{ cm}^2,$$
$$1\text{ cm}^2 = 10 \times 10\text{ mm}^2 = 100\text{ mm}^2$$

and

$$1\text{ ha} = 10\,000\text{ m}^2$$

The hectare is the preferred unit for measuring the area of land on a farm or industrial site, but for countries we use square kilometres.

$$\begin{aligned} 1\text{ km}^2 &= 1000 \times 1000\text{ m}^2 \\ &= 1\,000\,000\text{ m}^2 \\ &= 100\text{ ha} \end{aligned}$$

In *imperial units* the most common units of area are the square inch (sq in or in^2), the square foot (sq ft or ft^2), the square yard (sq yd or yd^2), the acre (which is 4840 square yards) and the square mile. The relationships between these quantities are:

$$1\text{ ft}^2 = 12 \times 12\text{ in}^2 = 144\text{ in}^2$$
$$1\text{ yd}^2 = 3 \times 3\text{ ft}^2 = 9\text{ ft}^2$$
$$1\text{ acre} = 4840\text{ yd}^2$$
$$1\text{ square mile} = 640\text{ acres}$$

Areas of squares and rectangles

The square

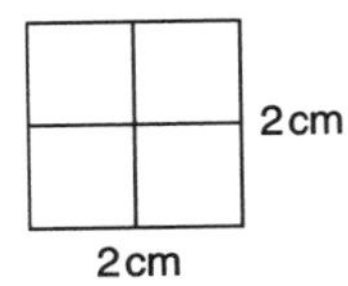

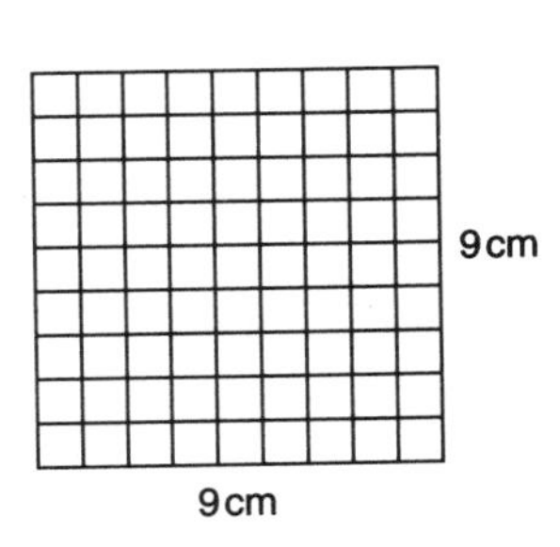

The area of a square postage stamp of side 2 cm is $2 \times 2\ \text{cm}^2$, i.e. $4\ \text{cm}^2$.
The area of a square computer disk holder of side 9 cm is $9 \times 9\ \text{cm}^2$, i.e. $81\ \text{cm}^2$.
In general, the area of a square is given by

$$\text{area} = (\text{length of side})^2$$

The rectangle

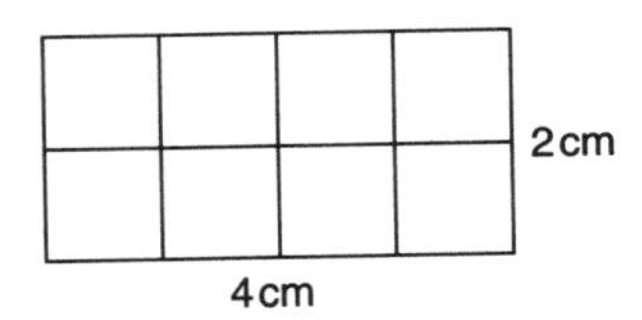

The area of a rectangular card measuring 4 cm by 2 cm is $4 \times 2\ \text{cm}^2$ i.e. $8\ \text{cm}^2$
In general, the area of a rectangle is given by

$$\text{area} = \text{length} \times \text{breadth}$$

Note: To find an area, all measurements need to be put in the same unit.

EXERCISE 5d

1 Find the area of a square of side
(a) 9 cm (b) 8.4 cm (c) $3\frac{1}{2}$ in.

2 Find the area of the following rectangles:

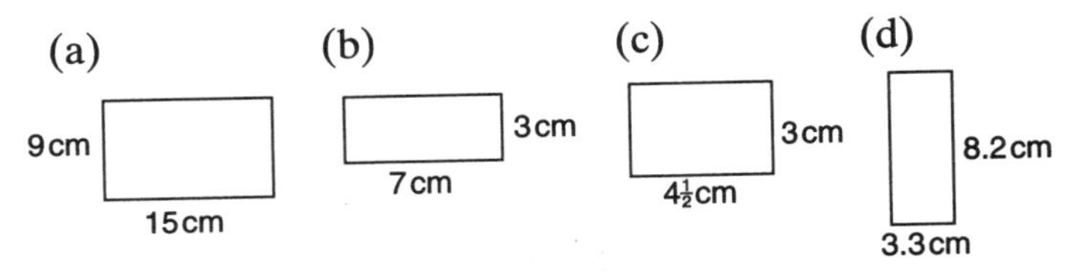

3

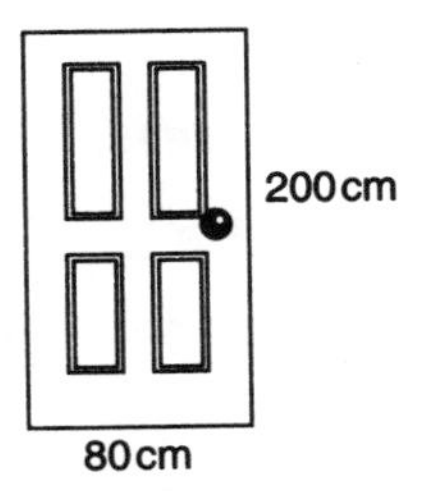

A door is 200 cm high and 80 cm wide.
Find (a) its area in cm^2 (b) its dimensions in metres (c) its area in m^2.

4

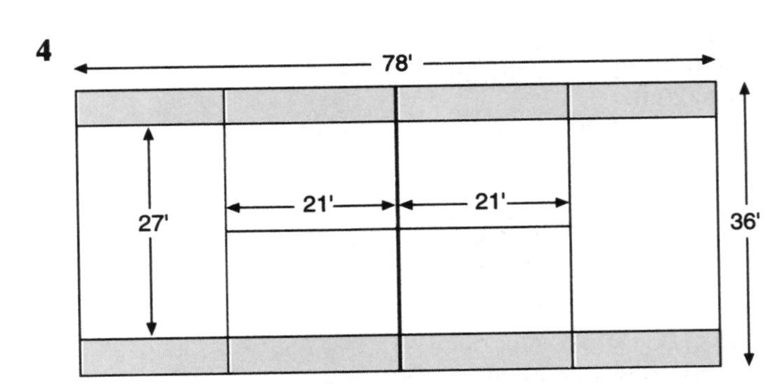

The diagram shows a tennis court.
Find the perimeter and area of
(a) a singles court (b) a doubles court.

5

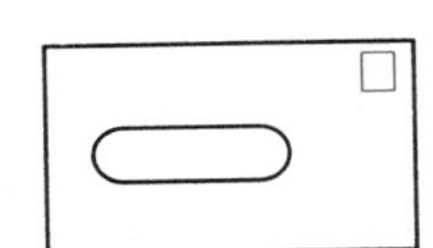

An envelope measures 204 mm by 120 mm. Find
(a) the perimeter of the envelope in millimetres
(b) the area of the envelope in mm^2
(c) the dimensions of the envelope in centimetres
(d) the area of the envelope in cm^2.
(Give your answer correct to 3 s.f.)

6

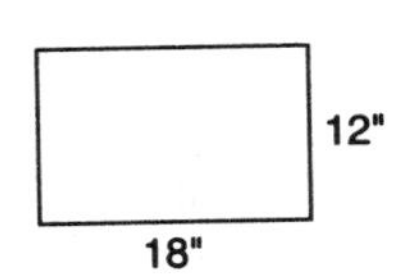

A rectangular floor tile measures 18 in by 12 in. Find
(a) its perimeter in (i) in (ii) ft
(b) its area in (i) in^2 (ii) ft^2.

QUESTION

George has 24 square floor tiles each with an area of 1 ft^2.

(a) How long is one edge of a tile?

(b) In how many different ways can he lay them in a rectangle?

(c) Which arrangement has the longest perimeter and which the shortest perimeter?

ANSWER

(a) 1 ft.

(b) One way of arranging 24 tiles in the shape of a 6 ft by 4 ft rectangle is shown below. In this case the perimeter of the arrangement is 6 ft + 4 ft + 6 ft + 4 ft i.e. 20 ft.

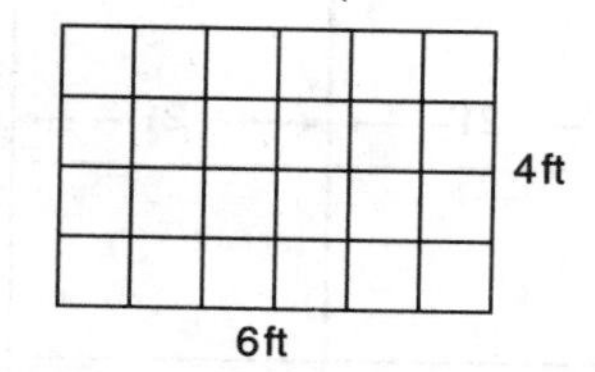

Other possible arrangements are 24×1, 12×2 and 8×3.

$\therefore$ four different arrangements are possible.

(c) If the rectangle measures 24 ft × 1 ft then the perimeter is 24 ft + 1 ft + 24 ft + 1 ft = 50 ft.
If the rectangle measures 12 ft × 2 ft then the perimeter is 12 ft + 2 ft + 12 ft + 2 ft = 28 ft.
If the rectangle measures 8 ft × 3 ft then the perimeter is 8 ft + 3 ft + 8 ft + 3 ft = 22 ft.
We have already found that the perimeter of a rectangle measuring 6 ft × 4 ft is 20 ft.
No other arrangement is possible without cutting some of the tiles.
The longest possible perimeter is therefore 50 ft and the shortest possible perimeter is 20 ft.

7 Ben has 16 square tiles, each of side 10 cm. (a) In how many different ways can he arrange them in a rectangle? (b) Which arrangement has (i) the longest perimeter (ii) the shortest perimeter? (c) How much longer is the longest perimeter than the shortest?

8 Sarah has 36 square tiles of side 3 in. She lays them out on a table to form a rectangle. (a) In how many different ways can she do this if the shortest acceptable width of the rectangle is 6 in? (b) Which arrangement has the longest perimeter? (c) Which arrangement has the shortest perimeter? What special name do we give to this shape?

9 The dimensions of a rectangle are whole numbers of centimetres and the perimeter of the rectangle is 30 cm. (a) How many different rectangles satisfy these conditions? (b) Which rectangle has (i) the largest area (ii) the smallest area?

Cubes and cuboids

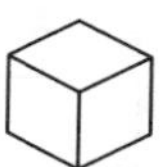

The volume of the cube shown here is 1 cubic centimetre, i.e. 1 cm^3.

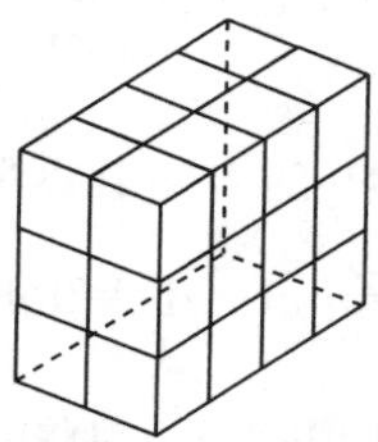

The name of a solid whose pairs of opposite faces are parallel rectangles is a cuboid.

We can work out the volume of the larger shape, the cuboid, by filling it with cubes of volume 1 cm^3 and counting the number of cubes. In this case we see that 24 cubes are needed, so the volume of the given cuboid is 24 cm^3. We can thus say that

$$\text{volume of a cuboid} = \text{length} \times \text{breadth} \times \text{height}$$

Note that the unit for all three dimensions must be the same.

Units of volume

In the *metric system* the most common units of volume are mm^3, cm^3 and m^3, where

$$1\ cm^3 = 10 \times 10 \times 10\ mm^3$$

i.e. $\quad 1\ cm^3 = 1000\ mm^3$

and $\quad 1\ m^3 = 100 \times 100 \times 100\ cm^3$

In the *imperial system* the units of volume are cubic inches (in^3 or cu in), cubic feet (ft^3 or cu ft) and cubic yards (yd^3) where

$$1\ ft^3 = 12 \times 12 \times 12\ in^3 = 1728\ in^3$$

and $\quad 1\ yd^3 = 3 \times 3 \times 3\ ft^3 = 27\ ft^3$

EXERCISE 5e

In each question from 1 to 4 the stack is made from cubes of side 1 cm. Find the number of cubes used to make each shape and hence write down its volume.

1

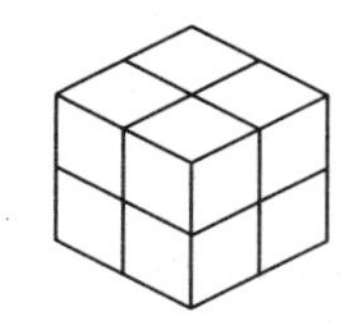

2

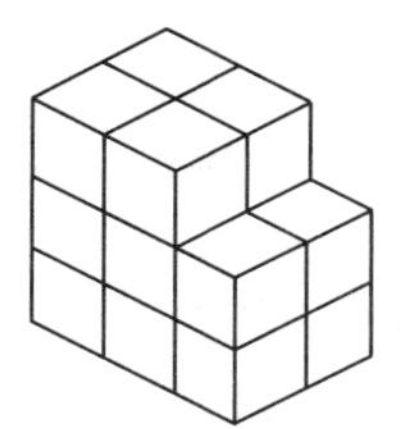

3

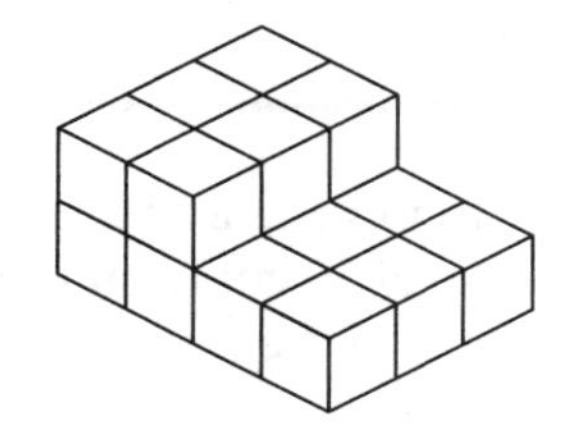

4

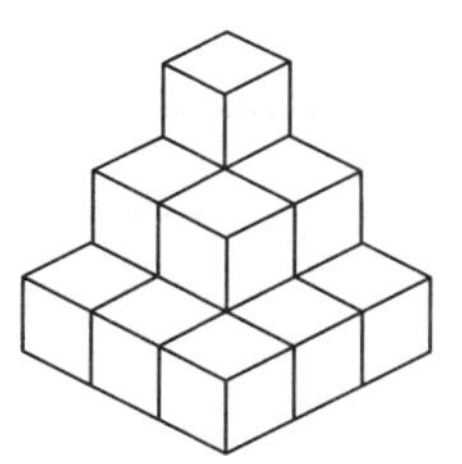

5 How many additional cubes are needed to turn the stack given in question 4 into a cube? (You are not allowed to take the original stack apart.)

6 The stack in question 1 is made from white cubes. Its outside is painted black and the stack then taken apart. How many of the small cubes have
(a) 3 black faces (b) 2 black faces?

QUESTION
How many cubes of side 2 cm are needed to fill the space inside a cuboid measuring 6 cm by 6 cm by 4 cm?

ANSWER

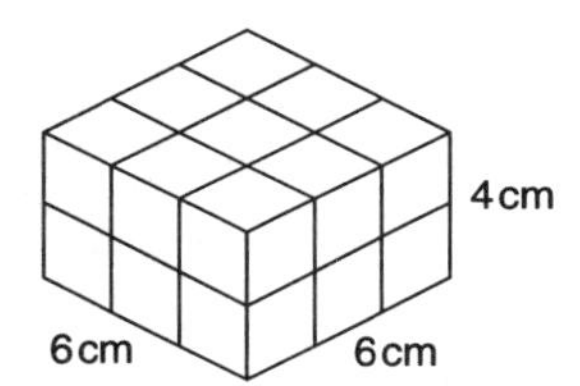

Looking down into the box, 9 cubes (3 rows with 3 in each row) of side 2 cm are needed to cover the base of the box.

These cubes fill the box to a depth of 2 cm. Another layer of 9 cubes is needed to fill the box completely.

Thus 18 cubes are needed to fill the space inside the cuboid.

---

7 The inside measurements of a rectangular metal storage box are 18 cm by 8 cm by 10 cm. How many cubes of side 1 cm are needed to fill the box?

8 Draw a cube of side 4 cm. How many cubes of side 2 cm would be needed to fill it?

Questions 9 to 12 refer to the information given below.

At a children's play centre they have a collection of coloured plastic cubes of different sizes, together with some rectangular boxes. Details are given in the table.

Plastic cubes		Open rectangular boxes			
Colour	Length of side cm	Box	Length cm	Breadth cm	Height cm
Red	1	A	4	3	2
Yellow	2	B	8	4	2
White	3	C	12	6	6

9 How many red cubes are needed to fill
(a) box A (b) box B (c) box C?

10 How many yellow cubes are needed to fill
(a) box B (b) box C?

11 How many white cubes are needed to fill box C?

12 Explain why box A cannot be filled completely (so that no part of a cube is projecting above the top of the box), using either all yellow cubes or all white cubes.

13 A cuboid is to be made from cubes of side 1 cm. Every dimension (i.e. length, width and height) must be at least 2 cm. (a) What are the dimensions of the smallest possible cuboid? How many cubes are needed to make it? (b) Can an acceptable cuboid be made from (i) 12 cubes (ii) 15 cubes? (c) Kate has 24 cubes. How many different cuboids can she make? List them.

QUESTION
Find the volume of a rectangular room measuring 8 m by 5 m by 3 m. If 4.5 m^3 of airspace is required for each person, what is the maximum number of people who should use the room at any one time?

ANSWER
Volume of rectangular room = length × breadth × height

$$= 8 \times 5 \times 3 \text{ m}^3$$
$$= 120 \text{ m}^3$$

One person needs 4.5 m^3 of air space.

∴ maximum number of people who can use the room is

$$\frac{\text{total airspace available}}{\text{amount of air needed by one person}}$$

$$= \frac{120}{4.5}$$

$$= 26.666\ldots$$

Thus the maximum number of people that should use the room at any one time is 26.

14

A cereal box for Pronto Puffed Wheat measures 12 in by 8 in by $2\frac{1}{2}$ in. How many cubic inches of puffed wheat will the box hold?

15 Ted and Wendy each have a small box in which to keep their tablets. Ted's box measures 25 mm by 20 mm by 6 mm and Wendy's measures 32 mm by 21 mm by 5 mm. Find the volume of each box in cubic centimetres. Who has the larger box and by how much?

16 Find the volume of each cuboid.

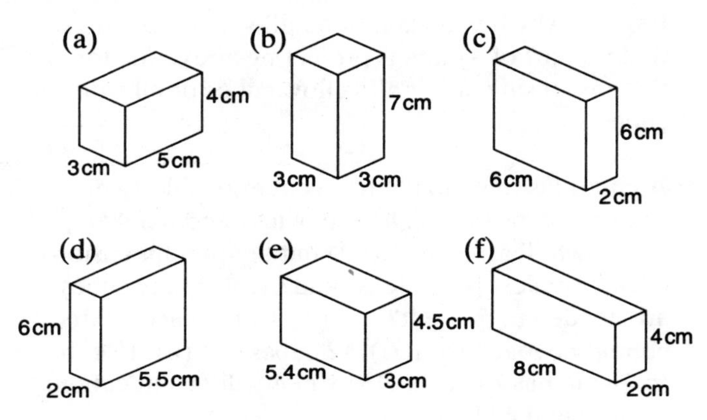

(g) Which cuboid has (i) the largest volume (ii) the smallest volume?

17 A classroom measuring 8 yd by 6 yd is to be used for a class of 32 students. If 5 yd^3 of airspace is required for each student, how high should the ceiling be?

QUESTION

A solid metal sheet is 3 m long, 80 cm wide and 15 mm thick. Find the volume of metal used to make this sheet. Give your answer in (a) cm^3 (b) m^3.

ANSWER

(a) (Work in centimetres.)

Length of sheet is 3 m $= 3 \times 100$ cm
$= 300$ cm

Width of sheet is 80 cm.

Thickness of sheet is 15 mm $= \frac{15}{10}$ cm
$= 1.5$ cm

Volume of metal in sheet
= length × breadth × thickness
$= 300 \times 80 \times 1.5\ cm^3$
$= 36\,000\ cm^3$

(b) (Work in metres.)

Length of sheet is 3 m

Width of sheet is 80 cm $= \frac{80}{100}$ m
$= 0.8$ m

Thickness of sheet is 15 mm $= \frac{15}{1000}$ m
$= 0.015$ m

Volume of sheet $= 3 \times 0.8 \times 0.015\ m^3$
$= 0.036\ m^3$

---

18 A swimming pool is 30 m long, 15 m wide and 2.5 m deep. It is filled with water to a level 50 cm from the top. What volume of water is there in the pool? Give your answer
(a) in m^3 (b) in litres. (1 m^3 = 1000 litres.)

19 Find the volume of a cube of sugar of side 12 mm. Give your answer in (a) mm^3 (b) cm^3.

20 (a) Find the volume, in cubic metres, of a rectangular piece of timber measuring 4 m by 20 cm by 8 cm.
(b) What is the price of this timber if it costs £85 per cubic metre?

21

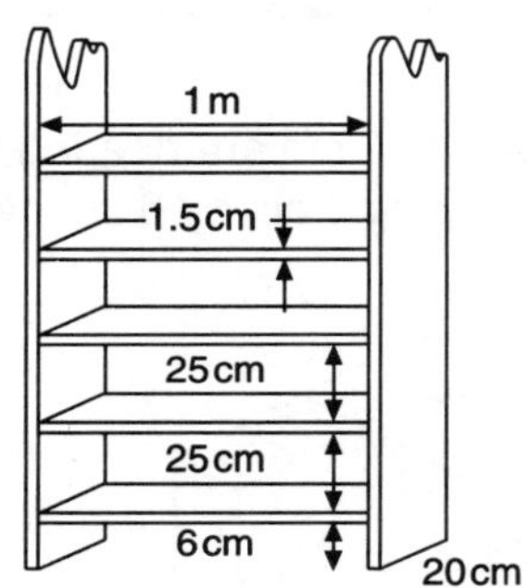

The shelves in a bookshop are erected in units 20 cm deep, 1 m wide and 25 cm apart. The undersurface of the lowest shelf is 6 cm above the floor and each shelf is 1.5 cm thick. No shelf must be more than 2 m above floor level.

(a) How high is the upper surface of the third shelf above floor level?

(b) What is the largest number of shelves possible in a single unit?

Books with a page size 240 mm × 188 mm, and which are 3 cm thick, are to be stored on these shelves. They are arranged in the usual way with their spines vertical and facing outwards.

(c) How many books can be arranged in this way (i) on one shelf (ii) in one unit?

(d) How much space is taken up by one book? Give your answer in (i) mm^3 (ii) cm^3.

(e) How much space is there on each shelf for storing books? (Assume that no book projects outside the dimensions of a shelf.)

22 A refuse bin is in the shape of a cuboid with a square base of side 60 cm. It is 90 cm deep and is to be filled with bricks measuring 20 cm × 10 cm × 7.5 cm.

(a) How much space is taken up by one brick? Give your answer in (i) cm^3 (ii) m^3. ($1\ m^3 = 100 \times 100 \times 100\ cm^3$.)

(b) Is it possible to place a number of these bricks into the bin in layers so that there is no spare space and the lid will close? If it is, how many bricks are there in the first layer?

(c) How many layers are needed to fill the bin completely?

(d) How many bricks are needed to fill the bin completely?

Capacity

Many three-dimensional shapes are used for holding liquid. The volume of liquid that a container holds is called its capacity. In the *metric system* capacity is usually measured in litres (ℓ).

Small units, such as medicines, are measured in millimetres (ml), i.e. thousandths of a litre (so 1000 ml = 1 ℓ). An ordinary teaspoon holds about 5 ml.

Because capacity is a particular kind of volume, the units of capacity are related to the units of volume we are already familiar with:

$$1 \text{ litre} = 1000\ cm^3$$
and
$$1 \text{ millilitre} = 1\ cm^3$$

In the *imperial system* the most common units of capacity are the fluid ounce (fl oz), the pint (pt), the quart (qt) and the gallon (gal):

$$20 \text{ fl oz} = 1 \text{ pt}$$
$$2 \text{ pt} = 1 \text{ quart}$$
and
$$1 \text{ gallon} = 8 \text{ pints}$$

EXERCISE 5f

In questions on capacity, all the given measurements are inside measurements.

QUESTION

(a) A medicine bottle has a rectangular cross-section measuring 5 cm by 3 cm and is 11 cm high. How much medicine will it hold in
(i) cm^3 (ii) litres (iii) millilitres?

(b) The bottle is full of cough medicine and Sean is told to take two 5 ml teaspoonfuls three times a day. How many days should the medicine last?

ANSWER

(a) (i) Capacity of the bottle $= 5 \times 3 \times 11\ cm^3$
$= 165\ cm^3$

(ii) Capacity of bottle in litres $= 165 \div 1000$ litres ($1000\ cm^3 = 1$ litre)
$= 0.165$ litres

(iii) Since $1\ cm^3 = 1$ ml, the capacity of the bottle is 165 ml.

(b) Sean takes two 5 ml of the medicine three times a day, i.e. he takes $2 \times 5 \times 3$ ml per day = 30 ml per day;
$\therefore$ the medicine will last $165 \div 30$ days i.e. $5\frac{1}{2}$ days.

1 An open rectangular tank is 30 cm long, 20 cm wide and 15 cm high. How much water will it hold in
(a) cm^3 (b) litres?

2 How many litres of water can be poured into a rectangular tank that has an internal volume of $1\ m^3$?

3 How many pint milk bottles can be filled from a 500 gallon tank of milk?

4 A recipe to make 2 lb of country pâté requires 4 fluid ounces of dry white wine.

(a) How many times can this recipe be made up from 1 gallon of wine?

(b) How many pounds of pâté does this produce?

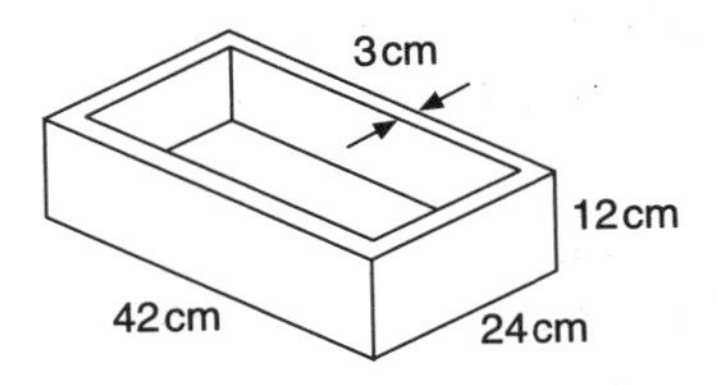

5 An open rectangular mould for making concrete blocks is shown in the diagram. The external measurements of the mould, which is everywhere 3 cm thick, are 42 cm by 24 cm by 12 cm.
Find (a) the volume of a concrete block made using this mould (b) the volume of material used to make the mould.

6

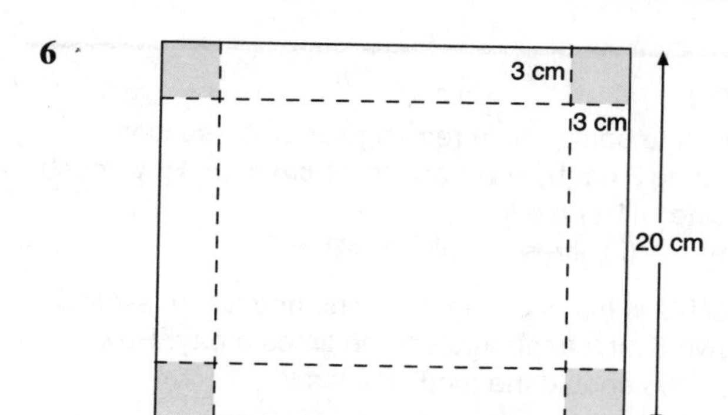

Four equal squares, of side 3 cm, are removed from the corners of a rectangular piece of card measuring 24 cm by 20 cm. The card is next folded about the dotted lines to form an open box.

(a) How deep is the box?

(b) What are the measurements of the base of the box?

(c) What is the capacity of the box?

Mass

When we buy meat or fruit or vegetables we usually ask for a particular weight. What we really want is a certain mass. The weight of an object depends on the pull of gravity on it, and this varies from place to place. The mass of an object is the amount of material in it.

In the *metric system* the most common unit of mass is the gram. Other units in everyday use that derive from the gram are the kilogram, milligram and tonne:

1 kilogram (kg) = 1000 grams (g)

1 gram (g) = 1000 milligrams (mg)

and 1 tonne (t) = 1000 kilograms (kg).

The most common units of mass in the *imperial system* are the ounce (oz), the pound (lb) and the ton, and occasionally the stone (st) and the hundredweight (cwt):

1 lb = 16 oz

1 st = 14 lb

1 cwt = 112 lb

and 1 ton = 2240 lb

Density

The mass of one unit of volume of material is called its density,

i.e. $\text{density} = \dfrac{\text{mass}}{\text{volume}}$

A goldsmith, for example, knows that the mass of 1 cm^3 of gold is 19.3 grams i.e. the density of gold is 19.3 g/cm^3.

EXERCISE 5g

QUESTION

(a) The mass of a sheet of silver is 8.7 grams. How many milligrams is this?

(b) A bag contains 1240 grams of apples. What is this in kilograms?

(c) 64 200 kilograms of potatoes are moved by road. How many tonnes is this?

ANSWER

(a) Since 1 g = 1000 mg

8.7 g = 8.7 × 1000 mg (Large unit to small unit, so multiply by 1000)

= 8700 mg

i.e. the mass of the sheet is 8700 mg.

(b) Since 1000 g = 1 kg

$1240\text{ g} = \dfrac{1240}{1000}\text{ kg}$ (Small unit to large unit, so divide by 1000)

= 1.24 kg

∴ the bag contains 1.24 kg of apples.

(c) Since 1000 kg = 1 tonnes,

$64\,200\text{ kg} = \dfrac{64\,200}{1000}\text{ tonnes}$ (Small unit to large unit, so divide by 1000)

= 64.2 tonnes

∴ 64.2 tonnes of potatoes are to be moved.

---

1 A tin of tomatoes has a mass of $\frac{1}{2}$ kg. How many grams is this?

2 A small tablet has a mass of 5 mg. How many grams is this?

3 A building society sends advertising material to 37 000 potential customers. Each one has a mass of 48 g. Find, in kilograms, the total mass of advertising material sent out.

4 A lorry, which when unloaded has a mass of 4.5 t, is loaded with one hundred and fifty 50 kg bags of potatoes. Find (a) the total mass of the potatoes in tonnes (b) the mass of the loaded lorry.

5 A wine enthusiast buys three 1 kg bags of sugar to make some wine. He needs 250 g sugar to make 4 litres of sweet raisin wine. How many litres of wine can he make from the sugar he bought?

6 A chef orders 12 kg of best fillet steak. How many servings can he hope to get from this order, if each steak is about 3 cm thick and weighs 200 g? (Assume that none of the meat is wasted.)

7 The instructions on a 5 kg bag of scientifically balanced puppy food which is suitable for puppies up to 18 months suggests giving a Cavalier King Charles spaniel 125 g per day. How many days should the bag last a family with one dog?

8 Find the mass of a metal bar measuring 3 m by 8 cm by 4 cm, if 1 cm^3 of the metal has a mass of 9.4 g. Give your answer in (a) grams (b) kilograms.

Metric and imperial equivalence

In everyday life we often need to convert from one system of units to the other. For example, the quantity of oil we need to put into an engine may be given in litres but the container we have may be graduated in pints, or a recipe may give the mass of the ingredients in kilograms and grams, whereas the scales we have may record pounds and ounces.

This mixture of metric and imperial units means that we need to know the rough equivalents between corresponding units. They are:

Length
8 km ≈ 5 miles
1 metre ≈ 39 inches (1 m is a little larger than 1 yd)
10 cm ≈ 4 inches

Area
1 hectare ≈ 2.5 acres

Mass
1 tonne ≈ 1 ton (1 tonne is a little less than 1 ton)
1 kg ≈ 2.2 lb
100 g ≈ 3.5 oz (100 g is about a quarter of a pound)

Capacity
1 litre ≈ 1.75 pints
1 gallon ≈ 4.5 litres

EXERCISE 5h

QUESTION
My petrol tank holds 70 litres. Roughly, how many gallons is this?

ANSWER

$$1 \text{ litre} \approx 1.75 \text{ pints}$$

so

$$70 \text{ litres} \approx 70 \times 1.75 \text{ pints}$$

$$= \frac{70 \times 1.5}{8} \text{ gallons}$$

$$= 13.125 \text{ gallons}$$

∴ 70 litres is about 13 gallons.

1 The cost of posting a first-class letter weighing not more than 60 g is 25 p and 38 p if it is not more than 100 g. What stamps should I put on it if a letter to be sent by first-class post weighs 2 oz on the kitchen scales?

2 (a) A petrol can has a capacity of 2 gallons. About how many litres is this?

(b) Which has the larger capacity: a drum that holds 50 litres or a tank that holds 12 gallons?

3 The area of a farm is 230 acres. Roughly how many hectares is this?

4 A recipe for wine requires 15 lb of sugar. How many 1 kg of sugar must be bought to be sure of having enough?

5 Which is the larger: (a) 1.5 lb or 550 g
(b) 5 gallons or 20 litres?

6 The distance from Glasgow to London is 395 miles. Roughly how many kilometres is this?

7

A demijohn holds 1 gallon of home-made wine. Roughly, how many 125 ml glasses can be filled from one demijohn of wine?

8 Eddy needs an 8 ft length of timber. It is sold in metric lengths which are sawn to the nearest 10 cm. What length should he ask for to be certain of having 8 ft?

QUESTION

Given that 1 metre ≈ 39 inches, find, correct to the nearest 10, the approximate equivalence in square feet of 30 m^2?

ANSWER

$$1 \text{ metre} \approx 39 \text{ inches}$$
$$= \tfrac{39}{12} \text{ feet}$$
$$= 3.25 \text{ ft}$$

so $1 \text{ m}^2 \approx 3.25 \times 3.25 \text{ ft}^2$
$$= 10.56 \text{ ft}^2$$

$\therefore$ $30 \text{ m}^2 \approx 30 \times 10.56 \text{ ft}^2$
$$= 316.875 \text{ ft}^2$$

i.e. $30 \text{ m}^2 \approx 320 \text{ ft}^2$ (to the nearest 10)

9 Which is the larger:
(a) 500 cm^2 or 70 in^2 (b) 3 in^2 or 3000 mm^2?

10 (a) If 1 m ≈ 1.09 yd, what is the approximate equivalent of 1 m^2 in yd^2? Give your answer correct to 3 s.f.

(b) A carpet costs £15.75 a square yard in one shop and £16.50 a square metre in another. Which is the cheaper?

Measuring instruments

Many measurements are obtained by noting the position of a pointer on a straight edge or circular scale. In some cases (for example a set of bathroom scales) the marker remains fixed and the scale moves.

EXERCISE 5i

QUESTION

Write down the value indicated by the pointer.

ANSWER

The value is between 10 and 11.
Between 10 and 11 there are 10 equal divisions, i.e. each division denotes $\frac{1}{10}$ or 0.1 of a unit. The pointer is opposite the eighth of these. The value indicated is therefore 10.8 cm.

In questions 1 to 10 write down the value indicated by the pointer.

1

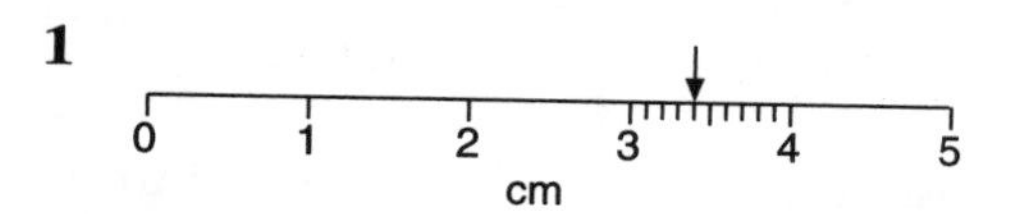

2

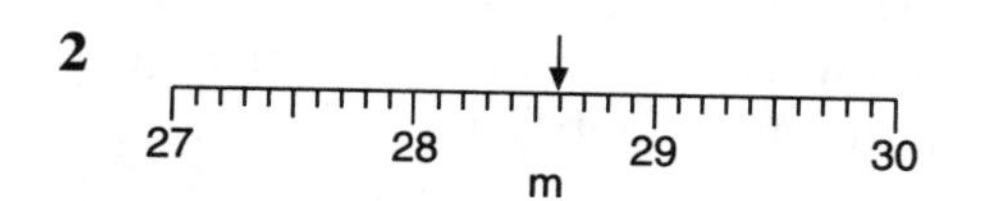

3

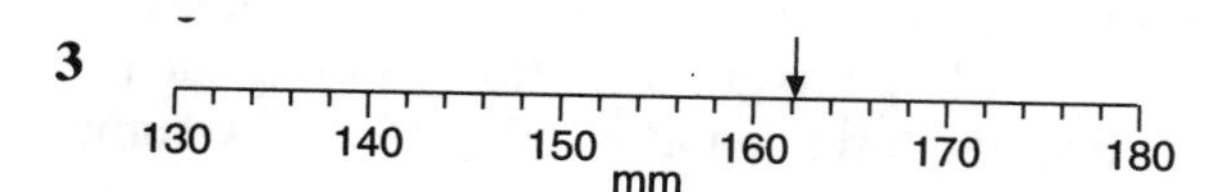

4

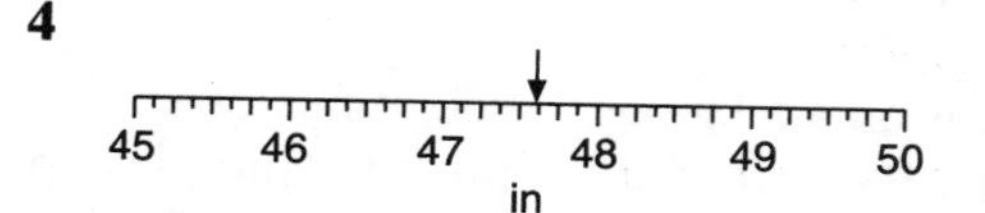

5

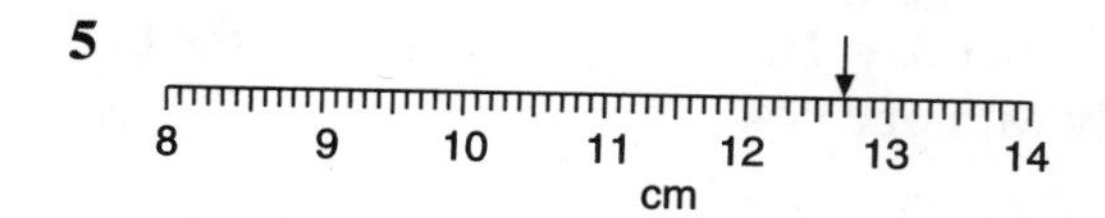

6

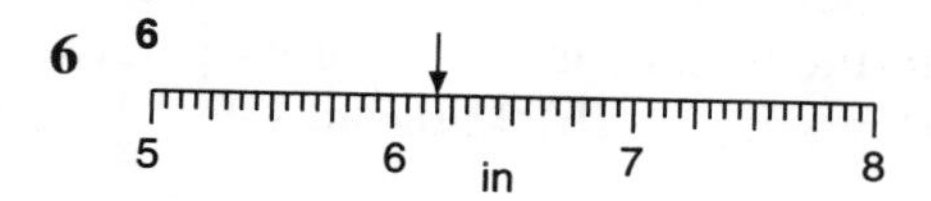

7

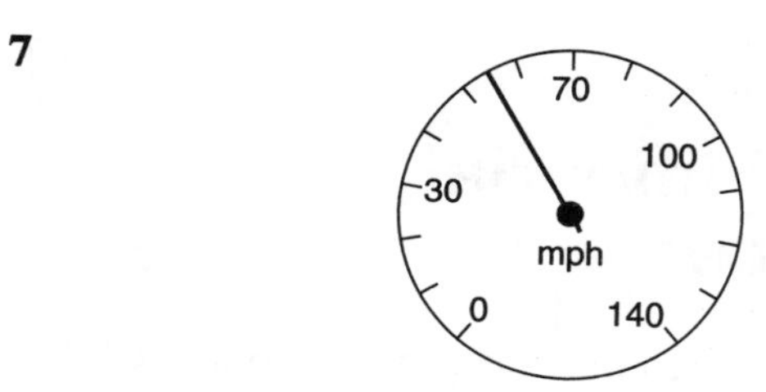

8

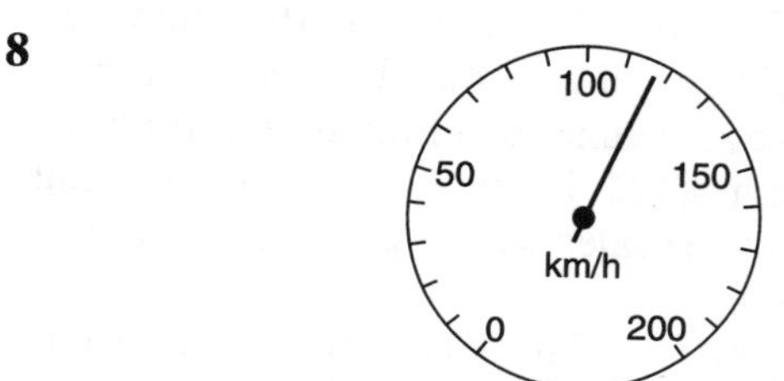

9

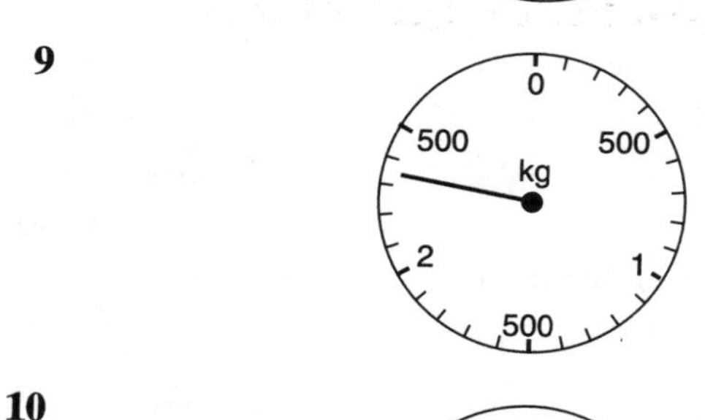

10

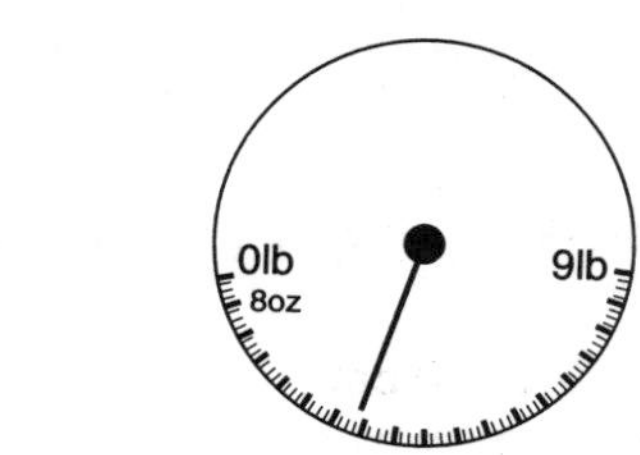

In questions 11 and 12 write down the weights of the two people that cause the pointer to take up the position shown.

11 **12**

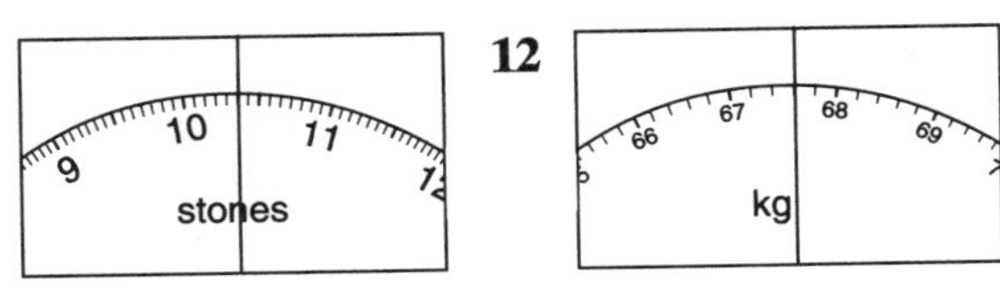

13

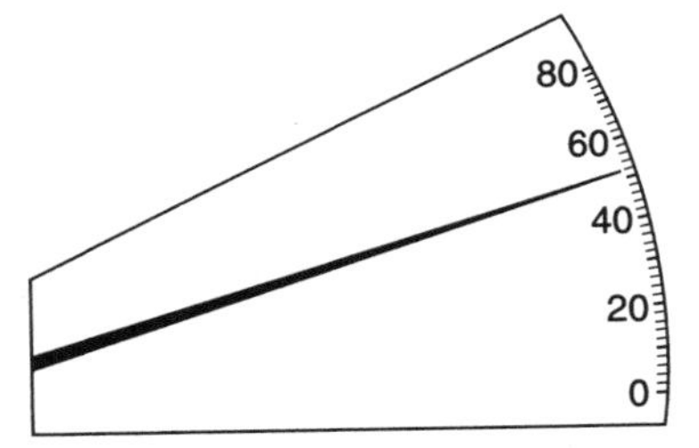

How many litres of petrol are in the petrol tank of this car?

14

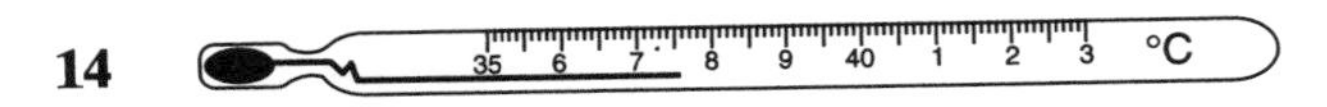

Estimate the temperature shown on this clinical thermometer.

15

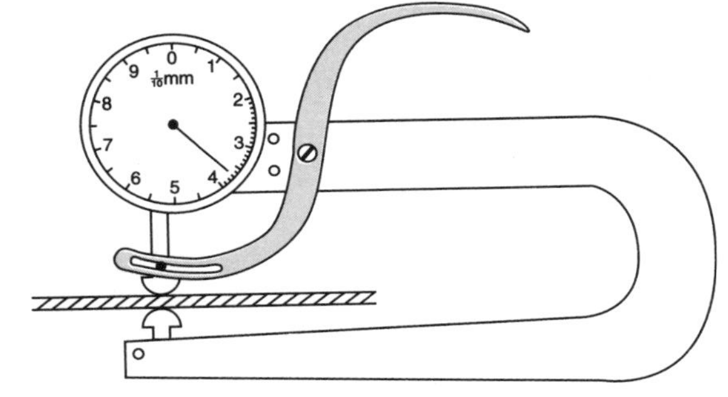

How thick is the piece of wood within the jaws of this gauge?

Multiple-choice questions 5

In questions 1 to 4 several alternative answers are given. Write down the letter that corresponds to the correct answer.

1 The lengths of four tables are: 1.85 m, 1800 mm, 186 cm and 1.847 m. The length of the shortest table is

A 1.847 m **B** 1800 mm
C 186 cm **D** 1.85 m

2 The area of a square tile is 225 cm^2. The perimeter of the tile is

A 60 cm **B** 30 cm
C 68 cm **D** 100 cm

3 A lorry weighs 3.5 tonnes when empty. It is loaded with 56 metal ingots, each weighing 0.08 tonnes. The total weight of the loaded lorry is

A 4.03 t **B** 48.3 t
C 4.48 t **D** 7.98 t

4

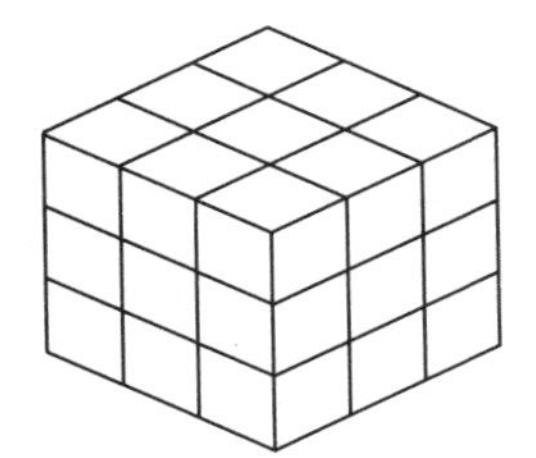

The cube is formed from 27 small white cubes. Its surface is painted red and it is taken apart. The number of small cubes that have exactly 4 white faces is

A 16 **B** 12 **C** 10 **D** 8

5 Niam makes up the following statements about different units of measurements. Which of the statements are true and which are false?

A A hectare is larger than an acre.

B An inch is smaller than 2 centimetres.

C A yard is longer than a metre.

D One litre is less than two pints.

6

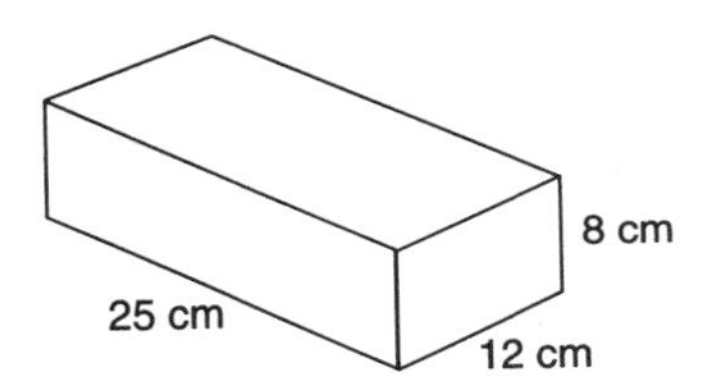

The diagram shows an open rectangular box with a base measuring 25 cm by 12 cm which is 8 cm deep.
The following statements have been made:
Statement 1. The area of the base of the box is 300 cm^2 and its capacity is 2400 cm^3.
Statement 2. The total area of the vertical sides of the inside of the box is 592 cm^2.
How are these two statements best described?

A True, True **B** True, False
C False, True **D** False, False

Self-assessment test 5

1 Change

(a) 9250 mm into cm (b) 1.05 km into m

(c) 42.6 cm into m (d) 100 cm^2 into mm^2

(e) 3 km^2 into m^2 (f) 4 cm^3 into mm^3

2

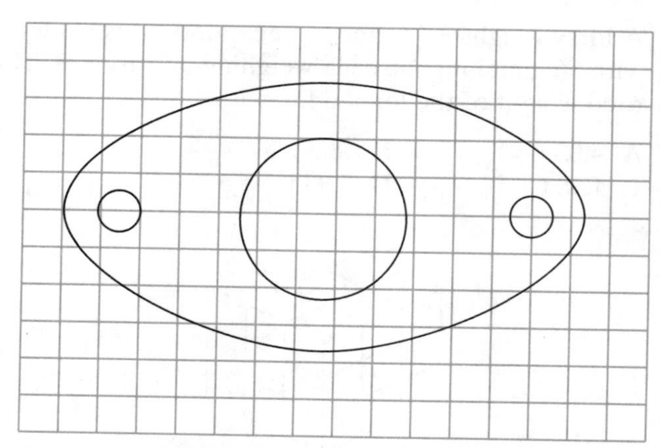

The diagram shows a gasket. By counting squares find its area.

3 A rectangular lawn measures 55 m by 34 m. Find
(a) its perimeter (b) its area.

4 (a) How many cubes of side 2 cm will fit into a cardboard box measuring 20 cm by 12 cm by 6 cm?

(b) Is it possible to fill a box measuring 18 cm by 12 cm by 6 cm with cubes of side
(i) 2 cm (ii) 3 cm (iii) 4 cm?
Give reasons for your answers.

5 Express (a) $3\frac{1}{2}$ yards in inches
(b) 124 inches in feet and inches (c) 108 ft^2 in yd^2
(d) 54 ft^3 in yd^3.

6 A book has 360 pages, a page size of 240 mm by 150 mm, and covers that are each 0.5 mm thick.

(a) Give the page size in centimetres. Hence find the area of one page in cm^2.

(b) (i) How many leaves are there in the book?
(ii) If one leaf is 0.1 mm thick, find the total thickness of the book including the covers. (One leaf is printed on both sides to give two pages)

(c) Find the area of paper used. Give your answer in m^2. Do not include the covers.

(d) The mass of the paper is 50 grams for each square metre, and the covers have a mass of 6 g. Find the mass of the finished book.

7

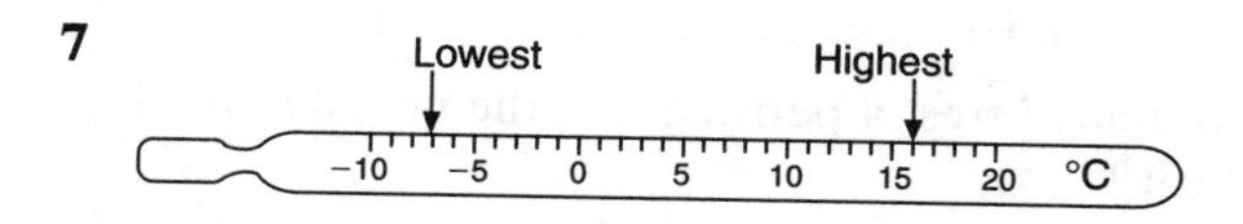

The thermometer shows, in degrees Celsius, the lowest and highest temperatures recorded one day last winter in New York.

(a) Find (i) the highest temperature recorded
(ii) the lowest temperature recorded.

(b) By how many degrees did the temperature change during the day?

CHAPTER 6

Understanding percentages

The meaning of percentage

'Per cent' means 'per hundred'.
12 per cent, which we write 12% for short, means 12 per 100 or $\frac{12}{100}$ or 0.12, and 6 per cent, i.e. 6%, means 6 per 100 or $\frac{6}{100}$ or 0.06.

Converting a percentage into a fraction

To convert a percentage into a fraction divide by 100 and simplify:

35% as a fraction is $\frac{35}{100} = \frac{7}{20}$

and 75% as a fraction is $\frac{75}{100} = \frac{3}{4}$

EXERCISE 6a

Express as a fraction in its lowest terms

1 25% **2** 55% **3** 60% **4** 48%

5 35% **6** 96% **7** 84% **8** 69%

9 120% **10** 260% **11** 196% **12** 325%

Converting a fraction into a percentage

To convert a fraction into a percentage multiply by 100:

$\frac{1}{2} = \frac{1}{2} \times 100\%$ i.e. 50%

$\frac{7}{8} = \frac{7}{8} \times 100\%$ i.e. 87.5%

$\frac{11}{10} = \frac{11}{10} \times 100\% = 110\%$

and $\frac{5}{36} = \frac{5}{36} \times 100\%$ i.e. 13.88 ...% or $13\frac{8}{9}\%$

EXERCISE 6b

Express as a percentage

1 $\frac{2}{5}$ **2** $\frac{17}{50}$ **3** $\frac{13}{20}$ **4** $\frac{2}{3}$ **5** $\frac{1}{12}$

6 $\frac{13}{8}$ **7** $\frac{27}{25}$ **8** $\frac{7}{18}$ **9** $\frac{12}{5}$ **10** $\frac{19}{7}$

Converting a percentage into a decimal

To convert a percentage into a decimal divide by 100:

$45\% = \frac{45}{100} = 0.45$

$67\frac{1}{2}\% = 67.5\% = \frac{675}{100} = 0.675$

and $137\% = \frac{137}{100} = 1.37$

EXERCISE 6c

Express as a decimal

1 20% **2** 65% **3** 47% **4** 73% **5** 2.5%

6 42.3% **7** 2.25% **8** 12.5% **9** 128% **10** 333%

Finding the percentage of a quantity

40% of 600 is $600 \times \frac{40}{100} = 240$

72% of 450% is $450 \times \frac{72}{100} = 324$

$37\frac{1}{2}\%$ of 192 is $192 \times \frac{75}{2} \times \frac{1}{100} = 72$

EXERCISE 6d

Find

1 30% of 8 **2** 10% of 37

3 15% of 60 **4** 125% of 44

5 $3\frac{1}{4}\%$ of 400 **6** $12\frac{1}{2}\%$ of 24

7 85% of 750 **8** $67\frac{1}{2}\%$ of 24

9 150% of 250 **10** 220% of 75

Interchanging percentages, decimals and fractions in everyday situations

EXERCISE 6e

In questions 1 to 5 express each percentage as a decimal.

1 In the car park 65% of the cars are foreign.

2 At a rugby international 74% of the spectators are males.

3 The clear-up rate for crimes in Oldborough is 34%.

4 Last year the sales of camcorders increased by 135%.

5 On a Thursday the number of customers at Sainsgate supermarket is 230% more than on a Monday.

QUESTION
At an MOT testing station 60% of the cars tested pass first time. Express this as a fraction in its lowest terms.

ANSWER

$$60\% = \frac{60}{100}$$

i.e. $60\% = \frac{3}{5}$

In questions 6 to 9 express each percentage as a fraction in its lowest terms.

6 At a factory 10% of the components from the press shop failed the quality test.

7 By choosing a smaller brick a bricklayer needs to order 20% more bricks.

8 In a warehouse 43% of the potatoes are reds and 57% are whites.

9 The target for Amien Computers is to increase sales next year by 35%.

QUESTION
(a) Out of the 20 nails in a box, 7 have round heads. What percentage is this?

(b) On a farm 0.63 of the land is planted with cereals. What percentage is this?

ANSWER
(a) 7 out of 20 is $\frac{7}{20} = \frac{7}{20} \times 100\%$
i.e. $\frac{7}{20} = 35\%$

(b) 0.63 is $0.63 \times 100\%$
i.e. $0.63 = 63\%$

---

10 Out of the 24 chocolates in a box, 6 have hard centres. What percentage is this?

11 At a disco 0.65 of the dancers are girls. What percentage is this?

QUESTION
45% of the residents in a home are men and the rest are women.

(a) What percentage of the residents are women?

(b) What fraction of the residents are men?

ANSWER
(a) If 45% of the residents are men then it follows that 100% − 45% i.e. 55% are women.

(b) Fraction of residents that are men is $\frac{45}{100}$ i.e. $\frac{9}{20}$.

---

12 In a library 32% of the books are reference books, which are not available for borrowing. What percentage of the books can be borrowed?

13 If 72% of the cost of a cigarette is tax what percentage is not?

14 Holiday World stated that 68% of the holidays they sold were for resorts in the Mediterranean. What percentage of the holidays they sold were for resorts that were not in the Mediterranean?

15 Each Wednesday evening at a leisure centre, members have to choose one of the activities, which are badminton, volleyball, gymnastics or dancing. If 14% choose badminton, 27% volleyball and 18% gymnastics, what percentage choose dancing?

16 Marmalade consists of 28% fruit, 58% sugar and the remainder water.
Find (a) the percentage of marmalade that is water
(b) the fraction that is sugar.

17 The cost of running a car is 28% petrol, 35% road tax, insurance and repairs, and the remainder depreciation. What percentage accounts for depreciation?

18 In a street $\frac{3}{5}$ of the properties are bungalows.

(a) What percentage is this?
(b) What percentage of the properties are not bungalows?

19 In a factory forty-four per cent of the workforce is under 24 years of age.

(a) What fraction is this?

(b) Can you say what fraction is older than 24?

(c) What fraction is older than 23?

20 The first all-British nuclear submarine was *HMS Valiant*. She had a displacement of 4000 tons, a crew of 90, was 285 ft long and 33 ft 3 in in the beam.

(a) If 35 cubic feet of water weighs 1 ton, find the number of cubic feet of water displaced by the submarine.

(b) If 54% of the space inside the ship is unavailable for the crew find
(i) the fraction of space available for the crew
(ii) the volume of space available for the crew
(iii) the amount of space available for each member of the crew.

(c) Express the width of the submarine (the beam length) as a percentage of its length.

Expressing one quantity as a percentage of another

To express 5 m as a percentage of 25 m, we first express 5 m as a fraction of 25 m;
i.e. 5 m is $\frac{5}{25}$ of 25 m
then $\frac{5}{25} = \frac{5}{25} \times 100\%$
$= 20\%$

$\therefore$ 5 m is 20% of 25 m

EXERCISE 6f

In questions 1 to 4 express

1 £50 as a fraction of £100

2 60 cm as a fraction of 200 cm

3 1 pint as a fraction of 8 pints

4 50p as a fraction of 25p

QUESTION
Express 65p as a fraction of £2.

ANSWER
(When the given units are different, one of the units must be converted into the other before the quantities are compared. We usually change the larger unit to the smaller unit.)

£2 = 200p

65p is $\frac{65}{200}$ of £2

i.e. 65p is $\frac{13}{40}$ of £2 ($\frac{65}{200}$ simplifies to $\frac{13}{40}$)

In questions 5 to 10 express the first quantity as a fraction of the second.

5 30p, £1

6 60 cm, 3 m

7 300 g, 4 kg

8 3 mm, 3 cm

9 700 kg, 2 tonne

10 4 pints, 2 gallons

11 In a sample of 500 light fittings that come off an assembly line, 25 are found to be faulty. What fraction is this?

12 In a box of 120 cassettes, 24 are damaged. What fraction is this?

13 At Varnley MOT vehicle testing station 7 out of 10 cars pass first time.

(a) What fraction is this?
(b) What fraction fail first time?

QUESTION
(a) 4 kg as a percentage of 80 kg

(b) 75p as a percentage of £2.50

ANSWER
(a) 4 kg is $\frac{4}{80}$ of 80 kg
But $\frac{4}{80} = \frac{4}{80} \times 100\%$
$= 5\%$
$\therefore$ 4 kg is 5% of 80 kg

(b) First change £2.50 to pence:
£2.50 = 250p
Now, 75p is $\frac{75}{250}$ of £2.50
But $\frac{75}{250} = \frac{75}{250} \times 100\%$
$= 30\%$
$\therefore$ 75p is 30% of £2.50

In questions 14 to 21 express the first quantity as a percentage of the second.

14 £8, £10

15 24 cm, 50 cm

16 400 m, 1 km

17 35p, £1.75

18 80 cm, 2 m

19 2 pints, 1 gallon

20 650 kg, 1 tonne

21 550 cm^3, 1 litre

22 Kim earns £180 per week and pays £30 a week at home for her keep.
What percentage does Kim (a) pay for her keep
(b) have left after she has paid for her keep?

23 When Ernie stood on the bathroom scales first thing one morning he weighed 11 st 6 lb. When he weighed again after lunch his weight was 11 st 8 lb. Express his lunchtime weight as a percentage of his weight first thing that morning. Give your answer to the nearest $\frac{1}{4}$%.

24 Suzanne bought a secondhand car for £5999 and sold it two years later for £3500. Express the price at which she sold it as a percentage of the purchase price. Give your answer correct to the nearest whole number.

Percentage of a quantity

30% of £50 is the same as finding 0.3 of £50

i.e. 30% of £50 = 0.3 × £50
= £15

EXERCISE 6g

Find

1 20% of £40

2 $12\frac{1}{2}$% of a population of 20 000

3 $37\frac{1}{2}$% of 64 cm

QUESTION
At a village fête £3400 is raised for charity. It is decided to give 40% to Barnardo's, 35% to the NSPCC and the remainder to the village hall improvement fund. How much goes to (a) Barnardo's (b) the village hall improvement fund?

ANSWER
(a) 40% of £3400 is $\frac{40}{100}$ of £3400
i.e. 0.4 of £3400
Barnardo's receive 0.4 × £3400 i.e. £1360.

(b) The village hall improvement fund receives
100% − 40% − 35%
i.e. 25% of the money raised
25% of £3400 is $\frac{25}{100}$ × £3400 = £850
The village hall improvement fund receives £850.

4 At a wedding 85% of the guests took wine with their meal. There were 80 guests. How many guests took wine with their meal?

5 At a pop concert 55% of the audience are female. There are 2400 people present. How many of those in attendance are (a) females (b) males?

6 A stallholder buys 300 shirts, knowing that 10% of them are unsaleable. How many shirts can he sell?

7 Deductions from Jean's wages amount to 40%. What is her take-home pay if she earns £320?

8 The constituents of gunpowder are: nitre 75%, charcoal 15% and sulphur 10%. How many kilograms of charcoal are needed to make 12 kg of gunpowder?

9 A salesperson is paid 5% commission on each sale with a value up to £300. For sales above this value the commission is $7\frac{1}{2}$%. (a) She takes two orders, one for £250 and one for £866. What commission can she expect to receive? (b) What is her commission on a sale valued at £300?

10

A restaurateur buys 30 kg of lamb. He estimates that it loses 15% in preparation, 30% in cooking, $12\frac{1}{2}$% for bones and $2\frac{1}{2}$% for trimming and carving.

(a) How many kilograms of useful lamb remains?

(b) If 100 g is allowed per serving, how many servings should be available from 30 kg of lamb?

(c) How many kilograms of lamb should be bought to provide 160 servings at 100 g per serving?

Percentage increase and decrease

Percentage increases or decreases are very important in everyday life. For example, wages usually increase by a given percentage, but often this doesn't mean very much until it is changed into an amount of money.

e.g. a 6% rise on £560 a week is worth an extra £33.60

whereas a 12% increase on £220 a week is worth only £26.40

EXERCISE 6h

QUESTION

Train fares are set to rise by 12%. Last month Leah's quarterly ticket cost £540. How much will it cost next quarter?

ANSWER

Increase is 12% of £540,

i.e. increase is $\frac{12}{100} \times £540$
$= 0.12 \times £540$
$= £64.80$

$\therefore$ cost of a new quarterly ticket is £540 + £64.80 = £604.80.

QUESTION

Paul Waite estimates the cost of building a new house at £84 000, of which 40% is for materials and the rest labour. By the time the house has been completed the cost of materials have increased by 15% and the labour costs by 12%. How much does the house actually cost him?

ANSWER

Estimated cost of materials = 40% of £84 000
$= \frac{40}{100} \times £84\,000$
$= 0.4 \times £84\,000$
$= £33\,600$

Estimated cost of labour = £84 000 − £33 600
= £50 400

Increase in the cost of materials = 15% of £33 600
$= \frac{15}{100} \times £33\,600$
$= 0.15 \times £33\,600$
$= £5040$

Increase in labour costs = 12% of £50 400
$= 0.12 \times £50\,400$
$= £6048$

$\therefore$ actual cost of the house = £84 000 + £5040 + £6048
= £95 088
= £95 100 (to the nearest £100)

1 On Wednesdays a store offers a discount of 10% on all sales over £50. Find the Wednesday price of (a) a pair of jeans marked £35 (b) a fireside chair marked £320 (c) a pair of trainers marked £50.

2 My electricity bill is £76.50, excluding VAT. How much must I pay if VAT is to be added at 8%?

3 A car bought for £12 000 loses 76% of its value over a 5 year period. Find its value after 5 years.

4 After 2 years a radio bought for £24 depreciates by 65%. What is it worth when 2 years old?

5 When a length of material is washed for the first time it shrinks by $2\frac{1}{2}$%. Sally buys some new jeans which are 90 cm long. What length can she expect them to be after their first wash?

6 The doctor advises Terry, whose present weight is 125 kg, to reduce his weight by 20%. What weight should he aim to get down to?

7 A price reduction of 30% is made on a three-piece suite costing £955. How much does the suite cost?

8 The population of Asherton is 50 000. Next year it is expected to rise by 10% and the following year by a further 8%. Find the expected population of Asherton (a) next year (b) the year after that.

9 Jane's weekly pay is £165 and 6% of this is deducted by her employer for pension contributions.

(a) How much is left after the pension contributions have been deducted?

(b) If Jane is given an increase of £15 per week, how much additional pension contribution must she pay?

10

	UK	England	Wales	Scotland	Northern Ireland
1961	52 807	43 561	2635	5184	1427
1971	55 928		2740	5236	1540
1981		46 821	2814	5180	1539
1991	57 801	48 208	2891	5107	1594
2001	59 719	49 921	2964	5148	1686
2011	61 110	51 289	3010	5078	1733

The table shows the populations in thousands, including projected figures for the year 2001 and the year 2011, for the various parts of the United Kingdom at ten year intervals.

(a) Copy the table and fill in the blanks.

(b) Find the percentage increase (or decrease) in population from 1961 to 1991 for (i) England (ii) Wales (iii) Scotland (iv) Northern Ireland.

(c) In which region of the United Kingdom has the population from 1961 to 1991 changed by
(i) the largest percentage
(ii) the smallest percentage?

(d) In which region of the United Kingdom is the percentage of the population expected to increase most from (i) 1991 to 2001 (ii) 1991 to 2011?

(e) For 1981 give the population of the United Kingdom and of each region, correct to the nearest million. Use these answers to find the fraction of the population, in its lowest terms, that lived in (i) England (ii) Wales.

Buying and selling

In a business, 'markup' is the gross profit given as a percentage of the cost of the goods sold.

EXERCISE 6i

QUESTION
Marshall (Footwear) buy trainers for £270 per dozen pairs and sell them at £33.75 a pair. Find the markup.

ANSWER
Cost price of one pair = £270 ÷ 12 = £22.50.
Retail price per pair is £33.75.
∴ gross profit per pair = £33.75 − £22.50 = £11.25.

$$\text{Markup} = \frac{\text{gross profit}}{\text{cost price}} \times 100$$

$$= \frac{£11.25}{£22.50} \times 100$$

$$= 50\%$$

The markup is therefore 50%.

1 Rosendale Computers made a gross profit of £61 600 on computer equipment costing £154 000. Find the markup.

2 Sidenham (Wholesale) Ltd bought goods for £470 000 and sold them for £680 000. Find (a) the gross profit (b) the markup.

3 Miles Denton made a profit of £3.4 m on sales of £8.8 m. Find (a) the cost price of the goods sold (b) the markup.

4 At Minoli's the food cost of preparing the speciality of the house is £4.50. What must the restaurant charge for the meal to make a gross profit of
(a) 50% (b) 60% (c) 75% (d) 100%?

5 The table gives the cost of preparing various courses at Bellini's Restaurant as a percentage of the total bill.

Course	Dish	Approximate percentage of the total cost of the meal
First	Hors d'oeuvres, soup	12
Main	Meat, fish, poultry	45
	vegetables	10
	potatoes	7
Third	Sweet, cheese, savory	20
Sundries	Roll and butter, condiments	6
		100

Sim pays £22 for a full meal that costs the restaurant £10 for raw materials and preparation.

(a) What percentage of the cost of the meal did he pay for his main course? (Don't forget the veg!)

(b) How much did he pay for (i) the meat (ii) his third course (iii) his main course?

(c) What markup did the restaurant add?

(d) If the restaurant were to add a markup of 100%, what would the same meal cost?

6 The lighting department in a department store turns in the following figures for the year 1994–5:

	£
Sales	180 000
Cost of goods sold	90 000
Wages + incentive payments	73 000
Share of fixed overheads	24 000
Net profit (or loss)	

(a) Does the department make a profit or a loss? (You have to decide which figures you add together and which you subtract.)

(b) What markup has the store used in this department?

(c) Which one figure in the list would be unchanged if the lighting department was closed?

(d) Lefebvre's, the well-known ladies' fashion house, is interested in renting the floor area used by the lighting department at a cost of £30,000 a year. It would employ its own staff.
   (i) Which one of the above figures would not disappear?
   (ii) Would you advise the store management to accept the offer, i.e. would it be better for Lefebvre's to have the space than to continue with the lighting department?
   (iii) Would the space be profitable with Lefebvre's renting it?

7

A furniture retailer sells a chair for £144, his sales markup being 80%. What did the chair cost him?

Taxes

Value Added Tax (VAT)

Value added tax is added to most goods and services. It is a tax collected for the central government and increases the basic cost by $17\frac{1}{2}$%. Some things, for example basic foodstuffs, children's clothes, newspapers and books, are zero-rated. This means that there is no tax on these items.

Income tax

Income tax is deducted from every person's taxable income, that is, on their earnings over and above their allowances. At present (January, 1996) the basic rate is 25%, but there is a reduced rate of 20% on the first £3900 of taxable income and a higher rate of 40% on taxable income above £25 500.

Other taxes

Apart from VAT and income tax the government collects other taxes, e.g. inheritance tax (a tax on what you leave when you die) and capital gains tax (a tax on the increase in value of an asset when it is disposed of). It also levies numerous taxes such as those on petrol, tobacco and alcohol, as well as the road fund licence, which are grouped together under the general heading of excise duty.

EXERCISE 6j

QUESTION

The marked price of a camcorder is £756, plus VAT at $17\frac{1}{2}$%. What must I pay for this camcorder?

ANSWER

The value of the VAT is 17.5% of £756 = 0.175 × £756
= £132.30

The price I must pay is £756 + £132.30 = £888.30

Alternatively, the price of the camcorder, including VAT, is (100% + 17.5%) i.e. 117.5% of £756 = 1.175 × £756
= £888.30

In questions 1 to 4 find the total purchase price, assuming that the rate of VAT is 17.5%.

1 A camera marked £120 + VAT.

2 A light fitting marked £68 + VAT.

3 A three course meal costing £8.50 + VAT.

4 An extension ladder marked £83.50 + VAT.

5 Shirley West bought several articles which were priced exclusive of VAT at $17\frac{1}{2}$%: a bucket at 60p, a pair of steps at £14.58, a dustbin at £7.20 and a clothes line at £13.12. Calculate the total bill including VAT.

6 A hi-fi system for my car is priced at £800 plus VAT at $17\frac{1}{2}$%.

(a) Find the total price including VAT.

(b) Walfords offers a discount of 10% off the total price while Radio Systems offers a cash discount of £65 off the marked price. Which shop gives the better deal and by how much?

7

E Pembroke (Wholesale Stationers)
Invoice 12345 **8 March 1996**

12 reams photocopying paper
at £2.89 per ream
VAT at $17\frac{1}{2}$% ________
Total
5% discount for settlement within
7 days otherwise strictly net.

Copy and complete this invoice to find the amount due (a) if the account is settled within 7 days
(b) if it is not settled within 7 days.

QUESTION

Des paid £869.50 for a set of four alloy car wheels. This price included VAT at $17\frac{1}{2}\%$. Find the marked price of each wheel excluding VAT.

ANSWER

(We do not know the marked price of the four wheels, but we do know that the VAT is 17.5% of the marked price, i.e. the price Des pays is 117.5% of the marked price.)

117.5% of the marked price is £869.50

i.e. 1.175 × marked price = £869.50

so marked price = £869.50 ÷ 1.175 = £740

i.e. the marked price of the four wheels is £740

Then the marked price of one wheel is £740 ÷ 4 = £185.

8 An electric typewriter costs £500.55, including value added tax at $17\frac{1}{2}\%$. A businessman has the VAT refunded at a later date, whereas a private customer must pay the full price. Calculate the difference between the two prices.

9 A businessman is charged £248.16, including VAT at $17\frac{1}{2}\%$, for four tyres for his van. Since he is in business he is able to claim repayment of the VAT. How much does each tyre actually cost him?

Sometimes a businessman is given a price including VAT, but what he needs to know is how much the VAT is. Assuming that the rate of VAT is 17.5%, this can be done using a simple formula:

amount of VAT

$$= \frac{17.5\%}{100\% + 17.5\%} \times \text{sale price including VAT}$$

For example, if the sale price of a chair, including VAT at $17\frac{1}{2}\%$, is £148 then

$$\text{amount of VAT} = \frac{17.5}{117.5} \times £148 = £22.04$$

10 How much VAT at $17\frac{1}{2}\%$ is included in the cost of a CD retailing at £12.99? Give your answer correct to the nearest penny.

11 Rangeworthy Manufacturing receive a request for late payment of a bill amounting to £1468.75. This includes VAT at $17\frac{1}{2}\%$. Unfortunately the accounts clerk fails to find the original invoice. How much VAT does this figure include?

12 At Enterprise Bookstores the markup is 75%.
(a) Find the wholesale price of a book that retails at £17.50. (b) They are worried that VAT will be added to books, but have decided that if it is they will absorb the cost, i.e. the price of their books will remain unchanged. If the sale price of the book remains at £17.50 but now includes VAT at $17\frac{1}{2}\%$, find the amount of VAT included. Give your answer correct to the nearest penny. (c) In this case how much profit do they make on this book?
(d) What is their markup now? Give your answer correct to the nearest whole number.

Saving

The most popular ways of saving are with building societies and banks, or the various types of National Savings. All these pay interest at least once a year.

Simple interest

If a building society advertises that it pays 6% p.a. on money invested in a particular account, it means that it will pay £6 for every £100 invested for a complete year.
It follows that if £700 is invested for 1 year at 6% then the amount of interest is 7 × £6, i.e. £42. If £700 is invested for 3 years at 6% then the total amount of interest will be 3 × £42 i.e. £126.
In words we have:

simple interest =

$$\frac{\text{sum invested} \times \text{rate per cent per annum} \times \text{time in years}}{100}.$$

Some people prefer to remember this as the formula

$$I = \frac{PRT}{100}$$

$$\text{For our example, simple interest} = \frac{£700 \times 6 \times 3}{100} = £126$$

Compound interest

Most accounts pay compound interest. This means that the first interest payment is added to the original amount invested, and so earns interest during the next interest period.

EXERCISE 6k

1 Alistair invests £1200 for 4 years at 7% p.a. simple interest. How much interest will he receive?

2 Beryl puts £550 into an account with the Cranley Building Society. The society pays simple interest of 5% p.a. How much interest will she earn if she leaves the money there for 3 years.

QUESTION
The Northern Building Society pays 7% per annum for money paid into its High Interest Account, interest being paid half-yearly. If £3000 is invested in this account and the interest is not withdrawn, find the amount in the account at the end of the first year.

ANSWER
Interest for first half-year is half of 7% of £3000

$= 0.5 \times 0.07 \times £3000$
$= £105$

The amount in the account at the end of the first half-year is £3105.

Interest for the second half-year is half of 7% of £3105

$= 0.5 \times 0.07 \times £3105$
$= £108.675$

The amount in the account at the end of the first year is

£3105 + £108.675
= £3213.675
= £3213.68 (to the nearest penny)

(Note that if the interest had been added yearly it would have been $0.07 \times £3000 = £210$, i.e. £3.68 less than it is when paid half-yearly.)

Sometimes income tax is deducted by the building society or bank and paid directly to the Inland Revenue. At present the lowest rate of tax is 20%, so that a gross interest rate of 5% gives a net interest rate of 4%, i.e. 5% reduced by 20% of 5%.
A typical building society notice reads
4% p.a. net = 5% p.a. gross

3 Ken puts £800 into a building society that pays interest of 8% per annum. If neither capital nor interest is withdrawn, how much is in the account at the end of one year if the interest is added
(a) yearly (b) half-yearly?

4 A lump sum of £1000 is to be invested for 2 years. Which account is the better investment: either (a) a savings account paying 4% per annum, the interest payable half-yearly or (b) an account with a fixed administrative charge of £7.50 and paying 5% per annum, the interest payable half-yearly?

5 Anne invests £12 000 in an income bond paying $5\frac{1}{2}\%$ p.a., the income to be paid monthly. Find the monthly income.

QUESTION
Edna puts £1200 in an account offering a fixed interest of 5% p.a. If the interest is left in the account at the end of each year, find the total interest earned after 3 years.

ANSWER
Interest for 1st year is 5% of £1200 = $0.05 \times £1200$
= £60
Amount in account at end of 1st year is £1200 + £60
= £1260
Interest for 2nd year is 5% of £1260 = $0.05 \times £1260$
= £63
Amount in account at end of 2nd year is £1260 + £63
= £1323
Interest for 3rd year is 5% of £1323 = $0.05 \times £1323$
= £66.15
Amount in account at end of 3rd year is £1323 + £66.15
= £1389.15
Total interest added is £1389.15 − £1200 = £189.15
(Note that although the rate of interest is fixed, the interest paid each year increases by a small amount.)

In questions 6 to 8 find the compound interest earned in each case.

6 £1000 is invested for 2 years at 8% in the Westminster Building Society.

7 £1000 is invested for 3 years at 4% in a Midford Bank deposit account.

8 £3000 is invested for 2 years at $5\frac{1}{2}\%$ with Westland County Council.

In questions 9 to 11 find the total in an account at the end of 3 years if the given amount is invested at the given rate of compound interest.

9 £1500 at $3\frac{1}{2}\%$ p.a. in National Savings Certificates.

10 £2500 at $4\frac{1}{2}\%$ p.a. in Haliabbey Investment Bonds.

11 £4600 at $5\frac{1}{4}\%$ in the Woodfield Building Society.

Compound growth tables

From these tables we can extract a number, called a multiplying factor, by which we can multiply the original quantity to show what it grows into for various percentage rates over different periods of time.

The table shows the multiplying factors for rates of growth from 2% to 15% over a 10 year period.

Rate of growth p.a.	Number of years									
	1	2	3	4	5	6	7	8	9	10
2%	1.020	1.040	1.061	1.082	1.104	1.126	1.149	1.172	1.195	1.219
3%	1.030	1.061	1.093	1.126	1.159	1.194	1.230	1.267	1.305	1.344
4%	1.040	1.082	1.125	1.170	1.217	1.265	1.316	1.369	1.424	1.480
5%	1.050	1.103	1.158	1.216	1.276	1.340	1.407	1.477	1.551	1.629
6%	1.060	1.124	1.191	1.262	1.338	1.419	1.504	1.594	1.689	1.791
7%	1.070	1.145	1.225	1.311	1.403	1.501	1.606	1.718	1.838	1.967
8%	1.080	1.166	1.260	1.360	1.469	1.587	1.714	1.851	1.999	2.159
9%	1.090	1.188	1.295	1.412	1.539	1.677	1.828	1.993	2.172	2.367
10%	1.100	1.210	1.331	1.464	1.611	1.772	1.949	2.144	2.358	2.594
15%	1.150	1.323	1.521	1.749	2.011	2.313	2.660	3.059	3.518	4.046

This table shows that if a population of 10 000 increases at a constant rate of 4% for 8 years then the multiplying factor is 1.369 and so the increased population is 10 000 × 1.369, i.e. 13 690.

EXERCISE 6I

In this exercise use the compound growth table given above. Give answers correct to 3 significant figures.

QUESTION

The population of Pullerton is 20 000. It is projected that each year, for the next 10 years, it will grow by 8%. What is the projected population of Pullerton (a) in 5 years' time (b) in 10 years' time?

ANSWER

(a) The table shows that the multiplying factor for growth of 8% over 5 years is 1.469.
Thus the projected population in 5 years' time is
20 000 × 1.469
= 29 380
= 29 400 (to 3 s.f.)

(b) Similarly the projected population in 10 years' time is
20 000 × 2.159
= 43 180
= 43 200 (to 3 s.f.)

1 The population of Wrigglesworth is 7000. It is expected to increase by 5% a year for the next 5 years. What is the projected population in 5 years' time?

2 If £100 is invested for 4 years at 6%, what sum will it amount to?

3 If £1800 is invested for 8 years at 6%, what sum will it amount to?

4 Baxters' turnover is planned to increase by 9% a year. About how long should it be before the turnover doubles?

5 The grey squirrel population of Dorney Wood has increased steadily by 15% a year for the last 5 years. 5 years ago it was estimated that it was 2500.

(a) How many squirrels are there in Dorney Wood now? (b) If the increase continues at the same rate, how many are there likely to be in 5 years' time?

6 The sales at Ashfords have increased steadily by 8% a year over the last 4 years. Four years ago they sold 850 units.

(a) How many have they sold this year?
(b) Assuming that the rate of increase remains constant how many do they hope to sell in 6 years' time?

Borrowing

Money borrowed to buy a house or flat is usually repaid with interest over a period of 25 or 30 years. To most people the most important fact is not what the total cost will be, but rather how much they have to pay each month. Building societies and banks therefore quote a monthly repayment on each £1000 borrowed. This amount varies with the rate of interest and the number of years over which the loan must be repaid.

Bank loans, credit sales and credit cards

A **bank loan** is usually repaid in monthly instalments over 2 to 5 years. It is not an expensive way of borrowing money.

A **credit sale** requires a down payment followed by monthly payments over a period of up to three years. This is an expensive way of borrowing which is why, by law, the annual percentage rate – the APR – must be clearly stated.

A **credit card**, such as Access or Visa, enables us to pay for goods and services up to an agreed limit, without using money. Each month the cardholder receives a statement which shows the amount due including interest. Although $2\frac{1}{2}\%$ a month looks small it works out equivalent to about 34% a year. Purchases paid for when they first become due are interest-free. This makes credit cards a very convenient way of buying things for cardholders who are able to clear their debt completely at the end of each month. Most credit card companies make a small yearly charge (about £15) to help cover their administration costs.

EXERCISE 6m

QUESTION

A building society offers a 25-year mortgage for monthly repayments of £11.50 per £1000 borrowed. (a) What are the monthly repayments on a mortgage of £60 000? (b) What is the total of all the repayments during the 25 years?

ANSWER

(a) The monthly repayment on £1000 is £11.50.
The monthly repayment on £60 000 is
$60 \times £11.50 = £690$.

(b) The total of 12 monthly repayments over 25 years is
$12 \times 25 \times £690 = £207\ 000$.
(This is more than 3 times the cost of the house!)

---

1 The Liverpool Building Society offers a 25-year mortgage for monthly repayments of £11 for each £1000 borrowed.
(a) What are the monthly repayments on a mortgage of (i) £30 000 (ii) £85 000?
(b) If the monthly repayments are £726 how much is borrowed?

2 The repayments on a 30-year mortgage of £50 000 are calculated at £11.25 per calendar month for each £1000 borrowed. What amount must be paid (a) per month (b) per year (c) over the full 30-year term?

3 Birmingham Building Society offers Sid Reeves a 90% mortgage on a bungalow whose purchase price is £80 000. (a) How much can he borrow? (b) How much must he pay himself? (c) The repayments are £12.25 per month per £1000 borrowed for 25 years. Find (i) his monthly repayments (ii) the total repayments over the 25 years.

4 A couple decide to buy a house priced £54 400. A building society is prepared to advance 80% of the purchase price. The monthly repayments are 95p per £100 borrowed for 20 years. (a) What is the amount borrowed? (b) What is the total cost of the house?

QUESTION

The cash price of a television set is £465. The credit sale terms are: a deposit of £140 followed by 36 monthly repayments of £11.95. Find (a) the total sale price (b) the amount that would be saved by paying cash.

ANSWER

(a) Total of monthly repayments is $36 \times £11.95 = £430.20$.
Total credit sale = deposit + repayments
= £140 + £430.20
= £570.20

(b) Amount saved by paying cash is £570.20 − £465
= £105.20

---

5 A secondhand car is offered for sale for £3800. If bought on credit the terms are a deposit of 25% plus 24 monthly repayments of £145. Find (a) the deposit (b) the total cost of buying the car on credit (c) the difference between the cash price and the credit price.

6 The marked price of a video recorder is £256. A buyer who pays cash is offered a discount of 5%. For a credit sale the terms are: a deposit of £75.50 plus 18 monthly payments of £11.92. (a) How much does the cash customer pay? (b) What is the total cost of buying on credit? (c) How much more does it cost to buy on credit than to pay cash?

7 Ray Woodford wants to buy a motorbike costing £3500 but cannot afford to pay cash. He can either (a) take a bank loan for £3500 repayable over 36 months at £121.60 per month, or (b) sign a credit agreement requiring a deposit of 20% (which he can afford) plus 30 monthly repayments of £123.70. Which is the cheaper way to buy the motorbike, and by how much?

8 Ali's Access statement at the end of February shows that he has spent £374.54. He must pay either £5 or 5%, whichever is the greater, within 7 days. The rate of interest on the balance is $2\frac{1}{2}\%$ per month. (a) How much must Ali pay immediately? (b) How much interest is due at the end of March? (c) If there are no further purchases and the minimum amount is paid at the end of March, how much is due at the end of April? (Give all amounts correct to the nearest penny.)

Multiple-choice questions 6

In questions 1 to 4 several alternative answers are given. Write down the letter that corresponds to the correct answer.

1 In a local election 27% of the electorate voted Labour, 15% voted Conservative and 23% voted Liberal Democrat. There are 48 500 registered voters. The number who did not vote is

A 13 095 **B** 31 525
C 16 975 **D** 7275

2 The population of Oxwich has increased by 5% a year for the last 5 years. Two years ago it was 1200. The population now is

A 1300 **B** 1323
C 1100 **D** 1452

3 A compact disc costs £11.99, including value added tax at $17\frac{1}{2}$%. The cost of the CD excluding VAT is

A £9.89 **B** £14.09
C £10.50 **D** £10.20

4 Liz puts £500 into her account with the Edinburgh Building Society. The rate of interest on this account is 6% a year, payable half-yearly. She doesn't withdraw any money during the year, so the amount she has in the account at the end of the year is

A £530.45 **B** £30.45
C £530 **D** £561.80

5 Wendy and John agree to buy a house for £75 000. The building society agrees to advance 90% of the purchase price provided they can find the remainder. The monthly repayments to the building society are £10.95 per £1000 borrowed for 30 years. Which of the following statements are true and which are false?

A Wendy and John must find £7500 and the building society agrees to advance £67 500.

B The monthly repayments to the building society amount to £821.25.

C The repayments to the building society amount to £8869.50 a year.

D By the time they have finished paying the house will have cost them £266 085.

6 A secondhand car is offered for sale at £6500. If bought on credit, the terms require a deposit of 30% plus 36 monthly repayments of £172. The following statements have been made.

Statement 1. The deposit is £1950 and the total of all the credit payments comes to £6192.
Statement 2. The total cost of the car if it is bought on credit comes to £8142, which is £1642 more than the cash price.
How are these two statements best described?

A True, True **B** True, False
C False, True **D** False, False

Self-assessment test 6

1 From a sample of 60 bags of crisps, 15 are found to be underweight. (a) What fraction is this? (b) What percentage is this?

2 When the council voted on a new bypass road, 63% voted for the bypass and 28% voted against it. What percentage abstained?

3 A college bought an extra 5 acres of land, and so increased the area of the campus to 48 acres. Express the acreage of the campus after the purchase as a percentage of the acreage before the purchase.

4 The cost of a package holiday for an adult is £574. The cost for a child is 70% of the adult price. Two adults and three children decide to take this holiday. How much will it cost them?

5 An employee earning £190 a week is offered an increase of either £13.50 or 7%. Which one would you advise her to take?

6 David Morgan offers a compact disc player at £150 plus VAT at $17\frac{1}{2}$%. Denhams offer the identical unit at £176 including VAT. Which store offers the better deal, and by how much?

7 Percy Sharman invests £20 000 in an income bond that pays $4\frac{1}{2}$% p.a., the income to be paid monthly. Find the monthly income.

8 Mrs Bunyan's Visa credit card account shows that she owes £436.78. She must pay either £5 or 5%, whichever is the greater, within 7 days. The rate of interest on the balance is $2\frac{1}{2}$% per month. (a) How much must Mrs Bunyan pay within 7 days?
(b) Assuming that she made the minimum payment, how much interest is added to the account at the end of the following month?

CHAPTER 7

Time and travel

The calendar

The calendar is the division of years into months, weeks and days and the method of ordering the years. For our calendar every month has either 30 or 31 days, except February which has 28 days in an ordinary year but 29 in every year exactly divisible by 4 (except the century years that are not divisible by 400 e.g. 1700, 1800, 1900).

A decade is a period of 10 years, for example the 1990s.

A millennium is a period of 1000 years.

The next millennium begins in the year 2000.

EXERCISE 7a

JANUARY

M	T	W	T	F	S	S
						1
2	3	4	5	6	7	8
9	10	11	12	13	14	15
16	17	18	19	20	21	22
23	24	25	26	27	28	29
30	31					

FEBRUARY

M	T	W	T	F	S	S
		1	2	3	4	5
6	7	8	9	10	11	12
13	14	15	16	17	18	19
20	21	22	23	24	25	26
27	28					

MARCH

M	T	W	T	F	S	S
		1	2	3	4	5
6	7	8	9	10	11	12
13	14	15	16	17	18	19
20	21	22	23	24	25	26
27	28	29	30	31		

APRIL

M	T	W	T	F	S	S
					1	2
3	4	5	6	7	8	9
10	11	12	13	14	15	16
17	18	19	20	21	22	23
24	25	26	27	28	29	30

MAY

M	T	W	T	F	S	S
1	2	3	4	5	6	7
8	9	10	11	12	13	14
15	16	17	18	19	20	21
22	23	24	25	26	27	28
29	30	31				

JUNE

M	T	W	T	F	S	S
			1	2	3	4
5	6	7	8	9	10	11
12	13	14	15	16	17	18
19	20	21	22	23	24	25
26	27	28	29	30		

JULY

M	T	W	T	F	S	S
					1	2
3	4	5	6	7	8	9
10	11	12	13	14	15	16
17	18	19	20	21	22	23
24	25	26	27	28	29	30
31						

AUGUST

M	T	W	T	F	S	S
	1	2	3	4	5	6
7	8	9	10	11	12	13
14	15	16	17	18	19	20
21	22	23	24	25	26	27
28	29	30	31			

SEPTEMBER

M	T	W	T	F	S	S
				1	2	3
4	5	6	7	8	9	10
11	12	13	14	15	16	17
18	19	20	21	22	23	24
25	26	27	28	29	30	

OCTOBER

M	T	W	T	F	S	S
						1
2	3	4	5	6	7	8
9	10	11	12	13	14	15
16	17	18	19	20	21	22
23	24	25	26	27	28	29
30	31					

NOVEMBER

M	T	W	T	F	S	S
		1	2	3	4	5
6	7	8	9	10	11	12
13	14	15	16	17	18	19
20	21	22	23	24	25	26
27	28	29	30			

DECEMBER

M	T	W	T	F	S	S
				1	2	3
4	5	6	7	8	9	10
11	12	13	14	15	16	17
18	19	20	21	22	23	24
25	26	27	28	29	30	31

The questions that follow refer to the calendar given above.

1 How many days are there in
(a) October (b) February?

2 Is this a calendar for a leap year?

3 Which month is (a) four months after July
(b) three months before October?

4 How many weekends are there between 1 March and 1 June?

5 In how many months of the year are there five Sundays?

6 Today is 23 September. (a) What day of the week is it? (b) What was the date last Saturday?
(c) What will be the date a week next Wednesday?

7 Yesterday was the second Saturday in September.
(a) What is the date today? (b) What was the date a week yesterday? (c) What will be the date next Monday?

8 Peg leaves on 12 August for a ten-night holiday in Corfu. What date is she due to return?

9 Sid Seward goes on holiday on 25 August and returns on 9 September. How many nights will he be away?

10 Sally's first term in college starts on 11 September and finishes on 15 December. (a) How many weeks is this?

Sally is given her first piece of coursework on the second Wednesday of term. It is to be completed and handed in so that her teacher has two weeks to mark it and can return the work to her on the last Wednesday of term. (b) On what date is Sally given her coursework? (c) How long does Sally have to work on it before she is due to hand it in?

Time

Each day is divided into hours, each hour into minutes and each minute into seconds, where

$$1 \text{ day} = 24 \text{ hours}$$
$$1 \text{ hour} = 60 \text{ minutes}$$
$$1 \text{ minute} = 60 \text{ seconds}$$

Using the 12-hour clock, we denote times before midday by the letters a.m. and times after midday by the letters p.m.

For example, 3 a.m. means 3 hours after midnight, i.e. in the 12-hour period before noon, whereas 3 p.m. means 3 hours after midday.

EXERCISE 7b

1 How long is it (a) from 8.15 a.m. to 11.00 p.m.
(b) from 10.38 a.m. to 12.49 p.m. (c) from 11 a.m. to 7 p.m. the next day?

2 David starts work at 8 a.m. He takes 20 minutes to travel to work and needs 15 minutes to get ready. What time should he aim to get up?

3 Laura went in on Saturday morning to work overtime. She clocked in at 8.22 a.m. and clocked off at 12.26 p.m. (a) How long did she work? (b) She is paid for complete periods of 15 minutes only. At what time could she have clocked off but still receive the same pay?

4 Given below are the television programmes for BBC and ITV one evening.

BBC1		ITV	
6.00	Stay Tooned	5.15	Time Trax
6.40	Pets Win Prizes	6.50	Celebrity Squares
7.20	Miss Marple	7.20	Stars in Their Eyes
8.00	Casualty	8.30	News
9.05	One Foot in the Grave	8.50	Stars in Their Eyes – The Result
9.30	News and Sport	9.05	Film: The Delta Force
9.55	Film: Firefox	11.25	World Cup – Looking Back
12.05 a.m.	Gloria Estefan	12.30	a.m. Film: Midnight Crossing
1.05–1.10	Weather	2.15	Hollywood Report

(a) How long is it (i) from the end of Stay Tooned to the beginning of Firefox (ii) from the end of Celebrity Squares to the beginning of Midnight Crossing?

(b) How many minutes is (i) News and Sport on BBC1 (ii) the ITV News?

(c) Which film is the longer, and by how much: Firefox or Midnight Crossing?

(d) Spike saw the last 10 minutes of Celebrity Squares and remained watching television until the end of The Delta Force. How long was this?

The 24-hour clock

Rail, bus and aircraft timetables use the 24-hour clock.

In the 24-hour clock, four figures are always used. The first two give the number of hours after midnight, and the last two the number of minutes past that hour.

In the 24-hour system 7.30 a.m. is written as 0730 or 07.30. The same time in the evening, 7.30 p.m., is written 1930 or 19.30, i.e. we add 12 to the hours number.

Similarly, 3.45 p.m. converts to 15.45.

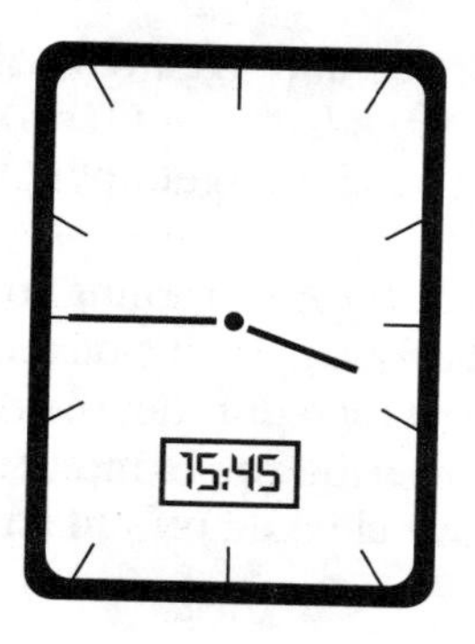

Most digital clocks and watches also use the 24-hour system. It is therefore important that we understand both systems and can convert quickly from one system to the other.

EXERCISE 7c

QUESTION

Doug Peake rings the station to find out the times of the early evening trains to Manchester. He finds that the most suitable train leaves at 18.28 and arrives in Manchester at 20.32. His mother has never used the 24-hour clock, so he has to convert these times into a.m./p.m. times for her.

(a) What time does he tell his mother (i) the train leaves (ii) the train is due to arrive in Manchester?

(b) How long, in minutes, is the train journey supposed to take?

(c) His mother wants to return home on the train leaving at 2.25 p.m. the following day. (i) How would this time be written in the timetable? (ii) If the homeward journey takes exactly the same time as the outward journey what time is the train due at the local station? Give your answer in a.m./p.m. time.

ANSWER

(a) (i) 18.28 is 6.28 p.m. (18.28 − 12.00).
(ii) 20.32 is 8.32 p.m. (20.32 − 12.00).

(b) From 6.28 p.m. to 7.00 p.m. is 32 minutes
from 7.00 p.m. to 8.32 p.m. is 1 hour and 32 minutes
∴ total time is (32 + 60 + 32) minutes, i.e. 124 minutes.

(c) (i) 2.25 p.m. is 14.25 in the 24-hour system.
(ii) Homeward journey takes 124 minutes, i.e. 2 hr 4 min.
If the train leaves at 2.25 p.m., it will arrive at the local station at 2.25 p.m. + 2 hr 4 min, i.e. at 4.29 p.m.

---

1 Len Dugg left work for home at five to six in the afternoon. Write this (a) in a.m./p.m. time (b) as it would appear on a 24-hr clock.

2 How many minutes are there (a) from 09.47 to 20.19 (b) from 04.44 to 18.29 (c) from 22.16 to 08.41 the next morning?

3 One day last winter, lighting-up time started at 16.54 and ended at 07.25 the next day. How long was this?

QUESTION
The timetable for buses between Linley and Southford for each weekday morning is given below.

Linley	dep	08.34	09.15	11.04	12.48
Dixton	dep	08.46	09.27	11.16	13.00
Ashford	arr	09.00	09.41	11.30	13.14
	dep	09.02	09.43	11.32	13.16
Frinton	dep	09.21	09.58	11.51	13.35
Wester	dep	09.34	10.08	12.04	13.50
Southford	arr	09.46	10.20	12.16	14.04

(a) At what time should Ann leave Ashford to get to Southford by 11 a.m.?
(b) How long does the 11.04 from Linley take to travel from Dixton to Wester?

ANSWER
(Try to use a straight edge, such as a ruler, to read across a table. In this table there are four columns of times. Each column refers to a different bus. Reading down any column shows the times at which that bus will arrive at, or depart from, the place named.)

(a) The latest time before 11 a.m. that Ann can arrive in Southford is 10.20. This bus leaves Ashford at 09.43.
∴ Ann must leave Ashford at 9.43 a.m.
(When the departure time only is given in a timetable, assume that this is also the arrival time. The bus will arrive, put down and pick up any passengers, then leave immediately.)

(b) The 11.04 from Linley departs from Dixton at 11.16 and arrives in Wester at 12.04. Time taken is the time from 11.16 to 12.04
i.e. 44 minutes (up to 12.00) + 4 minutes (after 12.00) = 48 minutes.

4 For this question use the table given in the example question above.

(a) At what time should Zena leave Linley to make
(i) the quickest journey to Wester
(ii) the slowest journey to Wester?

(b) How long does it take to travel from Dixton to Ashford?

(c) Colin Meare misses the 8.34 from Linley by 3 minutes. How long must he wait for the next bus? What time should he then arrive at Frinton? How much later is this than if he had caught the bus he had intended to catch?

(d) Betty lives in Ashford and has an appointment in Wester at 12 noon. If it takes her 10 minutes to walk to the bus stop, what is the latest time she can leave home to keep her appointment?

Time zones

If you fly to Majorca for a holiday, leaving the United Kingdom at 0800 you could find that you arrive in Majorca at 1200, even though your flight has taken 3 hours. Coming home, if you leave Majorca at 1830 and again enjoy a 3-hour flight you will arrive back in the United Kingdom at 2030. The reason for this apparent contradiction is that *local time* in Spain is one hour ahead of local time in the United Kingdom.

When it is 12 noon in London it is 10 p.m. in Sydney, Australia and 8 a.m. in Los Angeles. So that we know how local time in one part of the world is related to local time in another part, we divide the earth's surface into twenty-four time zones. Local time or clock time in all these zones is related to Greenwich Mean Time (GMT). (Greenwich was the site of the Royal Observatory just outside London.) In countries to the east of Greenwich the sun rises earlier, so their time is ahead of GMT. In countries to the west of Greenwich the sun rises later, so their time is behind GMT. The map on page 76 shows the time in each zone when it is 1200 GMT. The figures beneath this map show the number of hours each zone is ahead or behind GMT.

The zig-zag line drawn from the North Pole to the South Pole through the Pacific Ocean, so that it doesn't pass through any land mass, is called the International Date Line. If you cross this imaginary line from east to west (for example if you fly from America to China) you lose a day, that is, if it is 23 August as you approach the line from the American side the date changes to 24 August once you have crossed it. On the other hand, if you cross the date line in the opposite direction, i.e. if you go from west to east, then you move the date back one day and so gain a day.

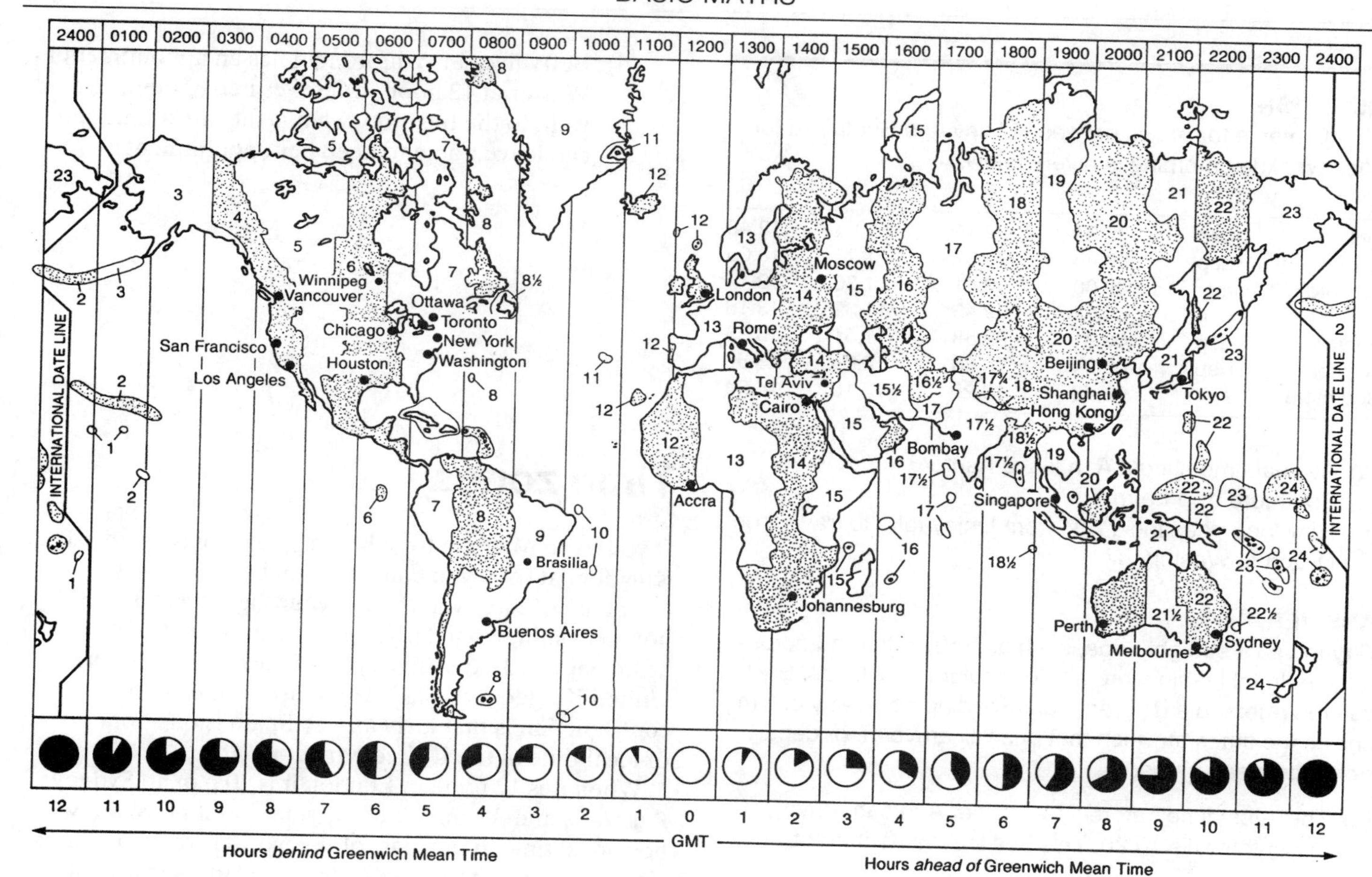

EXERCISE 7d

QUESTION

George and Olive Penny leave London Gatwick Airport at 10.30 a.m. to fly to San Francisco. The flight takes 10 hours. If the time in San Francisco is 8 hours behind the time at London Gatwick what time

(a) London Gatwick time will they arrive
(b) will they arrive, local time?

ANSWER

(a) (It is probably easier to answer a question like this using the 24-hour clock.)
When they arrive in San Francisco the time at London Gatwick
= 10.30 a.m. + 10 hours
= 10.30 + 10.00
= 20.30
= 8.30 p.m.
i.e. they arrive in San Francisco at 8.30 p.m. London Gatwick time.

(b) When it is 20.30 at London Gatwick the time in San Francisco is 8 hours behind
i.e. 20.30 − 8.00 = 12.30
∴ they arrive in San Francisco at 12.30 p.m. local time.

Use the information on the map above to answer questions 1 to 5.

1 How many hours is each of the following places ahead of Greenwich Mean Time (GMT)?
(a) Tel Aviv (b) Hong Kong
(c) Perth (d) Tokyo.

2 How many hours is each of the following places behind London time, i.e. GMT?
(a) Brasil (b) Vancouver
(c) Houston (d) New York.

3 When it is 12 noon in London, i.e. 1200 GMT, what time is it in
(a) Johannesburg (b) Melbourne
(c) Washington (d) Winnipeg?

4 When it is 3 p.m. in London what time is it in
(a) Rome (b) Beijing
(c) Toronto?

5 When it is 9 a.m. in London what time is it in
(a) Los Angeles (b) Melbourne
(c) Accra?

For the remaining questions in this exercise, the map may be found useful, but each problem can be solved without it.

6 The time in New York is 5 hours behind the time in London. What time is it (a) in New York when it is noon in London (b) in London when it is midnight in New York?

7 Moscow time is 3 hours ahead of London time, while the time in Ottawa is 5 hours behind London. What time is it (a) in Moscow when it is 3 a.m. in Ottawa (b) in Ottawa when it is midday in Moscow?

8 The distance from London to Bombay is approximately 4500 miles. A jet leaves London for Bombay at 11 a.m. and flies at an average speed of 500 miles per hour. (a) Approximately, how long does the journey take? (b) If the time is $5\frac{1}{2}$ hours ahead of London time, what time will it be in Bombay when the plane arrives?

9 During the summer months, we use British Summer Time (BST) in the UK. BST is one hour ahead of GMT. When it is 2 p.m. BST in London what time is it (a) in Shanghai, which is 8 hours ahead of GMT (b) in Chicago, which is 6 hours behind GMT?

10 What happens to the date as (a) you fly from Sydney to San Francisco, thereby crossing the International Date Line from west to east (b) you fly from Los Angeles to Tokyo and cross from east to west?

Distance tables

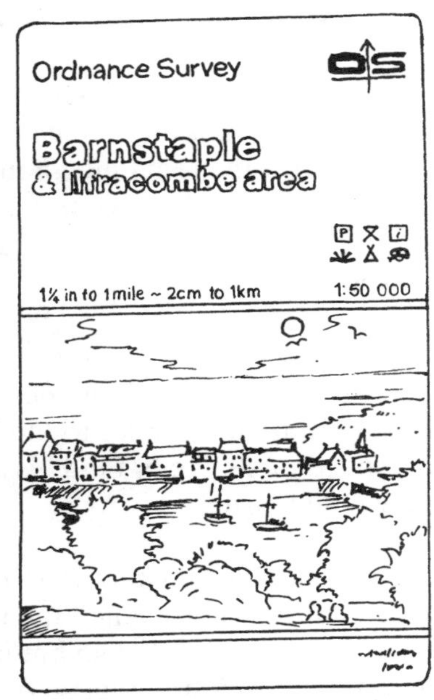

Many books of road maps give tables that enable us to find out quickly how far it is from one place to another.

EXERCISE 7e

Use this table to answer the questions that follow.

Distances are in miles

	London	Bristol	Cardiff	Dover	Glasgow	Liverpool	Norwich
Bristol	114						
Cardiff	155	44					
Dover	73	195	239				
Glasgow	394	366	378	467			
Liverpool	205	164	164	278	211		
Norwich	107	221	237	169	380	224	
Southampton	79	75	119	149	415	222	186

1 How far is it
(a) from London to Glasgow
(b) from Norwich to Dover?

2 Which two places are
(a) nearest together
(b) furthest apart?

3 Which place is
(a) nearest to Glasgow
(b) furthest from Liverpool?

4 How much further is Bristol from Norwich than Liverpool is from Cardiff?

5 How far is it
(a) from Cardiff to Glasgow via Liverpool
(b) from Liverpool to Dover via London?

Speed, distance and time

Speed compares distance with time. It is the distance travelled in one unit of time. Speed is frequently measured in metres per second (m/s), kilometres per hour (km/h) or miles per hour (m.p.h.).

Suppose a car travels 150 miles in 3 hours. The journey will include times when the car is moving slowly or even stationary. The steady speed that allows the car to travel the same distance in the same time is called the average speed. In this case, if the car travels 150 miles in 3 hours we say that the average speed of the car is 50 m.p.h. (miles per hour):

$$\text{average speed} = \frac{\text{total distance travelled}}{\text{total time}}$$

from which we also have

$$\text{total distance travelled} = \text{average speed} \times \text{total time}$$

and
$$\text{total time} = \frac{\text{total distance travelled}}{\text{average speed}}$$

EXERCISE 7f

1 A train travels 150 miles in 2 hours. Find its average speed.

2 Nina takes 3 hours to pedal 42 kilometres. Find her average speed.

3 An athlete takes 4 minutes to run 1500 metres. Find his average speed in metres per minute.

4 An aeroplane travels at an average speed of 450 m.p.h. for 3 hours. How far does it travel?

5 A lorry travels 275 km at 50 km/h. How long does this journey take?

QUESTION

In training, a long-distance runner takes 2 hours 20 minutes to run 14 miles. Find his average speed in miles per hour.

ANSWER

$$20 \text{ minutes} = \tfrac{20}{60} \text{ hours} = \tfrac{1}{3} \text{ h}$$
$$\therefore \text{ time taken} = 2 \text{ h} + \tfrac{1}{3} \text{ h}$$
$$= 2\tfrac{1}{3} \text{ h}$$
$$\text{average speed} = \frac{\text{total distance}}{\text{total time}}$$
$$= 14 \div 2\tfrac{1}{3} \text{ miles per hour}$$
$$= 14 \div \tfrac{7}{3} \text{ m.p.h.}$$
$$= 14 \times \tfrac{3}{7} \text{ m.p.h.}$$

i.e. his average running speed is 6 m.p.h.

6 An intercity express travels the 24 miles from Edgeley to Lexway in 15 minutes. Express this speed in
(a) miles per minute (b) miles per hour.

7 An international sprinter ran 200 metres in 24 seconds dead. Give his average speed in
(a) metres per second (b) metres per minute
(c) metres per hour (d) kilometres per hour.

QUESTION

A student returned from Manchester to her home in the south. She travelled for 1 h at an average speed of 35 m.p.h., followed by 3 h at an average speed of 55 m.p.h. Find her average speed for the whole journey.

ANSWER

Distance travelled = average speed × time taken.

Distance travelled in 1 h at 35 m.p.h. = 35 × 1 miles
= 35 miles

Distance travelled in 3 h at 55 m.p.h. = 55 × 3 miles
= 165 miles

∴ total distance travelled = 35 miles + 165 miles
= 200 miles

and total time taken = 1 h + 3 h = 4 h

$$\text{average speed} = \frac{\text{total distance}}{\text{total time}}$$
$$= \frac{200 \text{ miles}}{4 \text{ h}}$$
$$= 50 \text{ m.p.h.}$$

8 An aircraft travels for 4 hours at an average speed of 400 m.p.h., but then a headwind reduces its average speed to 350 m.p.h. for the remaining hour of the journey. Find (a) the total distance travelled
(b) the total time taken (c) the average speed for the whole journey.

9 Neal walks the $\frac{1}{2}$ mile from his home to the bus stop at an average speed of 4 m.p.h. and immediately catches the bus that takes him the 10 miles to the city centre at an average speed of 20 m.p.h. Find his average speed for the whole journey.

10 Andy wanted to make the 110 kilometre trip to Birmingham in 2 hours. He travelled the first 60 kilometres at an average speed of 45 km/h, and the next 30 kilometres at an average speed of 90 km/h. What must be his average speed for the final 20 kilometres if he is to arrive on time?

Distance–time graphs

EXERCISE 7g

QUESTION

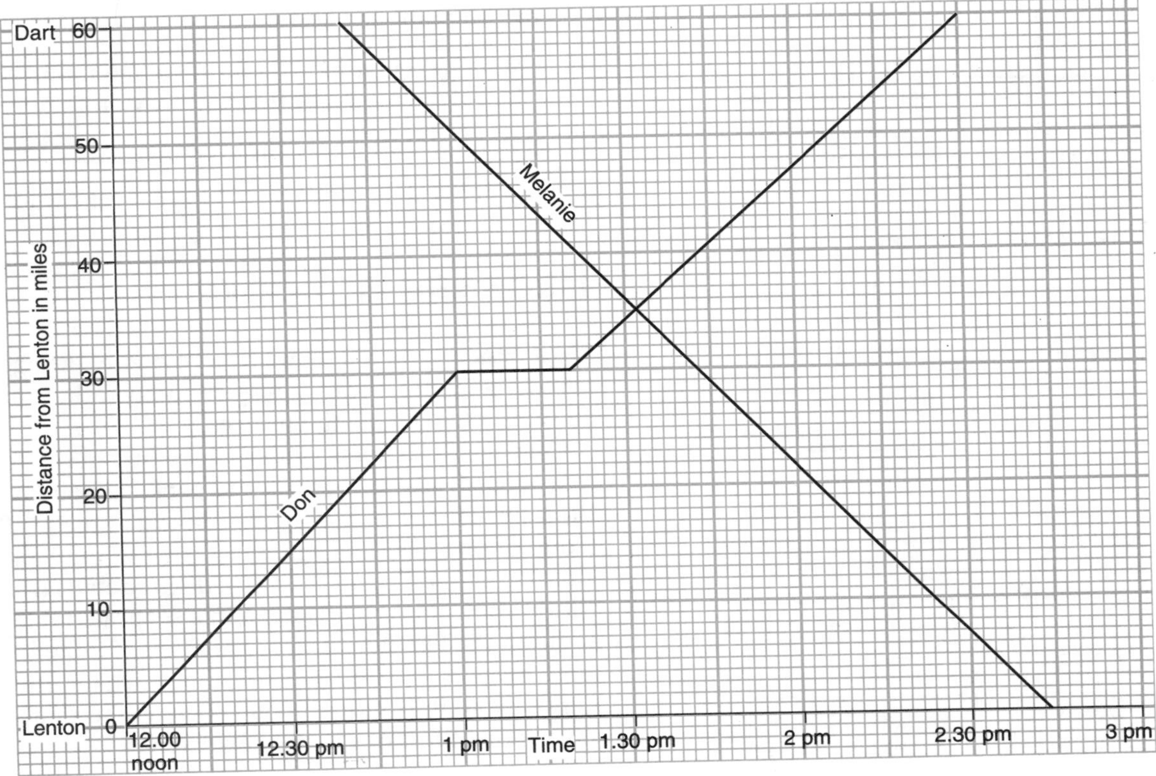

This distance–time graph shows the journeys of two motorists. Don leaves Lenton at 12 noon and drives to Dart, while Melanie drives from Dart to Lenton.

(a) Describe Don's journey and find the time he reaches Dart.

(b) Find Don's average speed for (i) the first part of the journey (ii) the whole journey.

(c) Describe Melanie's journey. What is her average speed?

(d) When and where do they pass?

ANSWER

(a) (On the time axis 30 small squares represents 1 hour, so each small square represents $\frac{60}{30}$ minutes, i.e. 2 min.) Don leaves Lenton at 12 noon, drives 30 miles by 1 p.m., rests for 20 minutes, then continues to Dart, at a slower speed than for the first part of the journey (the line representing the second part of the journey is not as steep as the one representing the first part), arriving there at 2.30 p.m.

(b) (i) Average speed for the first 30 miles
= 30 miles/1 hour
= 30 m.p.h.

(ii) Average speed for whole journey

$$= \frac{\text{total distance}}{\text{total time}}$$

$$= \frac{60 \text{ miles}}{2 \text{ h } 30 \text{ min}}$$

$$= \frac{60 \text{ miles}}{2.5 \text{ h}} \qquad (30 \text{ min} = \tfrac{30}{60} \text{ h} = 0.5 \text{ h})$$

= 24 m.p.h.

(c) Melanie leaves Dart at 12.40 p.m. and arrives in Lenton at 2.44 p.m., i.e. she takes 2 h 4 min.
∴ Melanie's average speed

$$= \frac{60}{2.0666\ldots} \text{ m.p.h.} \qquad (4 \text{ min} = \tfrac{4}{60} = 0.0666 \ldots \text{ h})$$

= 29.0 m.p.h. (to 3 s.f.)

(d) The point where the two graphs cross shows when and where Don and Melanie pass. They pass at 1.32 p.m. (16 small squares to the right of 1 p.m.) at a point 35 miles from Lenton.

1 Describe the journeys represented by each of the following distance–time graphs.

a

b

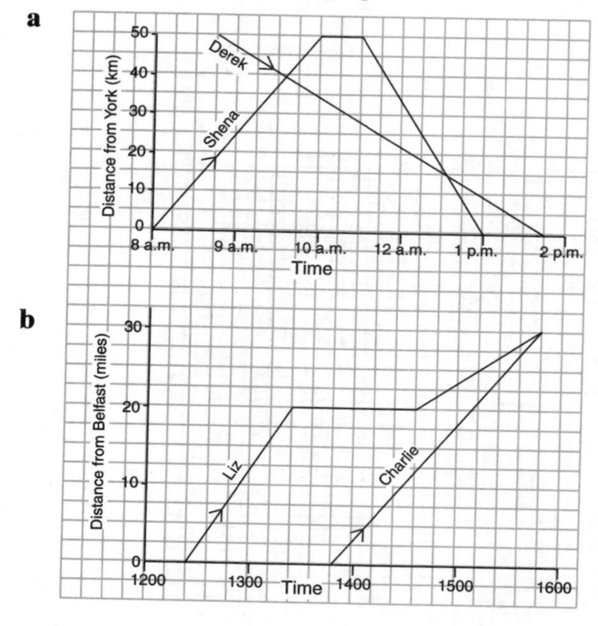

2

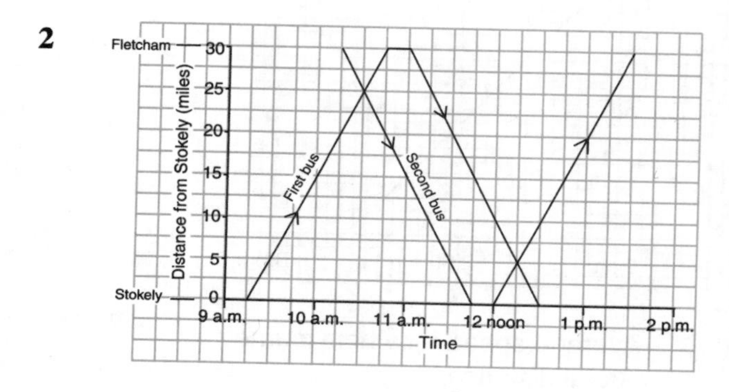

The graph shows two buses travelling between two towns.

(a) How far apart are the towns?

(b) How long does the first bus wait at Fletcham before returning to Stokely?

(c) Does the one bus overtake the other bus or do they pass one another moving in opposite directions? Where and when do they pass?

(d) What is the average speed of the first bus in travelling (i) from Stokely to Fletcham (ii) from Fletcham to Stokely?

3 A motorist leaves Caxton at 1020 to travel north to Dewchurch, which is 160 km away. He is able to travel at a steady 60 km/h and completes the journey without a stop. Draw a distance–time graph for this journey. Mark the distance axis from 0 to 200 km and the time axis from 1000 to 1300. Take 6 cm = 1 h and 1 cm = 10 km.

A second motorist leaves Eastwood, which is 40 km north of Dewchurch, at 1040 to drive to Caxton. He travels to Dewchurch at a steady 60 km/h, where he stops for 10 minutes before continuing his journey to Caxton, arriving there at 1240. Show this journey on your graph. Use your graph to find

(a) the time the first motorist arrives at Dewchurch

(b) the average speed of the second motorist between Dewchurch and Caxton

(c) when and where they pass

(d) the second motorist's average for the whole journey.

Package holidays

Most people, when they wish to go on holiday, go to a travel agent and buy a package holiday rather than make all the arrangements themselves.

On page 81 extracts from a travel brochure are reproduced. The details refer to package holidays in Bodrum, Turkey, either on half-board at the La Perla Hotel or on a bed-and-breakfast basis at the Sunrise Hotel or at the Sesin Hotel. The flight details from various UK airports are given in a separate table. In addition the bar chart shows the average daily temperatures and hours of sunshine each month in London and in Bodrum. You will need these tables to answer the questions in the next exercise.

EXERCISE 7h

Questions 1 to 5 refer to the bar chart.

1 What is the hottest month in Bodrum?

2 On an average day in August (a) how much hotter is it in Bodrum than in London (b) how many more hours sunshine are there in Bodrum than in London?

3 In September Sue and Eddy have booked to spend 14 days in Bodrum. In total, how many more hours sunshine can they expect than if they stay in London?

4 (a) On a single day in October how many more hours sunshine should there be in Bodrum than in London?

(b) During the month of May how many more hours sunshine should there be in Bodrum than in London?

5 In which month is the difference in temperature between London and Bodrum (a) greatest (b) least? Estimate these differences.

Prices are per person in £'s at time of going to press

Accommodation and Meal Arrangements	LA PERLA Half Board			SUNRISE Bed & Breakfast			SESIN Bed & Breakfast		
Accommodation Code	RIL			RIA			RIB		
Prices Based on	SH	WC	BC	PB	WC	BL	PB	WC	BL
Number of Nights	7	14	All	7	14	All	7	14	All
Adult/Child	Adult	Adult	Child	Adult	Adult	Child	Adult	Adult	Child
Departures on or Between									
27 April - 11 May	**309**	**469**	179	**289**	**389**	249	**239**	**295**	159
12 May - 18 May	**326**	**475**	199	**299**	**397**	269	**253**	**303**	179
19 May - 25 May	**357**	**527**	239	**329**	**452**	299	**280**	**330**	209
26 May - 30 May	**399**	**589**	249	**338**	**499**	309	**288**	**375**	209
31 May - 15 Jun	**369**	**551**	219	**344**	**473**	279	**293**	**355**	219
16 Jun - 22 Jun	**388**	**559**	229	**349**	**473**	299	**298**	**375**	219
23 Jun - 06 Jul	**388**	**572**	249	**356**	**482**	309	**305**	**389**	229
07 Jul - 13 Jul	**416**	**582**	269	**374**	**491**	319	**321**	**395**	249
14 Jul - 21 Jul	**435**	**620**	299	**392**	**547**	349	**337**	**422**	259
22 Jul - 08 Aug	**469**	**647**	329	**424**	**552**	379	**366**	**450**	289
09 Aug - 16 Aug	**462**	**642**	329	**417**	**532**	379	**360**	**450**	289
17 Aug - 23 Aug	**455**	**634**	319	**410**	**529**	369	**353**	**433**	279
24 Aug - 06 Sep	**438**	**599**	269	**394**	**517**	319	**338**	**419**	259
07 Sep - 20 Sep	**399**	**569**	239	**371**	**495**	299	**318**	**384**	239
21 Sep - 04 Oct	**369**	**530**	219	**347**	**450**	279	**296**	**345**	219
05 Oct - 26 Oct	**309**	**469**	209	**305**	**389**	269	**258**	**295**	179
Supplements per Person per Night	Full Board £4.80 Seaview £0.60			Half Board £4.80 Seaview £0.60			Half Board £4.80		
Reductions per Person per Night	3rd Adult sharing £8.80 Bed & Breakfast £2.00			3rd Adult sharing £3.00			3rd Adult sharing £2.10		

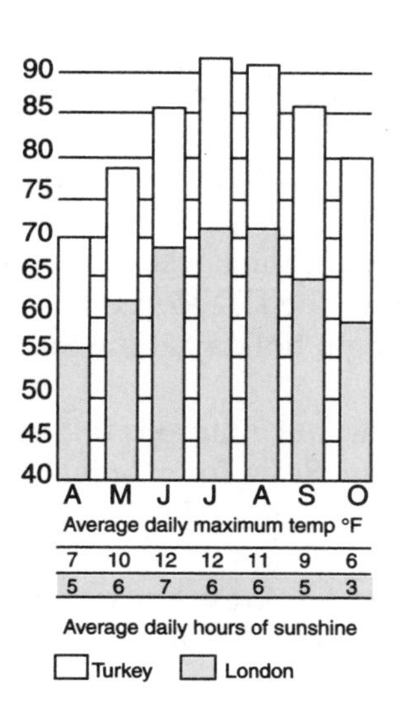

Dalaman Airport

Departure Airport	No of Nights	Day of Dept.	Time of Dept.	Day of Return	Time of Return	Departures	Flight Code	Supplement Per Person for Departures On or Between: 27 APR-30 MAY	31 MAY-6 JULY	7 JULY-21 JULY	22 JULY-8 AUG	9 AUG-28 OCT
GATWICK	7/14	SAT	21.45	SUN	07.00	30 APR-22 OCT	32385	£5	£5	£5	£7	£7
(4hrs)	7/14	WED	10.45	WED	19.45	27 APR-26 OCT	32386	£9	£9	£9	£11	£11
	7/14	WED	21.00	THU	06.15	4 MAY-19 OCT	32387	£0	£0	£0	£0	£0
STANSTEAD	7/14	WED	09.15	WED	18.30	4 MAY-26 OCT	32388	£7	£7	£7	£9	£9
BRISTOL	14	WED	21.00	THU	06.30	4 MAY-19 OCT	32389	£0	£7	£7	£9	£9
CARDIFF	7/14	WED	10.15	WED	19.45	4 MAY-19 OCT	32390	£19	£19	£0	£41	£21
BIRMINGHAM	7/14	WED	08.30	WED	18.00	4 MAY-26 OCT	32392	£22	£22	£22	£24	£24
EAST MIDLANDS	7/14	WED	19.45	THU	05.15	27 APR-26 OCT	32394	£12	£12	£12	£14	£14
MANCHESTER	7/14	SAT	20.45	SUN	06.45	30 APR-22 OCT	32396	£18	£18	£18	£20	£20
(4½ hrs)	7/14	WED	10.00	WED	19.45	4 MAY-19 OCT	32397	£32	£32	£32	£34	£34
	7/14	WED	21.00	THU	06.45	27 APR-26 OCT	32398	£15	£15	£15	£17	£17
NEWCASTLE	7/14	WED	19.30	THU	05.30	27 APR-26 OCT	32400	£24	£23	£0	£34	£25
GLASGOW	7/14	SAT	16.00	SUN	02.30	30 APR-22 OCT	32401	£9	£45	£65	£32	£31

QUESTION

(a) Two couples price a holiday, leaving home on 25 August for 14 nights, at the Sunrise Hotel on a bed-and-breakfast basis. Find the total accommodation costs.

(b) One of the couples decides to upgrade to half board and have a room with a sea view. How much extra does this couple have to pay?

ANSWER

(a) We go down the first column as far as the entry 24 Aug–06 Sep, since this includes 25 August, which is the date of departure. From here we go across until we come to the column headed 'Sunrise, Bed & Breakfast' with its sub-column '14', i.e. 14 nights. The entry here is 517. This is the price per person in pounds for the holiday.

From this, we calculate that the cost for four adults is $4 \times £517 = £2068$.

(b) The extra cost per person per night to upgrade from bed-and-breakfast to half board is £4.80 and the extra cost to have a sea view is £0.60, i.e. 60p.

For two people for 14 nights the total extra cost is $2 \times 14 \times £5.40 = £151.20$.

Do not use any flight information for questions 6 to 10.

6 Find the brochure price of a holiday for one adult staying (a) for 7 nights on half board at the La Perla, leaving on 18 June (b) at the Sesin for 14 nights on half board leaving on 29 August (c) at the Sunrise for 14 nights, on half board and with a sea view, leaving on 19 May.

7 What is the cost of a 14 night holiday for two adults on full board at the La Perla Hotel, leaving on 18 September?

8 Peter Gaines and his wife and three children leave on 26 July for a 14 night holiday at the Sesin Hotel on half board. How much will it cost them?

9 (a) What is the latest date on which a couple can leave the UK to get the cheapest rate for a 7 night holiday at the Sunrise?

(b) How much more is it to stay at the La Perla than at the Sesin for a 7 night holiday on half board starting on 22 June?

10 Joe and Meg Crew book a 14 night holiday for themselves and their two children at the Sunrise hotel. How much will the holiday cost them for bed and breakfast (a) if they leave on 23 June (b) if they leave on the last day of July?

QUESTION

The Brent family (husband, wife and three children) book a 14 night holiday on half board at the La Perla Hotel. They plan to fly from Birmingham on Wednesday 14 July.

(a) How much, in total, must they pay the travel agent if, in addition to the brochure price, £105.50 is added to cover insurance?

(b) When the holiday is booked the travel agent requires a deposit of 10% of the brochure price plus the cost of insurance. How much is this?

ANSWER

(a) Go down to 14 Jul–21 Jul (their departure date is 14 July), then across to the column headed 'La Perla', '14'. The entry in the table is 620. The cost for a child is found on the same line in the next column. It is headed 'child'.

The brochure price for one adult spending 14 nights at the La Perla leaving on 14 July is £620 and the cost for one child is £299.

∴ the cost for 2 adults is $2 \times$ £620 = £1240

and the cost for 3 children is $3 \times$ £299 = £897

Flight supplement from Birmingham on a Wednesday for a 14 night holiday between 7 and 21 July is £22 per person.

∴ total for the flight supplements is $5 \times$ £22 = £110

Total brochure price = £1240 + £897 + £110 = £2247

Total due to travel agent = total brochure price + cost of insurance = £2247 + £105.50 = £2352.50

(b) Deposit due is 10% of the brochure price, i.e. £2247 $\times \frac{10}{100}$ = £224.70

∴ amount due at time of booking = deposit + cost of insurance = £224.70 + £105.50 = £330.20

The remaining questions also require details found in the flight information.

11 How long is the flight time from Gatwick to Dalaman airport?

12 Sandra and Flo go to the travel agent to book a 14 night holiday in Bodrum. They wish to fly out on a Friday or a Saturday. From which airports can they fly?

13 Write down the flight supplement, i.e. the extra you have to pay, for

(a) a 7 night holiday from Gatwick leaving on Wednesday 5 August and returning on Wednesday 12 August

(b) a 14 night holiday from Bristol leaving on Wednesday 12 July

(c) a 14 night holiday from Manchester leaving on Saturday 19 July

(d) a 7 night holiday from Glasgow leaving on Saturday 3 May.

14 How much extra do the flight supplements come to for a family of four, 2 adults and 2 children, if they fly from East Midlands on a Wednesday in June?

15 Four couples book a 14 night holiday in Bodrum. They wish to fly from Newcastle. When should they fly to have the lowest flight supplement? Eventually they find it impossible to arrange the holiday during the cheapest time. Instead they decide to fly out on the first Wednesday in August. How much, in total, will it cost them in flight supplements?

16 Clive and Margaret book a room with a sea view for a 14 night holiday at the La Perla Hotel on half board. They leave Gatwick on the morning flight of Wednesday, 24 June.

(a) What is the brochure cost, excluding flight supplements?

(b) What do the flight supplements come to?

(c) Find the total cost of the holiday if insurance costs £89.90 and they take another £500 for spending money.

Foreign currency

When you go on holiday to a foreign country you have to use the currency of that country, e.g. pesetas in Spain, lire in Turkey or dollars in the United States. The number of units of a foreign currency you get for £1 is called the exchange rate. You can buy foreign currency from a bank, from some travel agents or through a building society. If you return home with spare foreign currency you will not get as many pounds for it as you paid. By offering to sell at one rate and buy back at a different rate, the company dealing in currencies is able to make money to meet its operating costs and to make a profit. Apart from buying and selling at different rates they also charge commission, typically 1%.

EXERCISE 7i

QUESTION
If £1 is equivalent to 190 Spanish pesetas, convert (a) £75 into pesetas (b) 7600 pesetas into pounds sterling (£).

ANSWER
(a) £1 = 190 pesetas
∴ £75 = 75 × 190 pesetas
i.e. £75 = 14 250 pesetas

(b) (Pesetas is often abbreviated to pta.)
190 pta = £1
∴ 1 pta = £$\frac{1}{190}$
∴ 7600 pta = 7600 × £$\frac{1}{190}$
i.e. 7600 pta = £40.

For questions 1 to 6 use the exchange rates given in the following table.

Pounds sterling	French francs	Spanish pesetas	US dollars	German Deutschmarks
£	(Ff)	(pta)	($)	(DM)
1	8.20	190	1.50	2.40

1 Dora needed French francs to go on holiday.
(a) How many francs did she get for £250?
(b) At the end of the holiday she was left with 1640 Ff. What was this worth in pounds?

2 Hank is going to Spain on holiday. What is the value of (a) £220 in pesetas (b) 10 640 pta in pounds?

3 Graham and Lyn are going to Orlando for a holiday. Some of the optional tours can be booked before they go. They sit down and work out the cost of the tours of their choice. If they book before they go it will cost them £288; if they wait until they get there the cost is $405. What advice would you give them? Do they book before they go, or wait until they get there?

4 Nia has always wanted a good pair of binoculars. While on holiday she sees a suitable pair in a German shop at 390 DM. She is aware that she can buy the same binoculars at home for £165 and decides against buying in Germany. Later in the holiday she is in France, where she sees a similar pair again. They are priced 1450 Ff. She decides to buy. Did she get the best available deal available?

5 Dennis has heard that it is much cheaper to buy his alcoholic drinks in France than locally. He and his wife take their car to France and load up with wines and spirits for which they pay 1342 Ff. At home they work out that the same goods would have cost £236. If the cost of the ferry trip was £38 including petrol costs, how much did they save?

6 What is the exchange rate if a tourist receives
(a) 248 US dollars in exchange for £160
(b) 7400 Spanish pesetas in exchange for £40
(c) 600 Deutschmarks for £250.

7 Franny Lee buys a bottle of perfume in a shop at Rome airport for 75 500 lire. If £1 is equivalent to 2422 lire, how much does he save if a similar bottle costs £38.50 in London?

8 A particular model of Ford car costs 12 750 pounds sterling in the UK, 30 000 Deutschmarks in Germany and 105 000 francs in France. In which country is the car (a) cheapest (b) dearest?
(£1 = 2.36 DM = 8.04 Ff.)

Travel insurance

It is essential to take out insurance cover if you go on holiday. The cost of insurance, and the extent of the cover, vary from one policy to another, but most policies cover lost luggage, hospital and medical expenses, loss of money and tickets, delays, personal accident and personal liability.

The table gives the premiums quoted by Travelwise Insurance Company.

Premium per person for European countries and other countries bordering the Mediterranean	
Up to 8 days	£21.95
9 to 15 days	£24.50
Each additional 7 days	£3.50

For countries other than those included above the rates are doubled. The rates for children under 16 on the date of departure are reduced by 50%. Children under 2 on the day of departure are insured free of charge.

EXERCISE 7k

Use the table in the text to answer the questions in this exercise.

QUESTION

Len and Judy Pask, together with their two children, Jonathan aged 11 and Richard aged 16, are going on holiday to Italy for 14 nights. How much will travel insurance cost them? How much extra would it have cost them if they had gone to Canada instead?

ANSWER

Since Richard is 16, the insurance costs for him are the same as for an adult.

The cost of insurance for one adult for 14 nights in the Mediterranean is £24.50.

$\therefore$ the cost for two adults plus the older child of 16 is $3 \times £24.50 = £73.50$.

As the cost of insurance for a child under 16 is 50% of that for an adult, the cost of insurance for Jonathan is $\frac{1}{2} \times £24.50 = £12.25$.

$\therefore$ total cost for the family of 2 adults and 2 children is $£73.50 + £12.25 = £85.75$.

Since the premiums are doubled for countries outside Europe, the cost of travel insurance for the family to go to Canada is $2 \times £85.75 = £171.50$.

1 How much does travel insurance cost for a family of three (father, mother and child aged 13 years) to go for a 15 day holiday in France?

2 John and Dorothy Bell and their children Mike (aged 13), Mandy (aged 10) and Tony (aged 8) propose taking a 14 night holiday in Crete. What would the insurance premiums come to?

3 Bill and Sandra Shirley are taking their 16-year-old daughter to the United States for a three week holiday. How much will the insurance premiums amount to?

4 What are the insurance costs for three adult couples plus four children, all under 16, to go on a twenty-one day holiday to Australia?

Multiple-choice questions 7

In questions 1 to 4 several alternative answers are given. Write down the letter that corresponds to the correct answer.

1 Sandy went to see a football match. As soon as the match was over she went home. She took 12 minutes to get to the bus stop, where she waited for 8 minutes before the bus arrived. The bus journey took 35 minutes and she took a further 15 minutes before she arrived home at 18.33. The match finished at

A 17.21 **B** 17.23 **C** 17.33 **D** 17.17

2 Yesterday was Wednesday, 16 April. My next visit to the dentist is a week tomorrow. This appointment is on

A Thursday 24 April **B** Friday 24 April
C Friday 25 April **D** Thursday 23 April

3 The time in London is 10 hours behind the time in Sydney. When it is 6 p.m. in London the time in Sydney is

A 4 a.m. **B** 8 a.m.
C 8 a.m. the next day **D** 4 a.m. the next day

4 Karen takes 3 minutes to run 600 metres. In kilometres per hour her speed is

A 12 km/h **B** 200 m/min
C 18 km/h **D** 2 km/h

5 Kath and Eddie book to take their young son Tim, aged 6, for a 10 night holiday in Spain. The brochure price is £370 per adult, with a 40% reduction for their son. To this price is added 60p per person per night for a sea view and insurance costs which are £22 per adult, children being charged at half the adult rate. Which of the following statements are true and which are false?

A The total cost of the insurance for the three of them comes to £57.20.

B If they did not take their son the cost of the holiday would be £239 cheaper.

C The amount they must pay to the travel agent is £1035.

D If they had decided against a sea view the total would have been less than £1000.

6 Before Mike went to France he changed £350 into francs at the rate of 8 francs to the pound. While on holiday he spent 2404 francs. When he got back home he changed his unspent francs into pounds at the rate of 9 francs to the pound.
The following statements have been made:
Statement 1. When he returned home the exchange rate had changed in his favour, so he got more pounds than he expected for his unspent francs.
Statement 2. The French francs Mike had spent cost him £300.50, so when he changed back his unspent francs he had £49.50.
How are these statements best described?

A True, True **B** True, False
C False, True **D** False, False

Self-assessment test 7

1 (a) How long is it from 2140 tonight to 0725 tomorrow morning?

(b) Sally is due in work by 8.00 a.m. She needs 20 minutes to get ready and 35 minutes to travel to work. What time should she aim to get up if she is to get to work 5 minutes early?

2 The extract given below shows the costs of package holidays at the Marina Hotel in Majorca.

Prices are per person in £

Accommodation and Meal Arrangements	MARINA Half Board			
Accommodation Code		MMA		
Prices Based on		PB	WC	BL
Number of Nights	7	10	11	14
Adult/Child	Adult	Adult	Adult	Adult
28 April - 11 May	203	225	238	289
12 May - 18 May	227	248	264	314
19 May - 25 May	248	275	290	339
26 May - 30 May	296	309	325	366
31 May - 15 Jun	258	302	318	369
16 Jun - 22 Jun	270	329	345	397
23 Jun - 06 Jul	280	347	363	417
07 Jul - 13 Jul	291	364	380	436
14 Jul - 21 Jul	308	385	402	456
22 Jul - 08 Aug	326	414	429	476
09 Aug - 16 Aug	322	403	419	474
17 Aug - 23 Aug	316	390	406	451
24 Aug - 06 Sep	309	375	391	435
07 Sep - 20 Sep	299	348	364	408
21 Sep - 04 Oct	273	315	330	372
05 Oct - 26 Oct	232	268	284	325
Supplements per Person per Night	Single Room £4.30			

Children under 16 are charged at $\frac{2}{3}$ the adult rate.

(a) Use this extract to find the brochure price of a holiday at the Marina for Jim Denton, his wife and two children, aged 7 and 11, if they leave on Friday 18 July for 14 nights.

(b) To the brochure price must be added £26 per person, because they wish to fly from Birmingham. At the time of booking the travel agent requires a 10% deposit plus the full cost of insurance, which is £28.95 per adult and £17.50 per child. The balance is to be paid eight weeks before they leave. How much must Jim pay when he books the holiday? How much remains to be paid eight weeks before they leave?

(c) While in Majorca they change £550 into pesetas at the rate of 186 pta to the pound. They spend 99 000 pta and when they return home change the pesetas that remain into pounds at the rate of 200 pta to the pound. How much do they receive for the unspent pesetas?

(d) In addition they spend £240 in English money. Find the total cost of the holiday. How much does this work out per person per night?

3 Given below is a typical timetable for Barry's working day.

7.10	Get up
7.25	Leave home
7.55	Arrive in work (5 minutes early)
10.20–10.30	Morning break
12.30–1.00	Lunch break
2.50–3.00	Afternoon break
5.00	Finish work
5.35	Arrive home
6.30–7.00	Main meal
8.30	Go out
11.30	Return home
11.45	Go to bed

(a) How long is it from the time Barry gets up until he is due to start work?

(b) How long is it from the time he gets up until he goes to bed?

(c) How long is he at home after work before he goes out?

(d) How much sleep does he normally get from one working day to the next?

(e) What is the length of his normal working day (i) including breaks (ii) excluding breaks?

(f) How much longer does he work in the morning than in the afternoon?

(g) How long does he spend at home, apart from the time he is in bed?

(h) Assuming that he is not paid for his breaks and that the above timetable is for each day from Monday to Thursday, how long must he work on Friday so that the length of his working week is $37\frac{1}{2}$ hours? (He gets a 10 minute unpaid break on Friday morning, just the same as any other day.)

4 Julie leaves home on 23 June for a 14 day holiday in Hong Kong. On what date does she return? Her non-stop flight leaves London at 1135 and arrives in Hong Kong at 0850 local time the next day. If the time in Hong Kong is 8 hours ahead of the time in London, how long was her flight?

The flying distance from London to Hong Kong is given as 5990 miles. Find the average flying speed, giving your answer correct to three significant figures.

On the return flight she leaves Hong Kong at 0240. The plane encounters a headwind which reduces its average speed to 440 m.p.h. How long should the return flight take? At what time should she arrive in London?

5

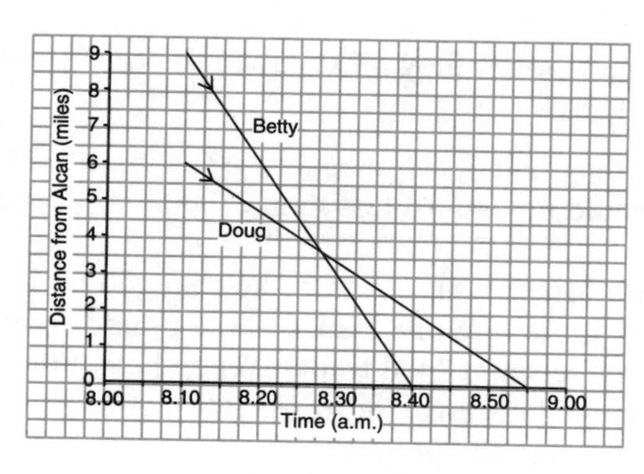

Betty and Doug both work for Alcan Industries. The graph show their journeys to work one morning.

(a) How far away does each of them live from the factory?

(b) By looking at the graph, which person travels to work faster, Betty or Doug?

(c) What time does Betty (i) leave home
(ii) arrive at work? How long does her journey take? Find her speed in m.p.h.

(d) What time does Doug (i) leave home
(ii) arrive in work? How long does he take? What is his average speed?

(e) Where and when do they pass?

(f) Suggest the means of transport each might be using.

CHAPTER 8
Earning money

Hourly pay

Most people get paid an hourly rate for working an agreed number of hours each week. Overtime is paid at a higher rate.

Commission

Salespeople are frequently paid a fairly low basic wage plus a percentage of the value of whatever it is they sell. This percentage is called *commission*. They are paid in this way to encourage them to sell their goods and services.

Piecework

Piecework is a form of payment that depends on the amount of work done, for example, the number of bags of potatoes you fill. Sometimes workers paid in this way also receive a fixed payment wage in addition to the piecework payment.

Salaries

Many jobs pay a salary rather than a wage. A salary is an agreed payment for a given number of hours a year. It is usually paid in twelve equal monthly instalments. Employees receiving a salary do not normally get paid extra for overtime.

EXERCISE 8a

QUESTION
Last week Ness Phillips worked 49 hours, 11 hours of which was overtime. Her hourly rate is £4.20 and overtime is paid at time-and-a-half. Find her gross pay for the week.

ANSWER
Basic working week is 49 h − 11 h = 38 h
Payment for 38 h at £4.20 per hour = 38 × £4.20
= £159.60
Hourly overtime rate at time-and-a-half is £4.20 + £2.10
= £6.30
Payment for 11 h overtime at £6.30 per hour is 11 × £6.30
= £69.30
Gross wage for the week is £159.60 + £69.30
= £228.90

1 (a) Sid Coleman works as a social worker. He earns £4.90 per hour for a 37 hour week. Find his gross weekly wage.

(b) Laura Peacock earns £5.35 per hour for a 38 hour week as a graphic designer with Marwick Walker & Partners. Find her gross weekly wage.

2 Vic Rice works in factory producing components for the electronics industry. His clocking-on and clocking-off times the week before Christmas are shown in the table.

Day	In	Out
Monday	8.00 a.m.	5.00 p.m.
Tuesday	7.59 a.m.	5.02 p.m.
Wednesday	7.58 a.m.	5.00 p.m.
Thursday	8.00 a.m.	6.30 p.m.
Friday	8.00 a.m.	1.30 p.m.
Saturday	8.00 a.m.	12.30 p.m.

Vic gets three unpaid breaks: mid-morning 10.00 to 10.15, lunch 12.00 to 12.30 and afternoon 3.00 to 3.15. On Friday he works until 1.30 p.m. but takes his usual morning break. He works overtime on Thursday and on Saturday morning, when he takes his usual morning break.

(a) What time is 'clocking-on' time?

(b) What time does he normally finish work for the day?

(c) On each of the days Monday to Thursday, how many hours does he get paid for at the basic rate?

(d) On which day(s), if any, is he late for work?

(e) How much overtime does he work?

(f) What is the length of the basic working week?

(g) Find his basic weekly gross wage if he is paid £4.92 per hour.

(h) How much overtime pay will he receive if overtime is paid at time-and-a-quarter?

(i) Find his gross wage for the week.

3 Jean Wallace works a basic week of 38 hours with the local solicitor. Overtime is paid at time-and-a-quarter. If her basic hourly rate is £4.80 find (a) her overtime rate (b) her basic gross weekly wage (c) her gross wage for a week when she does 8 hours overtime.

4 Chang Lee works for a builder who pays £5.40 an hour for a basic week of 37 hours. Overtime is paid at time-and-a-half. How much will Chang earn in a week when he works for 53 hours?

5 Nancy Kelly's timesheet for a week is given below:

	In	Out
Monday	1.58 p.m.	10.02 p.m.
Tuesday	2.00 p.m.	10.01 p.m.
Wednesday	1.45 p.m.	10.00 p.m.
Thursday	2.07 p.m.	9.55 p.m.
Friday	2.03 p.m.	10.03 p.m.
Saturday	1.57 p.m.	6.00 p.m.

Nancy is due to start work each day at 2 p.m. and to finish at 10 p.m. She is not paid for arriving early but loses 15 minutes any day she is more than 5 minutes late. She also loses 15 minutes if she leaves on a weekday before 10.00 p.m., but is paid time-and-a-half for each complete 15 minutes she works overtime – working on Saturday is counted as overtime.

(a) Has Nancy worked mornings, afternoons or nights?

(b) How many times (i) is she more than 5 minutes late (ii) does she leave early?

(c) How much overtime does she work?

(d) If she gets half an hour each day for her meal break (for which she is not paid), find the number of hours each week for which she is paid at the basic rate.

(e) Find her gross wage for the week if her basic rate of pay is £5 per hour.

QUESTION

Chris Walken sells computers. He receives a basic weekly wage of £65 plus commission at 3% on all sales over £5500 each week. Calculate his gross pay in a week when he sells computers to the value of £12 800.

ANSWER

Basic wage is £65
Commission on £12 800 − £5500,
i.e. on £7300 at 3% is 0.03 × £7300
= £219
Gross pay for the week is £65 + £219
= £284

6 Calculate the commission on sales of (a) £4500 at 3% (b) £11 500 at 5% (c) £44 000 at $2\frac{1}{2}$%.

7 An ice-cream seller receives a basic weekly wage of £85, to which is added commission at 15% on sales over £250. Find her gross wage in a week when her total takings amount to £545.

8 Glyn Close sells newspapers. Apart from his basic weekly wage of £90 he receives commission at 10% on sales over £50. Find his wage for a week when he sells newspapers to the value of £875.

9 Frances Blair receives a basic wage of £50 plus commission at 2% on the value of the goods she sells. Calculate her gross wage in a week when she sells goods to the value of £15 700.

10 Kent Deans manages Holiday Express. Apart from a basic monthly wage of £575 he is paid commission at the following rates:

Below £20 000	none
From £20 001 to £30 000	1.5%
Above £30 000	2.5%

Calculate his income in a month when he sells holidays to the value of £83 000.

11 Jean Hudson works in a factory assembling headlamps. She is paid a guaranteed weekly wage of £135, plus a bonus of 50p for every headlamp she assembles each day after the first 150. During a particular week the numbers of headlamps she completes are:

Monday	Tuesday	Wednesday	Thursday	Friday
185	184	188	189	182

Calculate her wage for the week.

12 Find the monthly salary of an employee whose annual salary is (a) £12 000 (b) £29 400 (c) £16 140.

13 Find the annual salary of a civil servant whose gross monthly pay is
(a) £1350 (b) £3920 (c) £2547.

14 Sam Norman is a salaried employee at an automotive factory. He receives £1375 per month gross. His brother, Grant, is employed at the same factory and receives an annual salary of £18 500. Which brother is the better off, and by how much?

Income tax

Anyone earning above a certain amount must pay income tax to the Inland Revenue. This money is used to help to meet government expenditure for such things as the National Health Service, the Armed Forces and the Social Services.

Self-employed people pay their income tax in a small number of equal payments, but most people pay under a *Pay As You Earn* (PAYE) system. Under this system tax is deducted by the employer from every pay. Given below are typical allowances for individuals and typical tax rates. These rates change in each Budget as the Chancellor of the Exchequer thinks fit.

Personal allowances		Income tax rates: Individual's rate %	Band of taxable income £
Basic	£3600	20	1 to 2800
Married couple	£1800	25	2801 to 25 200
One parent families	£1800	40	over 25 200
Basic (aged 65 to 74)	£4400		
Married couples (65 to 74)	£2450		
Basic (75 and over)	£4500		
Married couples (75 and over)	£2550		

EXERCISE 8b

In this exercise use the allowances and tax rates given in the text.

QUESTION

(a) George earns £12 500 a year and Daphne £15 480. Both are entitled to the basic allowance. How much taxable income does each have?

(b) They decide to get married and to split the married couple's allowance between them equally. How much taxable income does each have now?

ANSWER

(a) George's taxable income is
£12 500 − £3600 = £8900
and Daphne's taxable income is
£15 480 − £3600 = £11 880

(b) The married couple's allowance is £1800. If they split this equally, each is entitled to an extra £900 free of tax.

∴ George's taxable income is
£12 500 − £3600 − £900 = £8000
and Daphne's taxable income is
£15 480 − £3600 − £900 = £10 980

1 Find the taxable income for each of the following taxpayers:

(a) Barry Tubb who is single and earns £17 400 a year.

(b) Billy Vega, who is married, earns £15 670 a year, and receives the full married couple's allowance in addition to a basic personal allowance.

(c) Tim and Molly Garrett, a married couple in their late sixties. Tim's annual income is £10 750 and Molly's is £2500.

(d) Trish Waters, a single parent earning £9760 a year.

QUESTION

Abe Westman earns £18 760 a year. He is married and his wife does not work. Find (a) his total allowances (b) his taxable income (c) the amount of income tax due in a year.

ANSWER

(a) Since his wife does not work Abe can claim the full married couple's allowance for himself.
Total allowances are £3600 + £1800 = £5400.

(b) Taxable income = gross income − allowances
= £18 760 − £5400
= £13 360

Tax on first £2800 at 20% = 0.2 × £2800
= £560

Tax on the remainder i.e. on £10 560 (£13 360 − £2800) is 0.25 × £10 560
= £2640

∴ total tax due is £560 + £2640 = £3200.

2 Find the amount of tax due on a taxable income of
(a) £2400 (b) £14 550 (c) £9764
(d) £28 440 (e) £62 800.

3 Carol Arnold is single and earns £8533 a year. She pays tax by the PAYE system. Find (a) her taxable income (b) the amount of tax due for the year (c) the amount of tax deducted each week under PAYE. (Give the answers to (b) and (c) correct to the nearest penny.)

4 Rick Schreder is single and has a salary of £13 563 a year. How much tax does he pay?

5 Harry earns £14 740 a year and his wife earns £13 660 a year. They decide that the married couple's allowance is to be used by Harry. Find (a) the amount of tax Harry must pay (b) the amount of tax his wife must pay.

6 A married couple have a combined income of £35 000 a year.

(a) If the wife earns £5000 a year more than the husband how much does the wife earn?

(b) How much tax does each pay if they divide the married couple's allowance equally between them? Remember that both of them also have a personal allowance of £3600.

(c) Would it make any difference to the total tax they pay if the whole of the married couple's allowance was used by the wife?

7 Jon Jordon is in his eighties. He has an income of £10 500 a year and his wife, also in her eighties, has an income of £6730 a year. The married couple's allowance is used by Jon. (a) How much tax must Jon pay? (b) How much tax must his wife pay?

8 Louise Reed is single and receives a salary of £42 000 a year.

(a) How much tax must she pay in total in a year? (Don't forget that a taxable income over £25 200 is charged at 40%.) (b) If she gets a rise of £1000 a year how much more tax must she pay?

National insurance

National insurance contributions (NICs) are paid by all employees and their employers. When you are working your contributions are deducted from your pay by your employer. The employer adds the contributions he has to make for you, and pays the combined total to the government. Self-employed people have to make the full contributions themselves.

The main benefits of the scheme are:

(a) sickness benefits when you are unable to work;

(b) unemployment benefits when you are out of work;

(c) retirement and other pensions.

Employees who belong to certain company pension schemes can be contracted out of the state scheme. These people pay lower national insurance contributions. Typical rates for employees not contracted out are given below.

	Employee		Employer
(Earnings per month)	First £250	Balance	All
£0 to £249.99	0%	—	0%
£250 to £429.99	2%	9%	5%
£430 to £619.99	2%	9%	7%
£620 to £849.99	2%	9%	9%
Over £850	2%	9%	10.5%

EXERCISE 8c

Use the table in the text to answer the questions in this exercise.

QUESTION

Adrian Haynes earns £855 a month. (a) How much is Adrian due to pay each month in national insurance contributions (NIC)? (b) How much must his employer pay?

ANSWER

(a) Amount due on the first £250 is 2% of £250

i.e. $0.02 \times £250 = £5$

Amount due on the balance of £855 − £250 i.e. on £605 is 9% of £605

i.e. $0.09 \times £605 = £54.45$

$\therefore$ total NIC due is £5 + £54.45 = £59.45.

(b) Since Adrian earns more than £850 a month, Adrian's employer must pay 10.5% of his total earnings

i.e. $0.105 \times £850 = £89.25$

1 How much must Stephanie pay in national insurance contributions if she earns £650 a month?

2 Louis earns £1300 a calendar month. How much does he pay in national insurance contributions (a) for a calendar month (b) in a year (of 52 weeks) (c) a week?

3 Peter's annual salary is £18 960. (a) How much is this a month? (b) What are Peter's monthly national insurance contributions?

4 A factory worker earns £1100 a month, including overtime. Find the national insurance contributions paid by (a) the factory worker (b) her employer.

Pension schemes

More and more employees belong to pension schemes. A percentage is deducted from a person's earnings and this, together with a contribution from the employer, is invested to provide a lump sum that can be used to buy a pension on retirement. Many people agree to make larger percentage contributions as they get older.

EXERCISE 8d

QUESTION
Sara Brown earns £12 600 a year. She pays 6% of her salary into the pension scheme and her employer pays another 8%. Find (a) her gross monthly salary (b) her monthly pension deductions (c) the amount contributed each month by her employer (d) the total amount in the fund if these payments are made for 35 years.

ANSWER
(a) Gross monthly salary £12 600 ÷ 12 = £1050

(b) Monthly pension deduction is 6% of £1050
= 0.06 × £1050
= £63

(c) In addition the employer pays 8% of her gross monthly salary
= 0.08 × £1050
= £84

(d) Total paid into pension fund per month is
£63 + £84 = £147
∴ total paid each year is 12 × £147 = £1764
i.e. total paid in 35 years is 35 × £1764 = £61 740.
(The fund would be worth much more than this because of interest payments and the probable increase in the value of the investments.)

Find the monthly pension contribution for each of the following employees:

	Name	Monthly pay £	Pension contribution rate %
1	Roy Ovens	856	6
2	Lynda Brown	1366	5
3	Nia Pickles	2444	3
4	Colin Avery	799	8

Find the monthly pension contribution for each of the following employees:

	Name	Yearly salary £	Pension contribution rate %
5	Larry Young	9 072	6
6	Philip Reese	16 248	10
7	Sarah Davidson	34 644	8
8	Amjun Hussain	17 280	$5\frac{1}{2}$

For each of the following employees, find the weekly pension contribution. (Assume that there are 4 weeks in a month and 52 weeks in a year.)

9 Maisey Smith, weekly pay £256, pension contribution rate 4%.

10 Veronica Sweet, monthly salary £744, pension contribution rate 6%.

11 Frank Thomas, annual salary £10 400, pension contribution rate 5%.

12 Fay Dobson, annual salary £11 284, pension contribution rate $7\frac{1}{2}$%.

13 The benefits of a pension scheme are a lump sum on retirement equal to $\frac{3x}{80}$ of the final yearly salary, plus a yearly pension of $\frac{x}{80}$ of the final yearly salary, where x is the number of years worked. Olga Valli is earning £20 240 a year when she retires after contributing to the scheme for 40 years. Find (a) her lump sum (b) her annual pension.

14 Rework question 13 for Bill Adams who contributes for 35 years and is earning £16 440 a year when he retires.

Gross pay and net pay

Your gross wage or salary is the amount of money you earn before any deductions are made. Your net wage or 'take-home' pay is the amount that is left after all the agreed deductions have been made. These deductions include income tax, national insurance contributions, pension contributions, company leisure club fees, private medical insurance, and so on.

EXERCISE 8e

QUESTION

Lynda Baron earns £195.60 a week. Her deductions are: income tax £29.25, national insurance contributions £12.65 and pension contributions of £11.74. Find her take-home pay.

ANSWER

Total deductions = £29.25 + £12.65 + £11.74
= £53.64

Take-home pay = gross pay − deductions
= £195.60 − £53.64
= £141.96

Copy and complete the following table, which gives details of the weekly pay of five people employed at a leisure centre.

	Name	Gross pay	Income tax	NIC	Pension	Take-home pay
1	B. Jones	£212	£33.35	£14.81	£11.82	
2	S. Brown		£59.84	£26.60	£18.96	£237.60
3	P. Capstick	£568	£108.43	£46.85		£381.46
4	L. Brady	£290		£21.83	£16.08	£193.97
5	P. Lacey	£198	£30.47		£11.96	£142.02

6 Norma Deakin earns £300 a week. She pays tax at 20% on her income after the first £80, national insurance contributions of £1.25 plus 9% of her income after the first £60, and contributes 6% of her gross income to a pension scheme. Find (a) the income tax due (b) her national insurance contribution
(c) the amount due to her pension fund (d) her total deductions (e) her take-home pay.

7 Working in a bank, Jenny Cook has a take-home pay of £1050 per calendar month. Deductions from her gross pay amount to 30%. (a) What percentage of her gross pay is £1050? (b) Find (i) her gross monthly pay (ii) her gross annual salary.

8 Kim Forrest worked 49 hours last week. The first $37\frac{1}{2}$ hours are paid at the standard rate of £5.20 per hour and the remainder is overtime that is paid at time-and-a-half. She pays tax at 20% on her weekly income over £65, national insurance contributions of £19.84 and pension contributions of 6% of her gross income. Find
(a) her basic weekly wage i.e. excluding overtime
(b) the hourly overtime rate and the number of hours of overtime worked (c) the amount earned for overtime (d) her total wage for the week
(e) the amount of income tax due (f) her pension contribution (g) her take-home pay.

9 A wages clerk has to prepare a coin analysis so that she has the necessary cash to pay the workforce. Copy and complete the table.

Name	Wages	£20	£10	£5	£1	50p	20p	10p	5p	2p	1p
Norse	£187.86	180		5	2	50	20	10	5		1
Neale	£109.33										
George	£215.92										
Cox	£226.79										

Multiple-choice questions 8

In this exercise several alternative answers are given. Write down the letter that corresponds to the correct answer.

1 Celia's gross pay one week last month was £291.60. Her deductions were: income tax £39.70, national insurance contributions £21.68 and £17.47 as her pension contribution. Her pay after these deductions was

A £212.75 **B** £269.92
C £248.24 **D** £274.13

2 Pete worked 53 hours last week, 15 hours of which was overtime at time-and-a-half. His basic hourly rate is £6.30. His gross pay for the week was

A £333.90 **B** £500.85
C £453.60 **D** £381.15

3 Commission at $2\frac{1}{2}\%$ on sales of £53 000 amounts to

A £132.50 **B** £1325 **C** £2120 **D** £212

4 Last year May Bloom's taxable income was £18 600. The income tax due on this amount was 20% of the first £3200 plus 25% on the remainder. The amount of tax May had to pay was

A £4650 **B** £3720 **C** £4490 **D** £3850

Self-assessment test 8

1 At Castle Airproducts, each day, from Monday to Friday, employees work from 8 a.m. to 4.30 p.m. They get an hour for lunch, which is unpaid. (a) How many hours does an employee work (i) in a day (ii) in a week? (b) The basic hourly rate for shopfloor workers is £4.95. What is the basic weekly wage?

2 (a) James Clarke earns £27 400 a year and has a tax free allowance of £5750. Find his taxable income. (b) His taxable income is taxed as follows: the first £3000 at 20% and the remainder at 25%. How much income tax does James pay in a year?

3 Sally and Kerry are sisters. Sally gets a basic wage of £86 a week plus commission of 2% on all the sales she makes above £5000 while Kerry gets a basic wage of £110 plus 58p for each electrical appliance she assembles after the first 100. Which sister earns the greater wage in a week when Sally makes sales to the value of £27 000 and Kerry assembles 518 appliances?

CHAPTER 9

Household expenses

Shopping

First we consider shopping for food and drink.

EXERCISE 9a

Use the information given in the drawing to find the cost of:

1 (a) 2 lb carrots (b) 5 lb potatoes
(c) 3 lb beans (d) 2 lb parsnips

2 (a) 6 oranges (b) 4 lb apples
(c) 3 lb bananas (d) $1\frac{1}{2}$ lb grapes

3 (a) 2 lb swedes (b) $1\frac{1}{2}$ lb tomatoes
(c) $3\frac{1}{2}$ lb carrots (d) 1 cauliflower

Copy and complete these shopping lists. How much change will there be from £10?

4 3 lb carrots
2 lb parsnips
6 lb potatoes ______

5 6 oranges
2 lb bananas
4 lb apples ______

6 3 lb apples
2 lb tomatoes
5 oranges
3 lb peas ______

A board in the local greengrocers lists the following prices: peas 50p/500 g, potatoes 42p/kg, swedes 30p each, parsnips 35p/kg, cabbage 44p/kg, carrots 60p/kg.

7 Use this information to find the cost of
(a) 5 kg potatoes (b) 2 kg parsnips
(c) 3 kg cabbage (d) $1\frac{1}{2}$ kg carrots.

Copy and complete these shopping lists. How much change will there be from a £10?

8 2 kg carrots
2 kg parsnips
1 kg peas ______

9 $\frac{1}{2}$ kg carrots
1 kg parsnips
2 kg potatoes
1 swede ______

10 $2\frac{1}{2}$ kg carrots
2 kg parsnips
3 kg potatoes
$1\frac{1}{2}$ kg peas ______

Use your calculator to check the following supermarket bills. Say which are correct and give the correct answer for any that are added up incorrectly.

11	12	13	14	15
0.22	0.54	0.53	0.55	1.27
0.78	0.58	1.33	1.45	1.06
0.76	2.45	0.83	0.35	1.62
1.45	0.67	1.87	0.34	0.95
0.55	0.44	0.44	0.32	0.21
0.54	0.32	0.10	0.45	0.63
1.43	0.34	0.62	0.21	0.79
5.73	0.65	0.33	1.56	1.23
	3.42	1.97	1.32	1.43
	2.76	0.98	0.86	0.76
	0.97	0.54	0.65	0.62
	2.45	3.67	2.99	4.99
	2.99	**13.21**	1.88	1.77
	3.99		0.44	0.79
	23.57		4.49	0.77
			1.99	0.63
			20.85	**18.47**

Value added tax (VAT)

We have already discussed VAT in Chapter 6. It is a tax added to the sale price of a product or service each time it is sold. The current rate of VAT (1996) is $17\frac{1}{2}\%$, and it is payable on almost everything except food, children's clothes, children's shoes, books and newspapers. There is also a reduced rate of 8% payable on certain fuels.

EXERCISE 9b

In this exercise assume that VAT is $17\frac{1}{2}\%$ unless it is stated otherwise. Give any answers that are not exact correct to the nearest penny.

QUESTION

Eddie and Joy buy a new car costing £14 650 + VAT. Find (a) the VAT due (b) the total price of the car.

ANSWER

(a) VAT due is $17\frac{1}{2}\%$ of £14 650 = 0.175 × £14 650
= £2563.75

(b) Total cost of car = basic cost + VAT
= £14 650 + £2563.75
= £17 213.75.

Find the cash price of

1 A set of woodworking tools marked £85 + VAT

2 A tyre costing £56 + VAT

3 A compact disc costing £10.20 + VAT

4 A three-course meal costing £8.56 + VAT

5 Six dining chairs marked £44.99 each + VAT

6 A food mixer marked £64.30 + VAT

7 An electric fire marked £24.99 + VAT

QUESTION

A pair of walking boots costs £65.80 including VAT at $17\frac{1}{2}\%$. Find (a) the price excluding VAT (b) the VAT.

ANSWER

(a) If VAT is $17\frac{1}{2}\%$ then the purchase price of the boots is the price without the VAT + $17\frac{1}{2}\%$ of that price
i.e. $117\frac{1}{2}\%$ of the price of the boots without the VAT is £65.80
∴ 1% of the price without the VAT is £65.80 ÷ 117.5

So 100% of the price without the VAT is

$$\frac{£65.80}{117.5} \times 100 = £56$$

Thus the price of the walking boots without the VAT is £56.

(b) VAT on £56 at $17\frac{1}{2}\%$ = 0.175 × £56
= £9.80

(Check: price without VAT + VAT is £56 + £9.80 = £65.80, which agrees with the original statement in the question.)

8 The selling price of a carpet is £528.75 including VAT. How much does the carpet cost before the VAT is added?

9 When VAT is $17\frac{1}{2}\%$ the price of a cassette is £9.99. Find, correct to the nearest penny (a) the price excluding VAT (b) the price of the cassette including VAT if the rate of VAT is increased to 20%.

10 A wheelbarrow costs £28.20 including VAT at $17\frac{1}{2}\%$. Find (a) the price before the VAT was added (b) the price of the wheelbarrow including VAT if the rate is reduced to 15% (c) the reduction in the purchase price of the wheelbarrow.

Electricity bills

Electricity is measured in kilowatt hours (kW h). A kilowatt hour is the amount of electricity used in 1 hour by a fire or other appliance with a rating of 1 kilowatt. The number of such units used by a household in a quarter is the difference between the meter readings at the end and beginning of that quarter. In addition to paying for the number of units used there is a fixed or standing charge. Value added tax (currently 8% for domestic electricity) is added to the total. A bill for the Sample household is shown on p. 96.

EXERCISE 9c

QUESTION

Find the cost of running a 2.5 kW electric fire for 50 hours if electricity costs 8.51p per unit.

ANSWER

Number of units used
= rating in kilowatts × number of hours used
= 2.5 × 50
= 125.

Cost of 125 units at 8.51 per unit is 125 × 8.51p
= £10.64 (to the nearest penny)

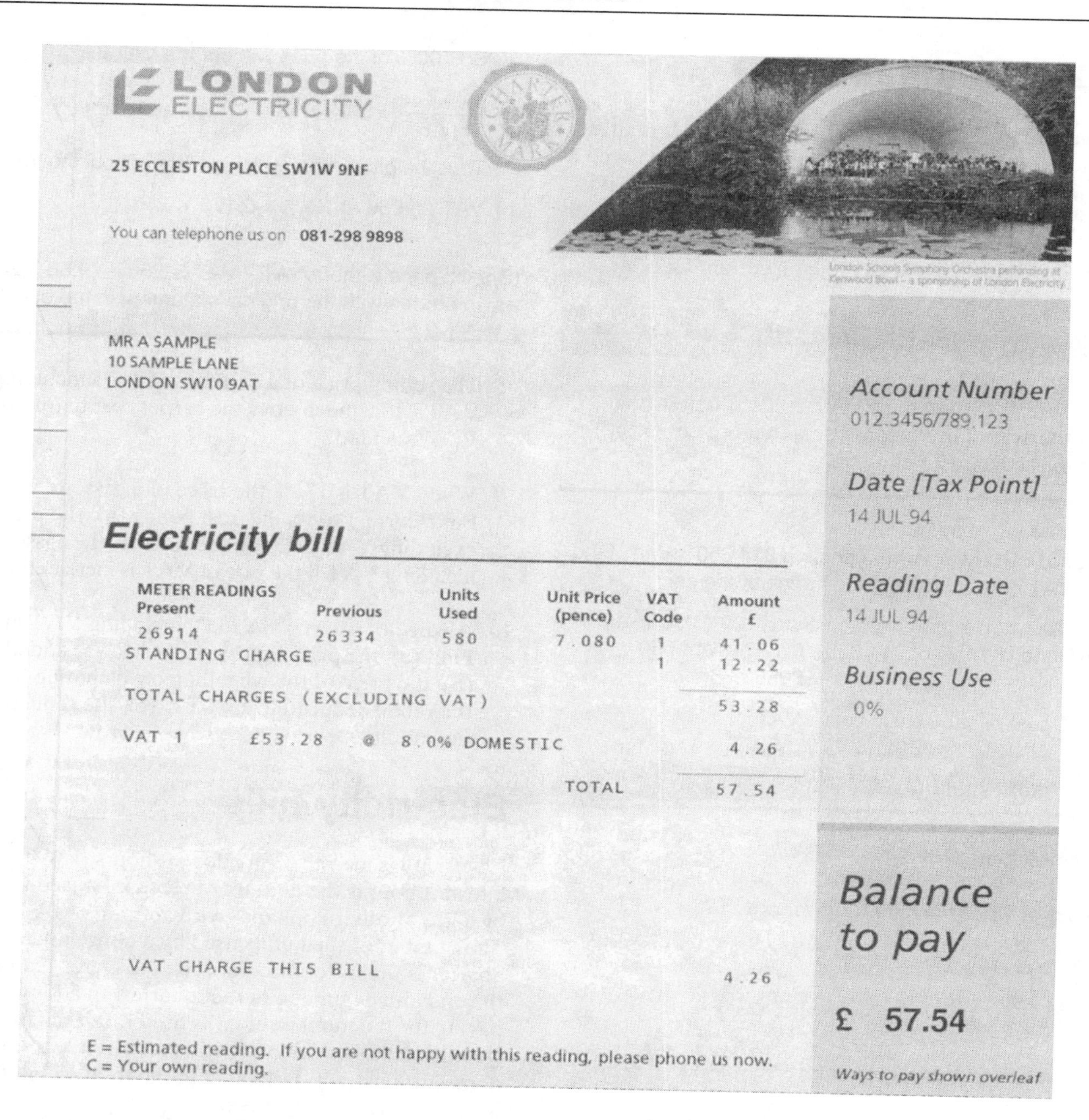

LONDON ELECTRICITY

25 ECCLESTON PLACE SW1W 9NF

You can telephone us on 081-298 9898

London Schools Symphony Orchestra performing at Kenwood Bowl – a sponsorship of London Electricity

MR A SAMPLE
10 SAMPLE LANE
LONDON SW10 9AT

Account Number
012.3456/789.123

Date [Tax Point]
14 JUL 94

Reading Date
14 JUL 94

Business Use
0%

Electricity bill

METER READINGS Present	Previous	Units Used	Unit Price (pence)	VAT Code	Amount £
26914	26334	580	7.080	1	41.06
STANDING CHARGE				1	12.22
TOTAL CHARGES (EXCLUDING VAT)					53.28
VAT 1 £53.28 @ 8.0% DOMESTIC					4.26
			TOTAL		57.54

VAT CHARGE THIS BILL 4.26

Balance to pay

£ 57.54

Ways to pay shown overleaf

E = Estimated reading. If you are not happy with this reading, please phone us now.
C = Your own reading.

1 Copy and complete the table, which shows the electricity meter readings for the Newman household last year.

Date	Meter reading	Number of units used in quarter
6 November	14 563	
		First
10 February	16 043	
		Second
4 May	17 267	
		Third
12 August	17 982	
		Fourth
8 November	18 544	

2 How many units of electricity are used if
(a) a 150 W lamp burns for 10 hours
(b) a 2 kW fire is used for 8 hours
(c) a 3 kW kettle is boiling for 3 minutes
(d) a 250 W computer is switched on for 12 hours?

3 How many hours will each of the following appliances run on 1 unit of electricity?

(a) a 100 W light bulb
(b) a 12 W light bulb
(c) a 2 kW fire
(d) a 250 W photocopier
(e) a 2.5 kW kettle
(f) a 150 W computer

4 Find the cost of using the following appliances for the times indicated if electricity costs 7.86p per unit.

(a) a 3 kW fire for 24 hours

(b) twelve 100 W bulbs, each for 6 hours

(c) 750 W iron for $2\frac{1}{2}$ hours

(d) a 350 W television set for 44 hours

Give each answer correct to the nearest penny.

5 At the Holiday Express travel agency they estimate that during the course of a week they use the following electrical appliances for the given times:
eighteen 60 W fluorescent tubes, each for 52 hours
one 2.5 kW electric kettle for 3 hours
three 125 W computer systems, each for 44 hours
Find

(a) the number of units of electricity used by
(i) the 18 tubes
(ii) the kettle
(iii) the 3 computer systems

(b) the total number of units used

(c) the cost of these units at 8.45p per unit.

QUESTION
The electricity meter readings in the Franklin household at the beginning and end of last quarter were 54 292 and 55 726 respectively. Electricity for domestic consumers costs 8.47p per unit; there is a standing charge of £18.40, and VAT is added to the total at 8%. Find (a) the number of units used (b) the cost of the electricity (c) the total due including VAT.

ANSWER
(a) Number of units used = 55 726 − 54 292
= 1434

(b) Cost of 1434 units at 8.47p per unit
= 1434 × 8.47p
= £121.46 (to nearest penny)

(c) Total cost excluding VAT
= standing charge + cost of electricity
= £18.40 + £121.46
= £139.86
VAT on £139.86 at 8% = 0.08 × £139.86
= £11.19 (to nearest penny)
∴ total cost including VAT = £139.86 + £11.19
= £151.05

Find the quarterly cost of electricity for each of the following households. Assume that the rate of value added tax is 8%.

Household	Meter reading: At beginning of quarter	Meter reading: At end of quarter	Number of units used	Cost per unit p	Standing charge £
6 Hegarty	16 792	18 112		8.21	16.84
7 O'Callaghan	37 421	38 440		7.98	18.42
8 Timshu	29 334	31 607		8.87	17.79

QUESTION
Find the cost of electricity for a quarter at Lawrie White Plastics if 18 654 units are consumed and the charges at commercial rates are: standing charge £16.95, first 1000 units 12.86p per unit, over 1000 units 9.67p per unit. VAT is added to the total at $17\frac{1}{2}$%.

ANSWER
Standing charge
= £16.95
Cost of 1000 units at 12.86p per unit is 1000 × 12.86
= £128.60
Cost of remaining 17 654 units at 9.67p per unit is 17 654 × 9.67p
= £1707.14 (to nearest penny)
Total cost excluding VAT
= £16.95 + £128.60 + £1707.14
= £1852.69 (to nearest penny)
VAT on £1852.69 at $17\frac{1}{2}$% is 0.175 × £1852.69
= £324.22 (to nearest penny)
∴ cost of electricity for the quarter
= £1852.69 + £324.22
= £2176.91

Find the quarterly cost of electricity for each of the following businesses. Value added tax should be added at $17\frac{1}{2}$%.

Business	Meter reading: At beginning of quarter	Meter reading: At end of quarter	Number of units used	Cost per unit: First 1000 units	Cost per unit: Additional units	Standing charge £
9 Black's Newsagents	24 078	27 962		12.53	7.95	15.85
10 Hodges Hardware	38 943	41 465		13.74	8.24	17.65
11 Mitchells Fashions	27 936	30 818		14.87	9.49	16.32

Gas bills

Gas is measured in units of 100 cubic metres. A formula is then used to convert the number of units used into kilowatt hours (kW h). There is a daily standing charge and VAT is added to the total to give the payment due.

EXERCISE 9d

QUESTION

The gas bill for the Marley household gives the following details:

standing charge: 93 days at 10.52p per day;
number of kW h used: 5296 at 1.477p per kW h.

If VAT is added at 8% find the total amount the Marleys must pay.

ANSWER

Standing charge for the quarter is 93 × 10.52p
= 978.36p
= £9.78 (nearest penny)

Cost of 5296 kW h at 1.477p per unit is 5296 × 1.477p
= 7822.192p
= £78.22 (nearest penny)

Standing charge + cost of gas is £9.78 + £78.22
= £88.00

VAT at 8% is 0.08 × £88.00
= £7.04

Total cost including VAT is £88.00 + £7.04
= £95.04

Given below is information from several different gas bills. In each case find the total amount due.

Name of householder	Number of days for standing charge	Daily cost of standing charge	Number of kW h used	Cost per kW h	Rate of VAT
1 Roux	97	10.03p	12 948	1.477p	8%
2 Yeo	87	10.73p	10 984	1.483p	8%
3 Tierney	105	11.07p	15 723	1.396p	10%
4 Cameron	94	12.35p	9 886	1.726p	10%
5 Davison	99	10.88p	11 932	1.603p	$17\frac{1}{2}$%

Telephone bills

As with electricity and gas bills, telephone charges are made up of a fixed charge plus charges for the calls made. Value added tax at the current rate is then added to the total. The fixed charge, which is paid in advance, pays for the rental of the line and equipment. The charge for each call depends on the distance away, the time taken and the time of day at which the call is made.

Household insurance

Insurance is a way of spreading risk. A large number of people pay a small sum, called a *premium*, to an insurance company. The insurance company will then pay out when property and/or belongings are damaged or stolen. Because a house cannot easily be carried away the premium to insure it is much cheaper than the premium to insure contents of the same value.

EXERCISE 9e

QUESTION

Find the annual insurance premium for a house valued at £75 000 if the premium is £1.75 per £1000.

ANSWER

Annual premium on £1000 is £1.75
∴ the annual premium on a house valued at £75 000 = 75 × £1.75 = £131.25

1 The Woodley Insurance Company will insure buildings at £1.65 per £1000, or part thereof. How much will the premium be on a property valued at (a) £54 000 (b) £88 000 (c) £135 500?

2

House contents can be insured for 35p per £100 covered. Find the premium on house contents valued at (a) £10 500 (b) £12 400 (c) £18 700.

3 If articles, such as cameras and jewellery, are covered for 'all risks' then they are covered at all times and in all places, whether inside the property or not. Premiums for this cover are obviously higher. How much does it cost to insure a video camera, valued at £985, for 'all risks' if the premium is 95p per £100 insured?

For each household listed in the table on the opposite page, find (a) the total premium (b) the weekly premium.

	Household	Value of property	Annual rate	Value of contents excluding 'all risks'	Annual rate	Value of 'all risks'	Annual rate
4	Evans	£55 000	£1.55 per £1000	£16 000	40p per £100	£3500	95p per £100
5	Patel	£78 000	£1.25 per £1000	£12 500	35p per £100	£4200	90p per £100
6	Kohl	£135 000	£1.35p per £1000	£34 000	45p per £100	£5600	£1.05 per £100

Council tax

Local councils need money to pay for the services they provide. Most of it comes from central government, but they raise some money locally by a tax on property. Every house, bungalow and flat is placed in one of eight bands depending on its value. All the properties within each band then pay the same yearly tax. The rates for one council are shown in the table.

Valuation band	Range of values	Amount of tax
A	Not exceeding £30 000	£230.73
B	Over £30 000 but not exceeding £39 000	259.18
C	Over £39 000 but not exceeding £51 000	287.64
D	Over £51 000 but not exceeding £66 000	316.09
E	Over £66 000 but not exceeding £90 000	373.00
F	Over £90 000 but not exceeding £120 000	429.92
G	Over £120 000 but not exceeding £240 000	486.82
H	Over £240 000	572.18

The amount given in the table assumes that two or more persons live in the house. For persons living alone this figure is reduced by 25%.

EXERCISE 9f

Use the information given in the text to answer the questions in this exercise.

QUESTION

Jenny Eschle lives alone in a house valued at £65 000. (a) Which valuation band is the property in? (b) How much council tax is she due to pay?

ANSWER

(a) A house valued at £65 000 lies within the range 'over £51 000 but not exceeding £66 000'. The property therefore belongs to band D.

(b) The tax due for a property in band D in normal circumstances is £316.09. Since Jenny lives alone she is entitled to a reduction of 25%

i.e. a reduction of $0.25 \times$ £316.09 = £79.02 (to the nearest penny)

$\therefore$ amount she has to pay is £316.09 − £79.02 = £237.07 (to the nearest penny)

1 Which band will a property be placed in if it is valued at (a) £95 000 (b) £56 000 (c) £225 000

2 Mr and Mrs Johnson live in a bungalow valued at £74 000. How much council tax must they pay?

3 (a) Wyn Coles lives alone in a house in band B. How much council tax must he pay? (b) How much more council tax would he have to pay if the house was revalued and placed in band C?

4 Sabina Shah lives in a flat valued at £85 000. (a) How much council tax is she due to pay? (b) She gets married and the couple live in her flat. By how much will the council tax on the property increase?

QUESTION

Midchester Borough Council encourage payment by direct debit. They require 10 equal monthly amounts. Any odd amount is to be made with the first payment. Frank Wilcox lives in a house in band F and decides to pay his council tax in this way. Find (a) his first payment (b) each subsequent payment.

ANSWER

The total amount due for a property in band F is £429.92, which gives 10 equal payments of £42.992. If he pays £42.99 each time he will pay too little, whereas if he pays £43 (£42.992 rounded up to the nearest penny) each time he pays too much. He can get over this problem by making 9 payments of £42.99 which have a total value of $9 \times$ £42.99 i.e. £386.91, and a first payment of £429.92 − £386.91 = £43.01. Thus

(a) his first payment is £43.01

(b) the other 9 payments are £42.99 each.

(**NOTE:** The first payment can never be lower than the other payments.)

5 Find for each of the following cases (i) the first payment (ii) each additional payment, if the finance department agrees to payment of the council tax in 10 equal monthly payments, provided that any odd amount is made with the first payment: (a) a property in band D occupied by a married couple (b) a house with a family of five valued at £45 000 (c) a flat valued at £85 000 occupied by a single person.

Cash flow

One of the biggest problems each of us faces can be summed up in the phrase 'cash flow'. Over the year as a whole we may have enough income to manage all right, but there will be certain times when our income is not enough to cover our expenditure. This problem can often be solved by careful planning. For example, it would be silly to arrange to have to pay the tax and insurance on the car, the TV licence, the council tax, the water rates, an electric bill and a telephone bill at the end of any one week or month – and certainly not out of your November pay with Christmas just around the corner.

EXERCISE 9g

1 The table shows Ben Clarke's probable income and expenditure for next year. (All figures are in pounds.)

(a) Copy and complete this table to find the amount he has left over or the amount he is short each month. Take each month separately. (The first three months are done for you.)

	Jan	Feb	Mar	Apr	May	June
Income	1380	1370	1360	1360	1360	1420
Expenditure	1050	1450	1100	1150	1550	950
Amount over	330		260			
Amount under		80				

	July	Aug	Sept	Oct	Nov	Dec
Income	1360	1360	1400	1400	1400	1550
Expenditure	1200	1480	1550	1350	1250	2000
Amount over						
Amount under						

(**NOTE:** Amounts 'under' are shown in a different line from amounts 'over'.)

(b) What is his total expected income for the year?

(c) Find his anticipated expenditure for the year.

(d) Should his income exceed his expenditure?

(e) Should it be possible to rearrange his payments so that he is not left short in any month?

2 Lana Martin's estimates of her income and expenditure for a year are given on page 101.

(All figures are in pounds.)

(Notes: The opening balance at the start of the year is £0. The closing balance at the end of January is the amount by which the income exceeds the expenditure, i.e. £210. This is the opening balance for February. A monthly balance is placed in brackets (for example (£385)) if what is paid out is greater than the income for that month. (The balances for the first four months have been done for you.))

(a) In a year how much does Lana spend (i) on rent (ii) on food (iii) on gas and electricity?

(b) Find Lana's opening and closing balance each month.

(c) Find (i) Lana's total estimated income for the year (ii) her total estimated expenditure for the year.

(d) In which months is her estimated expenditure greater than her income?

(e) Does she have any cash flow problems? i.e. are there any months in which her income plus her closing balance from the previous month is not enough to meet her expenditure?

(f) How much does she spend a year on bus fares? Express this as a percentage of her total income.

(g) Next year Lana's income is expected to rise by 5%. Estimate Lana's total income next year.

(h) Next year Lana expects her expenses to rise by 8%. Should her income exceed her expenditure next year?

(i) Express her rent as a percentage of her total income.

Income	Jan 1120	Feb 1120	Mar 1120	Apr 1160	May 1160	June 1160	July 1160	Aug 1160	Sept 1160	Oct 1160	Nov 1160	Dec 1160
Expenditure												
Rent	350	350	350	350	350	350	350	350	350	350	350	350
Food	160	160	160	160	160	160	160	160	160	160	160	160
Gas	38	38	38	38	38	38	38	38	38	38	38	38
Electricity	42	42	42	42	42	42	42	42	42	42	42	42
Phone			45			45			45			45
Water				255								
Council tax				380								
House insurance							184					
TV licence						120						
Life insurance	35	35	35	35	35	35	35	35	35	35	35	35
Credit cards	65	65	65	65	65	65	65	65	65	65	65	65
Bus fares	70	70	70	70	70	70	70	70	70	70	70	70
Holidays							600					
Christmas											450	
Regular saving	100	100	100	100	100	100	100	100	100	100	100	100
Other	50	50	50	50	50	50	50	50	50	50	50	50
Total expenditure	910	910	955	1545								
Monthly balance	210	210	165	(385)								
Opening balance	0	210	420	585								
Closing balance	210	420	585	200								

Multiple-choice questions 9

In this exercise several alternative answers are given. Write down the letter that corresponds to the correct answer.

1 Jane pays for 2 lb of carrots at 35p per pound and $1\frac{1}{2}$ lb of parsnips at 28p per pound by offering a £5 note. The amount of change she should receive is

A £3.88 **B** £4.37 **C** £4.02 **D** £4.23

2 The reading on a gas meter at the beginning of a quarter was 2420 and the reading at the end of the quarter was 2675. The number of units used during the quarter was

A 2675 **B** 5095 **C** 255 **D** 2420

3 The Homebank Insurance Company charges a yearly premium of £1.10 per £100 to cover articles for 'all risks'. The amount Sharon must pay to insure all her jewellery, valued at £2500, in this way is

A $27\frac{1}{2}$p **B** £2.75 **C** £275 **D** £27.50

4 The price of a pair of trainers is £45, including VAT at 20%. The cost of these trainers before VAT is added is

A £54 **B** £37.50 **C** £50.50 **D** £40

Self-assessment test 9

1 (a) Copy and complete the following bill:
5 lb bananas at 54p per pound
3 lb apples at 38p per pound
$1\frac{1}{2}$ lb grapes at £1.80 per pound
8 oranges at 22p each
4 grapefruit at 35p each

(b) How much change would you get if you paid for this order with a £10 note?

2 Silchester Double Glazing quotes £3546 + VAT at $17\frac{1}{2}$% to replace the windows in a house. How much is the customer expected to pay?

3 The Bennetts' electricity meter reading is 17 942 at the beginning of a quarter and 19 271 at the end. Electricity is charged at 8.92p per unit and there is a standing charge of £18.74.

(a) How many units did the Bennetts use during the quarter?

(b) How much does the electricity cost?

(c) How much is due to the electricity company?

(d) Find the total bill if VAT is added at 8%.

4 An insurance company charges £1.65 per £1000 for insuring a property and 55p per £100 for insuring contents. Penny and Arthur Cole wish to insure their bungalow for £85 000 and the contents for £22 000. How much will the insurance company charge for this cover?

CHAPTER 10

Other expenses

Fares and admission charges

Have you ever been puzzled by the different fares you can be asked to pay for a ticket to go on a journey by train? It often depends on the day of the week, the time of day and even on which train you travel. Likewise, if you go to the theatre the price of a seat depends on where you sit, whether it is an evening or matinée performance, what special discounts are offered and whether or not you belong to a group of a certain size. It is important to be aware of these differences, for in this way you can save yourself money.

EXERCISE 10a

QUESTION

Ticket prices for a musical are given in the table.

Seat type	Rows	Tues–Sat evenings £	Sat matinée £
Stalls	A–J	22.50	13.50
	K–R	20.00	12.00
	S–W	15.00	9.00
Circle	A–G	25.00	15.00
	H–P	20.00	12.00
Upper circle	A–E	10.00	6.00
	F–H	7.50	4.50

(a) Two adults attend on a Wednesday evening. How much do these seats cost if they sit (i) in row H of the stalls (ii) in row G of the upper circle?

(b) Don and his daughter Sarah attend the Saturday matinée and sit in row Q of the stalls. How much does Don pay if there is a 20% reduction for children?

ANSWER

(a) (i) Row H of the stalls is in the seat type 'stalls A–J'. These seats cost £22.50 each for an evening performance so the cost for two adults is 2 × £22.50 = £45.

(ii) Row G of the upper circle is in seat type 'upper circle F–H'. These seats cost £7.50 for an evening performance so the cost for 2 adults is 2 × £7.50 = £15.

(b) A seat in row Q of the stalls for the matinée costs £12. Reduction for a child is 20% i.e. reduction is 0.2 × £12 = £2.40
∴ cost of a seat for a child is £12 − £2.40 = £9.60
so cost of seats for 1 adult and 1 child is £12 + £9.60 = £21.60.

---

1 Cinema seats costs £5.50, £7.50, £9.50 and £12.50, and children are admitted at half price. Mr and Mrs Bowen take their three children to see *Jurassic Park*.
(a) What is the cheapest way of doing this?
(b) How much will it cost if they sit in the most expensive seats?

2 Seats for a special showing of *Pinocchio* cost £4.50, but for children they are reduced to two-thirds of the adult price. (a) How much must I pay for a seat for my son? (b) How much will it cost for a mother to take her three children?

3 The advertised prices of the seats for *Cinderella* are £7.50, £10 and £15. A discount of 40% is allowed for children. (a) What does it cost for a child to sit in the most expensive seat? (b) How much will it cost for a mother with her three children to sit in the cheapest seats? (c) How much cheaper is this than if she had chosen the next best seats?

4 The cheap-day return rail fare to London is £36.50 and children are carried at three-fifths of this rate. (a) Find the price of a child's ticket (b) How much will it cost for a family of five, including three children, to go to London for the day?

5 The prices of the seats for an 18-concert series are:

Seating area	Single ticket £
A	6.00
B	9.00
C	11.00
D	14.50
E	18.50

Parties of 8 or more: £1.00 off all tickets.
Attend all 18 concerts: 30% discount.
Attend any 8 concerts: 15% discount.
Attend any 3 concerts: 5% discount.

How much will it cost for

(a) a party of 10 to attend one concert if they sit in seating area D

(b) Marg Laffan to go to 8 concerts if she sits in seating area E

(c) Tim Salmon to attend all the concerts and sit in seating area C

(d) a party of 12 to attend 6 concerts in the cheapest seats?

(Tickets for more than 3, but fewer than 8, concerts are discounted at the rate for 3 concerts. Party deductions are given after discounts have been calculated.)

Rental charges

If you need to mix the concrete to lay the base for a garage, it is probably better to hire a mixer rather than to buy one. Similarly, most bridegrooms who want to get married in morning dress would hire the suit rather than buy it. On the other hand, there are some things, for example a television set, which you might like to own but simply cannot afford to buy. In a case like this you have to hire, otherwise you must do without. Similarly, many people live in rented houses or flats because they cannot afford to buy, or perhaps because they do not intend staying in a particular place for very long.

In contrast, some business firms hire their vehicles, even when they can afford to buy them. This is because they do not want to have a lot of capital tied up in vehicles which could be better used elsewhere in the business.

EXERCISE 10b

QUESTION
A television set costs £450 new. It can be rented for £15.50 a calendar month or £165 a year.

(a) If the set is rented, how much a year is saved by paying the rental yearly rather than monthly?

(b) Billy rents a set on monthly terms for 5 years. How much would he have saved by buying a new set? In a real-life situation why would he not save this amount?

ANSWER
(a) Rent for 12 months at £15.50 a month
$= 12 \times £15.50$
$= £186.$
Yearly rental is £165.
Amount saved by agreeing to the yearly rental
$= £186 - £165 = £21.$

(b) Monthly payments of £15.50 for 5 years amount to
$5 \times 12 \times £15.50 = £930.$
Cost of TV set new = £450.
Amount saved by buying rather than renting = £930 − £450 = £480.
This difference does not allow for the lost interest on the money used to buy the set, or for the cost of repairs or servicing for the set that is bought.

---

1 A TV set is offered for rent at £11.85 a calendar month or £132.50 a year. How much is saved by paying the rental once a year?

2 The rental for a flat is £86.50 a week. How much is this a year?

3 Kevin Newbury rents a flat for £6500 a year. How much is this a week?

4 A couple wish to hire 360 glasses for their wedding reception. They can either pay £3.50 a dozen, which includes the cost of any breakages, or pay £2.50 a dozen plus breakages at £3 a glass. When the glasses are returned 7 are found to be broken. Which way would have been the cheaper way of hiring the glasses?

5 The terms for hiring a concrete mixer from Blackwell Tool Hire are £10.75 per day or £31.50 per week. Sid Seward hires a mixer for five complete weeks and for 4 individual days of different weeks. (a) How much does he pay in hire charge? (b) Would it have been cheaper for him to buy a second-hand mixer for £165?

6 Sue Hamer rents a roof rack for her car. The rental is £2.50 plus 75p a day. How much does it cost her to rent it for (a) 5 days (b) 14 days?

Cost of running a motorcycle or car

It is possible that you will spend more money on a car or motorcycle than on any other single item, except possibly a house. Having bought our chosen means of transport we now look into the running costs.

EXERCISE 10c

QUESTION

George's motorcycle expenses for a year are: road tax £75, fully comprehensive insurance £750, depreciation £550, fuel 1200 litres at 55p per litre, servicing and repairs £100. If George travels 24 000 km during the year, find

(a) his total fuel costs

(b) his total costs

(c) how far he can travel on each litre of fuel

(d) his overall cost per kilometre, giving your answer correct to the nearest tenth of a penny.

ANSWER

(a) Total fuel cost = 1200 × 55p
= £660

(b) Total cost = £75 + £750 + £550 + £660 + £100
= £2135

(c) Number of kilometres per litre $= \dfrac{\text{distance travelled}}{\text{number of litres used}}$

$= \dfrac{24\,000}{1200}$ km

= 20 km

(d) Overall cost per kilometre

$= \dfrac{\text{total cost}}{\text{number of kilometres travelled}}$

$= \dfrac{£2135}{24\,000}$

$= \dfrac{213\,500}{24\,000}$p

= 8.8958 . . . p

= 8.9p (to nearest tenth of a penny)

1 Tyres for a car cost £50 each and have a life of 35 000 km. Find the cost of tyres per kilometre. Give your answer in pence, correct to two decimal places.

2 Sally Harding's car averages 35 miles per gallon on unleaded petrol. Calculate the cost of petrol per mile when it costs £2.80 a gallon.

3 Terry travelled 17 640 km last year on his motorcycle at an average of 21 km per litre.

(a) How much did he spend on petrol if it cost 58p per litre?

(b) If petrol accounts for 25% of his total costs, how much per kilometre did his motorcycle cost him for the year? Give your answer in pence correct to three significant figures.

4 Tom Lloyd's motorcycle uses 11 litres of petrol a week and averages 19.5 km per litre.

(a) How many kilometres does he travel (i) in a week (ii) in a year?

(b) Petrol costs 55p a litre, while other expenses, for depreciation, road fund licence, insurance and servicing, amount to £945. How much does his motorcycle cost him for the year?

5 Derek Jenkins estimates that he drives 18 000 miles a year. He has to choose between a car that does 36 miles to the gallon and another that does 30 miles to the gallon. Find (a) the difference in the yearly petrol consumption for the two cars (b) the additional cost for petrol if the car with the higher petrol consumption is chosen and petrol costs £2.80 a gallon.

Postage

The Post Office offers a wide range of services, two of the most important of which are collecting and delivering letters and parcels.

The rates for sending letters and parcels within the United Kingdom in January 1996 are given below. Notice that the costs go up in steps, for example all letters that are over 150 g but not more than 200 g cost 36p to send by second-class post. Because the charges go up in steps, a table of postage rates is an example of a step function.

Letters

Weight not over	First class	Second class	Weight not over	First class	Second class
60 g	25p	19p	500 g	£1.25	98p
100 g	38p	29p	600 g	£1.55	£1.20p
150 g	47p	36p	700 g	£1.90	£1.40p
200 g	57p	43p	750 g	£2.05	£1.45p
250 g	67p	52p	800 g	£2.15	Not
300 g	77p	61p	900 g	£2.35	admissible
350 g	88p	70p	1000 g	£2.50	over 750 g
400 g	£1.00	79p		Each extra 250 g	
450 g	£1.13	89p		or part thereof 65p	

Parcels	
Weight not over	Price
1 kg	£2.65
2 kg	£3.25
4 kg	£4.50
6 kg	£5.00
8 kg	£5.80
10 kg	£6.75
30 kg	£8.10

EXERCISE 10d

Use the tables in the text to answer the questions that follow.

QUESTION
Find the cost of posting

(a) 5 letters, by first-class letter post, 4 weighing 45 g and one weighing 275 g

(b) three parcels weighing $1\frac{1}{2}$ kg, $2\frac{1}{4}$ kg and $4\frac{3}{4}$ kg.

ANSWER
(a) The cost of sending one letter not more than 60 g by first class letter post is 25p
$\therefore$ the cost of sending 4 such letters is $4 \times 25\text{p} = £1$
The cost of sending one letter weighing 275 g, i.e. not more than 300 g, by first-class letter post is 77p
$\therefore$ total cost of sending the 5 letters is £1 + 77p, i.e. £1.77

(b) Posting one parcel not more than 2 kg by parcel post costs £3.25
Posting another parcel not more than 4 kg costs £4.50
Posting a third parcel not more than 6 kg costs £5.00
$\therefore$ total cost of posting the three parcels is £12.75

Assume that all letters are under 60 g unless it is stated otherwise.
In questions 1 to 8 find the cost of posting the items stated.

1 (a) Three letters by first-class post
(b) six letters by second-class post.

2 Two letters by first-class post together with three letters by second-class post.

3 Eight letters by second-class post, two of which weigh 215 g.

4 Four letters, each weighing 75g, by first class post.

5 Five letters by first class post together with two letters weighing 235 g by second class post.

6 (a) Two parcels, each weighing 1.3 kg
(b) three parcels, each weighing 3.5 kg, by parcel post.

7 1 parcel weighing $2\frac{1}{2}$ kg and one weighing $3\frac{3}{4}$ kg, by parcel post.

8 A parcel weighing 1600 g by (a) parcel post
(b) first-class letter post.

9 What does it cost to send a small parcel weighing 725 g by (a) parcel post (b) first-class letter post (c) second-class letter post?

10 How much does it cost to send a parcel weighing 2.3 kg by first-class letter post? Would this parcel be accepted for second-class mail?

11 How much more does it cost to send a package weighing 1.3 kg by first-class letter post than by parcel post? Why do some people choose to send such a package at the more expensive rate?

12 An electronics company wants to send a package containing some components to one of its other plants. Speed is important, so they decide to send it by first-class letter post. If the package weighs 4.5 kg, how much more expensive does this prove than to send it at the parcel rate?

13 How much cheaper is it to send out 1200 packages, each weighing 725 g, by second-class letter post than by parcel post?

14 A manufacturing company must, by law, send a copy of its annual report to every shareholder. The annual report for Duogate plc, which weighs 116 g, is to be sent to all 11 560 shareholders. How much is saved if these reports are sent by second-class rather than by first-class post? (In practice companies are able to negotiate lower rates for posting large amounts of mail.)

15 The postage book for BC Electronics shows that in one week they sent the following mail:
145 letters, each under 60 g, by first-class post
38 letters, each under 100 g, by first-class post
88 letters, each under 60 g, by second-class post
45 letters, each under 150 g, by second-class post
6 parcels, each weighing 2.6 kg, by parcel post.
Find the postage bill for the week.

Other step functions

Charges in multistorey car parks, printing costs for different numbers of books, and unit costs when different numbers of an item are bought are other examples of step functions.

EXERCISE 10e

1 The charges in a city-centre multistorey car park are:

Up to 1 hour	90p
Up to 2 hours	150p
Up to 3 hours	220p
Up to 4 hours	300p
Up to 5 hours	400p
Up to 6 hours	520p

Each additional hour or part of an hour costs 130p.

How much does it cost to park for (a) 40 minutes
(b) 1 hour 40 minutes (c) $3\frac{3}{4}$ hours
(d) 4 hours 20 minutes (e) 10 hours.

2 A printer charges the following rates for printing personal Christmas cards, which can be supplied in multiples of 25:

50 (minimum order)	79p each
Up to 100	68p each
Up to 200	53p each
Up to 300	49p each
Over 300	45p each

(a) How much will it cost to buy (i) 150 cards (ii) 225 cards (iii) 375 cards?

(b) How many cards must be bought if the buyer requires (i) 80 (ii) 189 (iii) 312?

(c) Pete estimates that he needs 120 cards. How many must he buy? How much will they cost him?

(d) Molly wants 168 cards. How many must she order? How much will they cost her?

3 A garage wishes to purchase a quantity of bonded leather, round key rings to give to customers. The cost of each ring depends on the number ordered, details of which are given below:

Price per ring in pence if number bought is				
100	200	400	600	1000
43	37	34	32	27

(Minimum order: 100 rings.)

(a) What is the cost per ring if the number ordered is (i) 150 (ii) 320 (iii) 950?

(b) How much will the total cost come to for (i) 180 (ii) 228 (iii) 1250 (iv) 78?

4 An estate agent charges the following rates for photocopying:

Number of copies	Cost per copy in pence
Single copy	15
2 to 10	12
11 to 20	10
Over 20	7

(a) Find the cost if a single page is photocopied (i) 5 times (ii) 12 times (iii) 25 times.

(b) Find the cost of 12 copies of one page and 4 copies of another page.

(c) A secretary gets 15 copies of a page of instructions, but on returning to the office finds that she should have got 30 copies. She returns to the estate agent to copy the other 15 pages. How much would she have saved if she had made 30 copies in the first place?

Multiple-choice questions 10

In this exercise several alternative answers are given. Write down the letter that corresponds to the correct answer.

1 Kelly travelled 9607 miles last year in her car and estimates that she averaged 6.5 miles on each litre of petrol. If petrol costs 50p a litre then the total cost of petrol for the year was

A £1478 **B** £624.46 **C** £739 **D** £480.35

2 The photocopying rates of a firm offering this service are:

Number of copies	Cost per copy in pence
Single copy	14
2 to 12	11
13 to 30	9
Over 30	6

The total cost of getting 5 copies of one sheet and 20 copies each of a second and a third sheet is

A £4.15 **B** £2.70 **C** £4.95 **D** £2.35

3 Using the postage rates given on page 104, Kerry calculated how much it would cost to send 3 letters, each weighing 40 g, by first-class post and 2 letters, each weighing 190 g, by second-class post. The amount he has to pay is

A £1.89 **B** £1.47 **C** £1.43 **D** £1.61

4 It costs Berry Walker £2.26 a day or £10.17 a week to hire an electric drill from Newbold Tool Hire. Berry needs the drill for 10 days. The amount he saves by hiring for a complete number of weeks rather than at the daily rate is

A £1.13 **B** £2.26 **C** £11.30 **D** £9.04

Self-assessment test 10

1 Seats for a London West End theatre vary from £12.50 for the cheapest seat to £45 for the most expensive. There is a 30% reduction for children. How much more would it cost for a family of 5, including 2 children, to sit in the most expensive rather than in the cheapest seats?

2 (a) The hire charge for a dehumidifier is £7.50 plus 56p a day. How much does it cost to hire a dehumidifier for (i) 3 days (ii) 2 weeks?
(b) A new dehumidifier costs £276. Which is the cheaper, and by how much: to hire a dehumidifier for 2 years or to buy a new one?

3 Use the table on pages 104 and 105 to find the cost of sending

(a) 8 letters by first-class post, 5 weighing 30g each and the remainder weighing 75g each

(b) 3 parcels weighing $2\frac{1}{2}$ kg, $2\frac{3}{4}$ kg and $4\frac{1}{2}$ kg.

4 A company wishes to buy a quantity of diaries to give away to customers. The cost of a diary depends on the number bought. The table shows how the price of a diary goes down as the number ordered goes up.

Number ordered	1	10	40	100
Price per diary	£3.19	£2.79	£1.99	£1.79

(a) What is the cost per diary if the number ordered is (i) 35 (ii) 80?

(b) How much is the total cost if the number bought is (i) 50 (ii) 150?

CHAPTER 11

Money in business and the community

Bank accounts and bank statements

Most people find it convenient to have a bank account. When you pay into your bank account you need to fill in a form. This form, called a **paying-in slip**, gives details of how the amount paid in is made up, i.e. it shows the number of £10, £5 notes, etc., as well as the total value of the cheques. The value of each individual cheque is written on the back of the slip. An example of a paying-in slip is given in the exercise.

If you have a bank account you will receive a **statement** at regular intervals. This statement shows details of all the payments that have been made into the account (called *credits*) and all the payments that have been made from the account (called *debits*). The figures in the right-hand column show the amount in the account (called the *balance*) after each transaction. The last figure in this column shows how much you have in your account at the close of business on the day the statement was prepared. A capital letter C after the figure means that you still have money in your account, whereas a capital letter D shows that you owe the bank money. An example of a statement is given in the exercise.

In order to operate a bank account you need to be able to write a cheque correctly. An example of a correctly written cheque from A. C. Baxter to pay S. P. Woodward £57.37 is given below. The numbers refer to different parts of the cheque and these are also explained below.

① Today's date. A cheque should not be dated in the future.

② The bank sorting code. All cheques drawn on accounts in this branch of the bank have this number on them. The number is repeated at the bottom of the cheque.

③ The name of the bank.

④ The address of the branch of the bank where the account is held.

⑤ The name of the person or organisation to whom the cheque is paid.

⑥ The amount to be paid written in words followed by the word 'only'. This discourages other words being added.

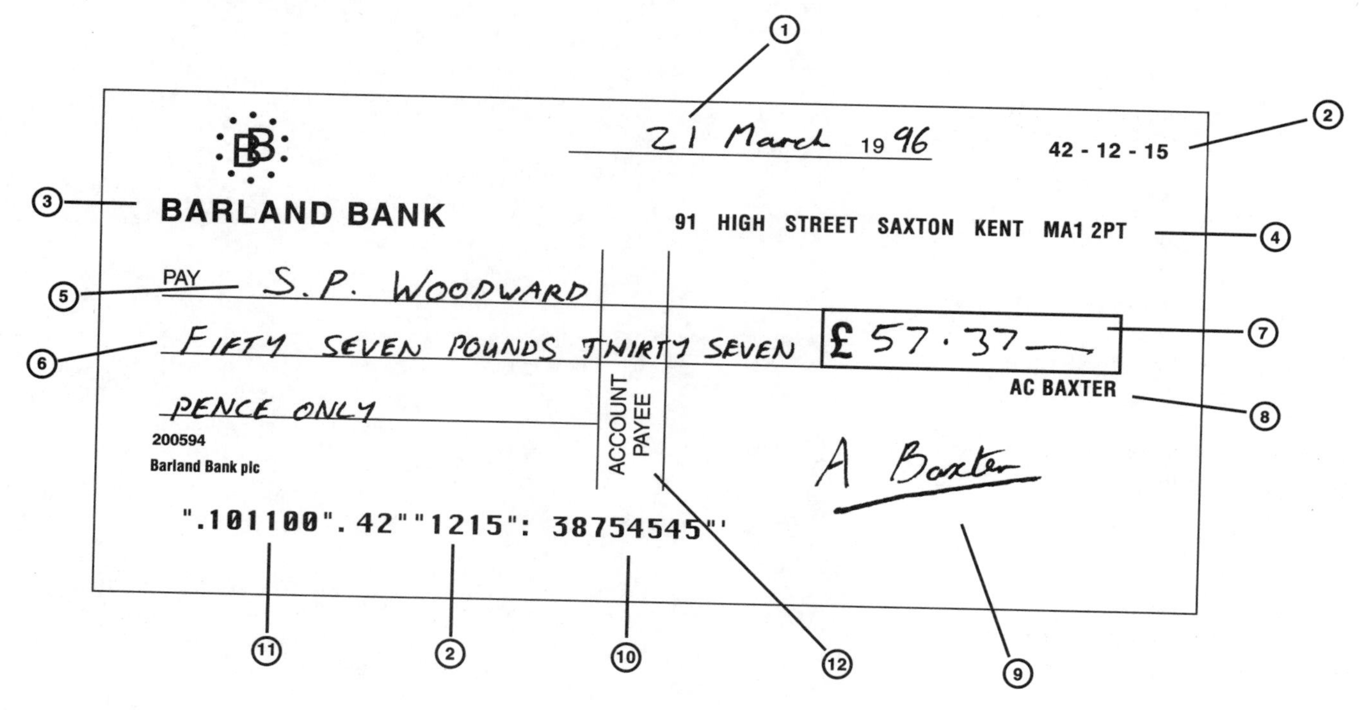

⑦ The amount to be paid written in figures followed by a line so that other figures cannot be added.

⑧ The name of the account holder is printed on the blank cheque.

⑨ The signature of the account holder.

⑩ Your account number, which is unique to you.

⑪ The number of the cheque. This also appears on the slip or stub which you keep. It allows you to trace one of your cheques easily.

⑫ The crossing with the words 'ACCOUNT PAYEE'. The cheque can only be paid into an account in the name of S. P. Woodward.

P. R. JAMES ESQ

Midshires Bank plc
34 Pentland Street
Pulborough
SE12 4TR

Statement of Account

1996	Sheet 47 Account No 56789234	Debit	Credit	Balance Credit C Debit D
AUG 1	BALANCE BROUGHT FORWARD			659.49C
AUG 8	101084	123.43		536.06C
AUG 10	101082	67.21		468.85C
AUG 13	101085	12.89		455.96C
AUG 17	101086	3.96		452.00C
AUG 23	N&G Build. Soc.	352.67		99.33C
AUG 26	MIDLAND GAS	44.76		54.57C
AUG 26	101087	25.43		29.14C
AUG 29	CENTRAL ELEC	56.92		27.78D
AUG 30	MIDSHIRE C.C.		864.66	836.88C
AUG 30	CHARGES	6.86		830.02C
SEP 1	101089	84.56		745.46C
SEP 5	101090	132.77		612.69C
SEP 7	SUNDRIES		75.42	688.11C
SEP 10	101088	88.47		599.64C

EXERCISE 11a

Use the statement to answer questions 1 to 11.

1 What was the balance in the account on
(a) 5 August (b) 23 August (c) 28 August?

2 Did the account go into debit at any time? If so, by how much, and for how long?

3 On which day(s) was there (a) most in the account (b) least in the account?

4 How much did the bank deduct for bank charges?

5 Percy James pays the gas board the same amount every month by banker's order. How much does he pay the gas board in a year?

6 Why do you think the cheque numbers do not appear on the statement in numerical order, even though they were probably written in numerical order?

7 How often do Midshire County Council pay Percy James? When do they pay him?

8 How much was paid out of the account during the month of August?

9 How much was paid into the account during the period of the statement?

10 What was the value of (a) the largest cheque (b) the smallest cheque, to pass through the account?

11 When the next statement arrives (a) what sheet number will it show (b) how much will the balance brought forward be?

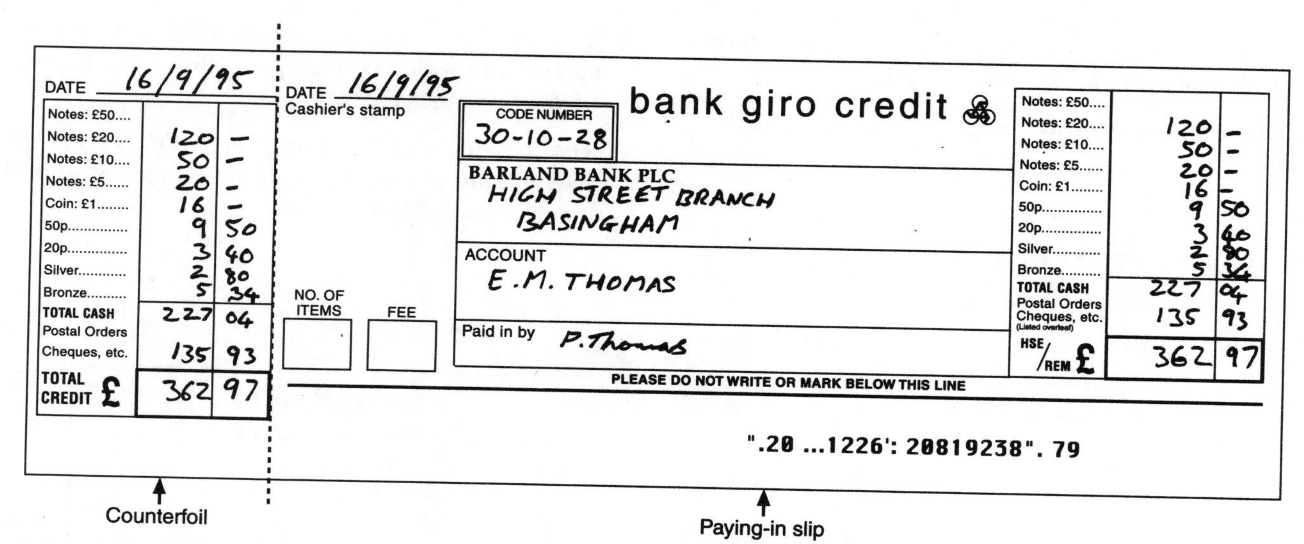

DATE 16/9/95		
Notes: £50....		
Notes: £20....	120	–
Notes: £10....	50	–
Notes: £5......	20	–
Coin: £1........	16	–
50p..............	9	50
20p..............	3	40
Silver............	2	80
Bronze..........	5	34
TOTAL CASH	227	04
Postal Orders Cheques, etc.	135	93
TOTAL CREDIT £	362	97

DATE 16/9/95
Cashier's stamp
CODE NUMBER 30-10-28
bank giro credit
BARLAND BANK PLC
HIGH STREET BRANCH
BASINGHAM
ACCOUNT E.M. THOMAS
NO. OF ITEMS
FEE
Paid in by P. Thomas

Notes: £50....		
Notes: £20....	120	–
Notes: £10....	50	–
Notes: £5......	20	–
Coin: £1........	16	–
50p..............	9	50
20p..............	3	40
Silver............	2	80
Bronze..........	5	34
TOTAL CASH	227	04
Postal Orders Cheques, etc. (Listed overleaf)	135	93
HSE/REM £	362	97

PLEASE DO NOT WRITE OR MARK BELOW THIS LINE

".20 ...1226': 20819238". 79

Counterfoil

Paying-in slip

12 Use this paying-in slip to answer the questions that follow.

(a) How much was paid in
(i) in notes (ii) in coin?

(b) How many (i) 50p coins (ii) 20p coins, were paid in?

(c) Three cheques were paid in. The value of one was £56.32 and the value of another was £37.89. What was the value of the third?

13 Make a copy of the paying-in slip shown above before it was filled in. Now enter the following details on it: notes – two £50, eighteen £20, fifteen £10; coin – twenty-seven 50p, thirty-four 20p, £8.95 in silver and £14.56 in bronze.

Complete the slip ready to take to the bank. Use today's date and your own name.

14 Make a copy of the counterfoil if the amount paid in was:

(a) twelve £20 notes, seventeen £5 notes, thirteen 50p coins and £7.34 in bronze

(b) eighteen £50 notes, nine £20 notes, sixty-seven 50p coins and forty-four 20p coins.

Building society accounts

Many people find it far more convenient to have an account with a building society than with a bank. This is because building societies pay interest on money in the account and usually have longer opening hours. One disadvantage of a building society account is that you cannot go into debit.

If you wish to invest money in a building society then you should look carefully at the different types of accounts. Some pay much higher interest than others, but this usually means that you must have a large amount invested and/or it takes longer to get your money out when you need it. An example of a page from an account book is given at the beginning of the next exercise.

EXERCISE 11b

Name Louise Waters *Roll number* 03 L 1563187

Date	Cashier's initials	Description	Withdrawn	Invested	Balance
15 FEB 96	EM	Balance brought forward			236.61
18 FEB 96	EM	CASH	50.00		186.61
20 FEB 96	PR	CHEQUE		23.18	209.79
28 FEB 96	EM	INTEREST		15.49	225.28
03 MAR 96	EM	CASH	100.00		125.28
03 MAR 96	PR	CHEQUE		26.39	151.67

03 MAR 96	EM	CHEQUE		26.39	151.67
14 MAR 96	EM	CASH	50.00		101.67
18 MAR 96	EM	CASH	20.00		81.67
24 MAR 96	PR	CHEQUE		97.42	179.09
24 MAR 96	EM	CHEQUE	52.18		126.91
27 MAR 96	PR	CASH	100.00		26.91
30 MAR 96	EM	CHEQUE		47.54	74.45
31 MAR 96	EM	CHEQUE		118.93	193.38
04 APR 96	PR	CASH	100.00		93.38
05 APR 96	EM	CHEQUE	82.54		10.84

Use this page from a building society account book to answer the questions that follow:

1 How much was in the account on (a) 20 February (b) 31 March (c) 20 March?

2 What was the largest amount taken out of the account on any one day?

3 How much was put into the account during March?

4 How much was taken out of the account during March?

5 How much cash was paid into the account between 25 February and 25 March inclusive?

6 How much did Louise receive in interest from the building society?

7 During the period that this page covers (a) how much was paid into the account in cheques (b) how much was withdrawn from the account by cheque?

8 Louise pays a cheque for £234.84 into the account on 6 April. On 8 April she goes to the building society and asks for a cheque for £51.77 to pay her electricity bill. She is surprised when she is told that it is not possible for her to draw a cheque on her account for £51.77 that day. Can you explain why?

Mortgages

If you ever wish to buy your own home you will probably need to borrow the money and pay it back over a great many years. The sum you borrow is called a **mortgage**. The money you borrow has been loaned to the society or bank by savers. Savers receive interest from the bank or building society for saving and the society lends it at a higher rate of interest to home buyers it believes are a good risk.

Money borrowed to buy a house or flat is usually repaid with interest over a period of 25 or 30 years. To most people the most important fact is not what the total cost will be but rather how much they have to pay each month. Building societies and banks therefore quote a monthly repayment on each £1000 borrowed. This amount varies with the rate of interest and the number of years over which the loan must be repaid.

EXERCISE 11c

QUESTION

A building society offers a 25-year mortgage for monthly repayments of £11.50 per £1000 borrowed.

(a) What are the monthly repayments on a mortgage of £60 000?

(b) What is the total of all the repayments during the 25 years?

ANSWER

(a) The monthly repayment on £1000 is £11.50.
The monthly repayment on £60 000 is $60 \times £11.50$
$= £690$.

(b) The total of 12 monthly repayments over 25 years is $12 \times 25 \times £690 = £207\,000$. (This is more than three times the cost of the house!)

---

1 The Bridgewood Building Society offers a 25-year mortgage for monthly repayments of £11 for each £1000 borrowed.

(a) What are the monthly repayments on a mortgage of (i) £30 000 (ii) £85 000?

(b) If the monthly repayments are £726 how much is borrowed?

2 The repayments on a 30-year mortgage of £50 000 are calculated at £11.25 per calendar month for each £1000 borrowed. What amount must be paid (a) per month (b) per year (c) over the full 30-year term?

3 Yearsley Building Society offers Tom Jones a 90% mortgage on a bungalow whose purchase price is £80 000.

(a) How much can he borrow?

(b) How much must he pay himself?

(c) The repayments are £12.25 per month per £1000 borrowed for 25 years. Find (i) his monthly repayments (ii) the total repayments over the 25 years.

4 A couple decide to buy a house priced £54 000. A building society is prepared to advance 80% of the purchase price. The monthly repayments are 95p per £100 borrowed for 20 years.

(a) What is the amount borrowed?

(b) What is the total cost of the house?

Life assurance

In the previous two chapters we saw that we can pay premiums to cover the cost of events that may or may not happen. We insure against an accident in the car or our house going on fire. In this section we look at assurance policies. An assurance policy is an agreement between an assurance company and an individual. For an agreed sum, paid at regular intervals (the premium), the company agrees to pay a lump sum when an event that must happen occurs, for example, when a person reaches the age of 60 or on the death of the person, whichever happens first. The table shows the yearly premium for men and women between 21 years and 50 years for each £100 assured on death.

The first premium is found from the table by choosing the premium corresponding to a person's age next birthday.

From the table, the yearly premium for a woman aged 34 now, i.e. who will be 35 on her next birthday, who is assured for £20 000 is

$$\frac{£20\,000}{£100} \times £6.20 = 200 \times £6.20 = £1240$$

A sum of £20 000 will be paid at death whether the premium has been paid for one year (total payments £1178) or 40 years (total payments £47 120).

Age	Premium		Age	Premium	
	Man £	Woman £		Man £	Woman £
21	5.25	5.05	36	6.75	6.39
22	5.30	5.07	37	6.85	6.50
23	5.35	5.10	38	6.90	6.62
24	5.40	5.15	39	7.06	6.78
25	5.45	5.20	40	7.22	6.94
26	5.51	5.26	41	7.40	7.12
27	5.57	5.32	42	7.58	7.30
28	5.63	5.40	43	7.80	7.54
29	5.71	5.48	44	8.06	7.80
30	5.81	5.58	45	8.37	8.10
31	5.93	5.70	46	8.78	8.50
32	6.15	5.82	47	9.28	9.00
33	6.27	5.94	48	9.50	9.60
34	6.39	6.06	49	10.62	10.30
35	6.53	6.20	50	11.45	11.10

EXERCISE 11d

QUESTION

Tim Reynold's life is assured for £45 000. Tim is 28.

(a) How much is the yearly premium?

(b) How much will the assurance company pay out if Tim dies at the age of 44?

(c) Tim lives until he is 62 and the yearly premium is due on his birthday.
(i) How much will have been paid in premiums?
(ii) How much more (or less) are the premiums paid than the sum assured?

ANSWER

(a) Tim is 29 next birthday, so the premium is £5.71 for each £100 assured.

The yearly premium is

$$\frac{£45\,000}{£100} \times £5.71 = £450 \times £5.71 = £2569.50$$

(b) They will pay £45 000 at whatever age he dies.

(c) The premiums are due each year on his birthday. From 29 to 62 he will have had 34 birthdays.
(i) Total premiums paid is 34 × £2569.50 = £87 363
(ii) The premiums exceed the sum assured by £87 363 − £45 000 = £42 363
(Things are not quite as bad as they look, since generous tax allowances are given on the premiums paid!)

Use the table in the text to answer the questions in this exercise.

1 What is the premium for each £100 assured for
(a) a man 46 next birthday
(b) a woman 45 next birthday?

2 What is the premium for each £100 assured for
(a) a woman aged 37 (b) a man aged 46?

3 A husband and wife are both 44 next birthday. Each of them wants to take out an assurance policy for £100 000. How much a year will these policies cost them altogether?

4

Name	Age	Sum assured
Joan Cartwright	38	£20 000
George Helman	44	60 000
Damon Southgate	25	75 000
Penny Gates	31	150 000

Use the details given in the table to find the annual premium due on a life assurance policy for the four people named.

Invoices

An invoice is a form that shows details of the goods or services supplied to a customer. It shows such details as the name and address of the customer and of the supplier, the quantity of goods ordered, the trade price, the recommended selling price, the rate of VAT due, and so on.

An example of an invoice is given below.

BUCKINGHAM FASHIONS
34 Pendine Road
Leicester LE4 3PQ

INVOICE No. 12345

Invoice to	Delivery address (if different)
Baxter & Co 15 Sutton Street London WC1A 4XJ	Baxters 456 High Street Quinton Birmingham B32 1LH

Your order No.	Date sent	Invoice date
54436	5/8/9–	7/8/9–

Product code	Description	Qty	Unit cost £	Gross cost £
X8-3345	Kays wordmaster	6	25.50	153.00
X7-5463	Pears pocket planner	4	15.90	63.60
			Sub-total	216.60
			Add VAT at $17\frac{1}{2}\%$	37.90
			Total	254.50

Terms:
1. If you receive faulty or damaged goods you must notify us immediately in writing.
2. Discount of 5% for payment within 10 days, otherwise strictly net.

EXERCISE 11e

In questions 1 and 2 copy and complete the invoice.

1

INVOICE

Pinhoe Stationery
123 Cathedral Way
Exeter

To: Hartleys
63 High Street
Frome
Somerset

Yr order No.	Date sent	Invoice date	Invoice No.

Quantity	Description	Unit price £	Amount £
30	Jiffy bags 10" × 8"	0.28	8.40
40	Lever arch files	2.10	
200	Suspension files	0.42	
55	Gusset files	1.99	
		Subtotal	
		Add VAT at $17\frac{1}{2}$%	
		Total	

2

INVOICE

Teleprince Office Supplies
34 Vauxhall Road
London

Customer	Delivery address
D K Evans Plastics	47a Leicester Road Poolbury Avon

Yr order No.	Date sent	Invoice date	Invoice No.

Quantity	Catalogue Code	Description	Unit price £	Amount £
45	037-63728	Diskette mailers	0.32	
3	037-54663	Mouse pads	2.99	
4	038-33225	Diskette storage boxes	5.99	
5 boxes	037-63744	$3\frac{1}{2}''$ diskettes	6.99	
			Gross total	
			Less discount at 10%	
			Subtotal	
			Add VAT at 20%	
			Total	

3 Make out to yourself an invoice from A. R. Goodman, The Computer Centre, 13 Leeds Road, Peterstow, for the following goods which are quoted at catalogue prices excluding VAT: 15 ELQ computer ribbons at £2.99 each, 6 boxes of PQ diskettes at £7.99 a box, 3 surge adaptors at £9.75 each and 4 boxes of continuous printer labels at £19.95 a box. Assume that the rate of VAT is $17\frac{1}{2}$%.

4 Rewrite the invoice for question 3 if a discount of 5% is allowed for orders over £100. Note that discounts are calculated before VAT is added.

Multiple-choice questions 11

In this exercise several alternative answers are given. Write down the letter that corresponds to the correct answer.

1 To buy a new camera on credit terms, Ainsley must put down a deposit of £36.42 and make 24 monthly payments of £5.74. The total cost of the camera is

A £101.34 **B** £105.30
C £137.76 **D** £174.18

2 A building society offers a 30 year mortgage for monthly repayments of £10.88 per £1000 borrowed. The total repayment, correct to the nearest £1000, on a mortgage of £75 000 is

A £293 800 **B** £293 000
C £294 000 **D** £293 760

3 The monthly cost per £100 assured, of a life policy for a person aged 33 is £6.27 for a man and £5.94 for a woman. Ken and Eve O'Callaghan, both aged 33, take out life policies for £55 000. The amount by which the monthly premium on Ken's policy is more than the premium on Eve's policy is

A £18.15 **B** £181.50
C £191.50 **D** £205.10

4 Jane Herian has a balance of £369.42 in the building society. She pays in two cheques, one for £76.59 and another for £13.83, and withdraws £100 in cash. Her balance after these transactions is

A £379 **B** £359.84 **C** £559.84 **D** £346.01

Self-assessment test 11

1 Copy and complete this invoice

INVOICE

Britac Office Supplies
27 Threadstone Road
Manchester

Customer	Delivery address
P L Lloyd Printers	154 Southland Road Rosebury West Midlands

Yr order no.	Date sent	Invoice date	Invoice no.

Quantity	Catalogue Code	Description	Unit price £	Amount £
3	P38-54628	2-hole punches	14.99	
2	P38-67363	Rotary trimmers	21.99	
5 packs	P40-42125	Small core tape	2.46	
5 packs	P40-77844	Large core tape	4.79	
			Gross total	
			Less discount at 10%	
			Subtotal	
			Add VAT at $17\frac{1}{2}$%	
			Total	

2 A building society offers a 25 year mortgage for monthly repayments of £12.32 per £1000 borrowed. (a) What are the monthly repayments on a mortgage of £74 000? (b) What sum has been borrowed if the monthly repayments are £591.36?

3 A secondhand motorcycle is offered for sale at £1785. If bought on credit the terms are: a deposit of £596 plus 36 monthly repayments of £46.44. Find (a) the total credit price (b) how much more (or less) it costs to buy the motorcycle on credit rather than to pay cash.

4 Use the bank statement on pages 110 and 111 to answer the following questions. (a) How much was in the account on 14 August? (b) How much was paid (i) into the account , (ii) out of the account, between 9 August and 9 September?

CHAPTER 12

Basic geometry

Parts of a revolution

In one hour the minute hand of a clock makes one complete turn.

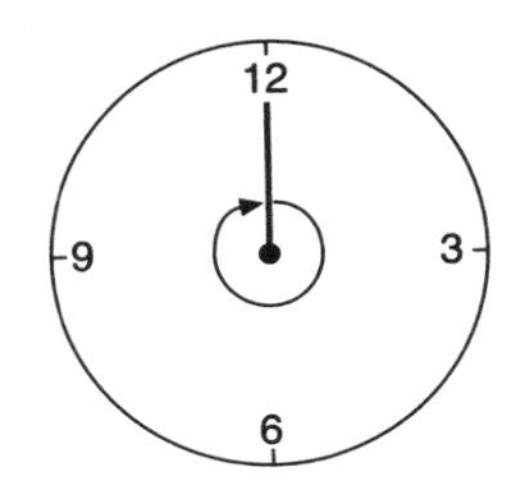

If one complete turn, or revolution, is divided into 360 parts, each part is called a degree. 360 degrees is written 360°.

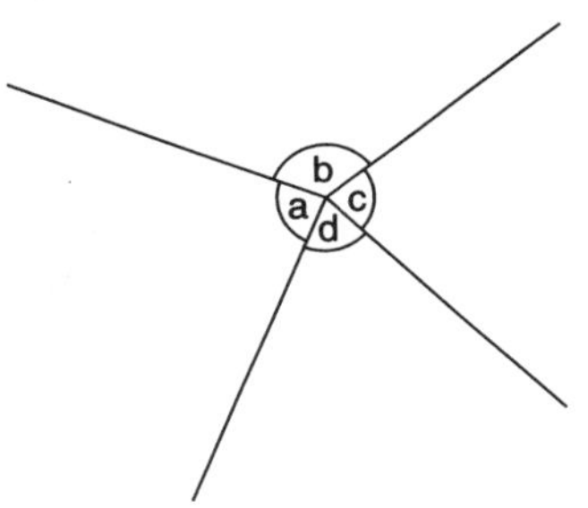

The sum of all the angles round a point is 360°:

$a + b + c + d = 360°$

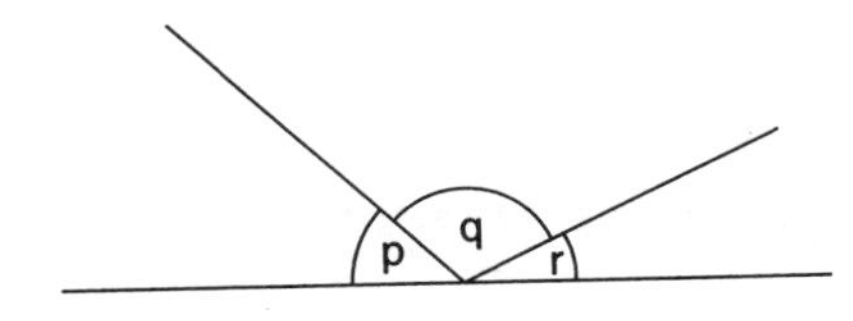

Half a turn is 180°.
The angles on one side of a straight line total 180°:

$p + q + r = 180°$

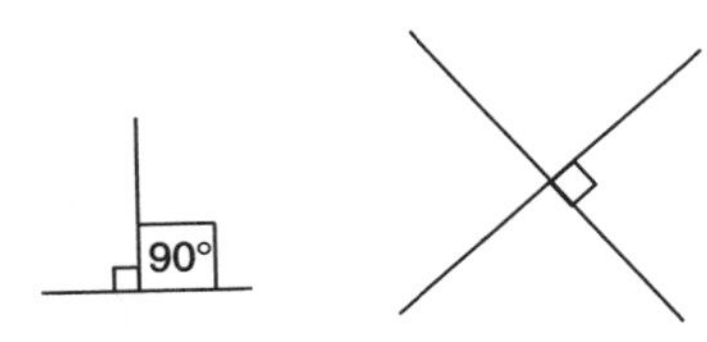

A quarter of a turn is 90°. It is called a right angle and is marked with the symbol ∟

EXERCISE 12a

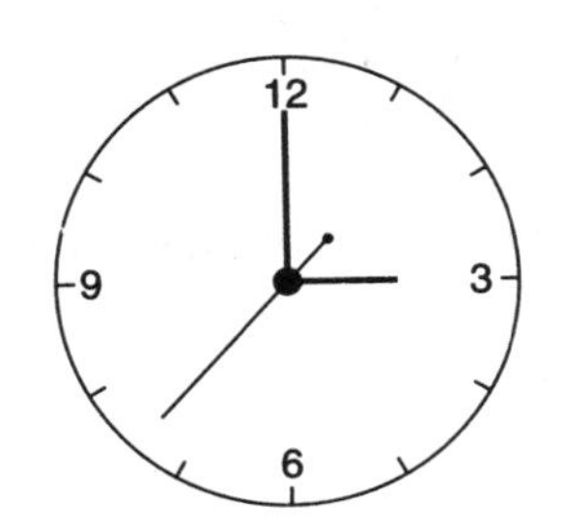

1 Give the fraction of a revolution that the *minute* hand of a clock turns through in

(a) $\frac{1}{2}$ hour (b) $\frac{1}{4}$ hour (c) $\frac{3}{4}$ hour
(d) 5 minutes (e) 20 minutes

2 State the number of degrees that the *minute* hand turns through in

(a) $\frac{1}{2}$ hour (b) $\frac{1}{4}$ hour (c) $\frac{3}{4}$ hour
(d) 5 minutes (e) 20 minutes

3 Find the fraction of a revolution represented by
(a) 90° (b) 180° (c) 270°
(d) 60° (e) 240°

4 Give the fraction of a revolution that the *hour* hand turns though in

(a) 6 hours (b) 9 hours (c) 1 hour
(d) 30 minutes (e) 5 minutes

5 State the fraction of a revolution that the *seconds* hand of a clock turns through in

(a) 30 seconds (b) 5 seconds
(c) 45 seconds (d) 2 minutes

6 Find how many degrees the *hour* hand of a clock turns through between

(a) 1 p.m. and 6 p.m. (b) 6 p.m. and 1 a.m.

7 Find how many degrees the *hour* hand of a clock turns through between

(a) 9 a.m. and 4 p.m. (b) 3 a.m. and noon
(c) 6 a.m. and 6 p.m.

Types of angles

An angle measures the amount of turn. An angle does not depend on the lengths of the lines that form it.

An angle less than 90° is called an **acute** angle.

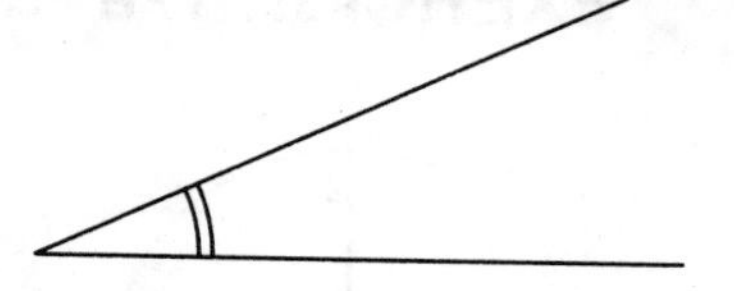

An angle bigger than 90° but less than 180° is called an **obtuse** angle.

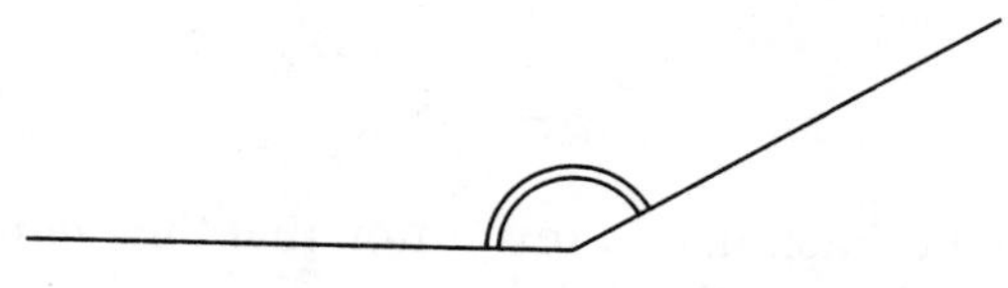

An angle bigger than 180° is called a **reflex** angle.

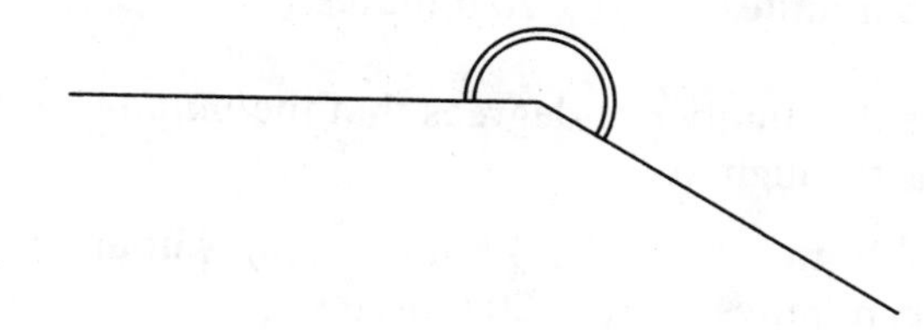

Look at these three angles:

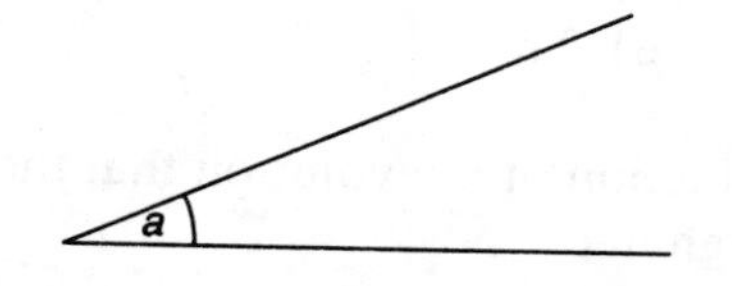

Angle a is acute – it is less than 90°. It is about 30°. About 3 angles this size would make a right angle.

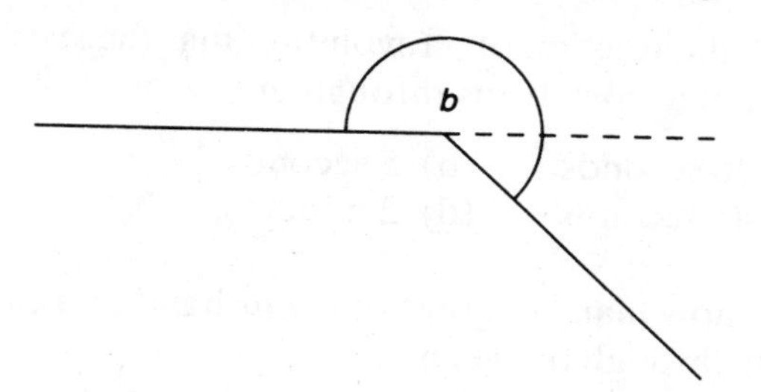

Angle b is bigger than 180° i.e. it is reflex. It is about 180° + 30°, i.e. it is about 210°.

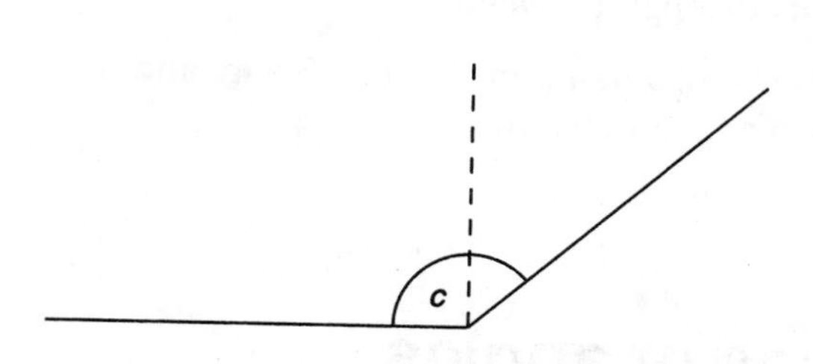

Angle c is between 90° and 180°, i.e. it is obtuse. It is about 90° + 45°, i.e. it is about 135°.

EXERCISE 12b

Is each of the following angles acute, obtuse or reflex? In each case guess the size of the angle.

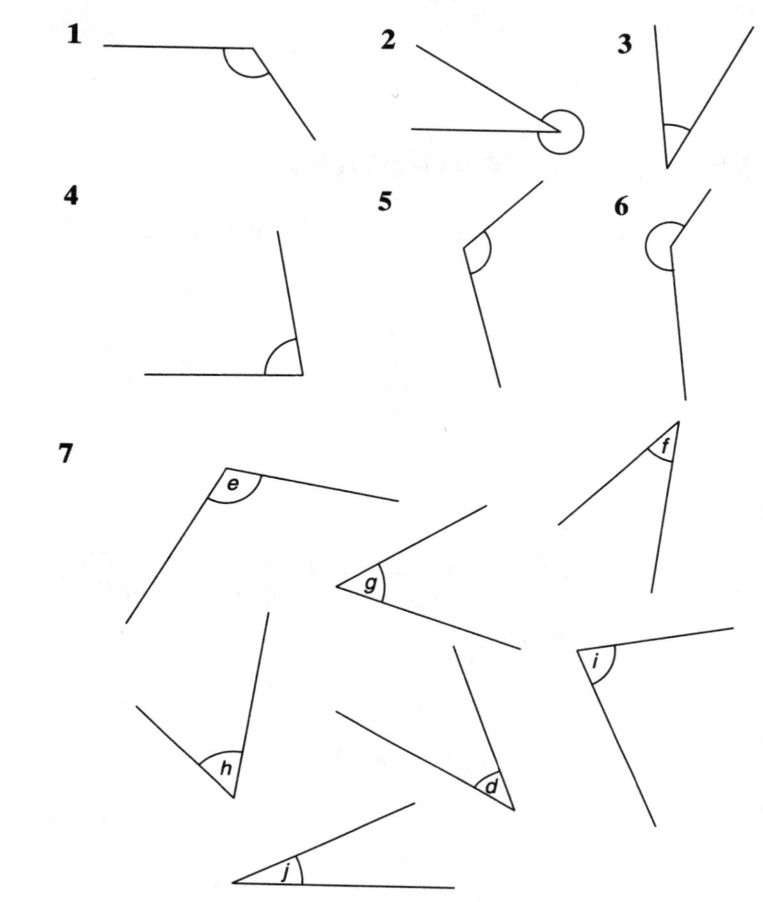

Without measuring decide which angles are

(a) bigger than d (b) smaller than d (c) equal to d.

Describing angles

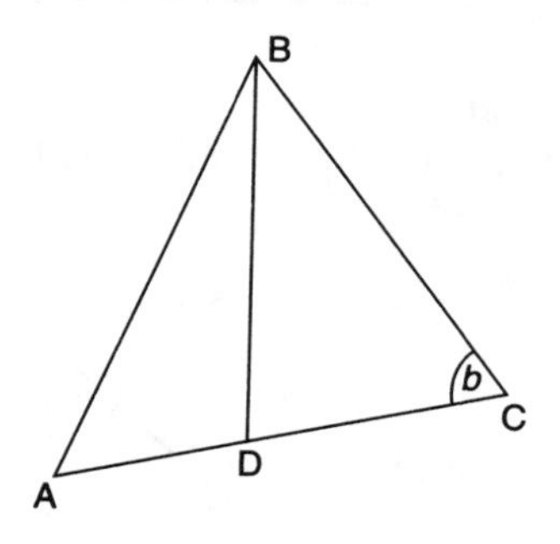

This shape contains several angles. We can refer to the angle at the corner A, i.e. the angle BAD, by writing

$\angle$BAD or B$\hat{A}$D or, since there is only one angle at A, by $\hat{A}$. Sometimes we put a small letter within the arms of the angle. In this shape B$\hat{C}$D is denoted by b.

At B we must use three letters to describe an angle, i.e. A$\hat{B}$D or A$\hat{B}$C or D$\hat{B}$C, depending on which one we want. Alternatively we could mark each angle with a small letter.

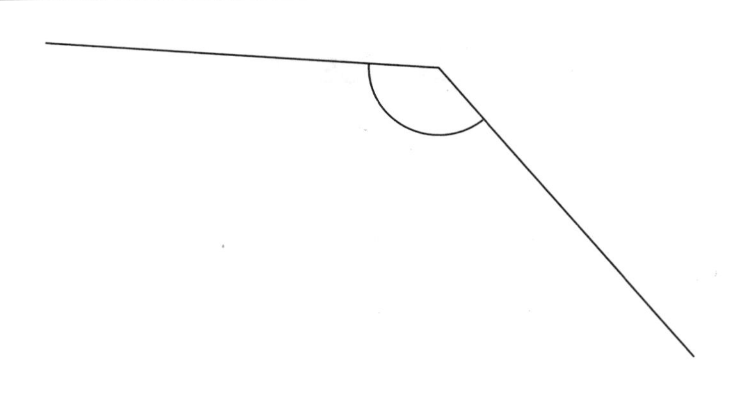

Using a protractor

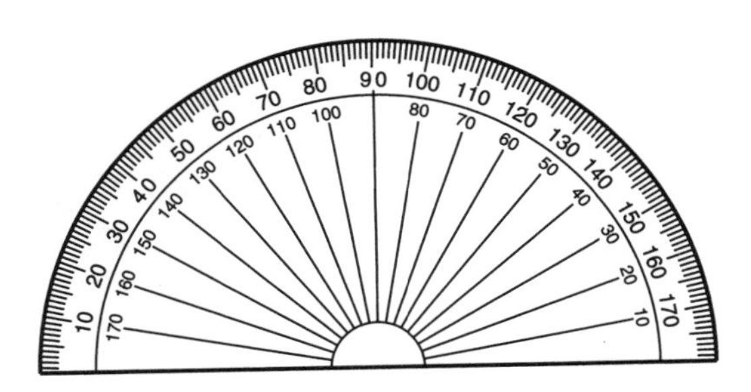

To measure angles we use a protractor. One is shown in the sketch. To measure an angle you need to follow these steps:

1. Guess the size of the angle – in particular ask yourself the question: is it less than 90° (i.e. is it acute), between 90° and 180° (i.e. obtuse) or is it bigger than 180° (i.e. is it reflex)?
2. If necessary extend the lines that form the angle so that they will reach the scale on the protractor.
3. Put the centre of the protractor on the point of the angle and lie the base line along one of the arms that make the angle.
4. **Starting from 0** count along the scale until you come to the other arm of the angle.
5. Write down the value you get. Does it make sense when compared with your guess? If not, start again from the beginning.

Now try out these steps on the two angles drawn below.

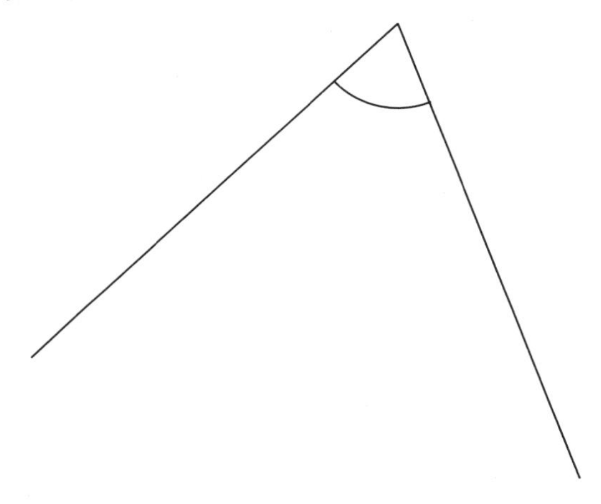

You should find that the size of the smaller angle is 68° and the size of the larger angle is 134°.

For a reflex angle measure the angle that makes up the full turn and take it away from 360°.

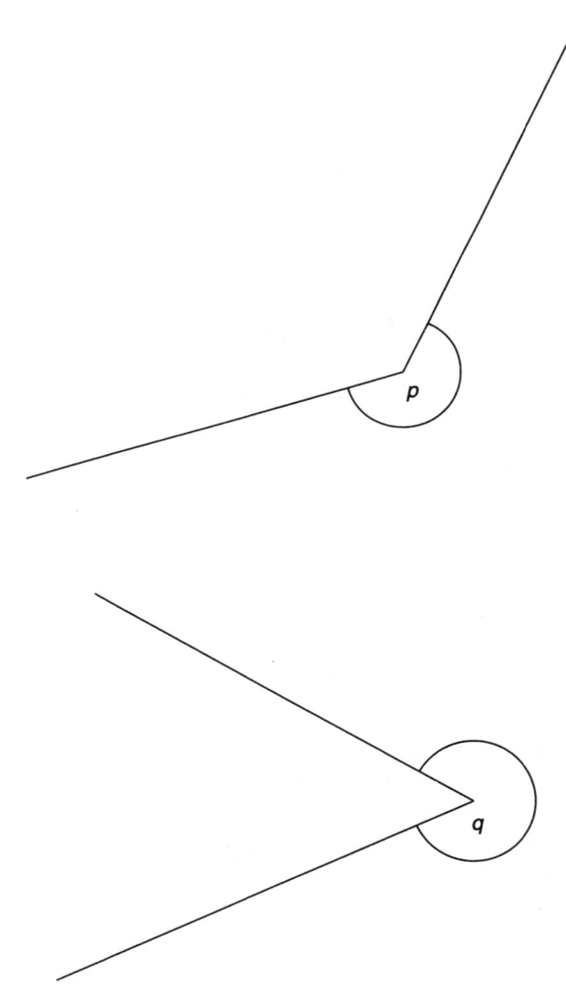

The unmarked angle is 132°, so $p = 360° - 132°$.
$= 228°$

The unmarked angle is 53°, so $q = 360° - 53°$
$= 307°$

EXERCISE 12c

Measure the following angles.

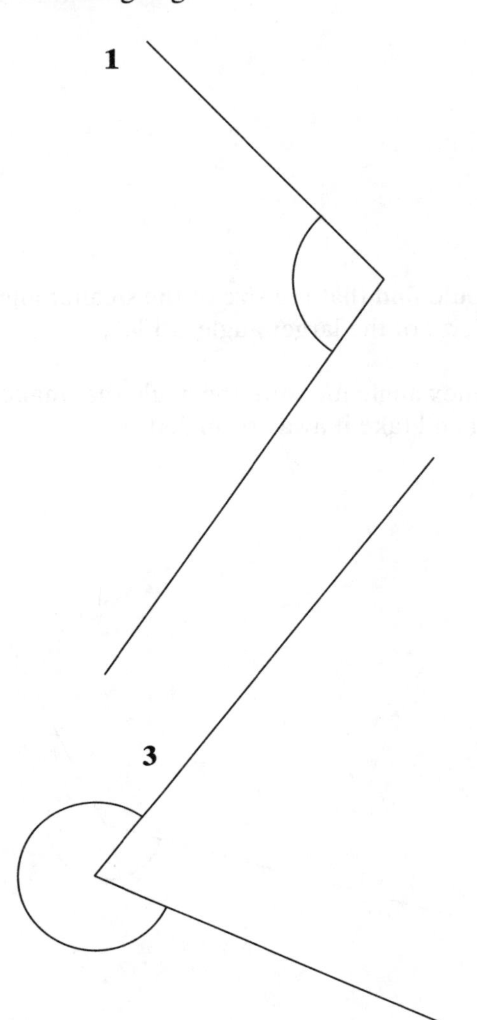

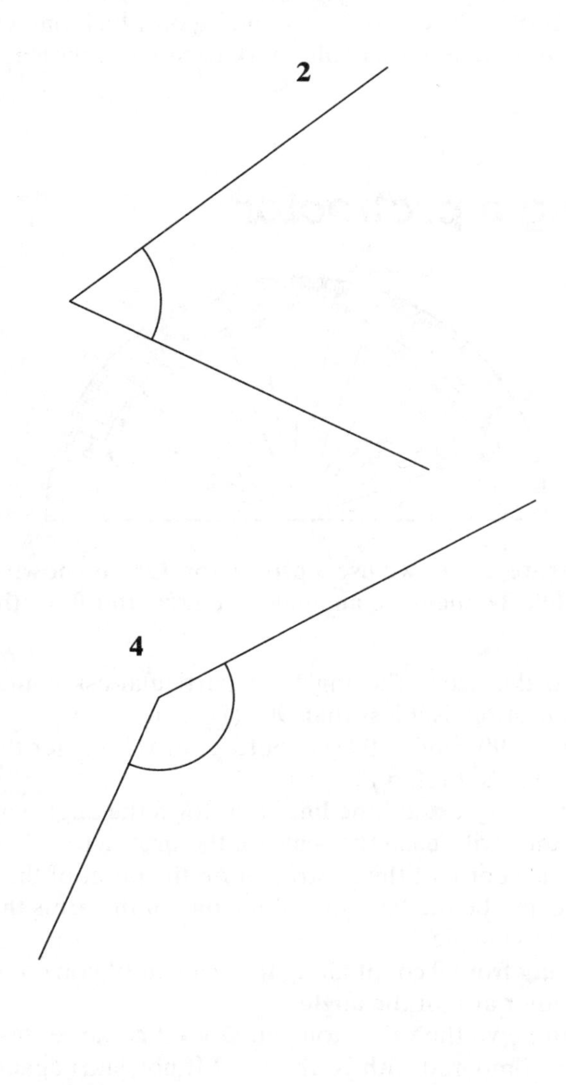

Perpendicular lines

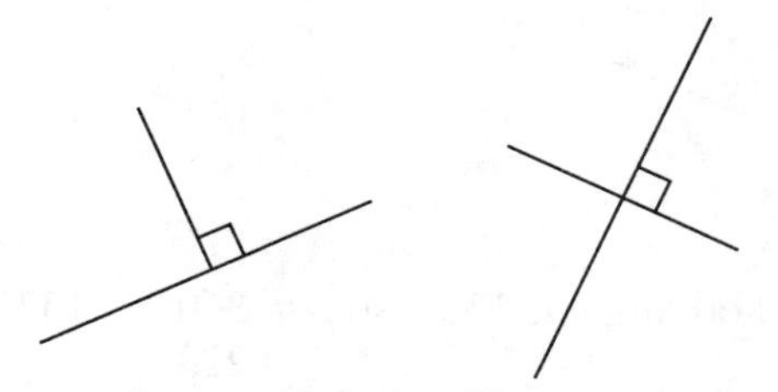

'Perpendicular' means 'at right angles'. If two lines are perpendicular they are at right angles to each other.

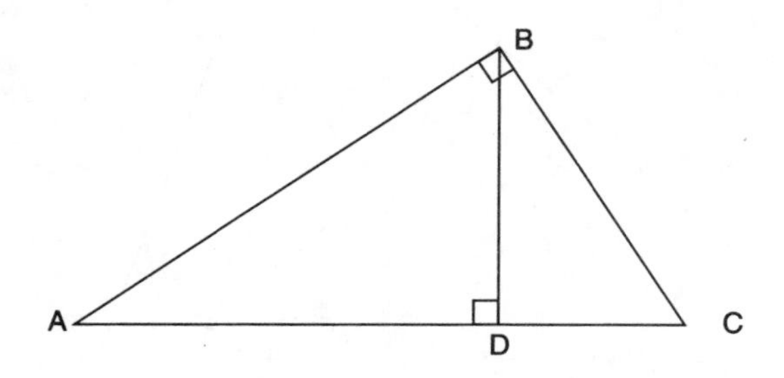

In the diagram BD is perpendicular to AC and AB is perpendicular to BC.

Parallel lines

Parallel lines go in the same direction. Parallel lines are often marked by arrows.

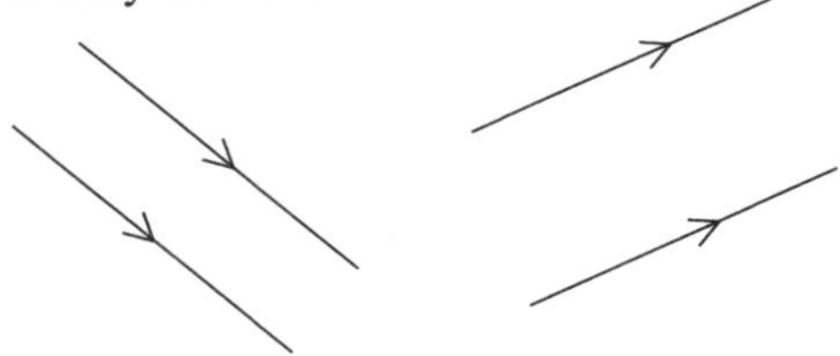

EXERCISE 12d

The sketch shows the front of a bungalow. Each point where two lines meet is marked by a capital letter. We can refer to lines using capital letters. For example, the line CD is the ridge of the roof.

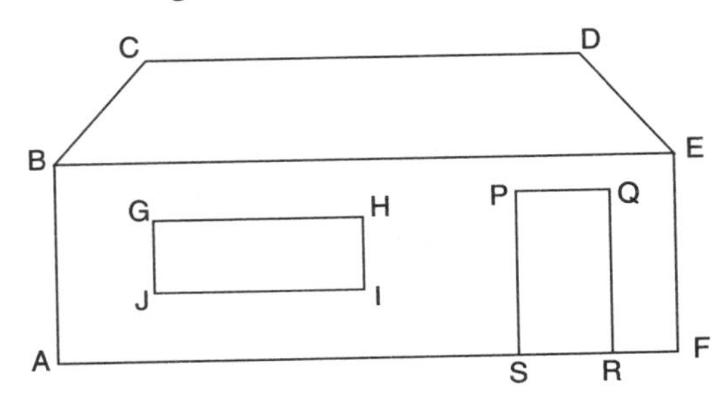

1 Name three lines that are parallel to CD.

2 Name three lines that are perpendicular to BE.

3 Name a line that is parallel to QR but shorter than it.

4 Name a line that is parallel to PS but longer than it.

5 Name a line that is not parallel to BE.

6 Name a line that is neither parallel nor perpendicular to any other line on the sketch.

Angle facts

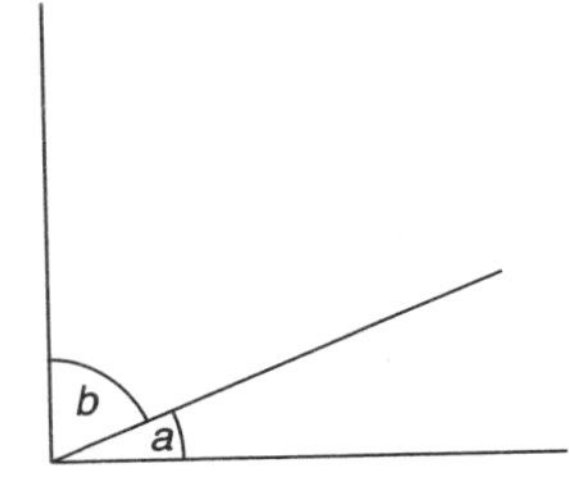

Angles that add up to $90°$ are *complementary angles*:

$a + b = 90°$;
a is the complement of b
and b is the complement of a

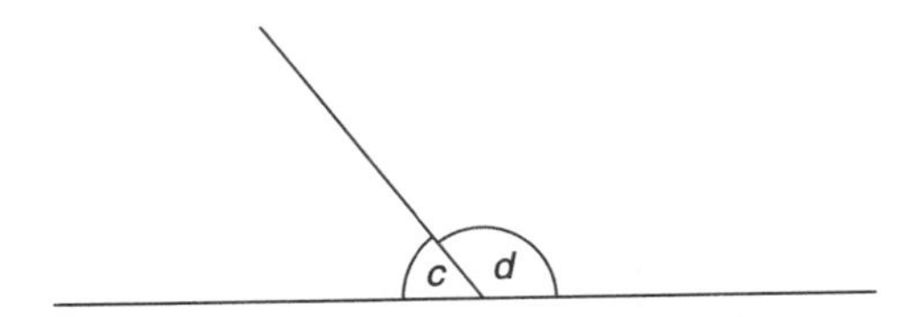

Angles that add up to give $180°$ are *supplementary angles*:

$c + d = 180°$;
c is the supplement of d
and d is the supplement of c

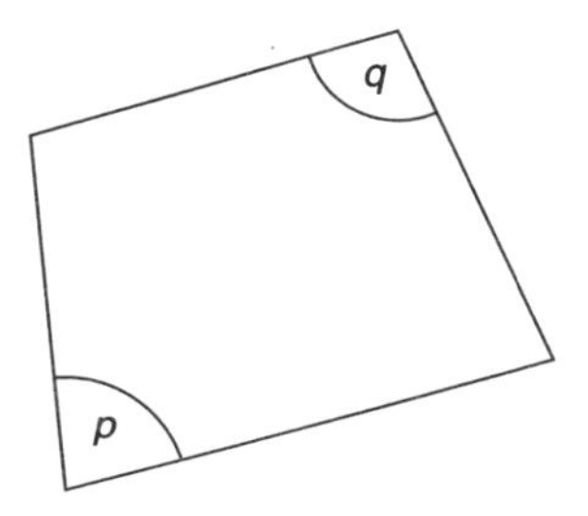

Similarly $p + q = 180°$, so p is the supplement of q and q is the supplement of p.

Vertically opposite angles are equal:

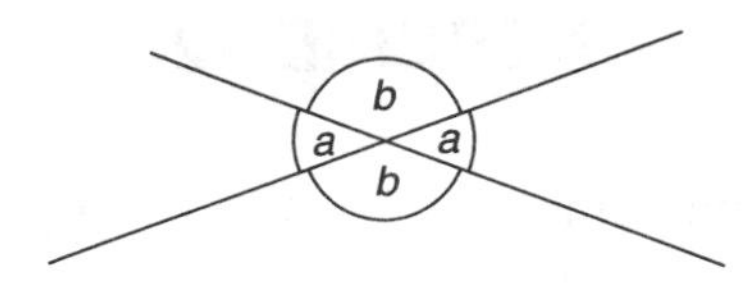

Angles and parallel lines

When a straight line cuts two parallel lines, various angles are formed.

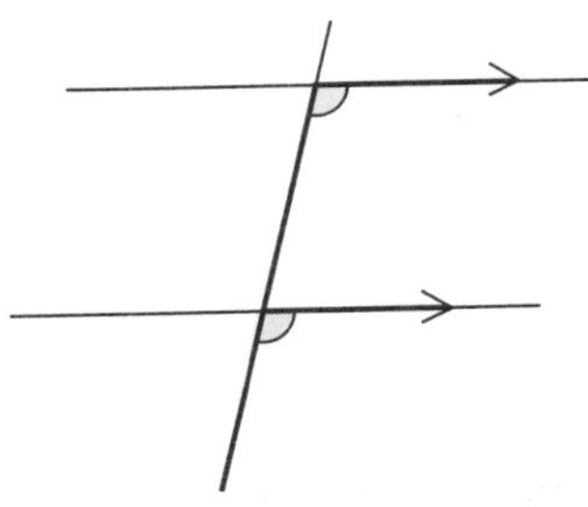

Corresponding angles are equal.
(Look for the letter F.)

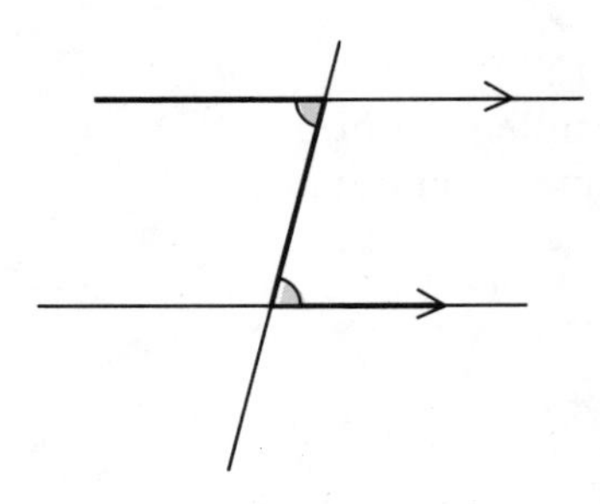

Alternate angles are equal.
(Look for the letter Z.)

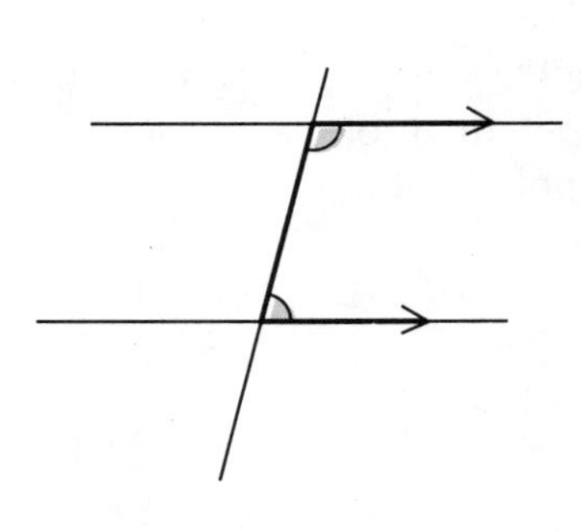

Interior angles add up to 180°.
(Look for the letter U.)

EXERCISE 12e

1 Find the complement of (a) 60° (b) 20° (c) 37° (d) 72° (e) 45°.

2 Find the supplement of (a) 130° (b) 45° (c) 93° (d) 176° (e) 90°.

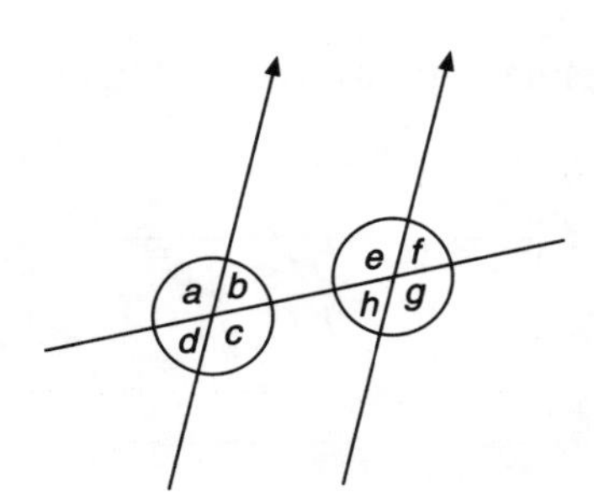

3 Use this diagram to pick out two pairs of (a) vertically opposite angles (b) corresponding angles (c) alternate angles (d) interior angles.

In the remaining questions find the size of each marked angle.

4

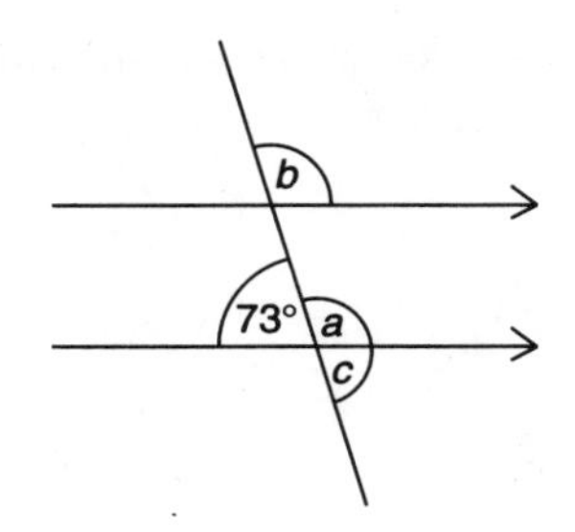

5

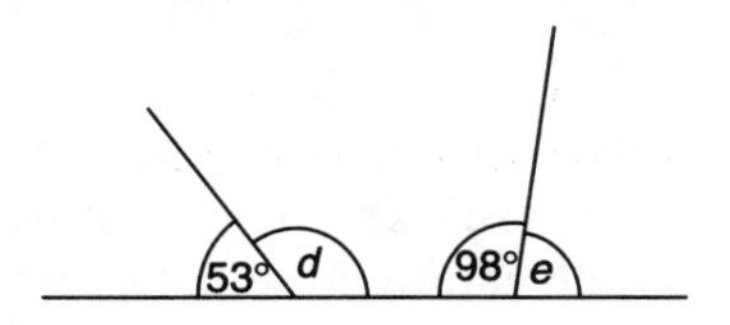

6

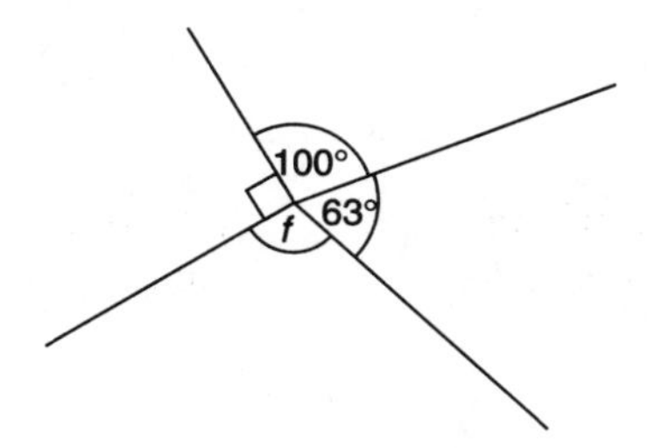

7

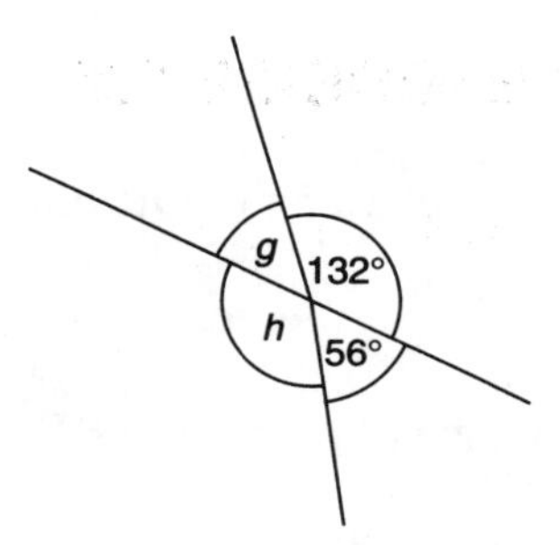

8

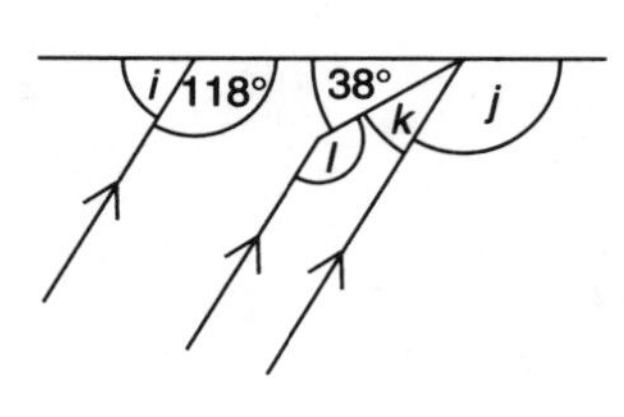

9

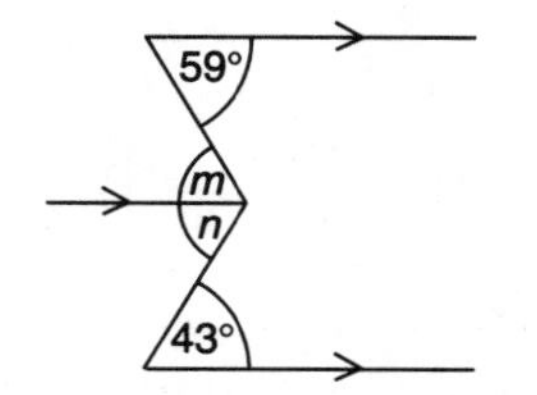

Triangles

A triangle has three sides and three angles.

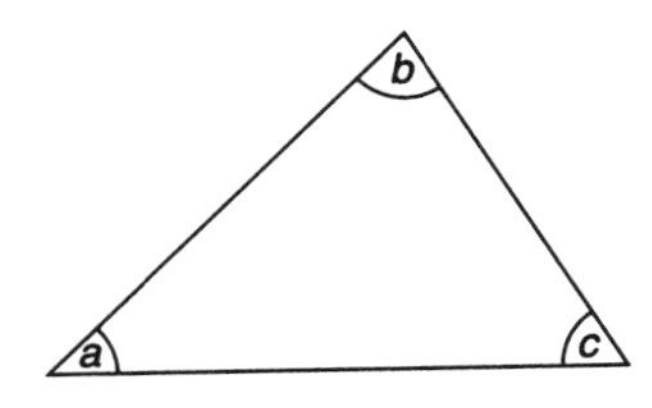

The sum of its angles is always 180°:

$a + b + c = 180°$

Depending on the size of the largest angle in the triangle we give the triangle a different name.

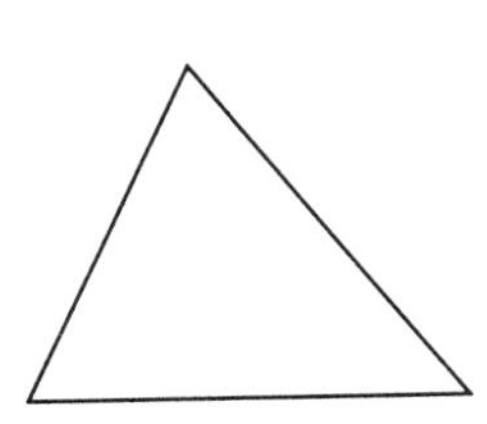

An acute-angled triangle.
The largest angle is less .
than 90°

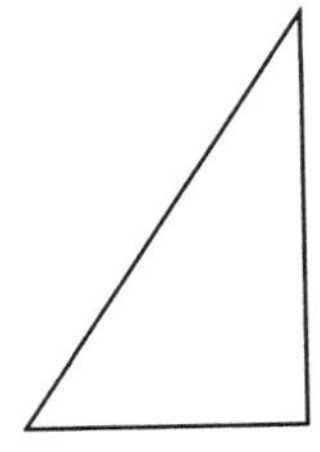

A right-angled triangle.
The largest angle is 90°.

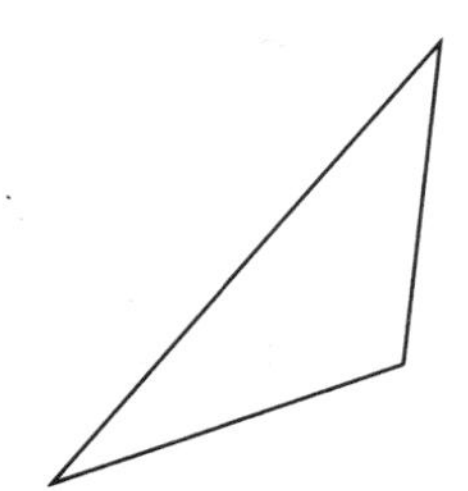

An obtuse-angled triangle.
The largest angle is more than 90°.

Special triangles

Some triangles have special names.
In an *equilateral* triangle all three sides are the same length and all the angles are 60°.

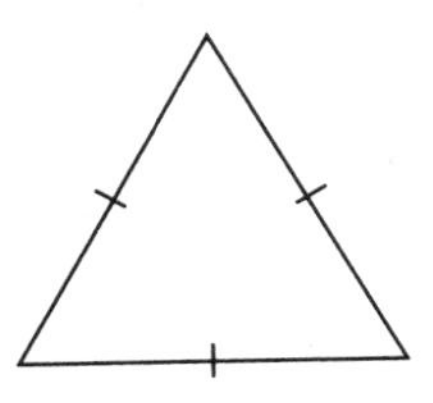

If a triangle has two equal sides it is called an *isosceles* triangle.

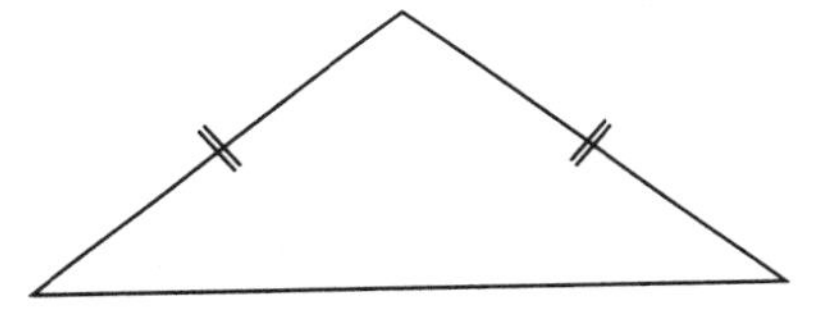

EXERCISE 12f

Find the angles marked with letters.

1

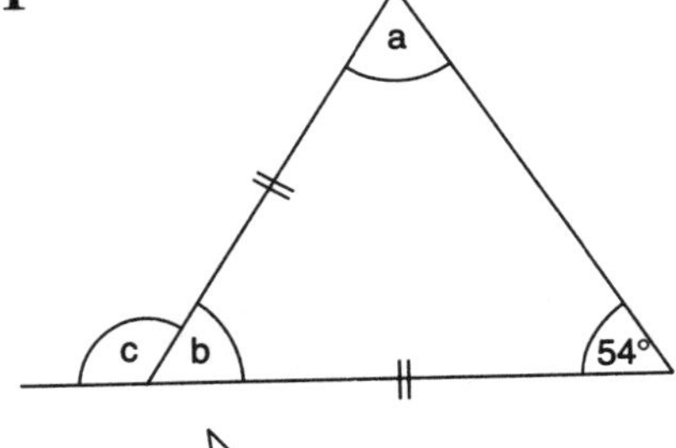

2

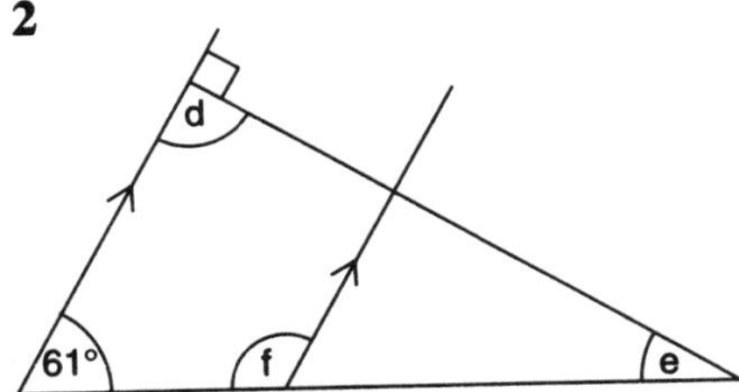

3

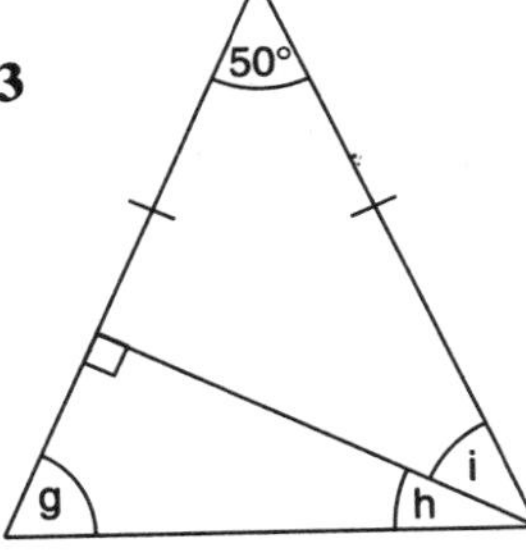

4

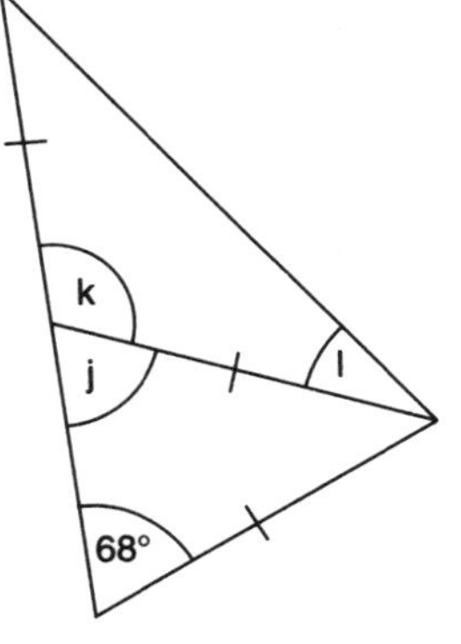

5

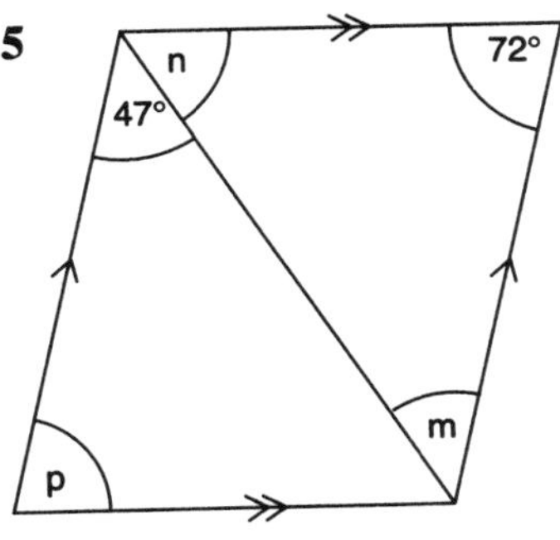

6

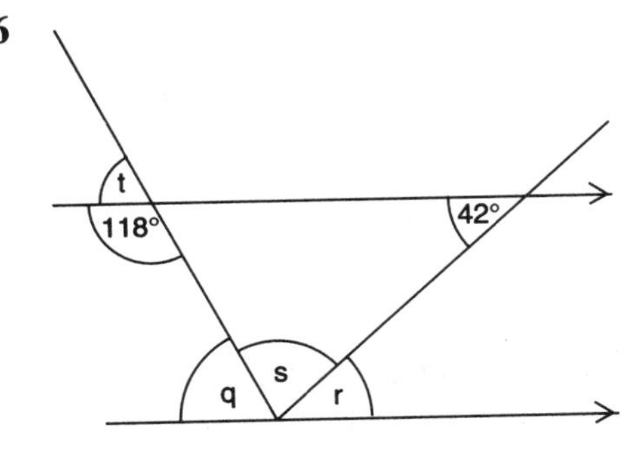

7

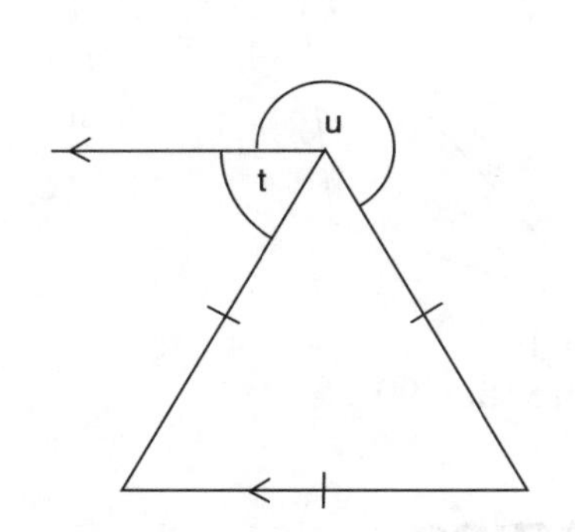

8

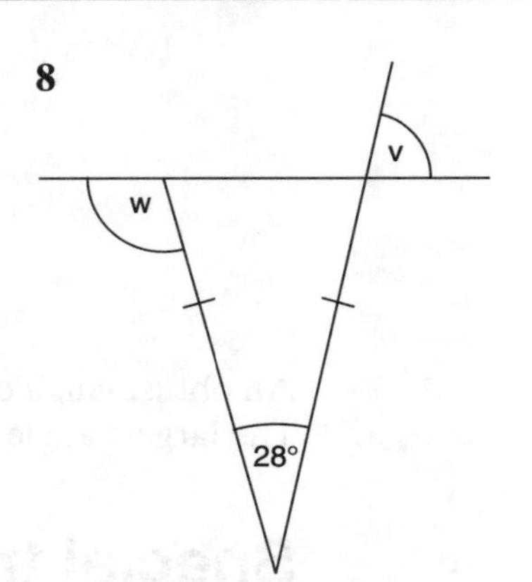

9

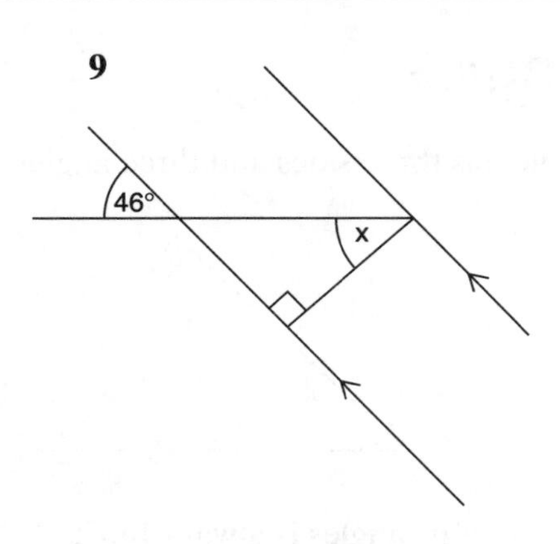

Drawing accurate triangles

A: Given three sides

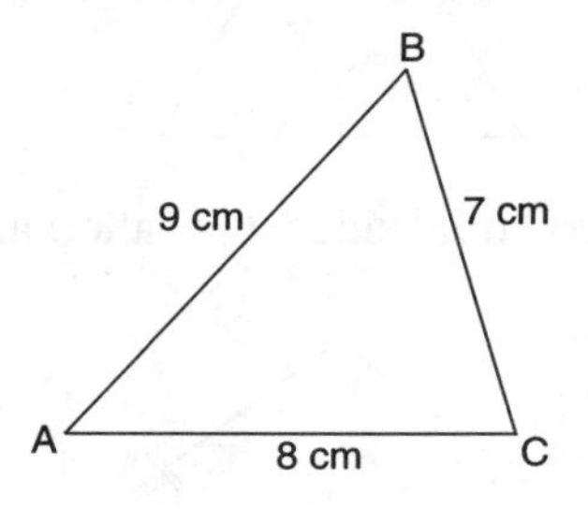

To draw this triangle, draw AC first.

Next set your compasses to 9 cm and, with the point on A, draw an arc as shown.

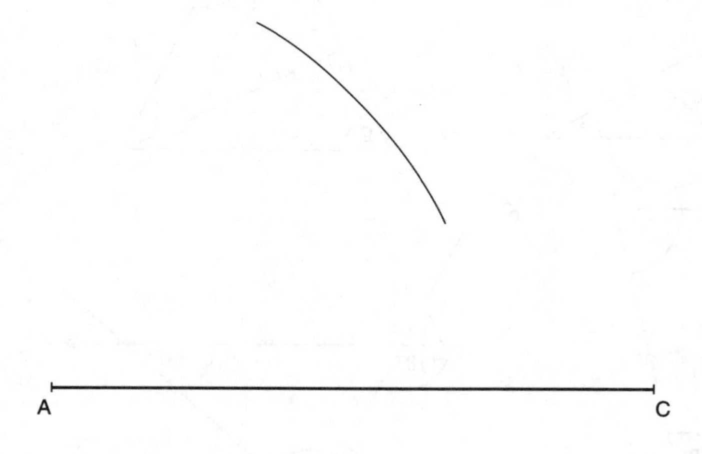

Then set your compasses to 7 cm and, with the point on C, draw an arc to cross the first arc. Where the arcs cross gives the position of B.

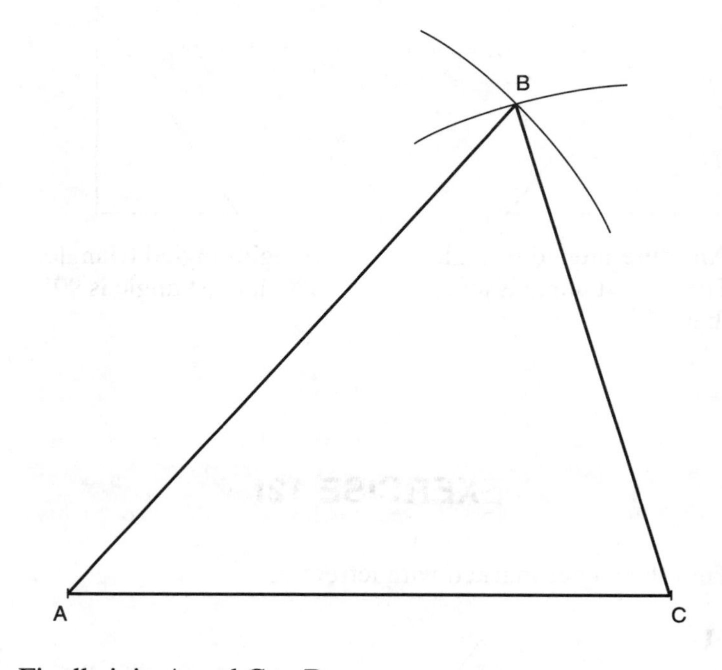

Finally join A and C to B.

B: Given two sides and the angle between them

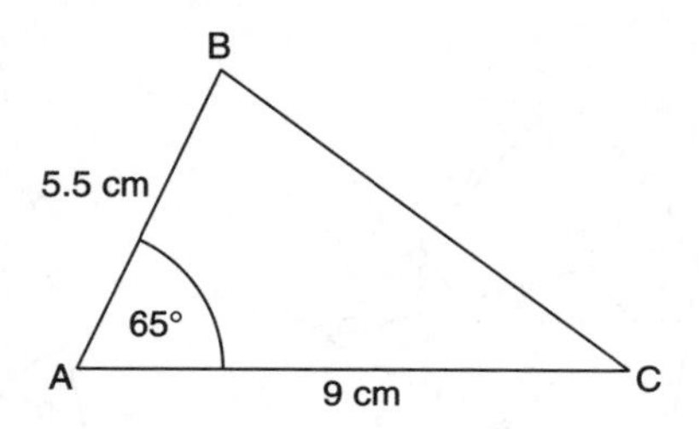

To draw this triangle, draw AC first.

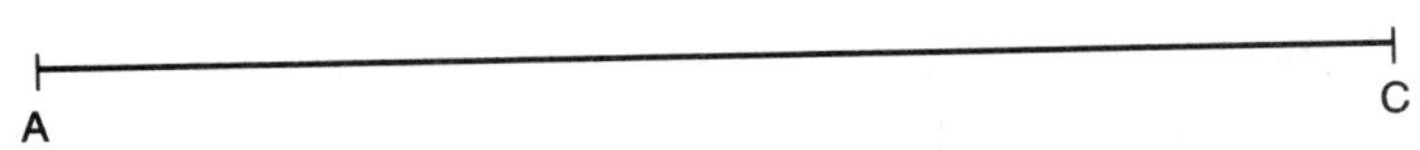

Then use a protractor to make an angle of 65° at A.

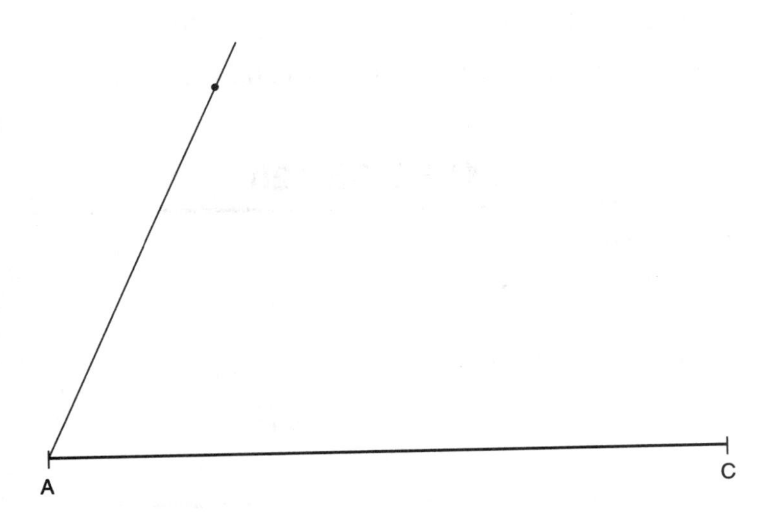

Next measure AB = 5.5 cm to give the position of B.

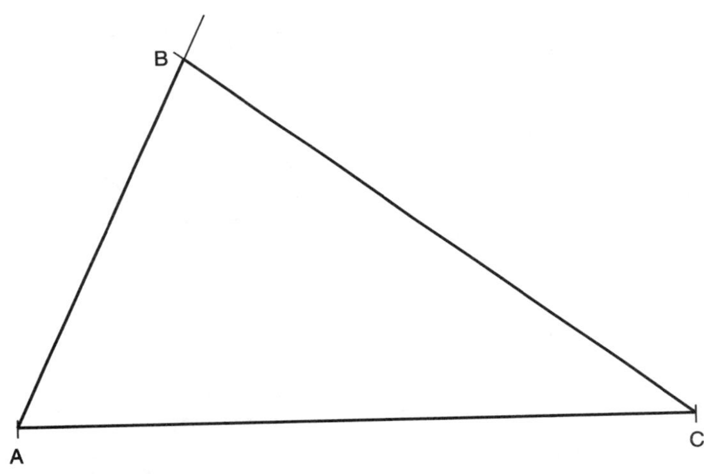

Finally join BC.

C: Given one side and two angles

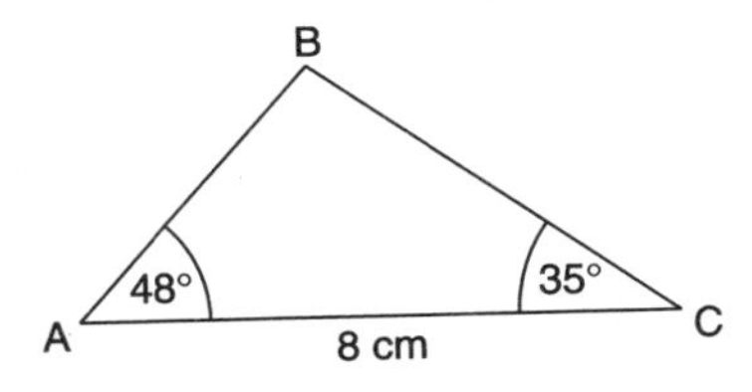

To draw this triangle, draw AC first.

Next, use a protractor to draw an angle of 48° at A and one of 35° at C.

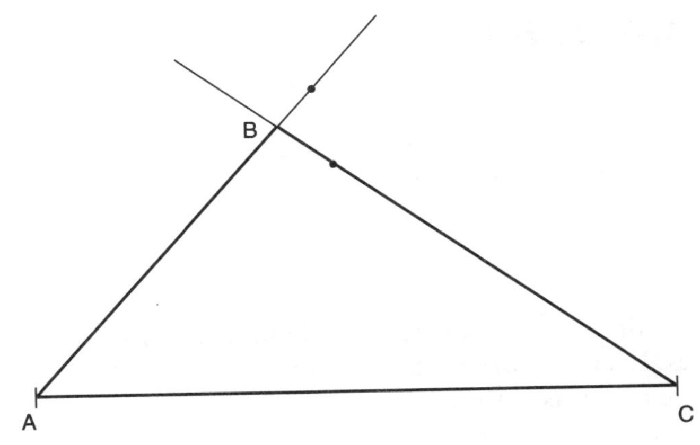

The point where the two arms cross gives the position of B.
(*Note:* If the angle at B had been given instead of the angle at C then the angle at C could have been found from the fact that the sum of the three angles of a triangle is 180°.)

EXERCISE 12g

Make accurate drawings of the following triangles.

1

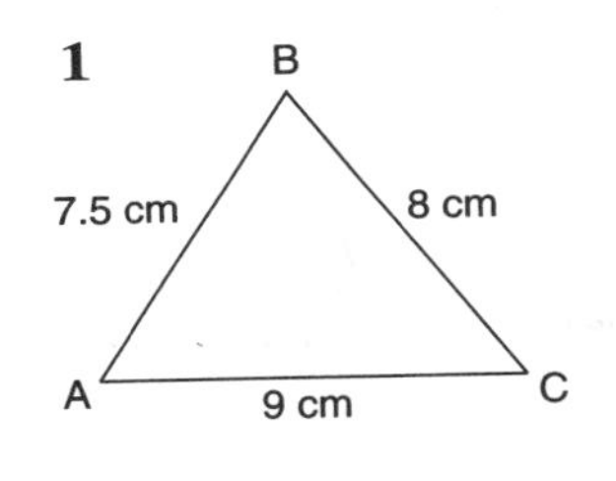

2

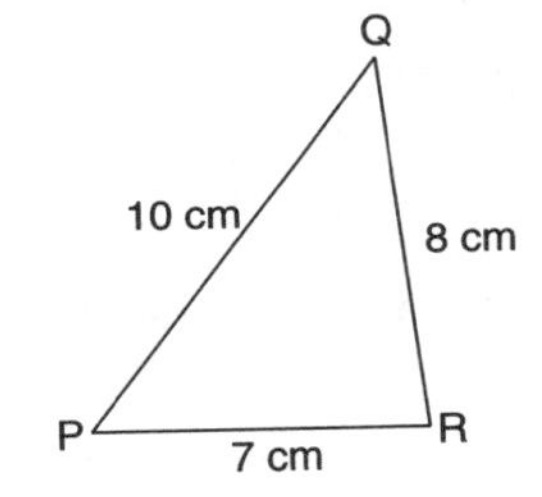

3

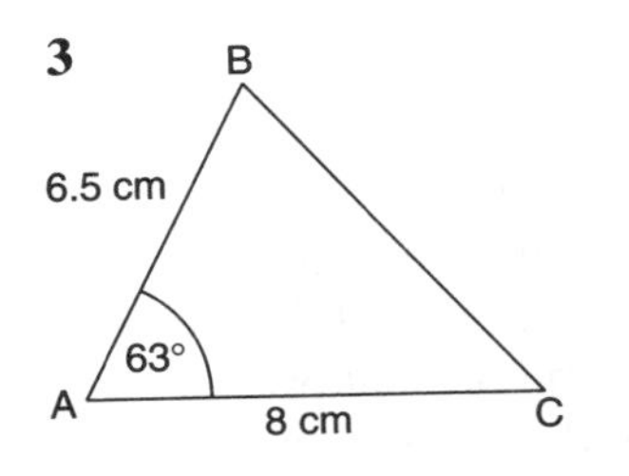

4

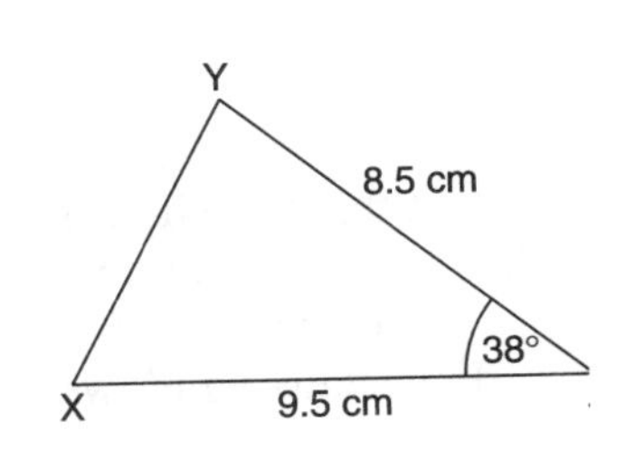

5

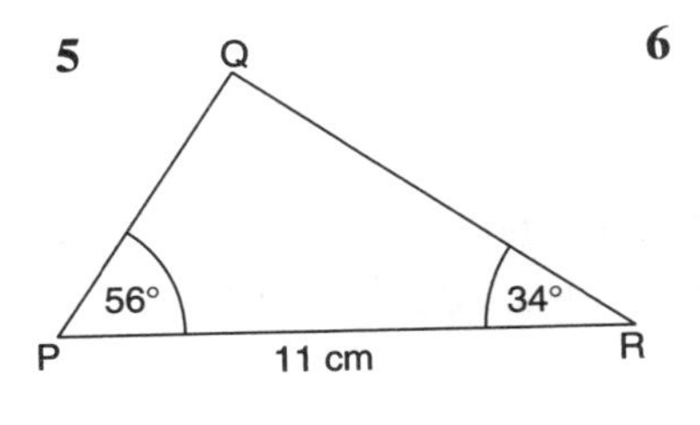

6

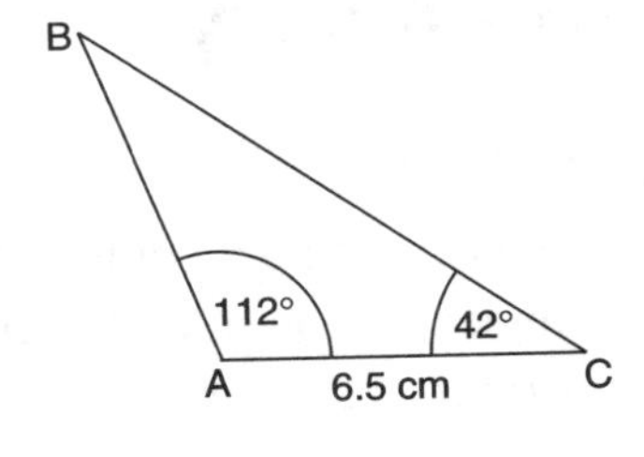

Quadrilaterals

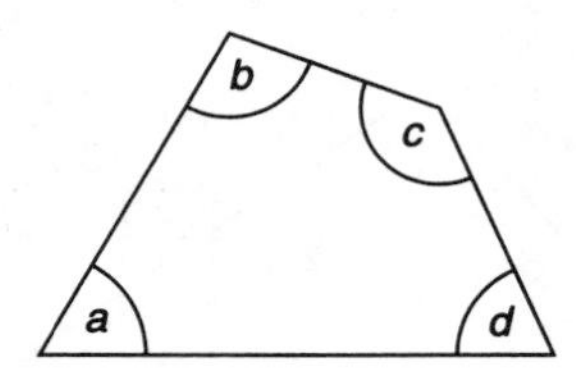

A quadrilateral is a plane figure bounded by four straight lines. Every quadrilateral has four angles, and the sum of these angles is always 360°:

$$a + b + c + d = 360°$$

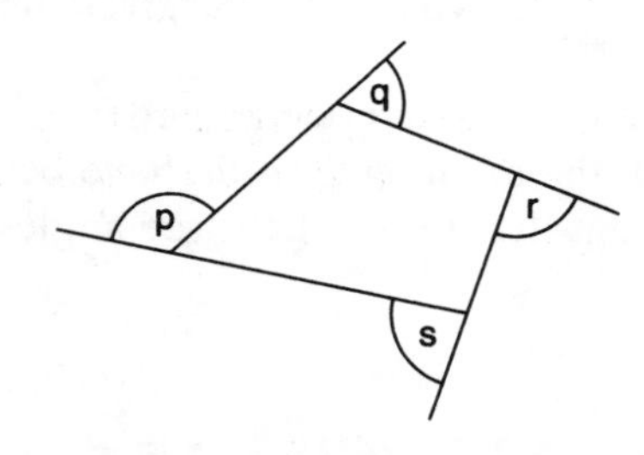

The sum of the exterior angles of a quadrilateral is 360°:

$$p + q + r + s = 360°$$

Some of the quadrilaterals with special names are shown below.

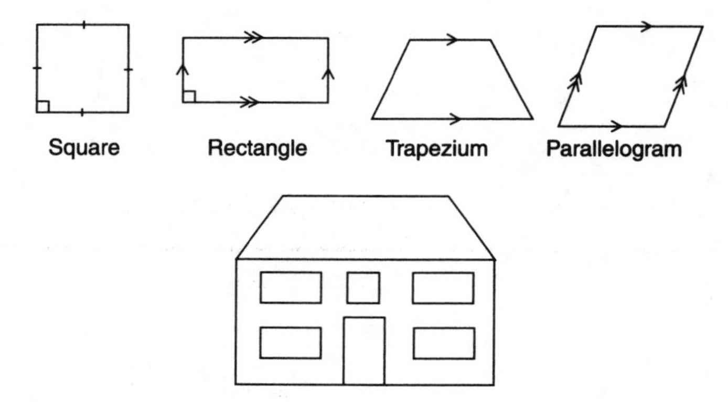

Look at this sketch of the front of a house.
What special name do you give to the shape of
(a) the roof (b) the front door (c) one of the downstairs windows (d) one of the upstairs windows (e) the front of the house excluding the roof?

Summary

So far, the results we have are:

Angles around a point add up to 360°.
Angles on one side of a straight line add up to 180°.
A right angle is 90°.
Vertically opposite angles are equal.
Corresponding angles are equal.
Interior angles of a triangle add up to 180°.
The sum of the angles in a quadrilateral is 360°.

For the next exercise you will need all these results.

EXERCISE 12h

QUESTION
Find the size of angle x.

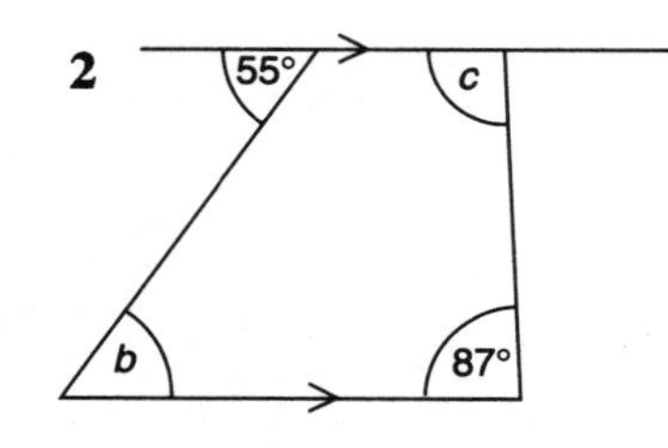

ANSWER

$$108° + 97° + 90° + x = 360°$$
$$295° + x = 360°$$
$$x = 360° - 295°$$

i.e. $x = 65°$

Find the sizes of the marked angles.

1

102°
97°
a
68°

2

55°
c
b
87°

3

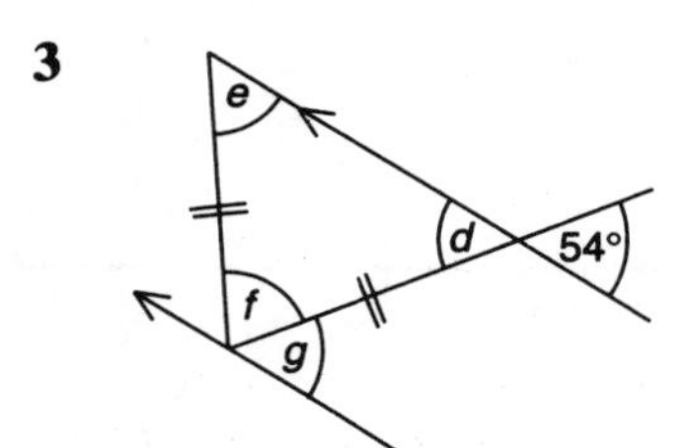

4

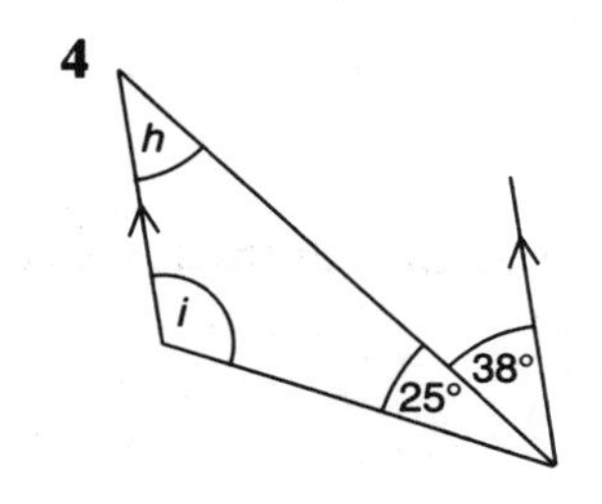

5

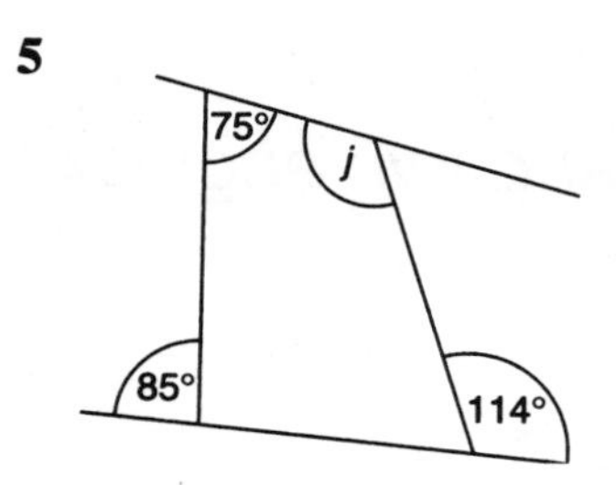

6

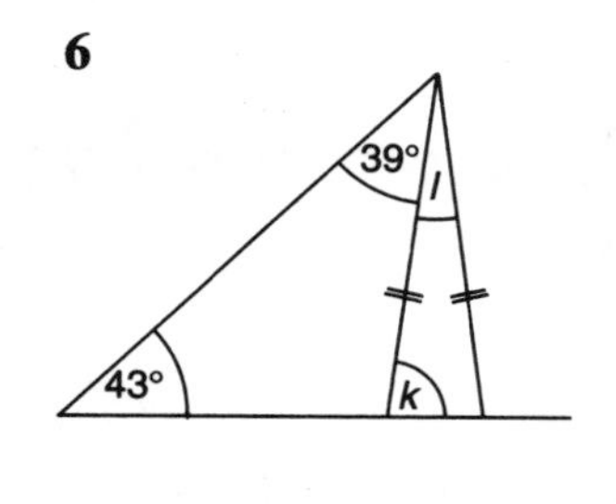

7

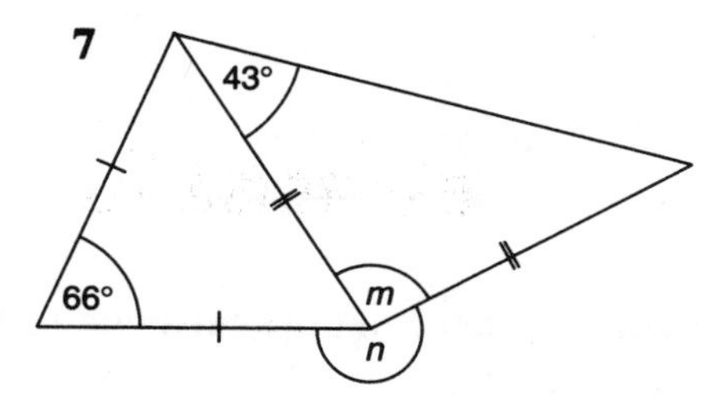

8

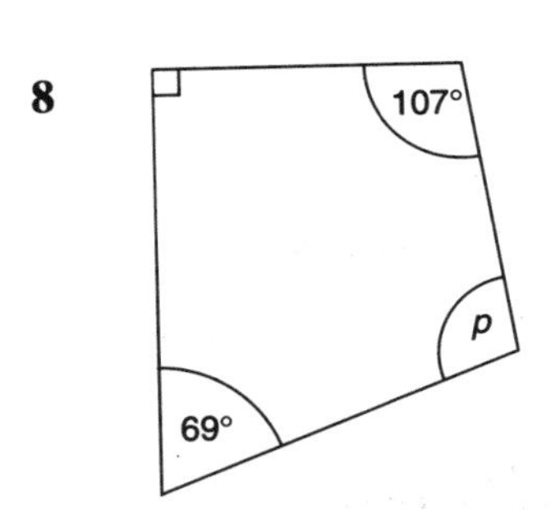

9

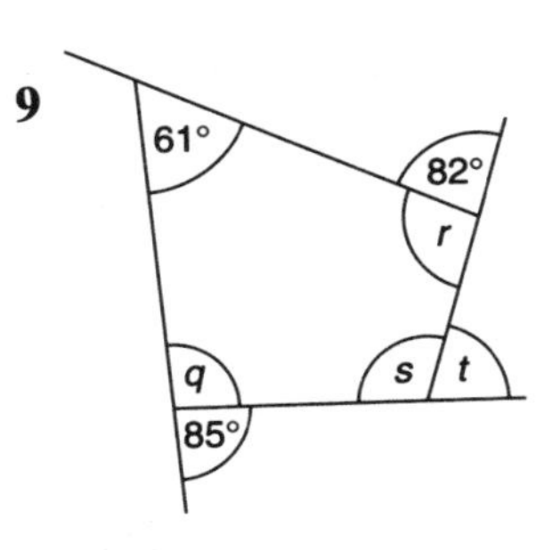

Pythagoras

An important result connecting the lengths of the sides of a right-angled triangle has been known for more than a thousand years. It is called Pythagoras' result and states that:

In a right-angled triangle, the square of the longest side (the hypotenuse) is equal to the sum of the squares of the other two sides.

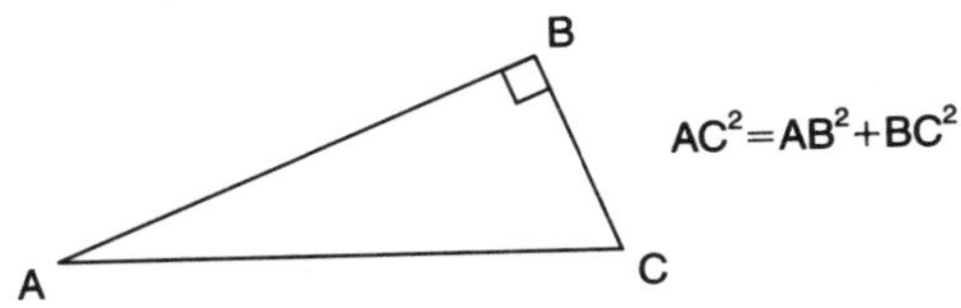

The simplest right-angled triangle has sides of lengths 3, 4 and 5 units. We can use these lengths to verify Pythagoras' result

since $5^2 = 5 \times 5 = 25$

and $3^2 + 4^2 = 9 + 16 = 25$

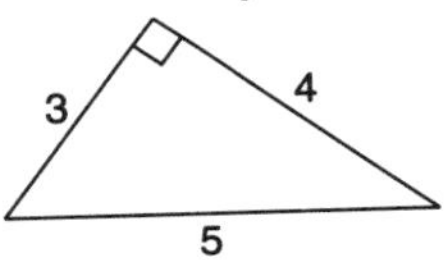

i.e. the square of the longest side is equal to the sum of the squares of the other two sides.

If the square of the longest side is not equal to the sum of the squares of the other two sides then the triangle does not contain a right angle;

for example, $AC^2 = 6^2 = 36$

and $AB^2 + BC^2 = 4^2 + 5^2$

$= 16 + 25$

$= 41$

A, 6 cm, 4 cm, C, 5 cm, B

AC^2 is not equal to $AB^2 + BC^2$, so there is no right angle in the triangle.

EXERCISE 12i

In questions 1 to 4 use the result of Pythagoras to decide whether or not $A\hat{B}C = 90°$.

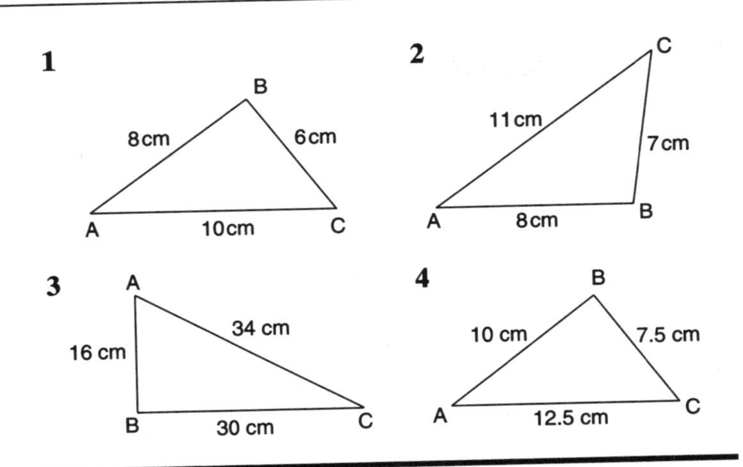

QUESTION

A rectangular piece of wood measures 36 cm by 15 cm. How far is it along a diagonal from one corner to the opposite corner?

ANSWER

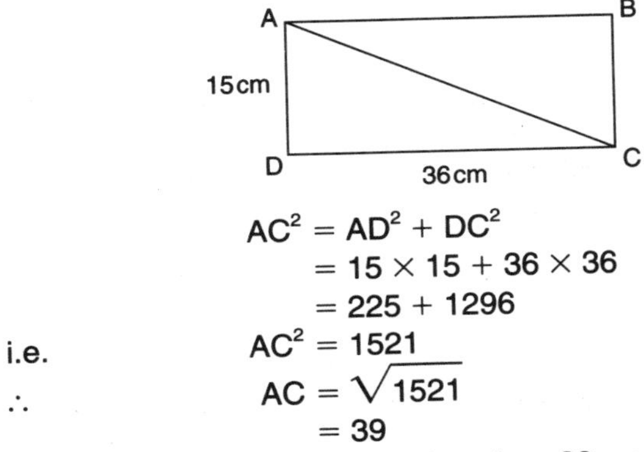

$$AC^2 = AD^2 + DC^2$$
$$= 15 \times 15 + 36 \times 36$$
$$= 225 + 1296$$

i.e. $AC^2 = 1521$

$\therefore$ $AC = \sqrt{1521}$

$= 39$

The length of the diagonal is therefore 39 cm.

5

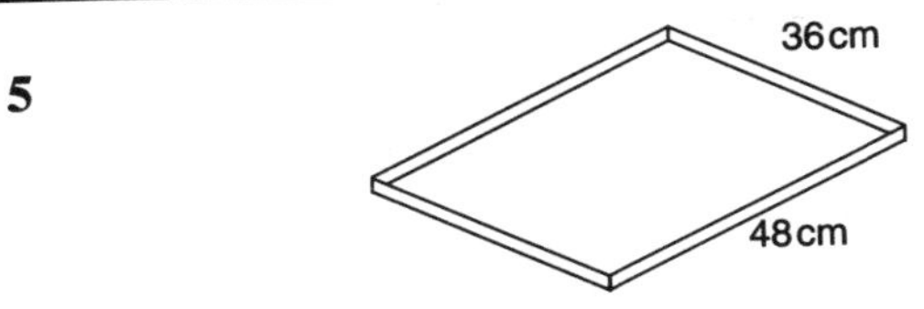

A rectangular metal tray measuring 36 cm by 48 cm has a lip 2 cm high round its edge. What is the length of the longest wooden stick that can be laid flat on the surface of the tray?

6

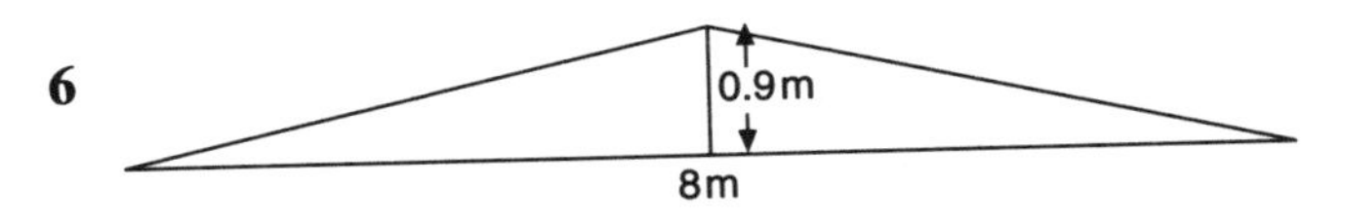

The sketch shows a simple symmetrical roof truss. Find the length of each sloping timber.

7 The rectangular concrete base for a house is to measure 9.3 m by 12.4 m. To check that it is square the builder measures the distances between opposite corners. What should they be?

QUESTION

A ladder AB, of length 5.5 m, is placed against a vertical wall so that its foot is 3.3 m from C, the base of the wall. How far up the wall does the ladder reach?

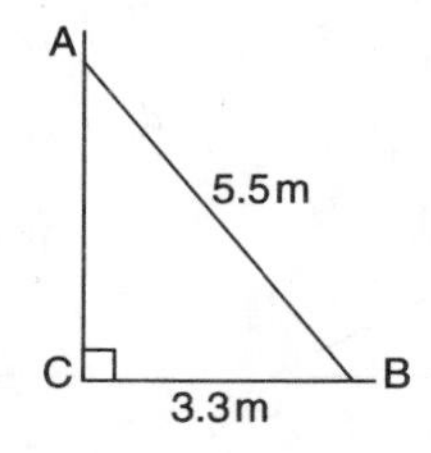

ANSWER

The triangle contains a right angle, so Pythagoras' result applies;

i.e. AB^2 (the square of the longest side)

$= AC^2 + CB^2$

(the sum of the squares of the other two sides).

$\therefore \quad 5.5^2 = AC^2 + 3.3^2$

i.e. $30.25 = AC^2 + 10.89$

We can write this the other way around,

i.e. $AC^2 + 10.89 = 30.25$

$\therefore \quad AC^2 = 30.25 - 10.89$

$= 19.36$

so $\quad AC = \sqrt{19.36}$

i.e. $\quad AC = 4.4$ m

8 The path from one corner of a rectangular field to the opposite corner is 65 m long. If the field is 39 m wide, how long is it?

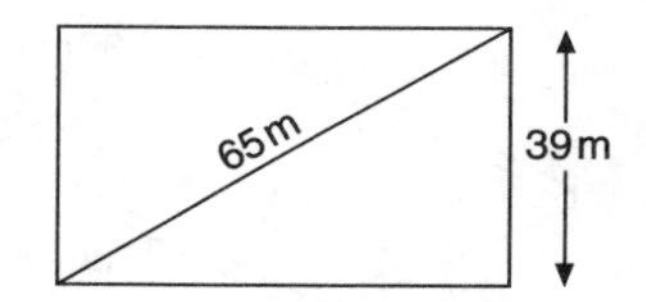

9 A ladder 6 m long is placed with its foot 3.6 m from the base of advertising hoarding. How high up the hoarding does the ladder reach?

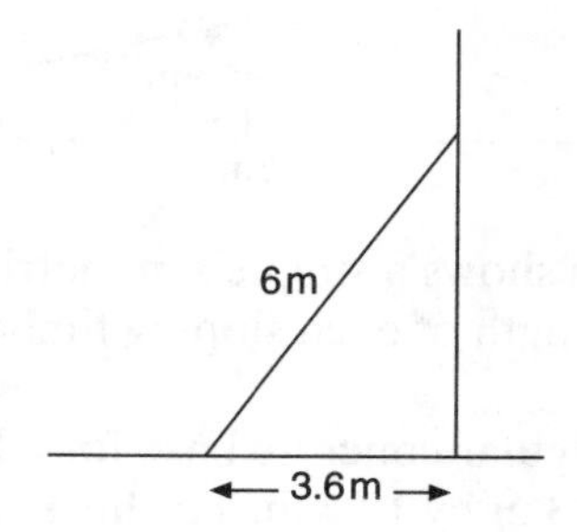

Sometimes lengths do not work out exactly.

QUESTION

The sketch shows a triangular sail ABC in which $A\hat{B}C = 90°$.

AB = 2.1 m and BC = 6.3 m.

Find, correct to 3 significant figures, the length of AC.

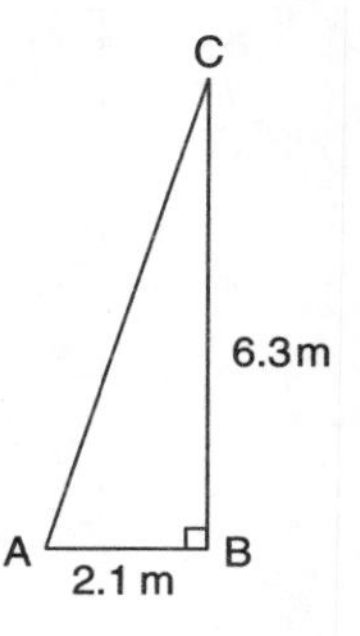

ANSWER

$AC^2 = AB^2 + BC^2$

$= 2.1^2 + 6.3^2$

$= 4.41 + 39.69$

$= 44.1$

$\therefore \quad AC = \sqrt{44.1}$

$= 6.640\ 78\ldots$

$= 6.64$ (to 3 s.f.)

i.e. the length of AC is 6.64 m.

In questions 10 to 12 give your answers correct to 3 s.f.

10

An envelope measures 16 cm by 11 cm. Find the length of a diagonal.

11

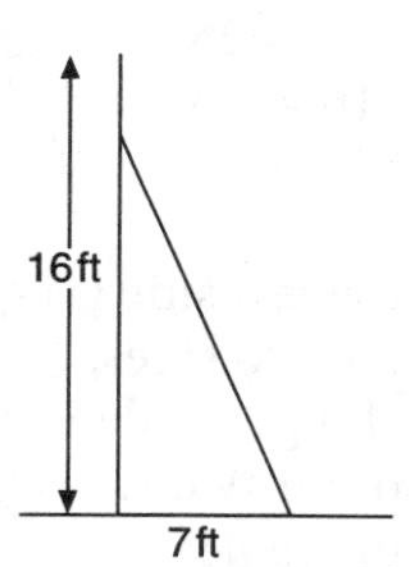

11 A flagpole is 16 ft high and is supported by a metal stay attached to a point 1 ft below the top of the pole and secured to a point on the ground 7 ft from its base. How long is the stay?

12

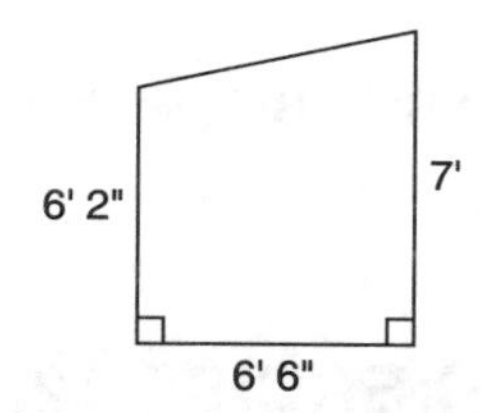

The sketch shows the cross-section through a garden shed. Use the given dimensions to find the length of the sloping roof.

Multiple-choice questions 12

In this exercise several alternative answers are given. Write down the letter that corresponds to the correct answer.

1

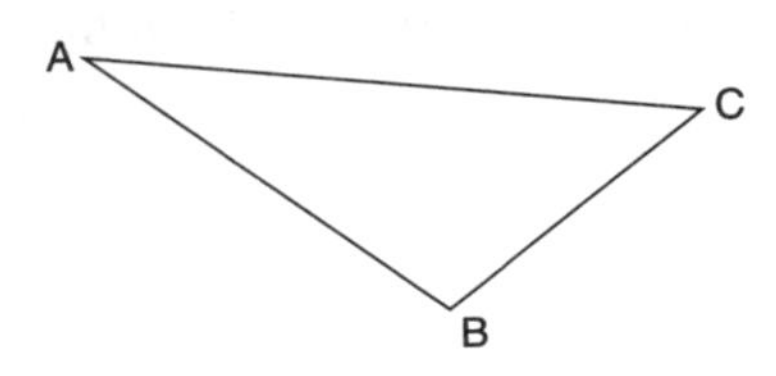

In triangle ABC the angle ABC is

A acute **B** obtuse **C** reflex **D** a right angle

2

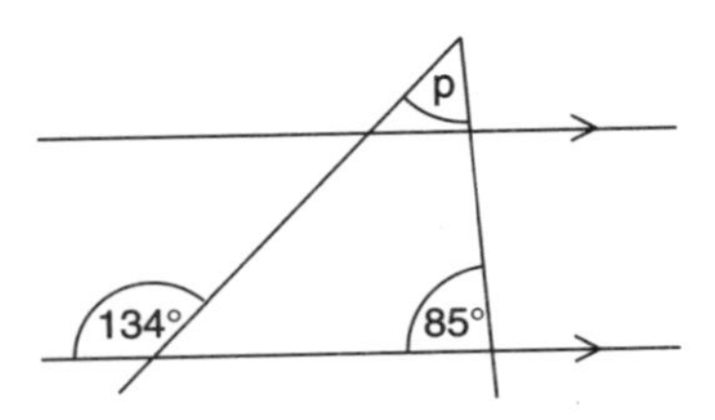

The value of the angle marked p is

A 46° **B** 49° **C** 12° **D** 29°

3 One of the base angles of an isosceles triangle is 66°. The sizes of the other two angles in this triangle are

A 57° and 57° **B** 66° and 68°
C 67° and 67° **D** 66° and 48°

4

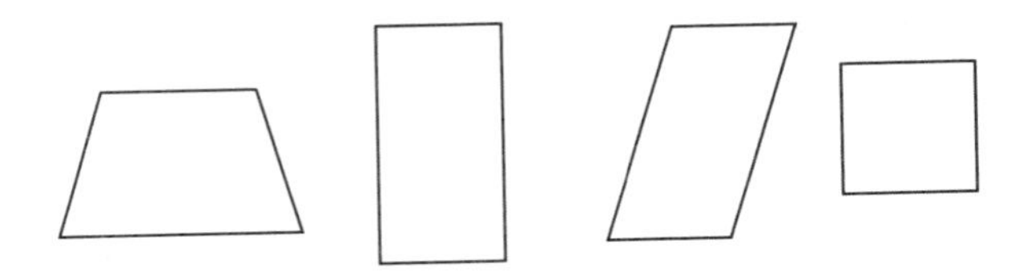

Which of these quadrilaterals has more than two axes of symmetry?

A the square **B** the parallelogram
C the trapezium **D** the rectangle

5

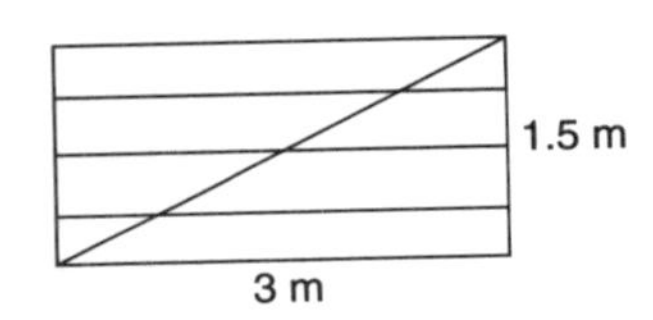

Correct to the nearest centimetre, the length of the diagonal brace for this gate is

A 450 cm **B** 335 cm **C** 336 cm **D** 324 cm

Self-assessment test 12

1 (a) How many degrees does the hour hand of a clock turn through between (i) 12 noon and 4 p.m. (ii) 3 a.m. and 8.30 a.m. (iii) 4 a.m. and 4 p.m.?

(b) How many degrees does the seconds hand of a clock turn through in
(i) 20 seconds (ii) 55 seconds?

2

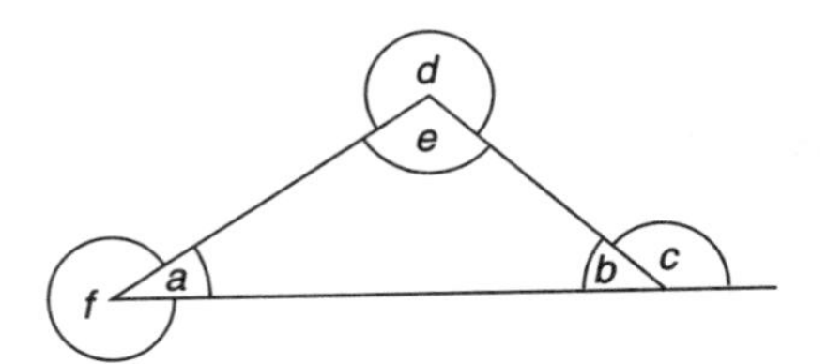

Which of the angles marked by letters are
(a) acute (b) obtuse (c) reflex?

3 Find the size of each marked angle:

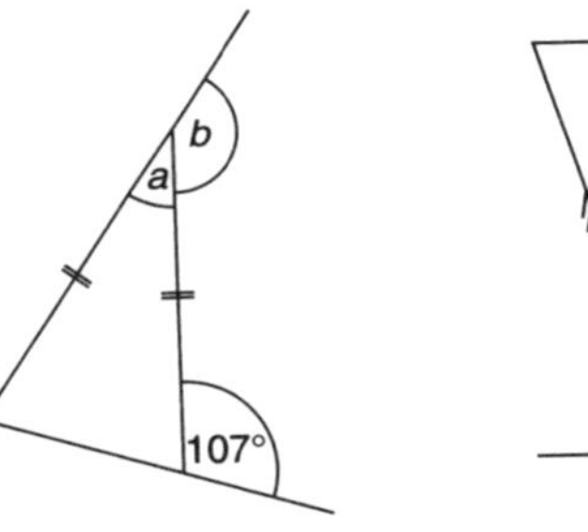

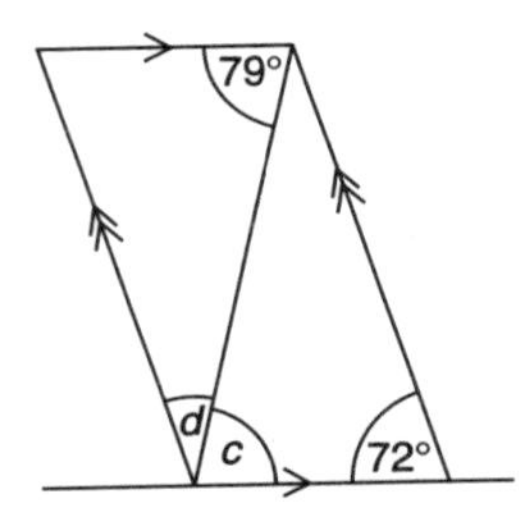

4 Which of the following statements are true and which are false?

(a) The sum of two acute angles is always bigger than 90°.

(b) The difference between two obtuse angles is always less than 90°.

(c) If three of the angles of a quadrilateral are each 105° then the size of the remaining angle is 45°.

(d) If two angles are supplementary their sum is 90°.

(e) The supplement of 143° is the same as the complement of 55°.

5 (a)

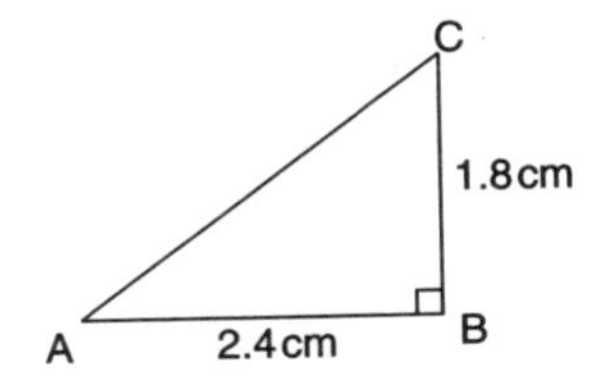

What is the length of AC?

(b)

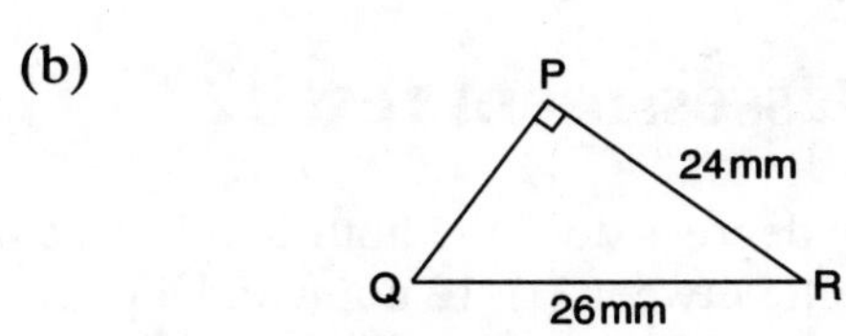

How long is PQ?

(c)

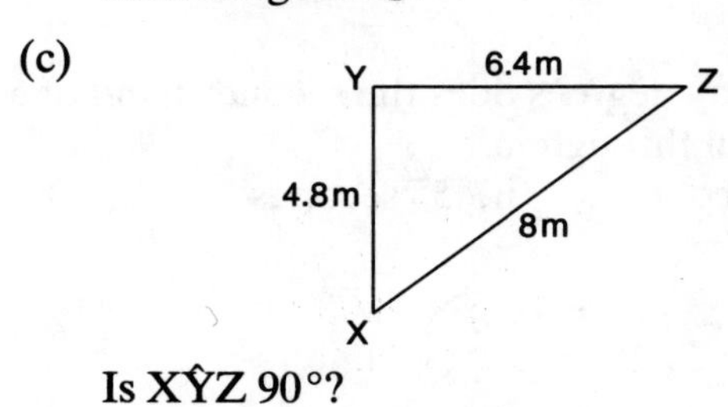

Is $X\hat{Y}Z$ 90°?

6

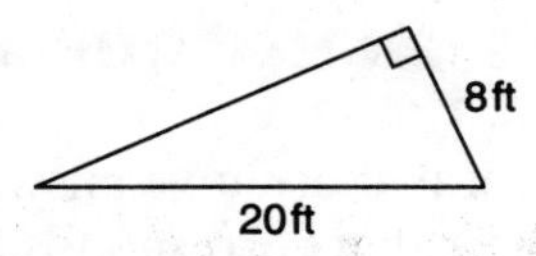

One of the roof trusses used to span a factory unit 20 ft wide is shown in the sketch. If one of the sloping timbers is 8 ft long find the length of the other.

CHAPTER 13

Areas involving quadrilaterals and triangles

Reminders

In Chapter 5 we found that:

the area of a square is equal to the length of a side multiplied by itself,

and the area of a rectangle is equal to a long side multiplied by a short side.

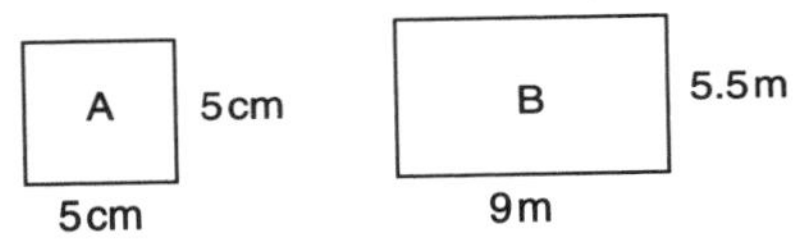

For example, the area of A is 5×5 cm^2 i.e. 25 cm^2 and the area of B is 9×5.5 m^2 i.e. 49.5 m^2.

Compound shapes

In this section we find the area of shapes that can be split into squares and/or rectangles.

EXERCISE 13a

QUESTION

Find the area of each shape:

(a)

(b)

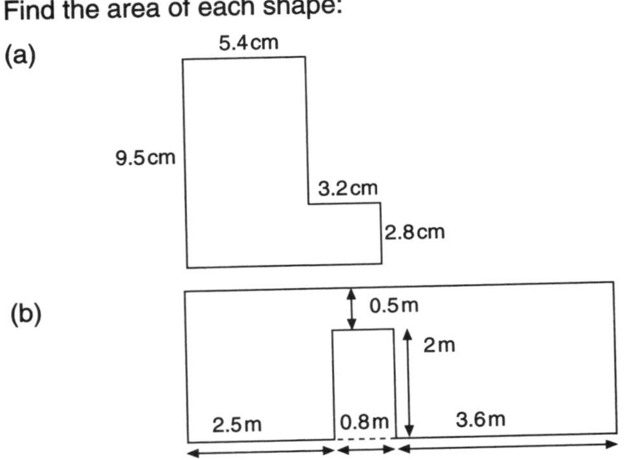

ANSWER

(a)

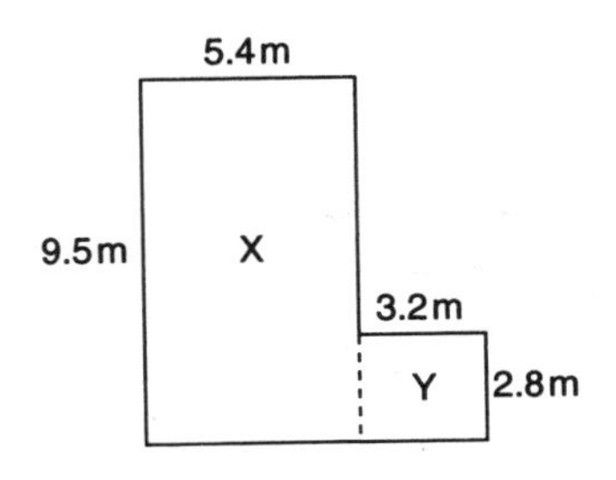

(Divide the shape into two rectangles.)

Area of X $= 9.5 \times 5.4$ cm^2 $= 51.3$ cm^2

area of Y $= 3.2 \times 2.8$ cm^2 $= 8.96$ cm^2

$\therefore$ total area $= 51.3$ cm^2 $+ 8.96$ cm^2

$= 60.26$ cm^2.

(b)

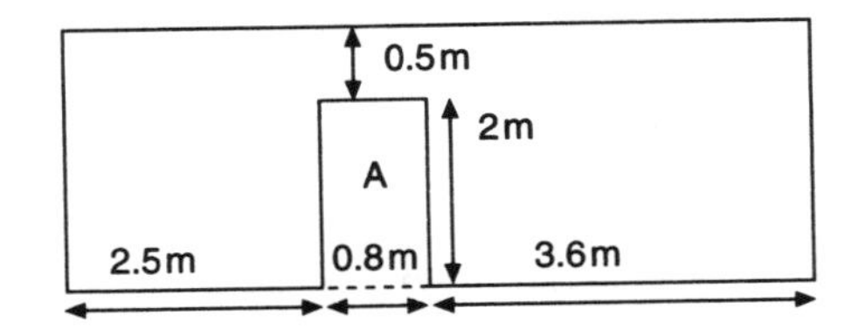

(To find the required area find the area of the large rectangle and subtract from it the area of the small rectangle.)

Length of large rectangle is 2.5 m + 0.8 m + 3.6 m

= 6.9 m

height of large rectangle is 2 m + 0.5 m = 2.5 m

$\therefore$ area of large rectangle is 6.9×2.5 m^2 $= 17.25$ m^2

and area of small rectangle is 2×0.8 m^2 $= 1.6$ m^2

$\therefore$ required area is 17.25 m^2 $-$ 1.6 m^2 $= 15.65$ m^2.

In questions 1 to 10 find the area of each shape. (All measurements are in cm.)

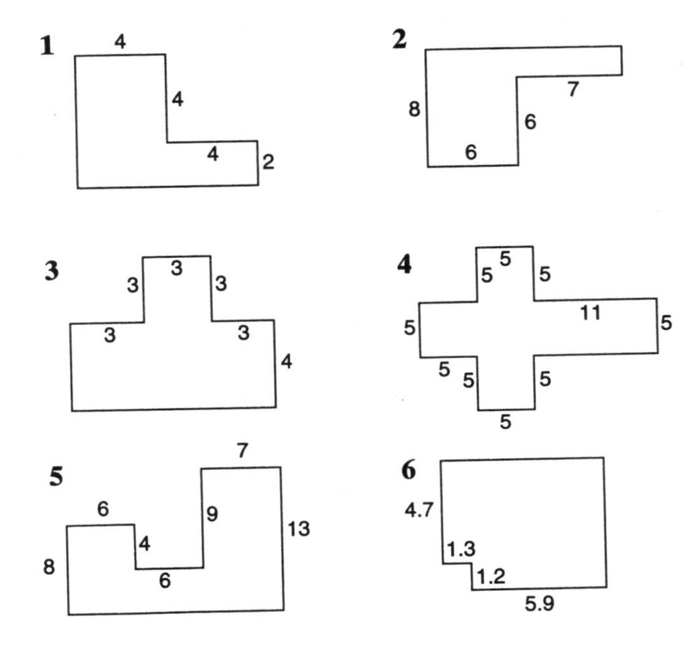

7

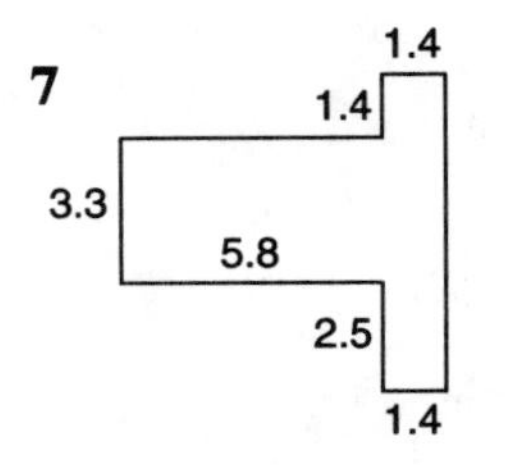

8

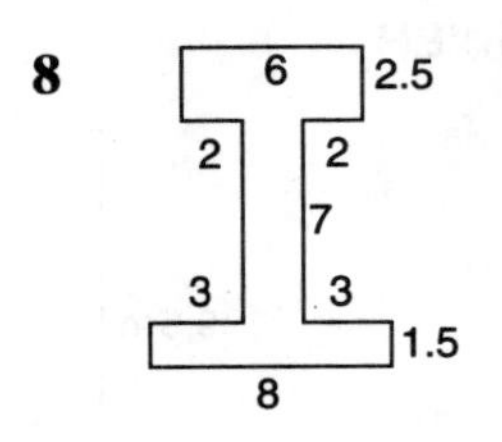

9

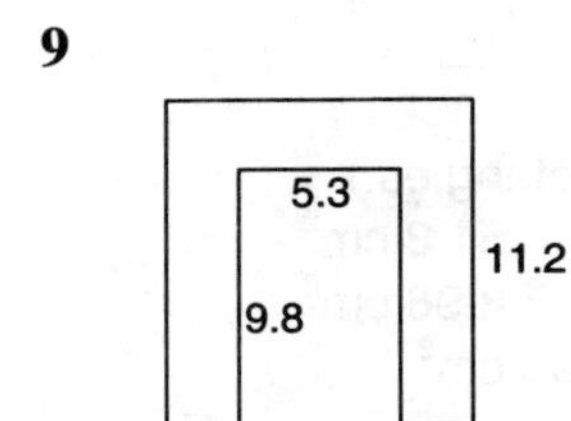

10

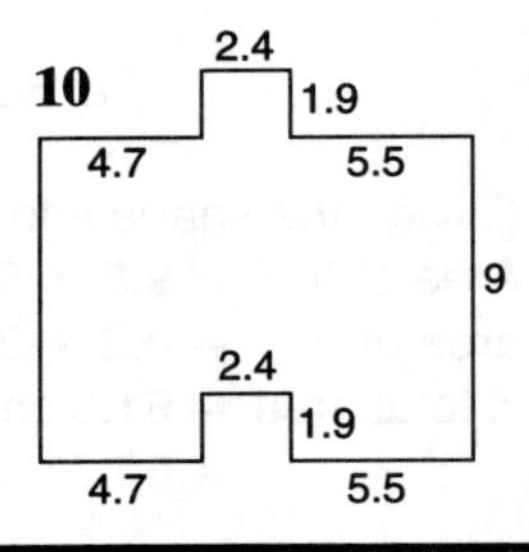

QUESTION

Find the floor area of the shop floor shown in the diagram. All dimensions are in metres.

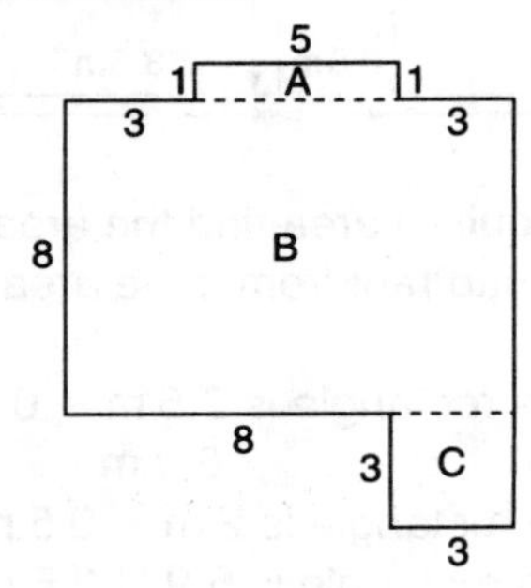

ANSWER

(The broken lines split the shop floor into 3 sections, marked A, B and C.)

Area of A (a rectangle) is $5 \times 1\ \text{m}^2 = 5\ \text{m}^2$
area of B (a rectangle) is $8 \times 11\ \text{m}^2 = 88\ \text{m}^2$
area of C (a square) is $3 \times 3\ \text{m}^2 = 9\ \text{m}^2$
$\therefore$ total floor area of the shop is $(5 + 88 + 9)\ \text{m}^2 = 102\ \text{m}^2$.

11 Find the area of this piece of sheet metal:

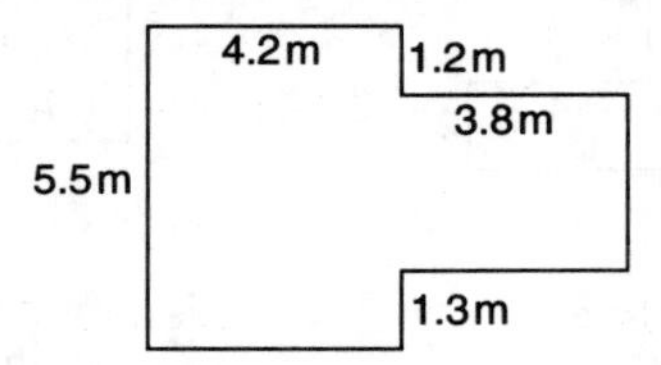

12 Find the area of this wooden cross:

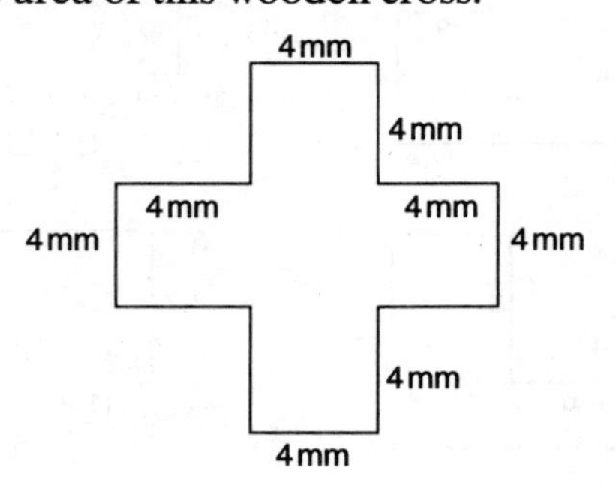

13 The diagram is the plan of my lounge.

(a) Draw your own diagram and on it mark the length of each side.

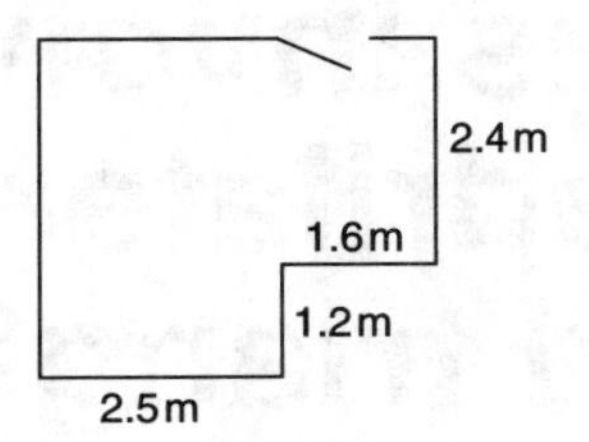

(b) Find (i) the length of skirting board used, if there is one door 75 cm wide (ii) the area that can be carpeted.

14

A mount for a photograph is cut from a rectangle measuring 23.8 cm by 16.5 cm by removing a rectangle measuring 17.2 cm by 10.3 cm.
Find the area of (a) the original card (b) the photograph (c) the border.

15

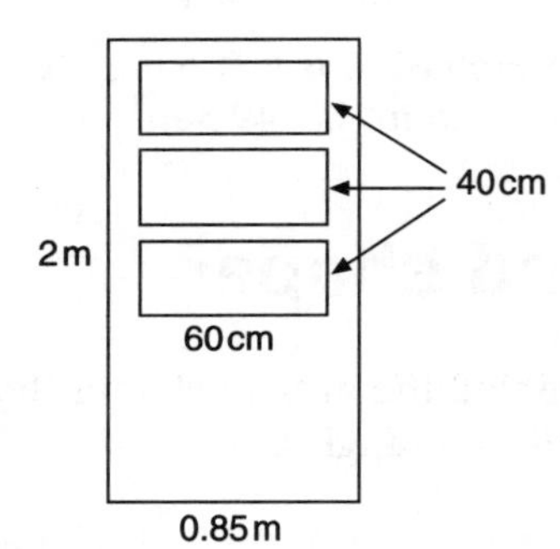

A wooden door has three glass panels, as shown in the diagram. Find (a) the area of each panel
(b) the area of the painted surface of the door that is visible from one side.

Area of a triangle

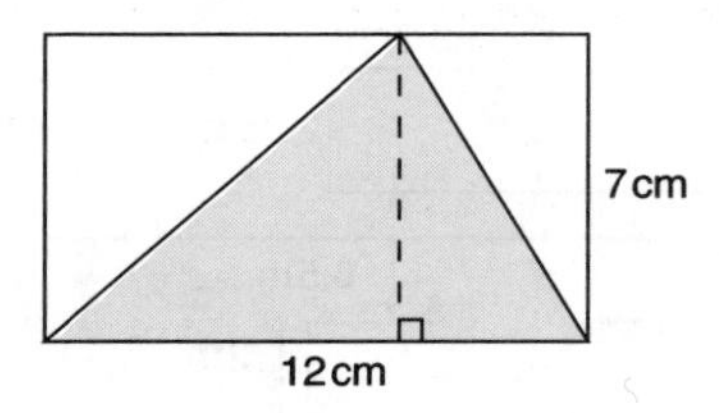

The area of the shaded triangle is equal to half the area of the rectangle that surrounds it.

Area of rectangle is $12 \times 7\ cm^2$, i.e. $84\ cm^2$;
so area of triangle is $\frac{1}{2} \times 12 \times 7\ cm^2$, i.e. $42\ cm^2$.

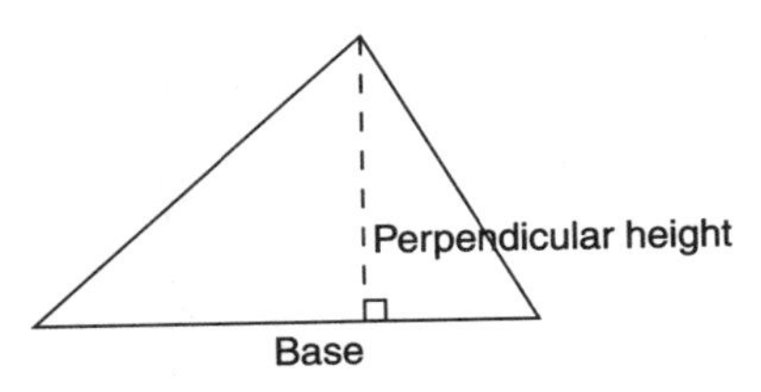

In general,
area of a triangle $= \frac{1}{2} \times$ base $\times$ perpendicular height

EXERCISE 13b

QUESTION
Find the area of each triangle:

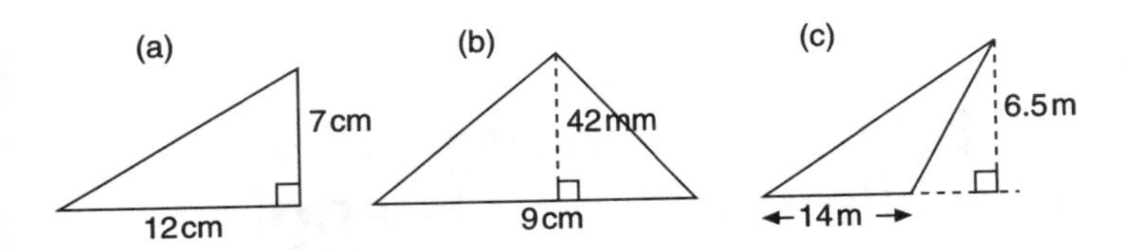

ANSWER
Area of a triangle $= \frac{1}{2} \times$ base $\times$ perpendicular height.
Take care that both distances are given in the same unit.

(a) Area $= \frac{1}{2} \times 12 \times 7\ cm^2$
$= 6 \times 7\ cm^2$
$= 42\ cm^2$

(b) (Give both measurements in centimetres.)
Length of base is 9 cm and the height of the triangle is 4.2 cm.
Area $= \frac{1}{2} \times 9 \times 4.2\ cm^2$
$= \frac{1}{2} \times 37.8\ cm^2$
$= 18.9\ cm^2$

(c) (The perpendicular height is sometimes shown by a line that does not lie within the triangle.)
Area $= \frac{1}{2} \times 14 \times 6.5\ m^2$
$= 7 \times 6.5\ m^2$
$= 45.5\ m^2$

Find the area of each triangle:

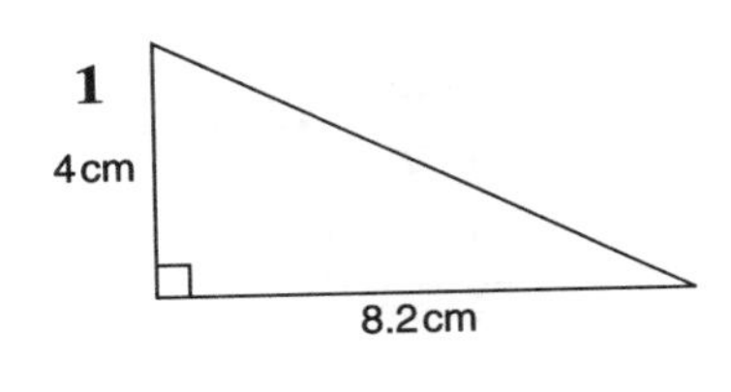

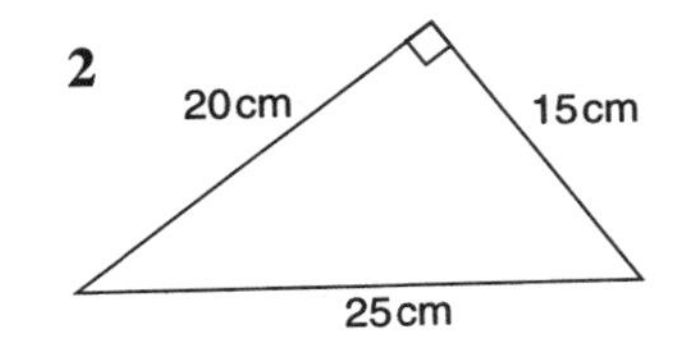

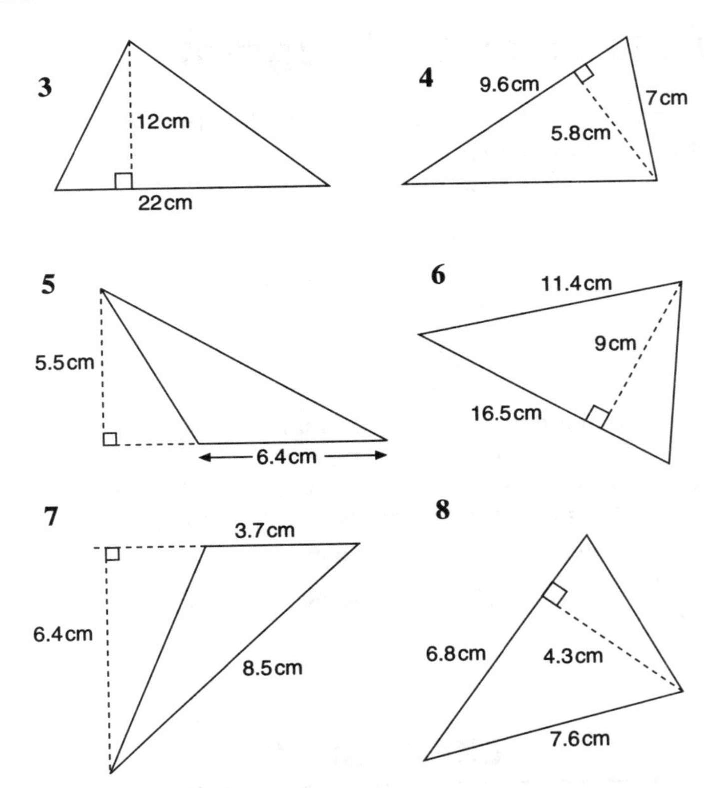

Area of a trapezium

A trapezium is a quadrilateral with just one pair of opposite sides parallel.

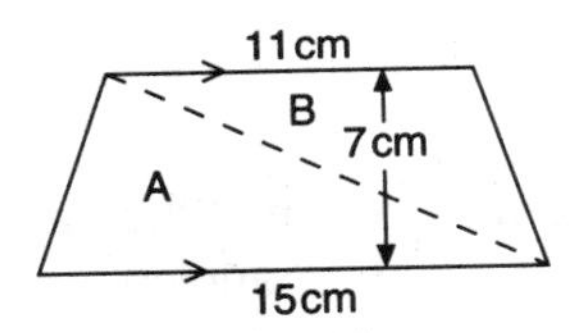

A trapezium can be divided into two triangles. The area of each triangle is then found and the two areas added together to give the area of the trapezium.
In the diagram here

area of A $= \frac{1}{2} \times 15 \times 7\ cm^2 = 52.5\ cm^2$

area of B $= \frac{1}{2} \times 11 \times 7\ cm^2 = 38.5\ cm^2$

$\therefore$ area of trapezium $= 52.5\ cm^2 + 38.5\ cm^2$
$= 91\ cm^2$

The area of a trapezium is also equal to half the sum of the parallel sides multiplied by the perpendicular distance between them,
i.e.

area of given trapezium $= \frac{1}{2}(15 + 11) \times 7\ cm^2$
$= \frac{1}{2} \times 26 \times 7\ cm^2$
$= 91\ cm^2$

Area of a parallelogram

A parallelogram is a quadrilateral with both pairs of opposite sides parallel.

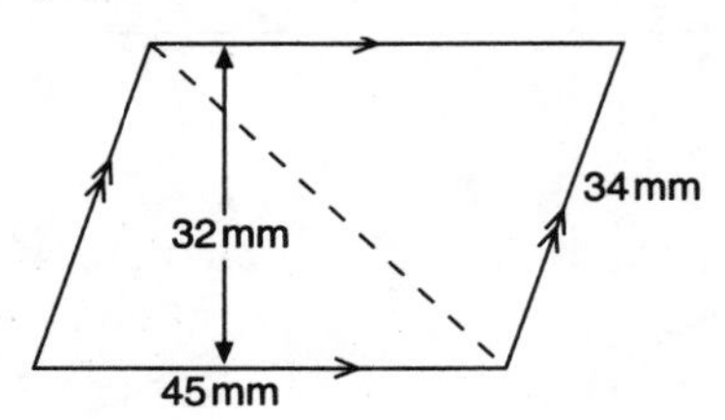

The area of a parallelogram is equal to the sum of the areas of two identical triangles, i.e. the area of parallelogram is equal to the length of one side multiplied by the perpendicular distance between that side and the side opposite it. In the above diagram,

$$\text{area of parallelogram is } 45 \times 32 \text{ mm}^2 = 1440 \text{ mm}^2$$

EXERCISE 13c

QUESTION

Find the area of each shape:

(a)

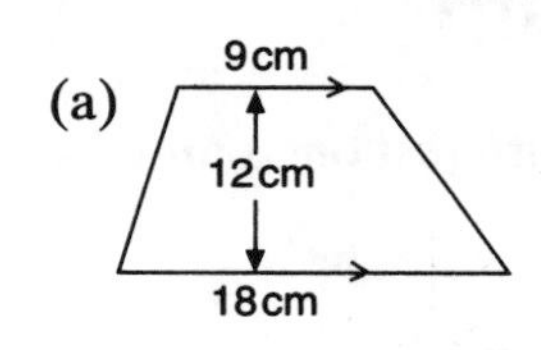

(b)

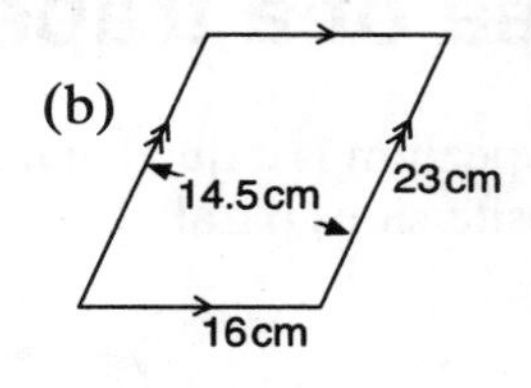

ANSWER

(a) Area of trapezium $= \frac{1}{2}$ (sum of the parallel sides) $\times$ perpendicular distance between them

$= \frac{1}{2}(18 + 9) \times 12 \text{ cm}^2$
$= 0.5 \times 27 \times 12 \text{ cm}^2$
$= 162 \text{ cm}^2$

(b) Area of parallelogram = length of one side $\times$ perpendicular distance between that side and the one parallel to it

$= 23 \times 14.5 \text{ cm}^2$
$= 333.5 \text{ cm}^2$

Find the area of each shape:

1

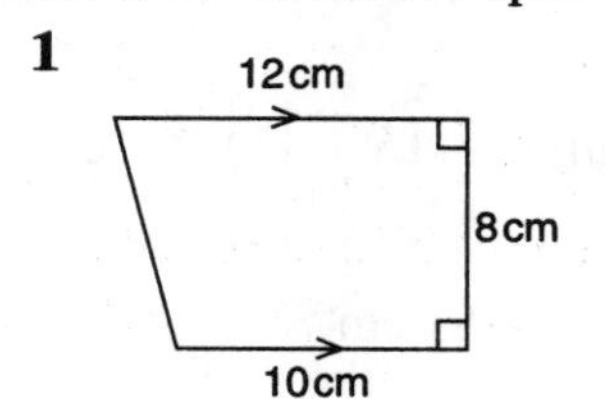

2

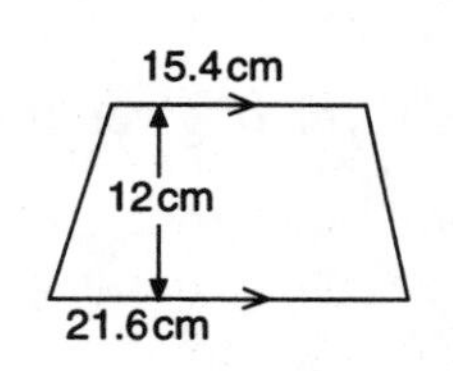

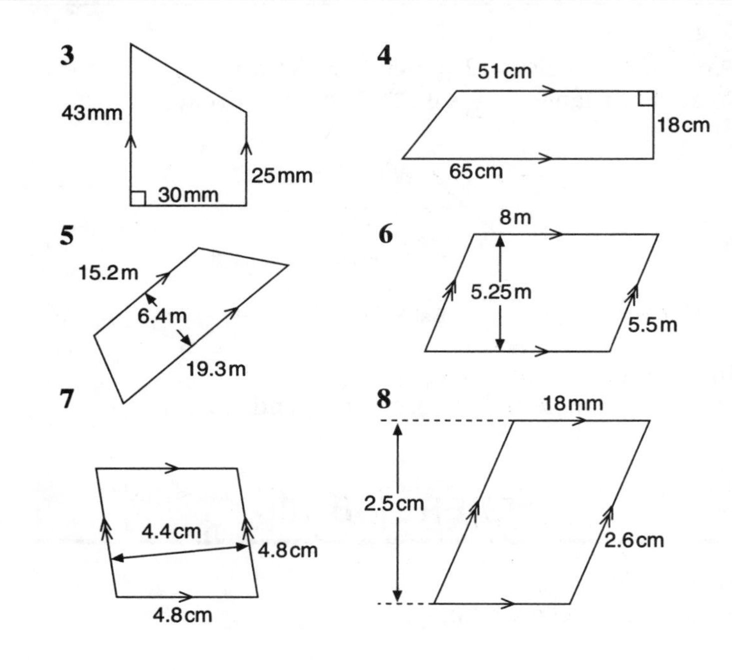

Problems involving quadrilaterals and triangles

EXERCISE 13d

QUESTION

Given below are the templates for four blanks that will be drilled and bent to form components used in the manufacture of a machine. Each machine requires two components made from an A blank, two from a B blank, two from a C blank, and six made from a D blank. Find

(a) the area of sheet metal used to make each blank;

(b) the total area of metal required for the blanks used to make one machine. Give your answer correct to the nearest whole number.

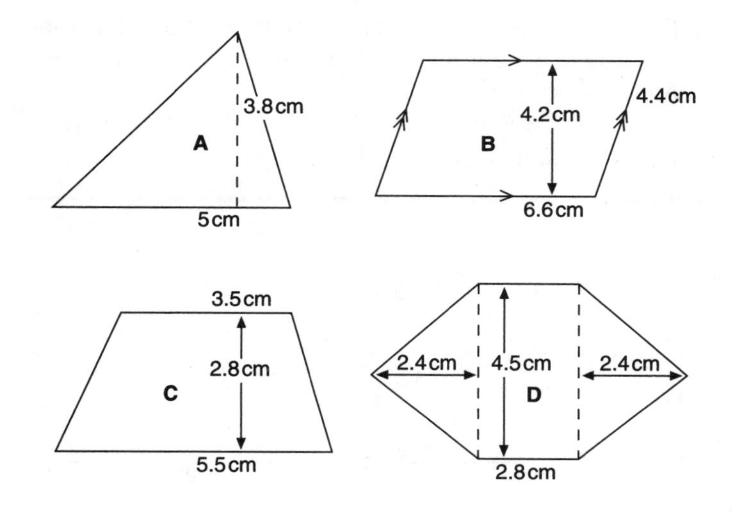

ANSWER

(a) Area of A $= \frac{1}{2} \times 5 \times 3.8\ \text{cm}^2$
$= 9.5\ \text{cm}^2$

Area of B $= 6.6 \times 4.2\ \text{cm}^2$
$= 27.72\ \text{cm}^2$

Area of C $= \frac{1}{2}(3.5 + 5.5) \times 2.8\ \text{cm}^2$
$= 4.5 \times 2.8\ \text{cm}^2$
$= 12.6\ \text{cm}^2$

Area of D = area of rectangle + 2 × area of one triangle
$= 2.8 \times 4.5\ \text{cm}^2 + 2 \times \frac{1}{2} \times 4.5 \times 2.4\ \text{cm}^2$
$= 12.6 + 10.8\ \text{cm}^2$
$= 23.4\ \text{cm}^2$

(b) Total area of sheet metal required is 2 × area A + 2 × area B + 2 × area C + 6 × area D
$= 2 \times 9.5 + 2 \times 27.72 + 2 \times 12.6 + 6 \times 23.4\ \text{cm}^2$
$= 19 + 55.44 + 25.2 + 140.4\ \text{cm}^2$
$= 240.04\ \text{cm}^2$
$= 240\ \text{cm}^2$ (to the nearest whole number)

---

1 Find the area of each of the following plastic shapes.

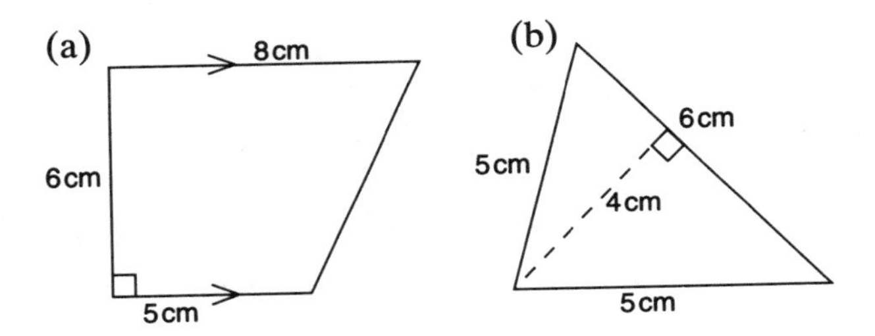

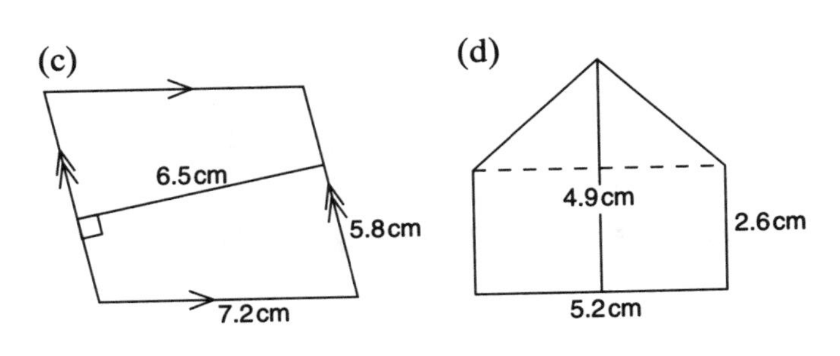

2 The diagram shows the end wall of a bungalow. Find its area.

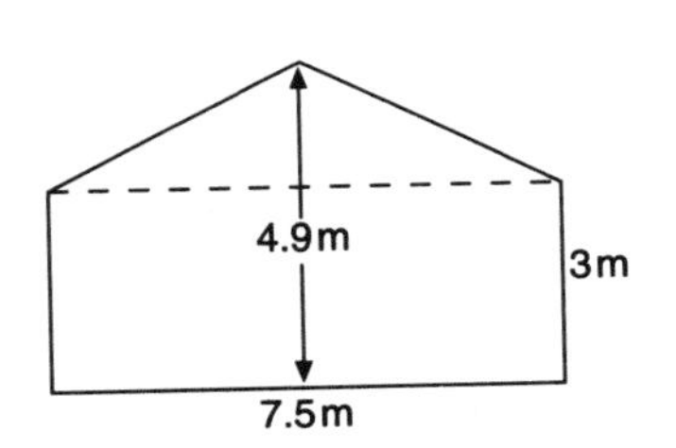

3

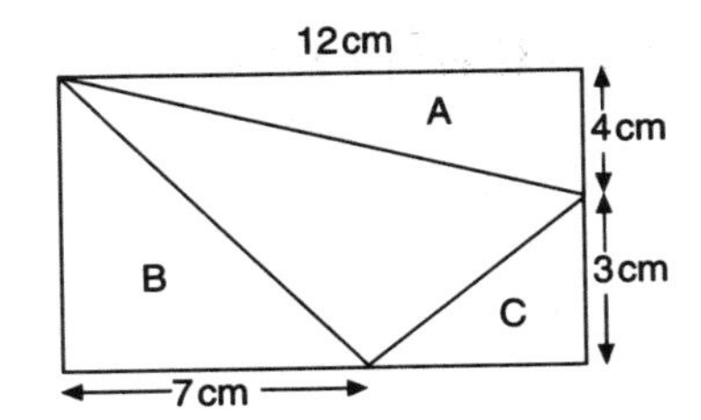

The diagram shows a rectangular sheet of card measuring 12 cm by 7 cm. The triangles marked A, B and C are cut off. Find (a) the area of each of the marked triangles (b) the area of the triangle that remains.

4

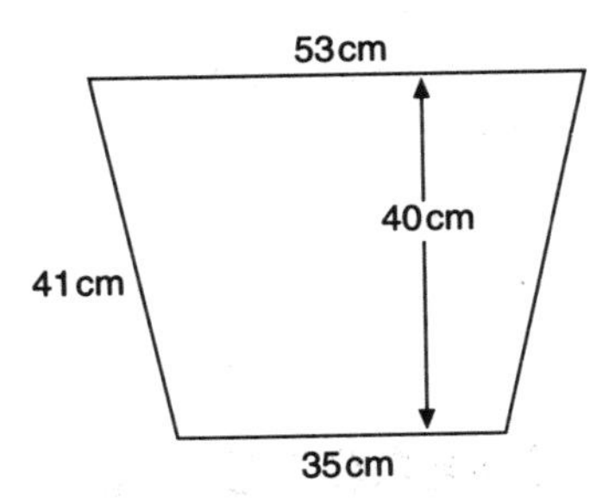

A water trough on a farm has a cross-section which is a trapezium. Use the dimensions given on the sketch to find the area of the cross-section.

5

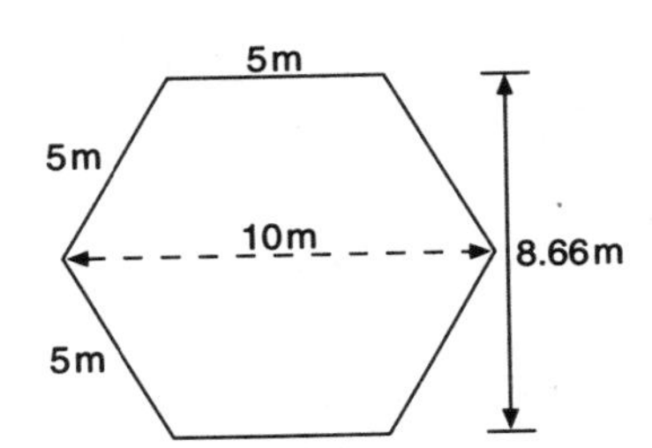

The diagram shows the base of a hexagonal bandstand. Find the area of the base of the bandstand, giving your answer correct to three significant figures.

6

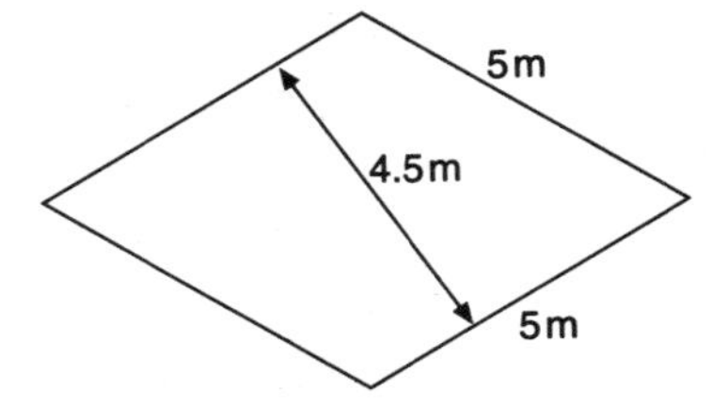

A bed that has been prepared for tulips is in the shape of a diamond. All its sides are 5 m long and opposite sides are 4.5 m apart. Find (a) the area of the bed (b) the number of tulip bulbs that should be bought to fill the bed if each square metre requires 120 bulbs. (Assume that a diamond is a parallelogram with its four sides equal.)

7

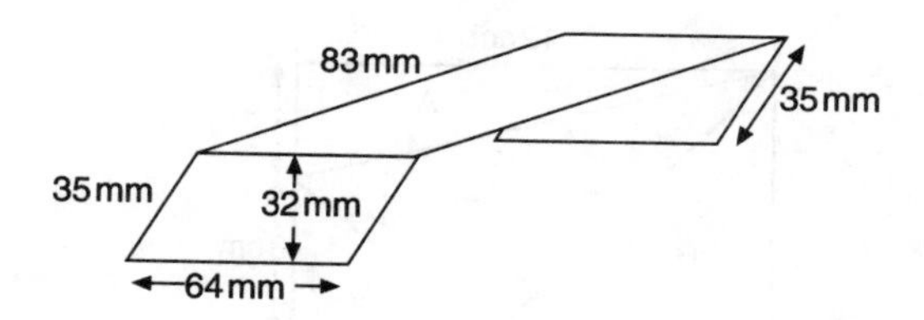

The sketch shows a small component needed in the manufacture of a machine. It is made by bending a flat piece of metal into a rectangular top supported by two identical sides, each in the shape of a parallelogram. Use the dimensions given on the sketch to find the area of the template from which the component is formed. Give your answer in square centimetres, correct to the nearest whole number.

8

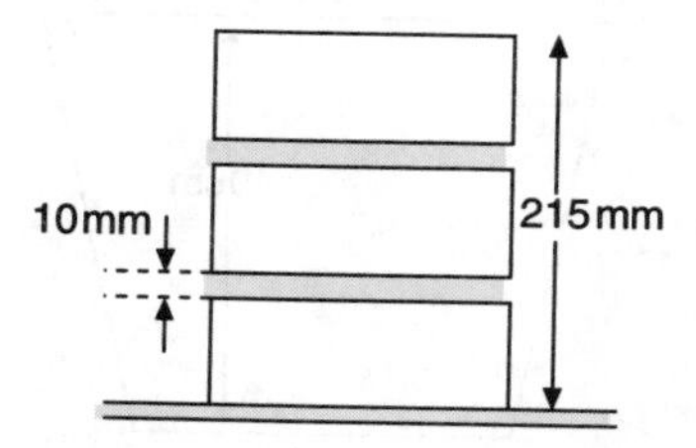

(a) Three building bricks, when laid one on top of the other, each separated by a layer of cement 10 mm thick, reach a height of 215 mm above the level of the cement laid at the base. Find the thickness of one brick.

(b) Find the dimensions of a brick if its thickness is two-thirds its width and it is twice as long as it is wide.

(c) A wall is built to a height of 2.25 m by laying all the bricks longways. How many courses are needed? (Assume that the thickness of cement at the base and under each course of bricks is 10 mm.)

Surface area of a cuboid

A cuboid has three pairs of identical opposite faces i.e. six faces altogether. The total surface area of a cuboid is found by adding together the areas of the six faces.

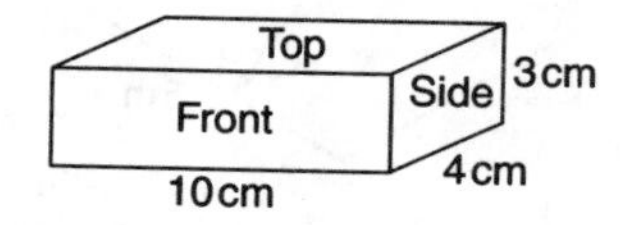

Area of the top is $10 \times 4\ \text{cm}^2 = 40\ \text{cm}^2$
$\therefore$ area of top and bottom is $80\ \text{cm}^2$
Area of the front face is $10 \times 3\ \text{cm}^2 = 30\ \text{cm}^2$
$\therefore$ area of the front face and the back face is $60\ \text{cm}^2$
Area of one side is $4 \times 3\ \text{cm}^2 = 12\ \text{cm}^2$
$\therefore$ area of the two side faces is $24\ \text{cm}^2$

Therefore the total area of the six faces is
$(80 + 60 + 24)\ \text{cm}^2 = 164\ \text{cm}^2$

EXERCISE 13e

In questions 1 to 4 find the total surface area of each shape.

1 A brick measuring 25 cm × 12.5 cm × 8 cm.

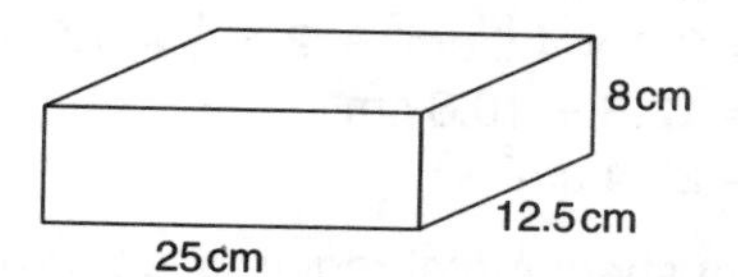

2 A rectangular room measuring 5.5 m by 4.5 m × 2.3 m.

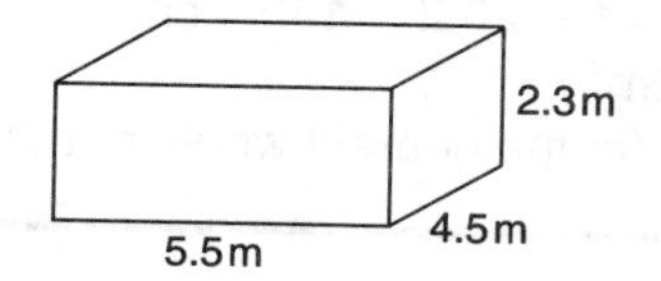

3 A rectangular box for sending wedding cake through the post measuring 65 mm by 50 mm by 18 mm.

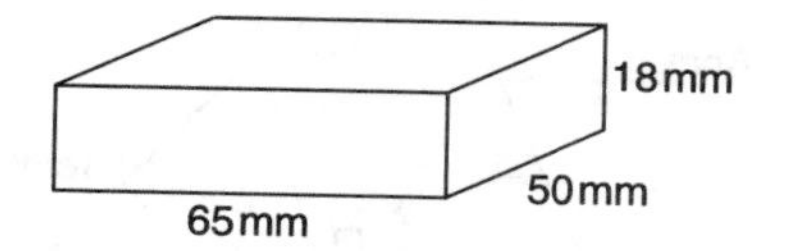

4 A book measuring 240 mm by 185 mm by 30 mm. Give your answer in sq cm correct to 3 s.f.

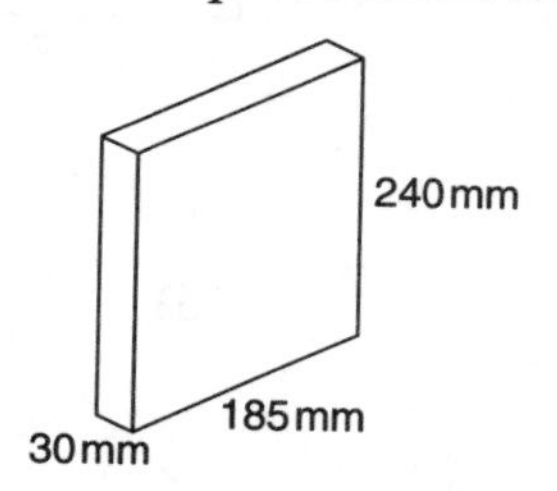

Multiple-choice questions 13

In this exercise several alternative answers are given. Write down the letter that corresponds to the correct answer.

1

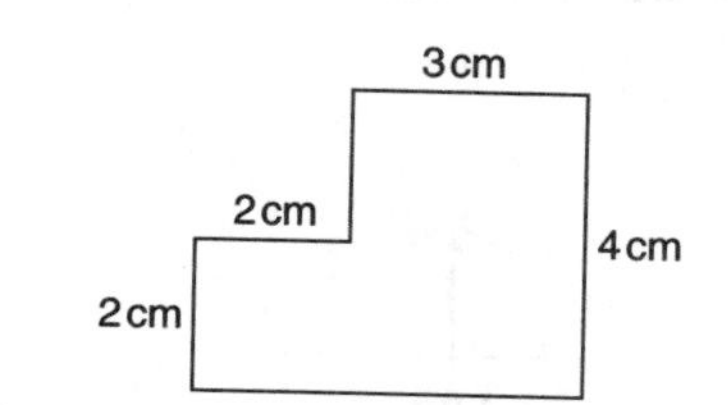

The area of this shape is

A 16 cm **B** $16\ \text{cm}^2$ **C** 18 cm **D** $18\ \text{cm}^2$

2

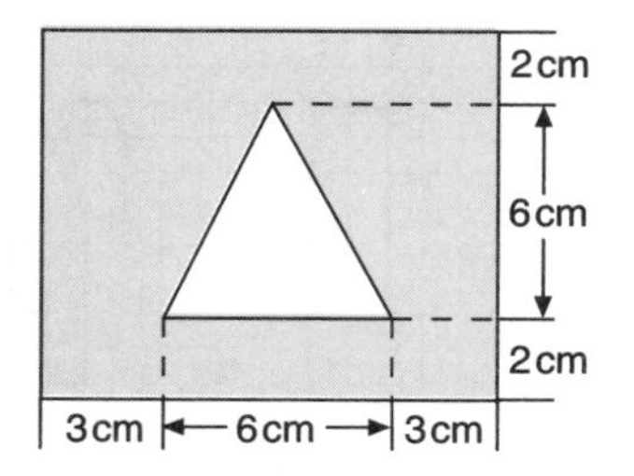

The area of the shaded region is

A 120 cm^2 **B** 44 cm^2 **C** 102 cm^2 **D** 22 cm^2

3

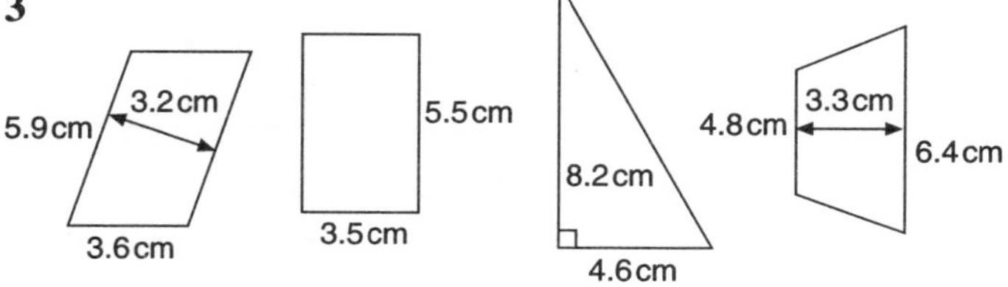

The largest of these areas is

A the trapezium **B** the triangle
C the parallelogram **D** the rectangle

4

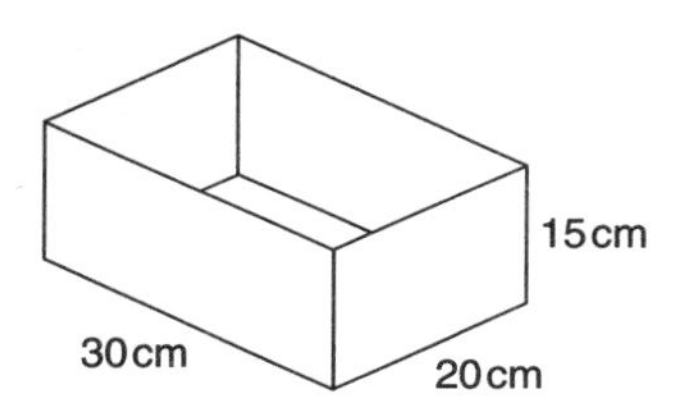

The total outside area of this lidless cardboard box is

A 9600 cm^2 **B** 2700 cm^2
C 1500 cm^2 **D** 2100 cm^2

Self-assessment test 13

1 Find the perimeter and area of each shape.

(a)

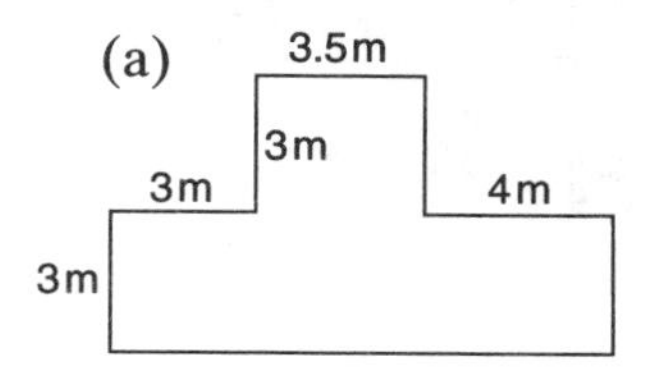

(b)

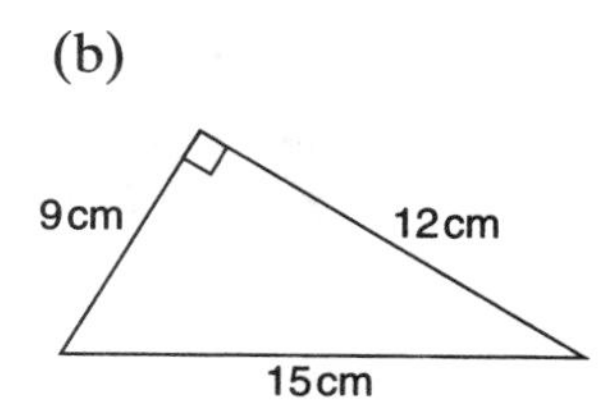

(c) (d)

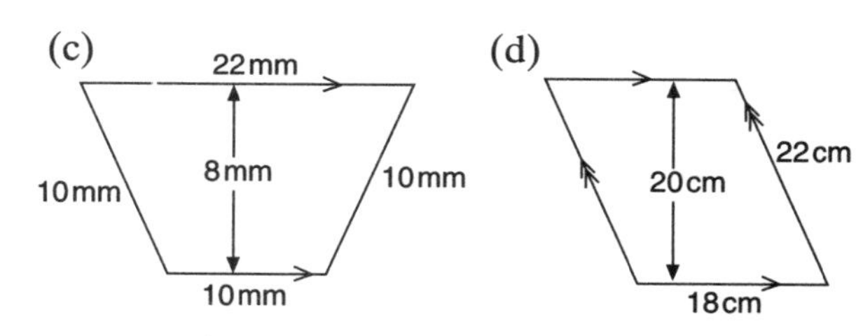

2

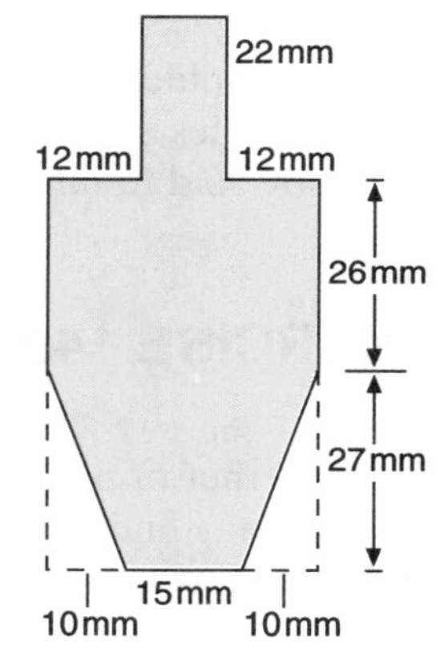

The sketch shows the cross-section of a glazing bar that is 2 m long and is to be used in the construction of a skylight. The bar has been machined from a length of timber with a rectangular cross-section measuring 8 cm by 4 cm.

(a) Find, in square centimetres, the area of (i) the original cross-section (ii) the cross-section after it has been machined.

(b) What percentage of the wood is wasted?

CHAPTER 14

Symmetry and similarity

Line symmetry

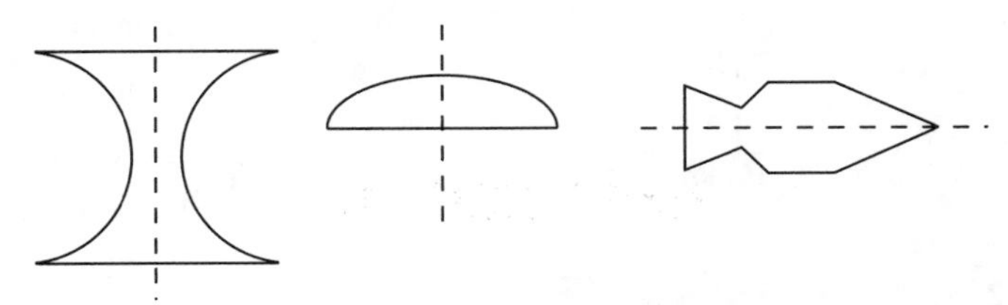

Each of these shapes can be folded along the dashed line so that one half of the shape lies exactly over the other half. Shapes that do this are said to have *line symmetry*.

EXERCISE 14a

1 For each shape say whether or not the dashed line is a line of symmetry. You may find it useful to place a mirror along the dashed line.

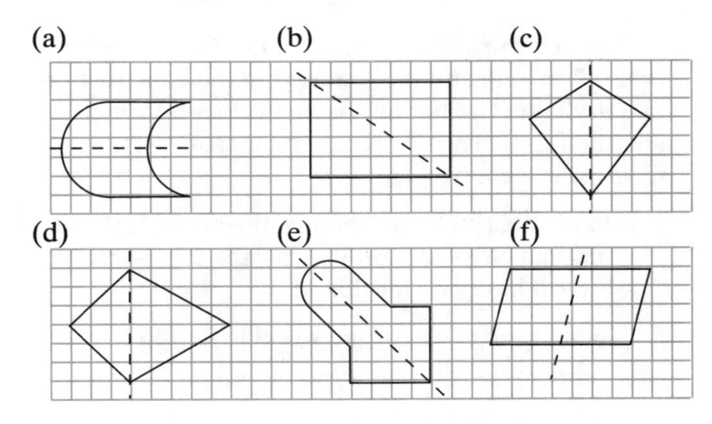

In questions 2 to 7 each figure has line symmetry. Copy the figure and draw the line of symmetry.

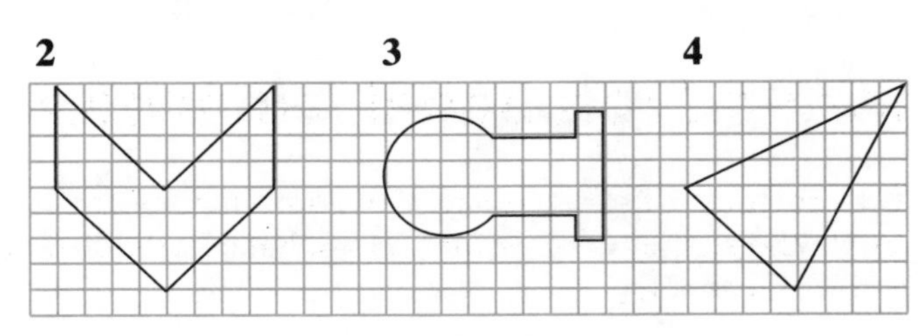

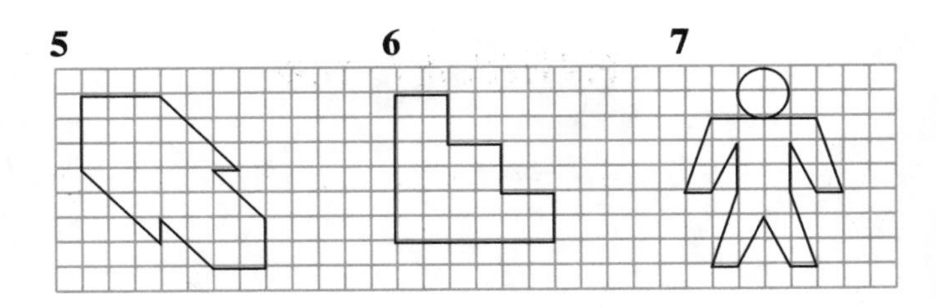

In questions 8 to 13 copy each drawing and complete the figure so that the dashed line is a line of symmetry.

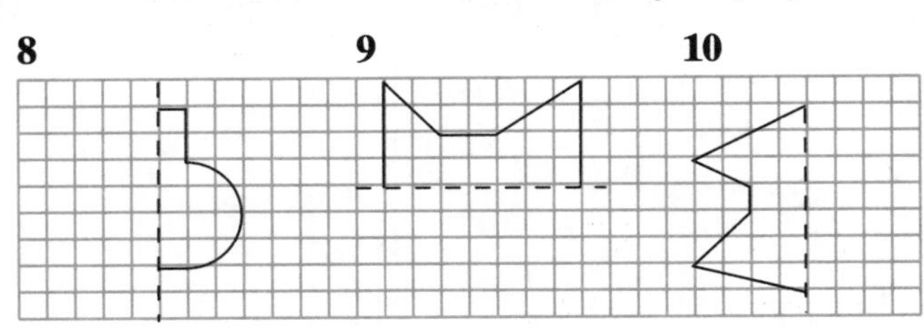

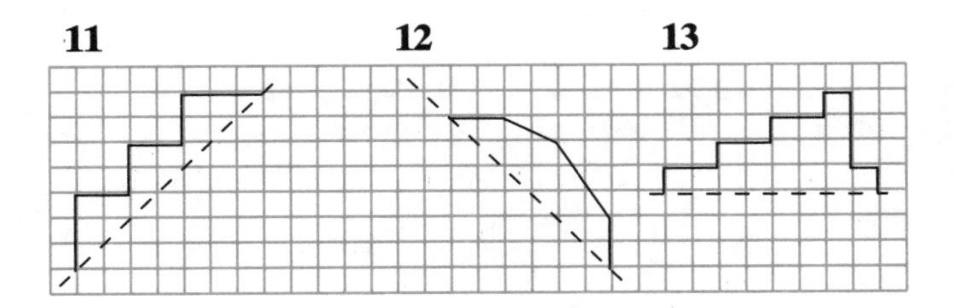

Two or more lines of symmetry

A rectangle has two lines of symmetry:

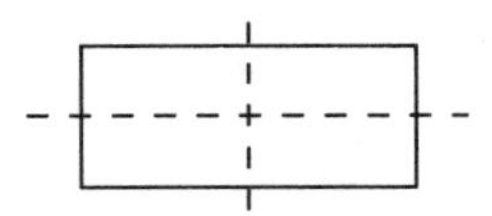

An equilateral triangle has three lines of symmetry:

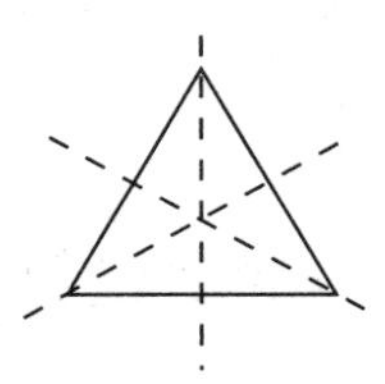

A square has four lines of symmetry:

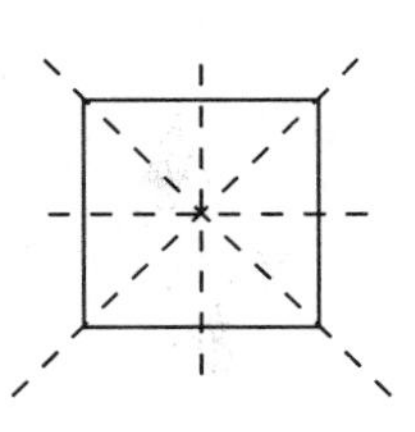

EXERCISE 14b

Copy each diagram and mark as many lines of symmetry as you can find.

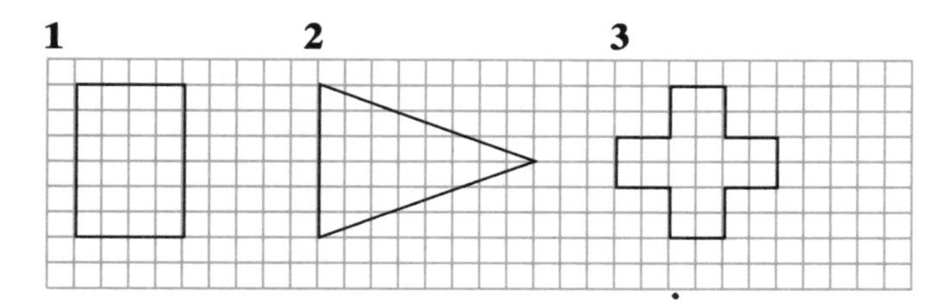

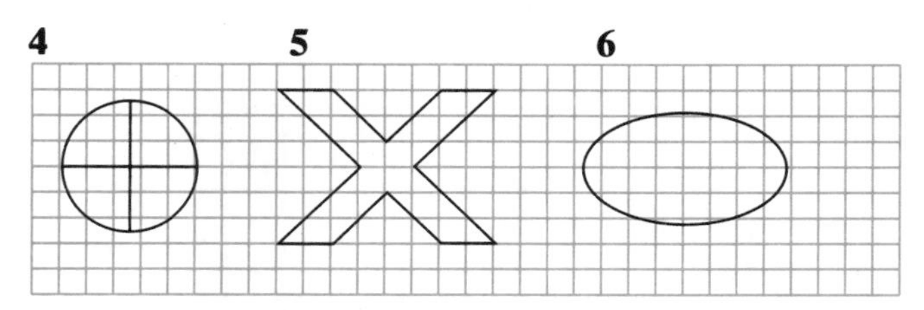

In questions 7 to 10 copy each drawing and complete the figure so that the dashed lines are lines of symmetry.

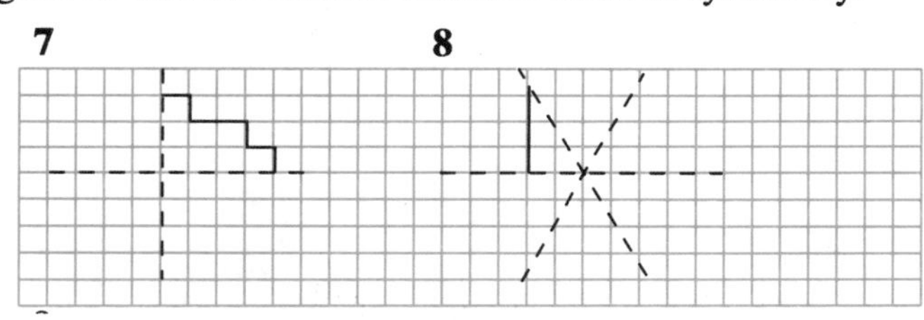

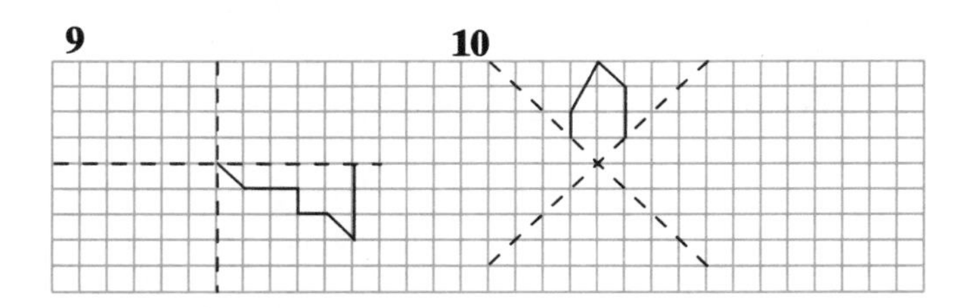

11 Draw a quadrilateral that has
(a) 1 line of symmetry
(b) 2 lines of symmetry
(c) 4 lines of symmetry
(d) no lines of symmetry.

Rotational symmetry

This shape appears on many French cars. If we rotate it through half a turn about its centre we would be unable to tell that it had been moved.

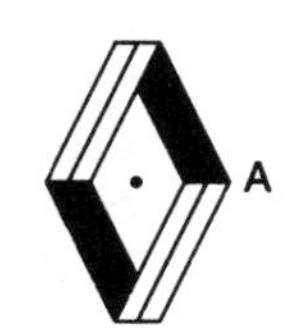

Follow the position of A as we turn the shape through half a revolution clockwise about its centre (marked with a dot). We need two such turns to get A back to its starting point. This shape has rotational symmetry of order 2.

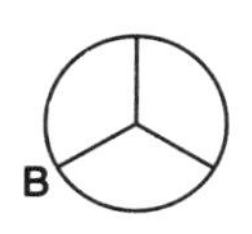

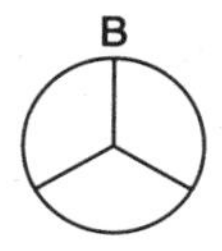

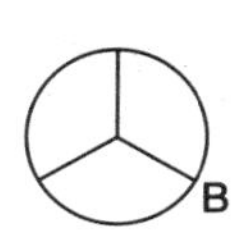

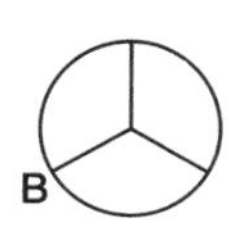

For this shape, turning it through 120° leaves its position looking unchanged. Three turns, each of one-third of a revolution, are needed to bring B back to its starting point. This shape has rotational symmetry of order 3.

EXERCISE 14c

In questions 1 to 6 give the order of rotational symmetry for each shape.

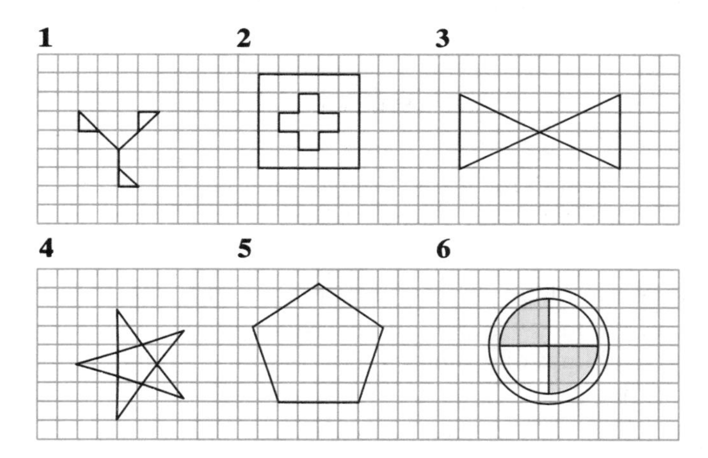

7 Do any of the shapes given in Exercise 14b questions 1 to 6 have rotational symmetry? If they do, give the order of that symmetry.

8 Draw a shape of your own choice (and not given in this chapter) that has rotational symmetry of order
(a) 2 (b) 3 (c) 4.

Line and rotational symmetry

In the previous exercise we saw that some shapes, for example the shapes in questions 2 to 6, have both line and rotational symmetry.

EXERCISE 14d

For each shape give (a) the number of lines of symmetry (b) the order of rotational symmetry. (If the answer to either part is 'none' then say so.)

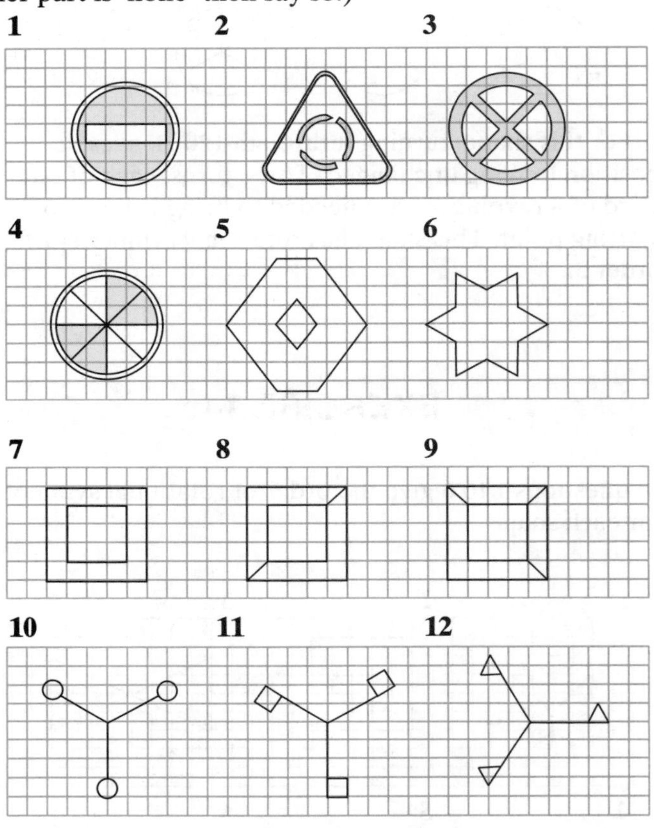

13 Draw a shape of your own choice that has (a) 1 line of symmetry and rotational symmetry of order 2 (b) 2 lines of symmetry and rotational symmetry of order 2.

14 This shape (called a regular hexagon) has 6 equal sides and 6 equal angles. (a) How many lines of symmetry does it have? (b) What order of rotational symmetry does this shape have?

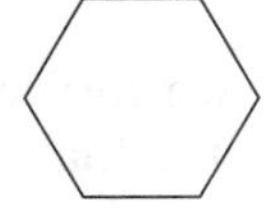

Congruence

Two shapes are congruent if they have exactly the same size and shape. If one shape is turned over or round it will fit exactly over the other.

Examples of congruent shapes are:

EXERCISE 14e

In questions 1 to 6, for each pair of figures say whether or not the second figure is an exact copy of the first. If you are unsure try using tracing paper.

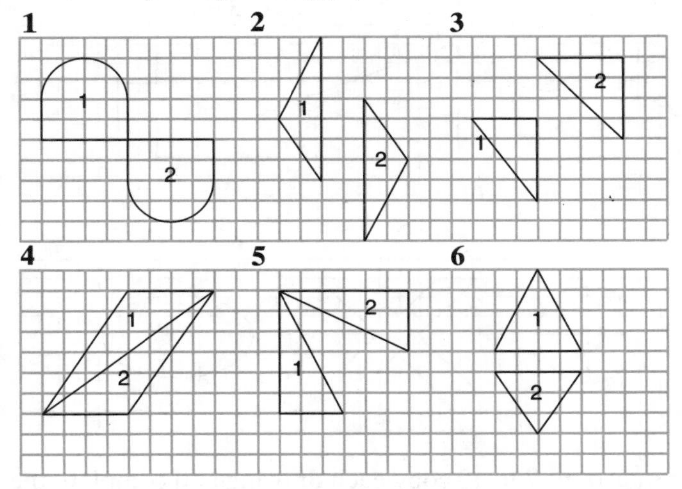

In questions 7 to 12 use line symmetry and/or rotational symmetry to decide whether or not the given shapes are congruent. In some cases the two shapes are joined together.

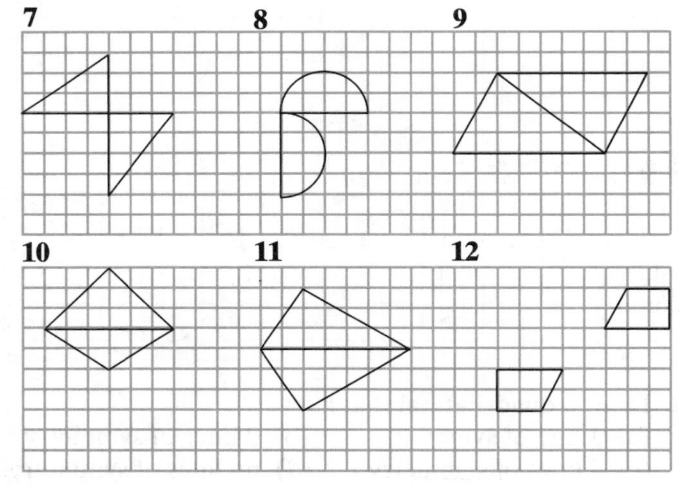

In questions 13 to 18 use one straight line to divide the given figure into two congruent shapes.

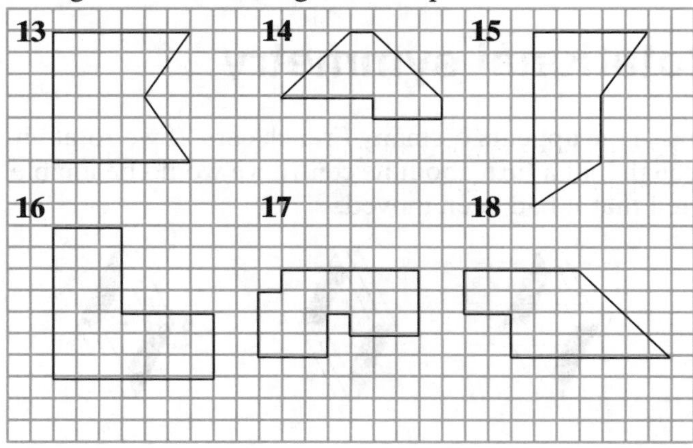

19

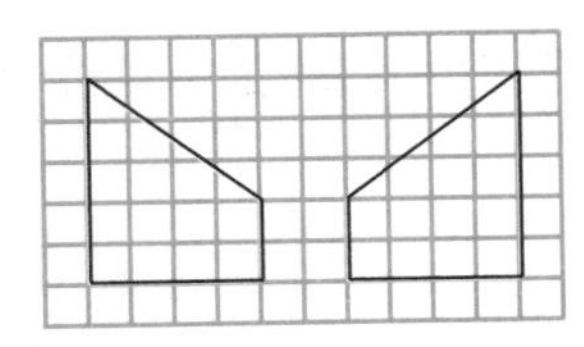

Find as many different ways as you can of fitting these two congruent shapes together so that their common edge is an axis of symmetry for the new shape. One way is given below.

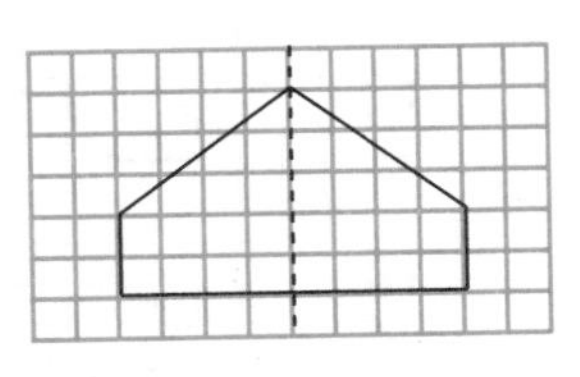

20

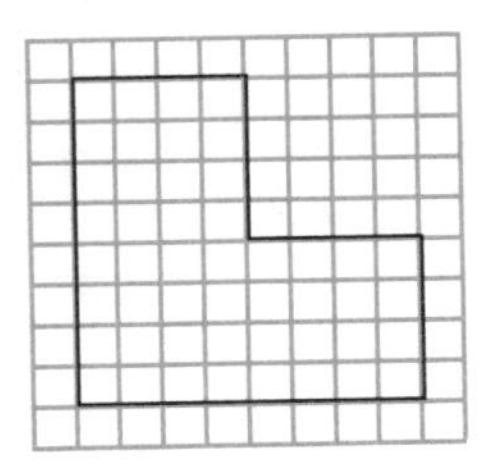

A farmer has a large, L-shaped field which he wishes to divide into four congruent shapes. How does he do it?

Tessellation

Identical shapes that fit together to cover a flat surface, without leaving any gaps, are said to *tessellate*. For example

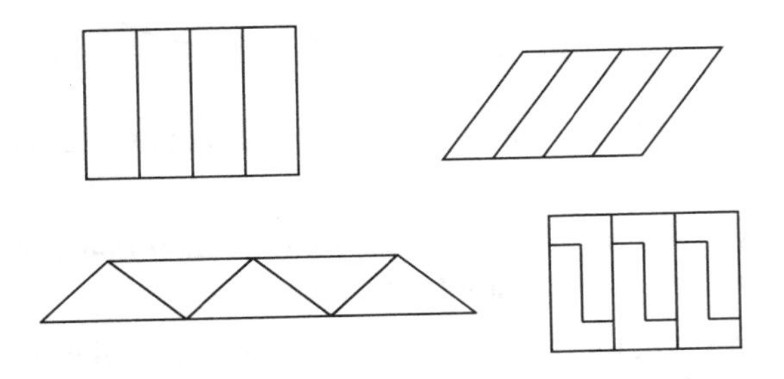

Tessellations can sometimes be made using more than one shape. For example

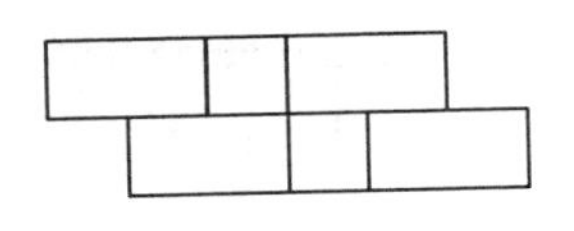

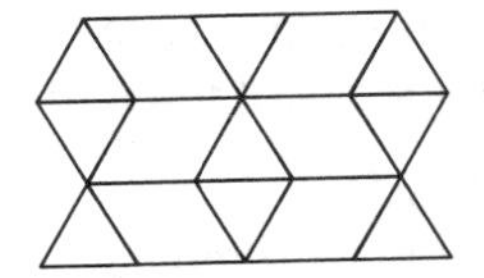

EXERCISE 14f

Use squared paper to show that each of these shapes tessellate.

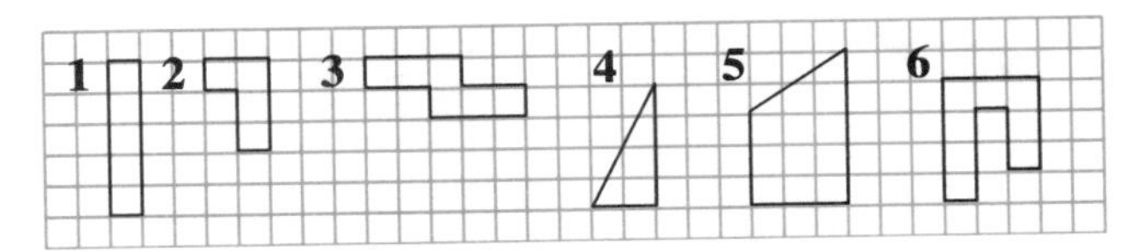

Similarity

If all the dimensions of a cube are increased by a factor of 2 then the area of each face is increased by a factor of 2×2, i.e. 4, and the volume of the cube is increased by a factor of $2 \times 2 \times 2$, i.e. 8.

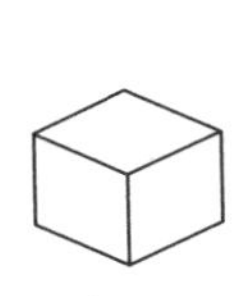

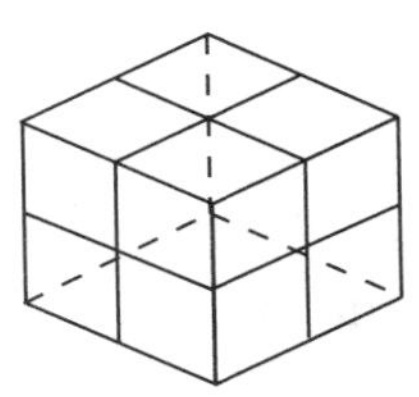

Every solid can be thought of as the sum of a number of very small cubes. It follows that if all the dimensions of a solid are doubled (i.e. multiplied by a factor of 2) then its surface area will be 4 times as big and its volume will be 8 times as big.

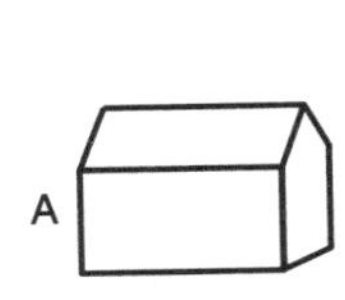

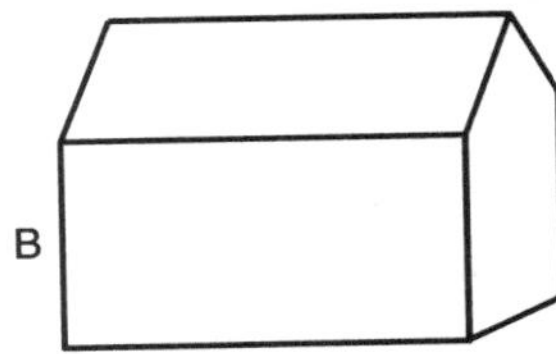

Two models of the same house, A and B, are such that B is twice as high, twice as wide and twice as long as A.

The area of each wall in B is 4 times the area of the corresponding wall in A and the area of B's roof is 4 times the area of A's roof.

Comparing their volumes, the volume of any room in house B is 8 times the volume of the corresponding room in house B. For example the volume of B's lounge is 8 times the volume of A's lounge.

If two figures or objects have exactly the same shape we say that they are **similar**. Some examples are given below.

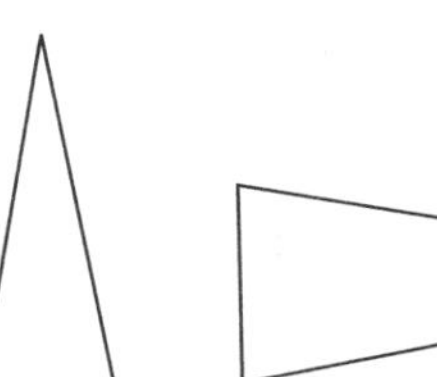

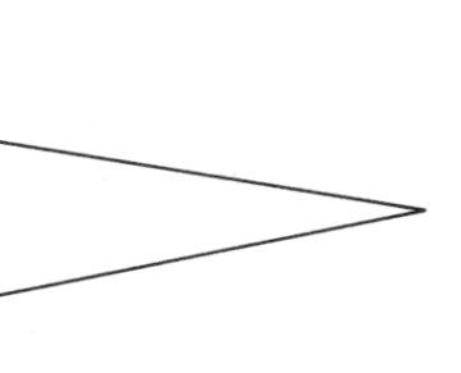

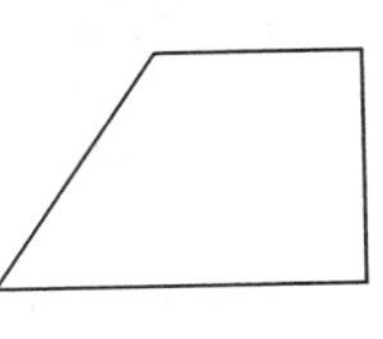

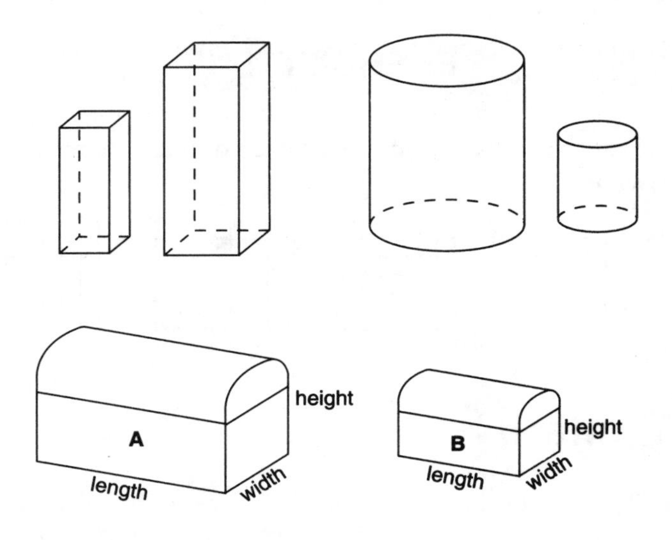

If two shapes, A and B, are similar then

$$\frac{\text{height of A}}{\text{height of B}} = \frac{\text{width of A}}{\text{width of B}} = \frac{\text{length of A}}{\text{length of B}}$$

$$= \frac{\text{any length on A}}{\text{the corresponding length on B}}$$

always gives the same value.

EXERCISE 14g

QUESTION

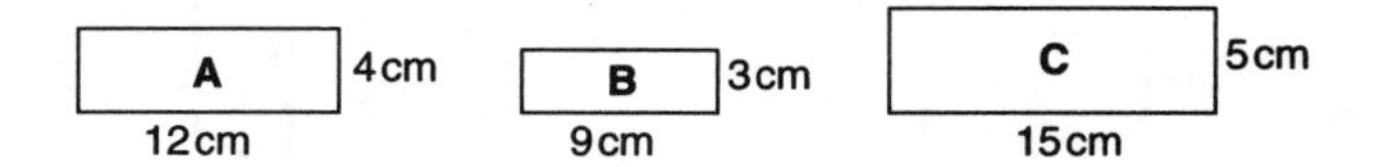

Show that (a) rectangles A and B are similar
(b) rectangles A and C are not.

ANSWER

(a) For rectangles A and B,

$$\frac{\text{length of A}}{\text{length of B}} = \frac{12}{9} = \frac{4}{3} \text{ and } \frac{\text{width of A}}{\text{width of B}} = \frac{4}{3}$$

Since each fraction gives the same value the rectangles are similar.

(b) For rectangles A and C,

$$\frac{\text{length of A}}{\text{length of C}} = \frac{12}{15} = \frac{4}{5} \text{ and } \frac{\text{width of A}}{\text{width of C}} = \frac{4}{6} = \frac{2}{3}$$

These fractions are different, so the rectangles are not similar.

1 Which of the following pairs of shapes are similar and which are not?

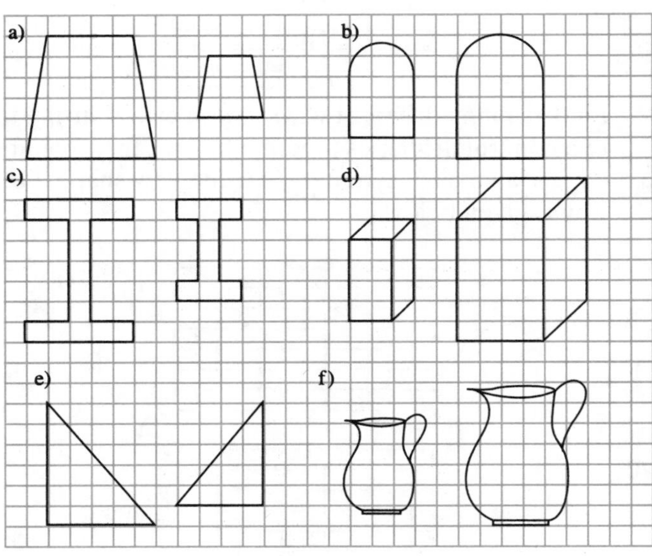

2

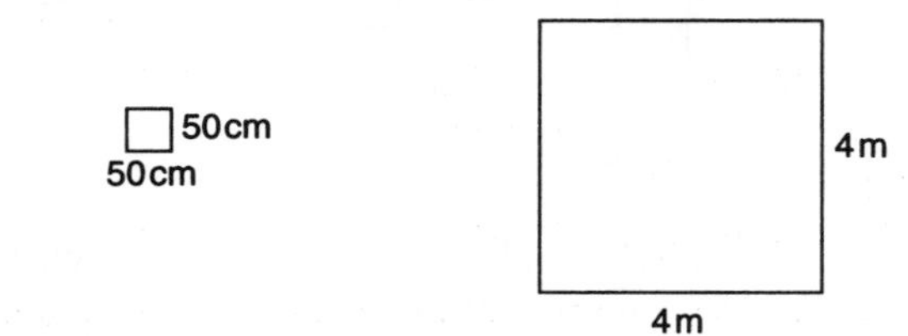

(a) Are these two shapes similar? (b) Draw a sketch to show how many slabs of side 50 cm are needed to cover a yard measuring 4 m × 4 m?

QUESTION

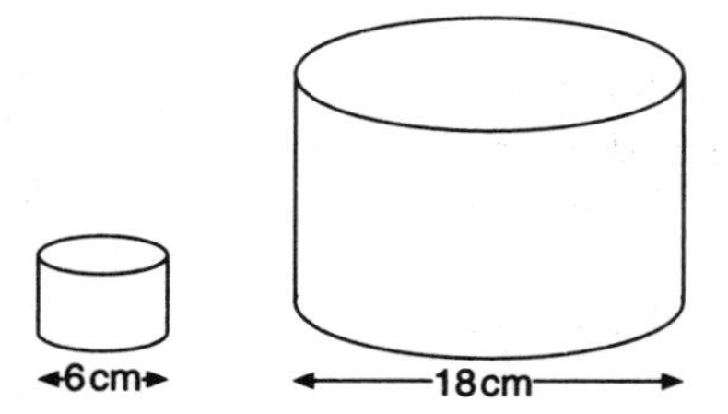

The diameters of two similar cylindrical cans are 6 cm and 18 cm.

(a) What factor do you multiply the smaller diameter by to get the larger diameter?

(b) What factor do you multiply the area of the base of the smaller can by to get the area of the base of the larger can?

(c) What factor do you multiply the capacity of the smaller can by to get the capacity of the larger can?

(d) If the capacity of the smaller can is 0.5 litres find the capacity of the larger can.

ANSWER

(a) 6 must be multiplied by 3 to give 18.

(b) Since each unit of length is increased to 3 units, each unit of area will increase to 3×3 units, i.e. 9 units. The multiplying factor is therefore 9.

(c) Since each unit of length is increased to 3 units, each unit of capacity will increase to $3 \times 3 \times 3$ units, i.e. 27 units. The multiplying factor is therefore 27.

(d) The capacity of the larger can is 27 times the capacity of the smaller can, so the capacity of the larger can is 0.5×27 litres $= 13.5$ litres.

3

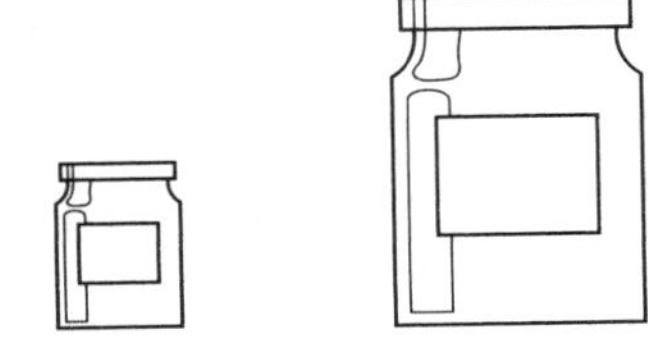

Two jars of sweet pickle are similar in shape and content.

(a) If the larger jar is twice as tall as the smaller jar, what is the multiplying factor to find the amount of pickle in the larger jar if you are given the amount in the smaller jar?

(b) The smaller jar contains 100 g. How much is in the larger one?

4

A gardener has two similar flower pots. The diameter of the top of the larger pot is three times the diameter of the top of the smaller pot. The smaller pot is filled with potting compost, which is then tipped into the larger pot. How many times must this be done to fill the larger pot?

5

The larger bottle of Gloy is similar to the smaller bottle but is twice as tall.

(a) The smaller bottle holds 2 fluid ounces. How much does the larger bottle hold?

(b) The smaller bottle cost 80p. How much will the larger bottle cost if it is priced at the same rate?

6 In Jamaica it is commonplace to carve objects out of wood and then paint them. The sketch shows two similar wooden carvings that have been painted.

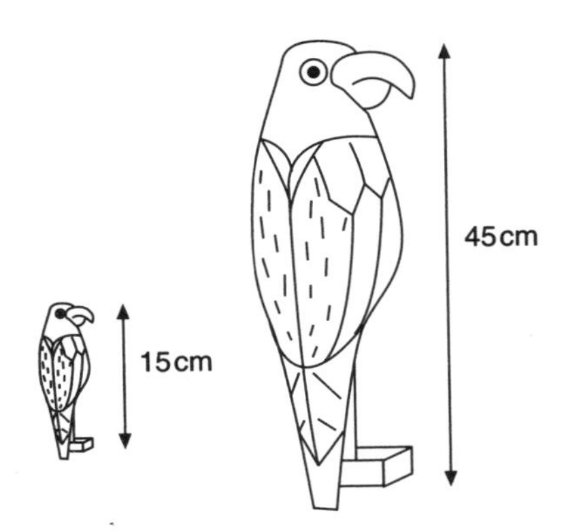

(a) What number do you multiply the surface area of the smaller carving by to give the surface area of the larger one?

(b) How much more paint is needed to cover the larger carving than the smaller one?

(c) Assuming that they are made from the same type of wood, how many times heavier is the larger carving than the smaller one?

7 A toyshop sells two sizes of models of a particular articulated lorry with its trailer. The width of the smaller model is 3 cm and the width of the larger model is 4.5 cm.

(a) What fraction (as a common fraction or as a decimal) must the length of the smaller lorry be multiplied by to give the length of the longer lorry?

(b) The surface area of the base of the trailer attached to the smaller lorry is 18 cm^2. What is the surface area of the trailer that is attached to the larger lorry?

(c) The cab of the smaller lorry has a capacity of 12 cm^3. What is the capacity of the cab of the larger lorry?

8

The model of an engine is $\frac{1}{72}$ full size and has a mass of 50 g. The total *surface* area of the engine is therefore 72×72 times as much as the surface area of the model. Find the mass of the engine, assuming that it is made from the same materials as the model, in
(a) grams (b) kilograms (c) tonnes.
(Give each answer correct to 3 s.f.)

Multiple-choice questions 14

In this exercise several alternative answers are given. Write down the letter that corresponds to the correct answer.

1 The number of lines of symmetry in a rectangle is

A 0 **B** 1 **C** 2 **D** 3

2

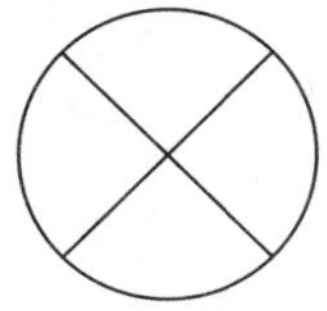

This figure has rotational symmetry of order

A 1 **B** 2 **C** 3 **D** 4

3

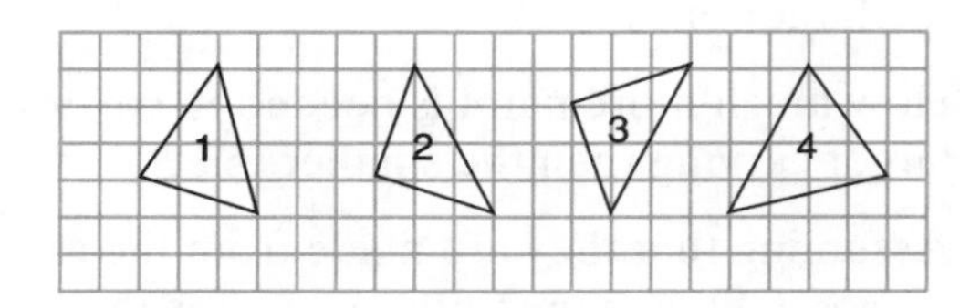

The two shapes that are congruent are

A 1 and 2 **B** 2 and 3 **C** 3 and 4
D 1 and 4

4

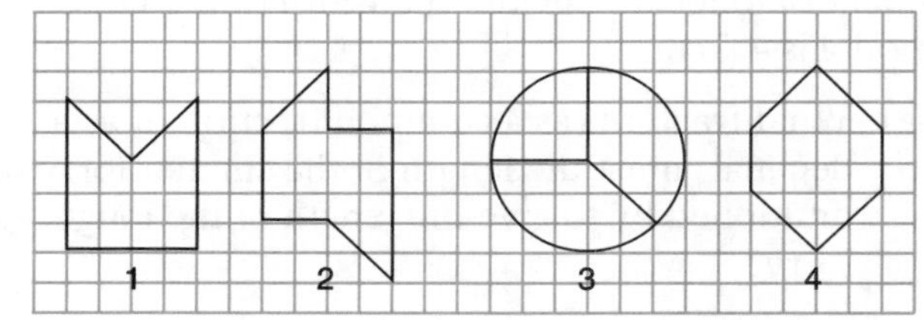

The only shape that has both line symmetry and rotational symmetry is

A 1 **B** 2 **C** 3 **D** 4

Self-assessment test 14

1

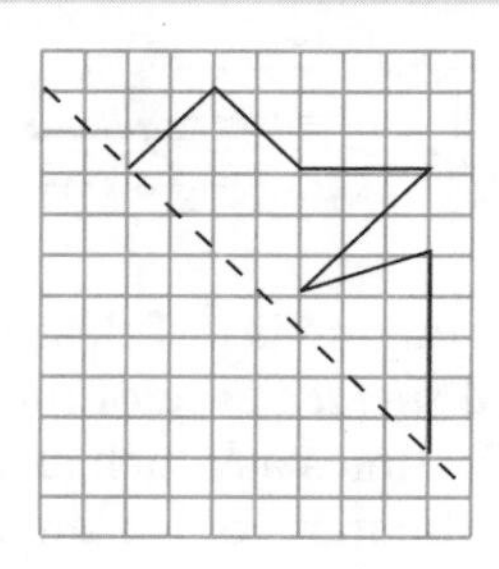

Copy the drawing and complete the figure so that the dashed line is a line of symmetry.

2

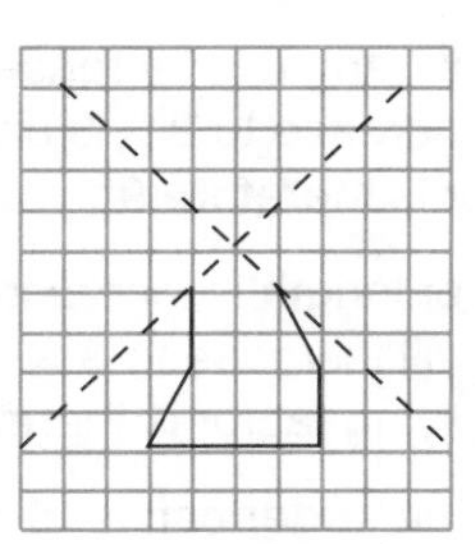

Copy the drawing and complete the figure so that both dashed lines are lines of symmetry.

3

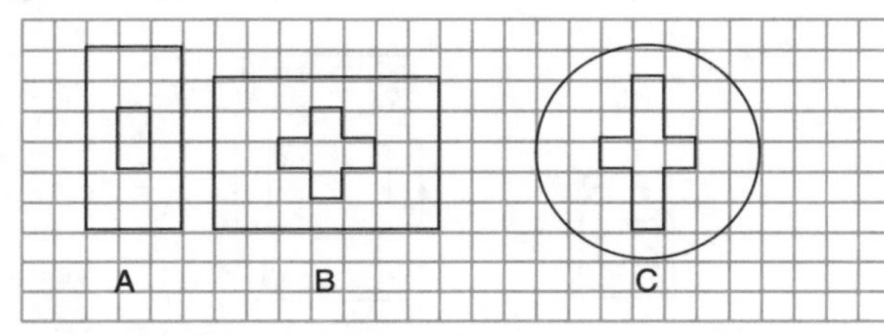

For each shape state (a) the number of lines of symmetry (b) the order of rotational symmetry.

4

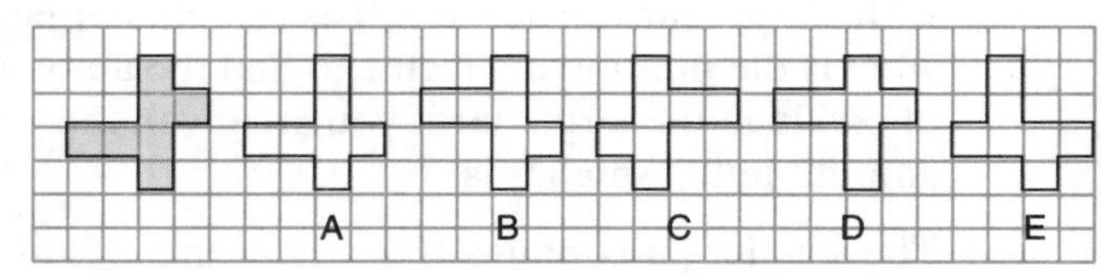

Which shapes are congruent with the shaded figure?

5 State whether or not the following pairs of shapes are congruent.

(a) (b)

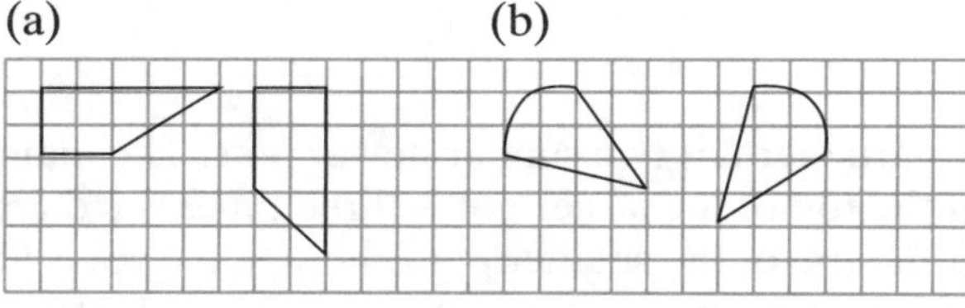

(c) (d)

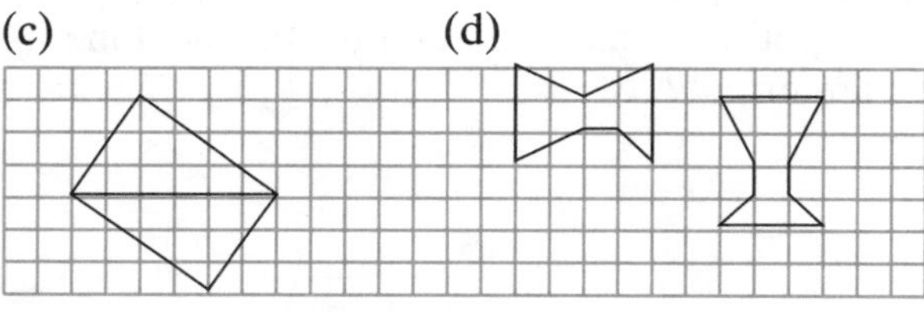

6

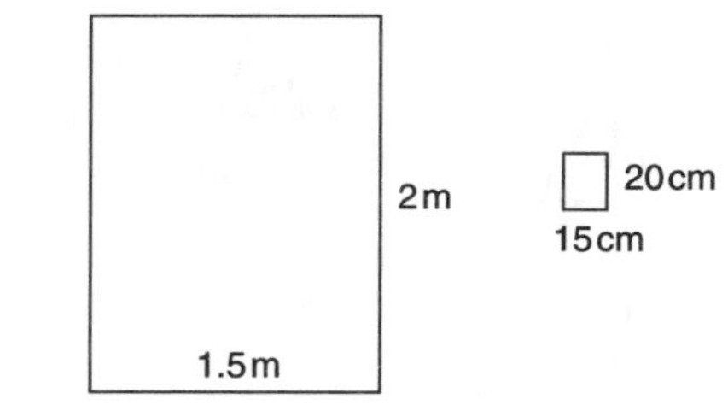

A bathroom wall measuring 2 m by 1.5 m is to be covered with rectangular tiles measuring 20 cm by 15 cm. (a) Are the two shapes similar? Justify your answer. (b) How many tiles are needed?

7 The diagram shows two similar open rectangular metal boxes.

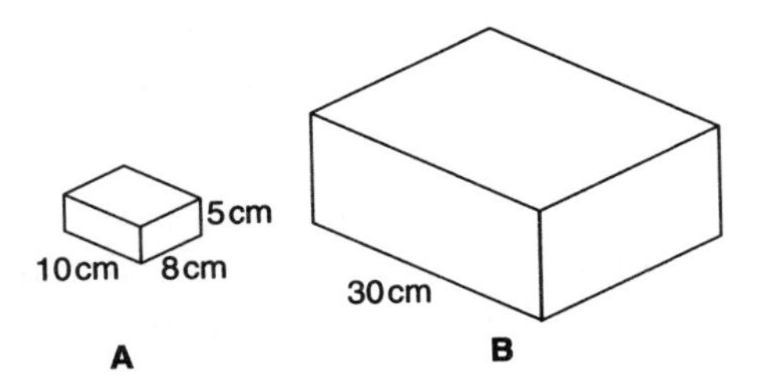

By what number must we multiply (a) the height of the A to get the height of the B (b) the width of A to get the width of B (c) the area of the largest face of A to get the area of the largest face of B (d) the capacity of A to get the capacity of B?

CHAPTER 15

Solids

Cubes

We are all familiar with cubes in everyday life, for example, an Oxo cube or a child's building block.

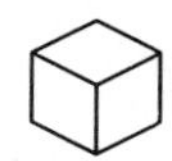

Every cube has 6 square *faces*.
Two faces meet in an *edge*. A cube has 12 edges.
Three faces, and three edges, meet at a *corner*. A corner is sometimes called a *vertex*. A cube has 8 corners.

An outline that we can cut out and fold to make a 3-dimensional shape is called its *net*. One net for a cube is given below.

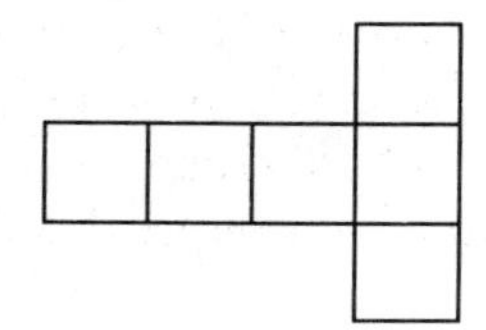

Cuboids

A cuboid is a rectangular block.

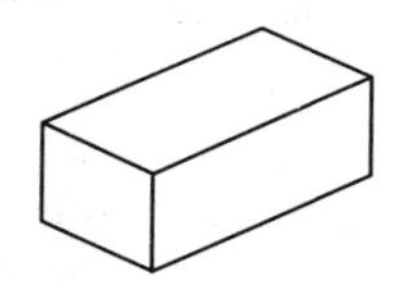

EXERCISE 15a

1

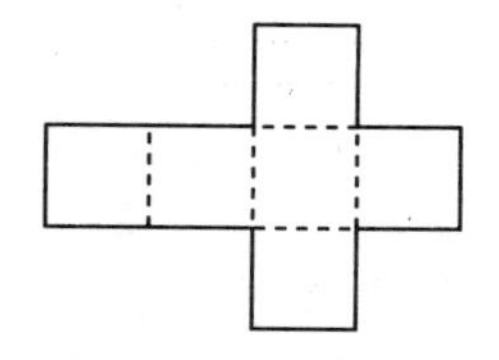

(a) Draw this net on squared paper four times the size you see here. Cut it out and fold it along the dashed lines. Join the edges together using adhesive tape.

(b) Use your cube to check the number of faces, edges and corners given in the text.

2

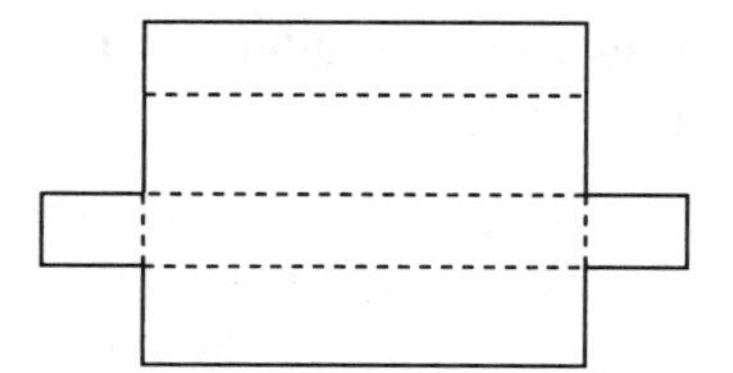

This is a net for a cuboid. Draw this net on squared paper four times this size. Cut it out and fold it along the dashed lines. Join the edges together using adhesive tape.

(a) Count the number of faces. What name do you give to their shapes?

(b) Count (i) the number of edges
(ii) the number of corners.

(c) How do the numbers of faces, edges and corners compare with those for a cube?

Prisms

Any shape that has the same cross-section all the way along its length is called a *prism*. The shape of the cross-section gives the name to the prism.

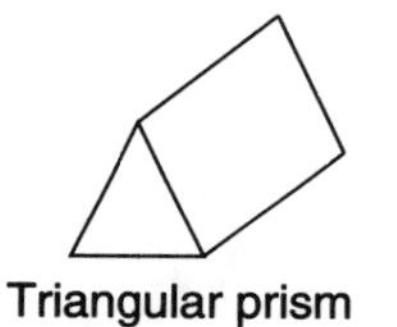

Triangular prism

Trapezoidal prism

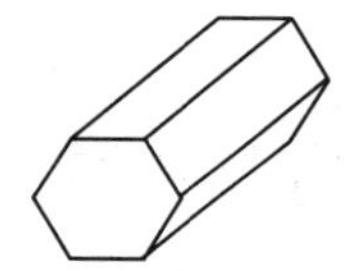

Hexagonal prism

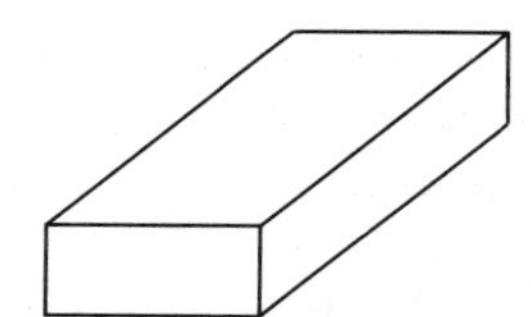

A rectangular prism, also called a cuboid

EXERCISE 15b

1

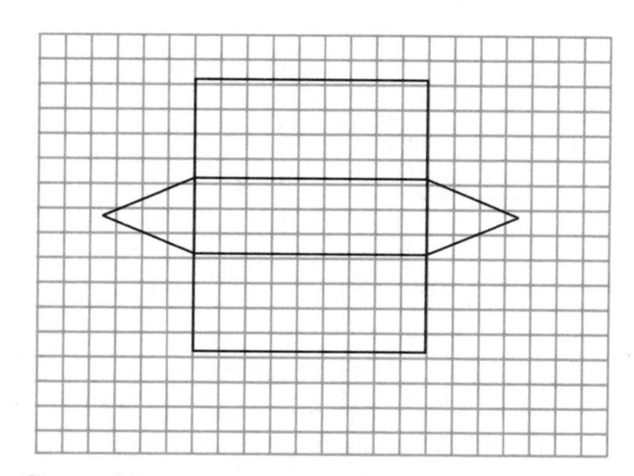

(a) Copy this net on to squared paper making each square of side 1 cm. Cut it out, fold it and stick the edges together to form a prism. What type of prism have you made?

(b) How many faces does it have? How many of these faces are (i) rectangles (ii) triangles?

(c) How many (i) edges (ii) corners, does it have?

2

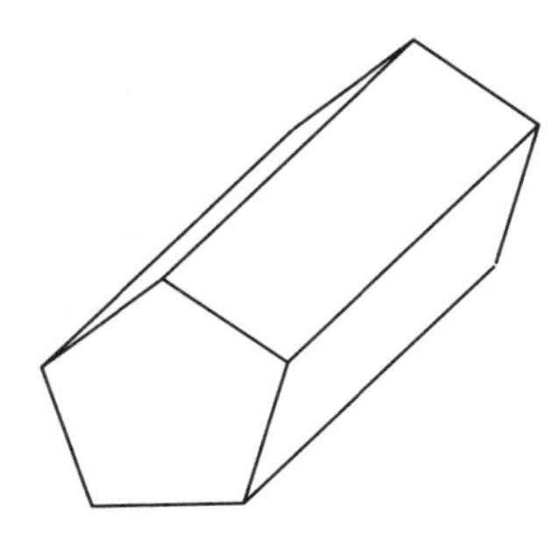

(a) What word describes the shape of the cross-section of this solid?

(b) What kind of prism do you call it?

(c) How many (i) faces (ii) edges (iii) corners, does this solid have?

(d) How many of the faces are (i) rectangles (ii) not rectangles?

Pyramids

A 3-dimensional shape that has a flat base, and which comes up to a point, is called a *pyramid*. The type of pyramid is determined by the shape of the base. For example, a pyramid with a square base is called a *square pyramid*. A pyramid with a triangular base has a special name; it is called a *tetrahedron*.

EXERCISE 15c

1

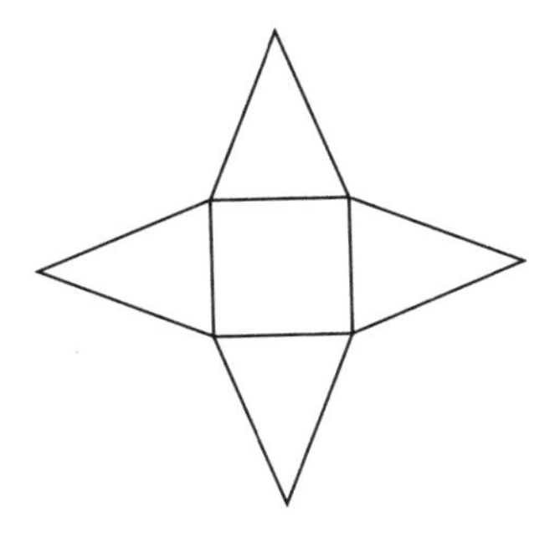

(a) This net, shown half-size, is for a square pyramid. Copy it, cut it out and stick the edges together.

(b) How many faces does it have? Describe the shapes of the faces.

(c) How many (i) edges (ii) corners, does it have?

2 (a) Sketch a pyramid that has a five-sided base.

(b) How many faces does it have? What is the shape of each face apart from the base?

(c) How many (i) edges (ii) corners, does it have?

2-D representation of 3-D shapes

Drawing a three-dimensional (3-D) shape on a flat sheet of paper, i.e. in two dimensions (2-D), is not easy. Two methods, each with their own advantages and disadvantages, are given below.

Oblique drawings

You will probably find squared or dotted paper helpful to start with, but you should progress rapidly to drawing most shapes easily on plain paper.

Here is how to make an oblique drawing of a cube on squared paper.

(a) Draw the front face.

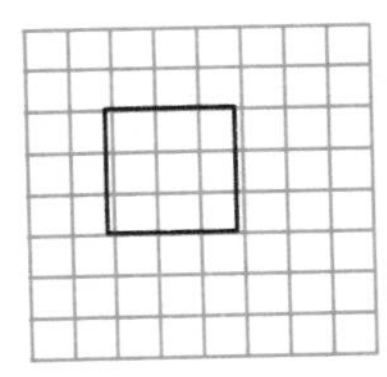

(b) Draw the opposite face the same size but slightly offset from the first.

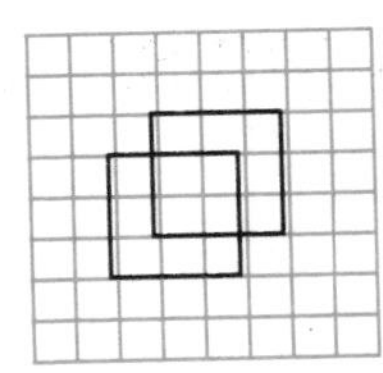

(c) Join the matching corners.

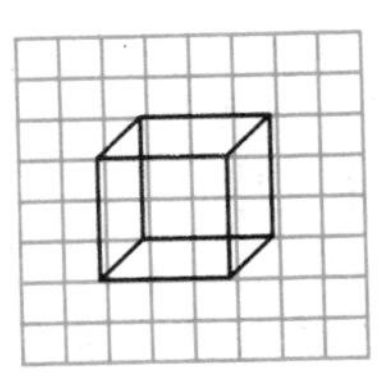

The convention is that we use solid lines for edges we can see, but dashed lines for edges we know exist but cannot see, i.e. for hidden edges.

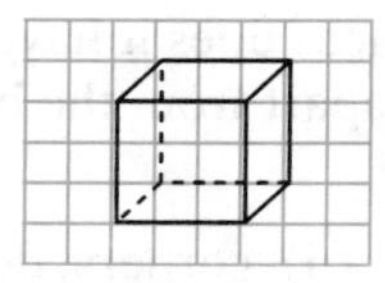

Using this convention, the cube we have drawn above is now redrawn.

Now try drawing a cuboid, first using all solid lines, and then dashed lines for the edges that you cannot see.

Isometric drawings

Isometric drawings are easier to do on isometric graph paper or on isometric dot paper, but with a little practice can be drawn effectively on plain paper.

Here is how to make an isometric drawing of a cuboid on isometric graph paper.

(a) Draw the top face. The top face of a cuboid is a rectangle but is drawn here as a parallelogram.

(b) Draw the four vertical edges, all of which are parallel and equal in length.

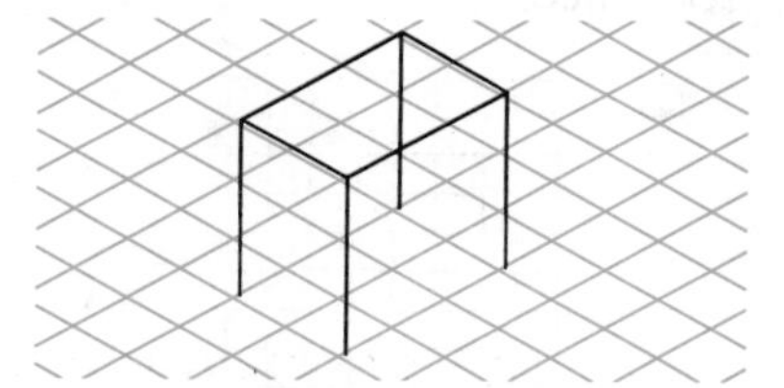

(c) Join the matching bottom corners.

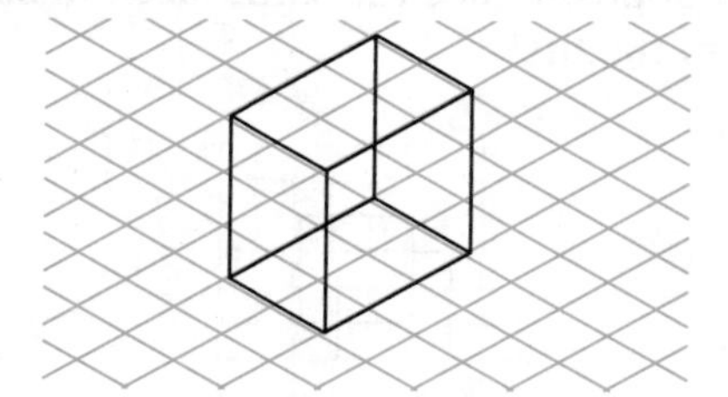

The corresponding drawing using isometric dot paper is given here.

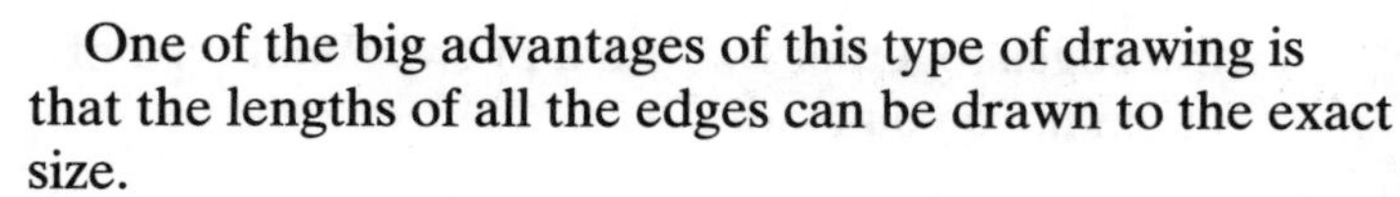

One of the big advantages of this type of drawing is that the lengths of all the edges can be drawn to the exact size.

You do not have to draw the lines in the order in which they are given above, but it is probably wise to decide on an order that is suitable for you and stick to it.

EXERCISE 15d

Several different oblique drawings of solids, together with their dimensions in cm, are given below.

(a) Look at each shape in turn, study it, then close the book and see if you can make your own oblique drawing of it from the picture you have in your mind. (Should you find this difficult, make a freehand sketch, and put the dimensions on it, before you close the book.)

(b) Make an isometric drawing of each shape using either isometric graph paper or isometric dot paper. (See that you place the paper in the correct position in front of you, i.e. as it has been positioned in the text.)

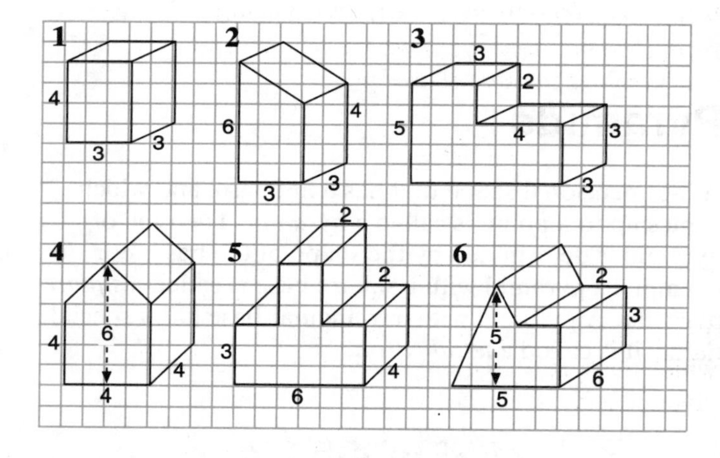

Questions 7 and 8 give isometric drawings. Sketch the corresponding oblique drawings.

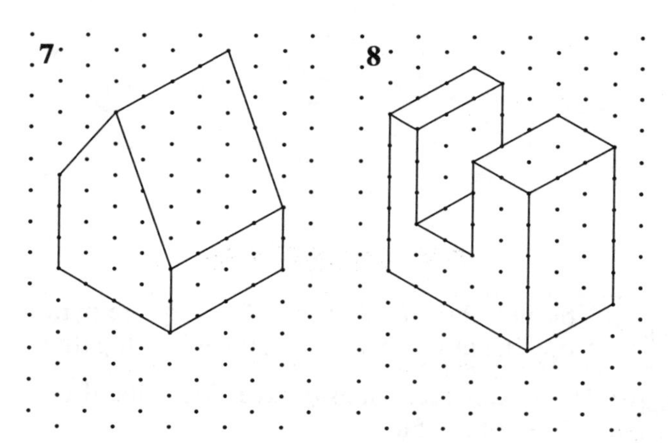

Plans and elevations

Consider this ordinary plastic beaker.

Looking directly down on it from above, it appears as two concentric circles; the outer circle is the rim of the beaker and the inner circle is the bottom of the beaker.

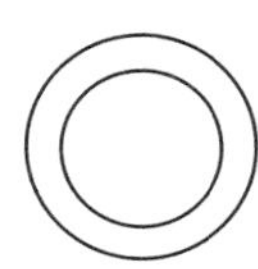

When we look from the side the beaker looks like a trapezium.

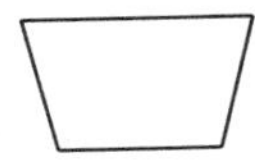

What we see when we look at a shape from above is called its *plan*.
What we see when we look from the front is called the *front elevation*, and what we see when we look from the side is called the *side elevation*.

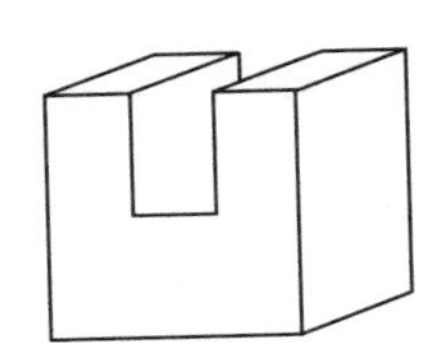

The plan, front elevation and side elevation of a cube, which has a rectangular groove cut out of one face, are given below.

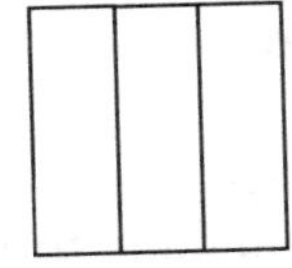

Plan

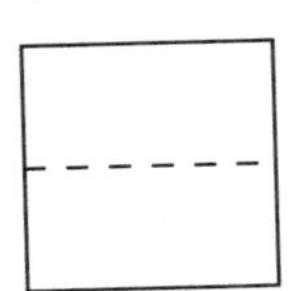

Front elevation

Side elevation

(**Note**: Hidden edges are shown by a dashed line.)

EXERCISE 15e

QUESTION
The drawing shows an I-shaped pillar which can be used to support machinery. Draw the plan, front elevation and side elevation.

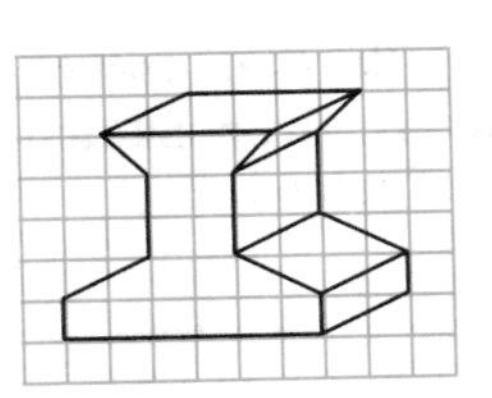

ANSWER

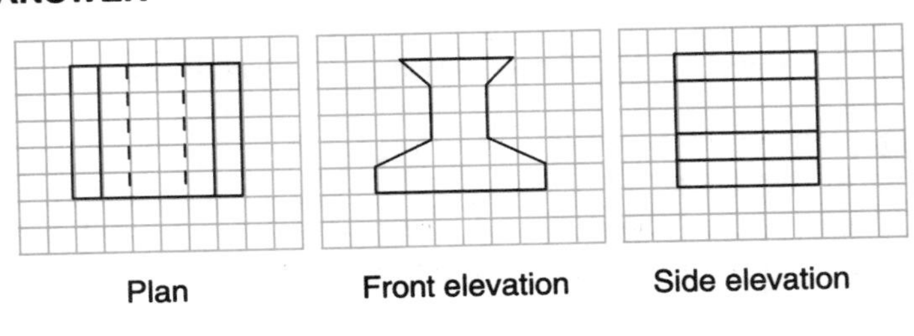

Plan　　Front elevation　　Side elevation

In questions 1 to 6 sketch the plan, front elevation and side elevation.

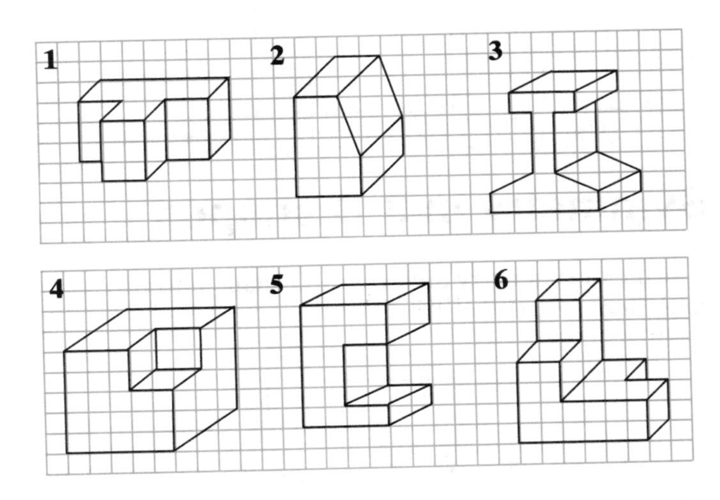

In questions 7 to 10 draw the view of each solid from the direction marked with an arrow.

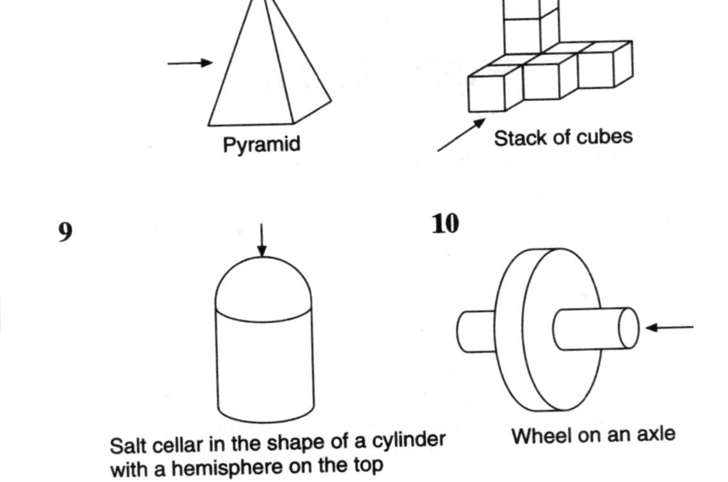

In questions 11 to 13, the plan, front elevation and side elevation for a solid are given. Sketch the solid.

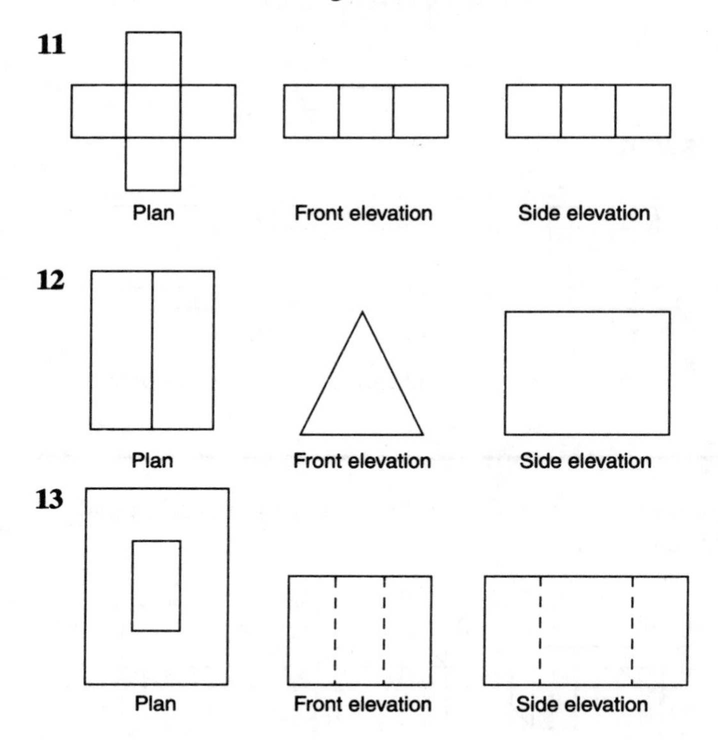

Symmetry in 3-D shapes

A plane of symmetry divides a 3-D shape into two congruent shapes.

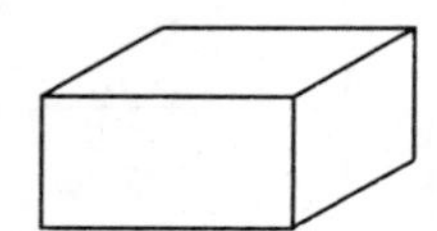

This cuboid has 3 planes of symmetry. Each one is shown below.

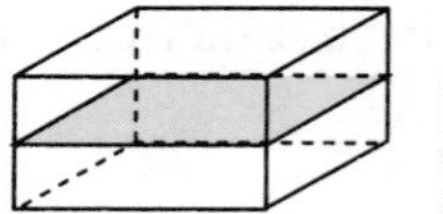
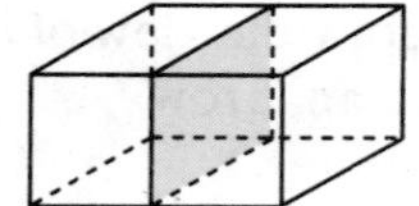
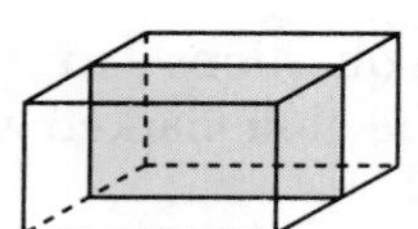

EXERCISE 15f

For each solid, decide whether or not the shaded plane is a plane of symmetry.

1

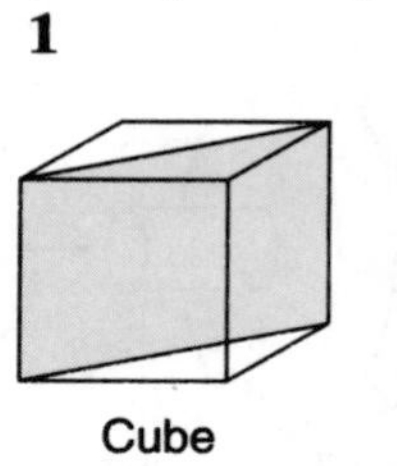

Cube

2

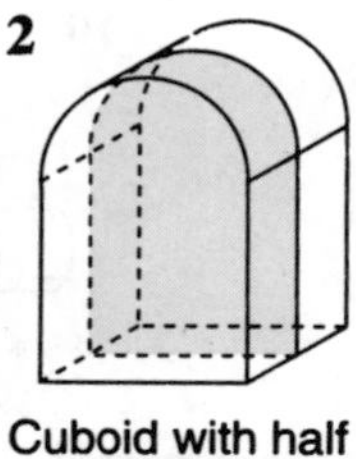

Cuboid with half a cylinder on top

3

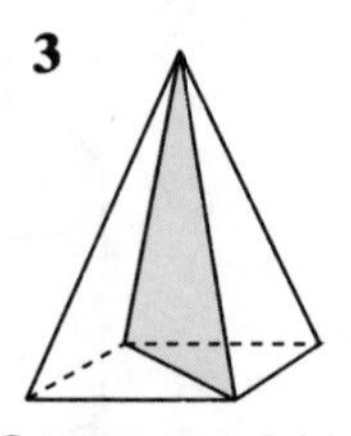

Square pyramid

4 **5**

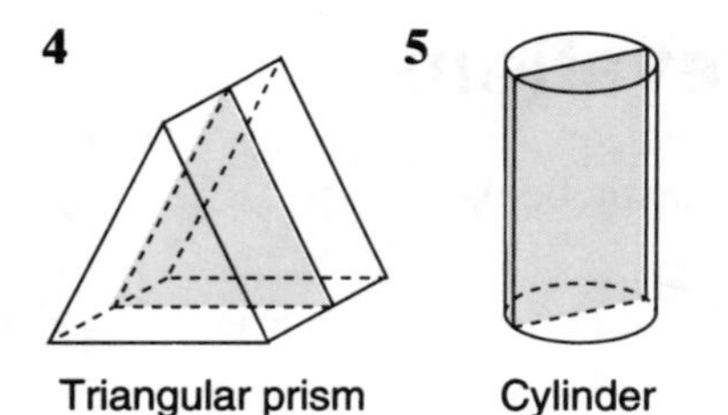

Triangular prism Cylinder

6

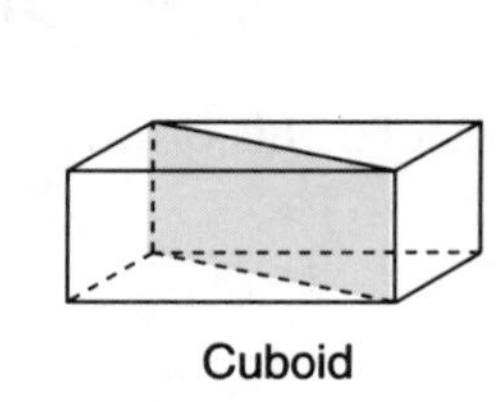

Cuboid

How many planes of symmetry can you find for the solids given in questions 7 to 12?

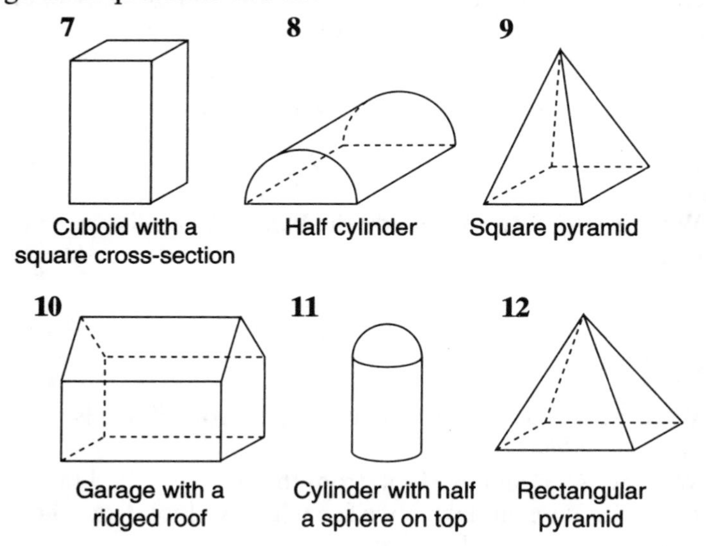

Multiple-choice questions 15

In this exercise several alternative answers are given. Write down the letter that corresponds to the correct answer.

1

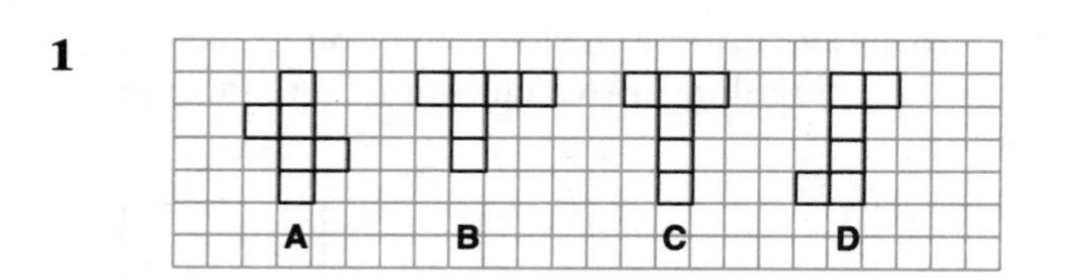

The sketch shows four different nets enclosing 6 squares. The only one that cannot be folded to form a cube is the net marked

A A **B** B **C** C **D** D

2

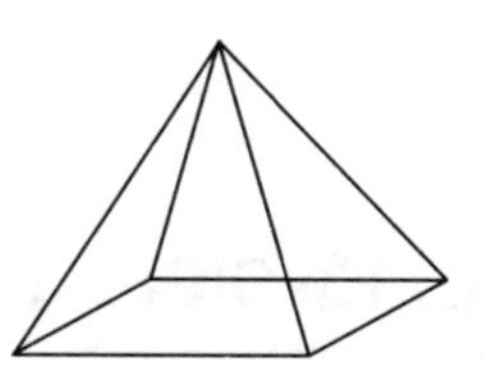

For this solid the number of edges exceeds the number of faces by

A 5 **B** 4 **C** 3 **D** 2

3

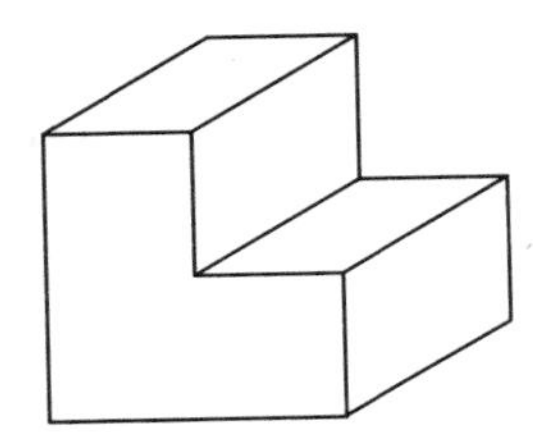

For this solid the number of planes of symmetry is

A 1 **B** 2 **C** 3 **D** 4

4

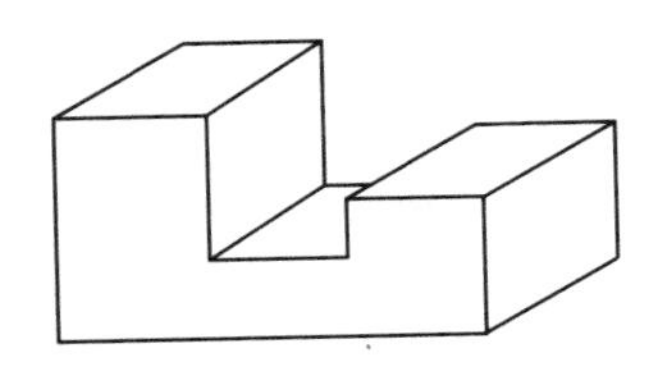

The sketch of a solid is shown above. Its plan is

A

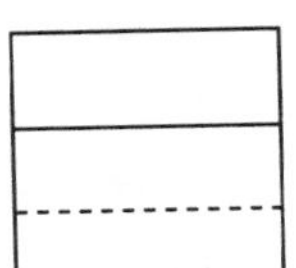

B

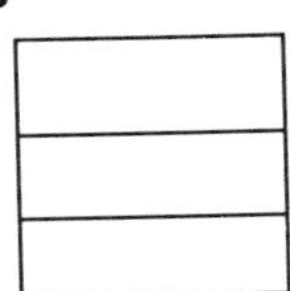

C

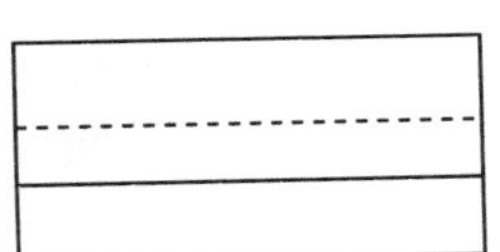

D

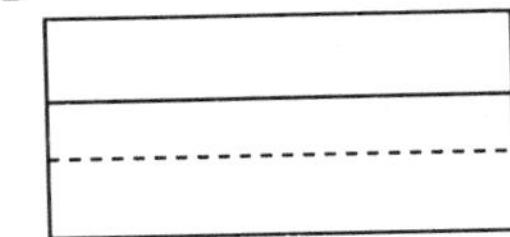

Self-assessment test 15

1

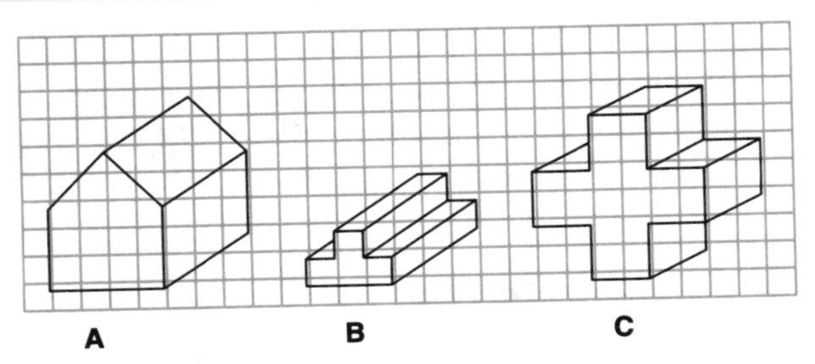

For each of these prisms state

(a) the number of (i) edges (ii) corners

(b) the number of faces that are (i) rectangular
(ii) not rectangular.

2

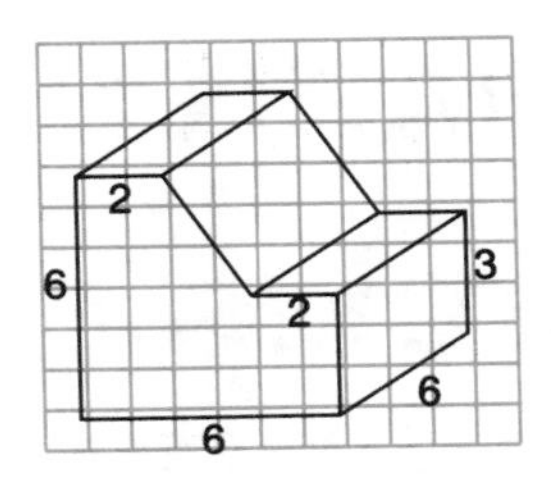

Use isometric graph paper or isometric dot paper to make an isometric drawing of this shape.

3

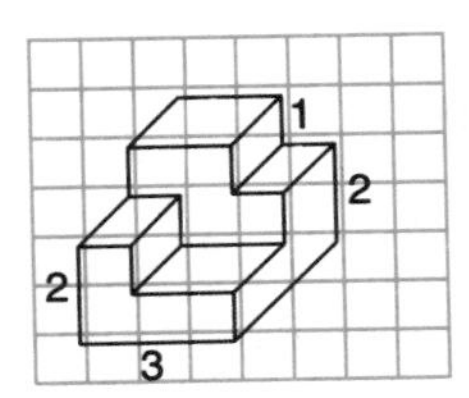

Draw the plan, front elevation and side elevation of this shape.

4

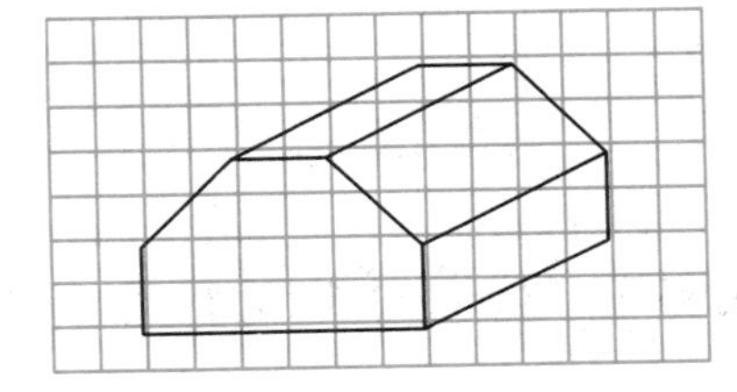

How many planes of symmetry does this shape have?

CHAPTER 16

Circles and cylinders

The basics

The names of the main parts of a circle are shown in the diagram.

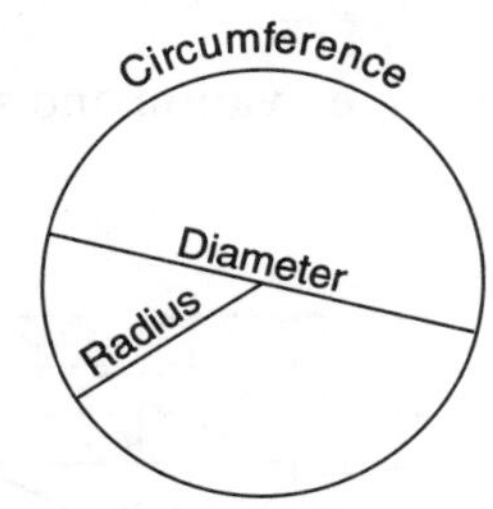

The *diameter* of a circle is the distance across the centre from edge to edge.

The radius is the distance from the centre to a point on the edge. It follows that

diameter = 2 × radius

The distance round the edge of a circle is called the *circumference*. For any circle the circumference is just over three times the length of the diameter.

EXERCISE 16a

1 The top of a tin of baked beans is an example of a circle. Name other objects that have circular parts to them.

2 For this question you need a tape measure and three or four circular objects, e.g. a can of soup, a dinner plate, a bicycle wheel, a coin.

Copy the following table.

Object	Diameter mm	Circumference mm	$\frac{\text{Circumference}}{\text{Diameter}}$

(a) Take your first object, for example the can of soup. Measure the distance across the top of the can in millimetres. Write it in your table.

(b) Next measure the distance round the can using your tape measure. Write this in the column headed 'Circumference'.

(c) Finally, write the value you get by dividing the value in the third column by the value in the second column. Give each value correct to 1 decimal place.

Repeat your measurements and calculations for the other objects you have available. Do your results confirm that the distance round the object is roughly three times its diameter?

QUESTION

Find, roughly, the circumference of a circular table if its diameter is 90 cm.

ANSWER

Circumference is roughly 3 × diameter = 3 × 90 cm
= 270 cm

---

3 Find, roughly, the circumference of a bicycle wheel that has a diameter of (a) 50 cm (b) 64 cm.

4 A clock face has a radius of 5 inches.
(a) What is its diameter? (b) What, roughly, is its circumference?

5 A car wheel is 75 cm in diameter.

(a) What, roughly, is its circumference?

(b) About how far does the car travel forward when the wheel makes one complete turn?

(c) Roughly, how far does the car travel forward when the wheel revolves 50 times? Give your answer (i) in cm (ii) in m.

The Greek letter π

The ratio $\frac{\text{circumference of circle}}{\text{diameter of circle}}$ is denoted by the Greek letter π (pronounced 'pie'). Its exact value cannot be worked out. While 3 is a very rough approximate value, and 3.142 is better, it is usually more convenient to use the value on your calculator.

Then $C = \pi D$

and $C = 2\pi r$ (since diameter = 2 × radius)

EXERCISE 16b

In this exercise, and the remaining exercises in this chapter, unless stated otherwise, use the value of π on your calculator and give answers correct to three significant figures.

1 Press the π button on your calculator and write down the value in the display. Write this value correct to
(a) 2 decimal places (b) 3 significant figures
(c) 3 decimal places.

QUESTION

Find the circumference of the top of a soup tin that has a diameter of 9.6 cm.

ANSWER

Circumference $= \pi D$
$= \pi \times 9.6$ cm (π × 9 . 6 =)
$= 30.2$ cm (3 s.f.)

2 Find the circumference of a circle with

(a) diameter 6 cm
(b) diameter 8.3 cm
(c) diameter 35.3 mm
(d) radius 3.9 cm
(e) radius 23.7 cm
(f) radius 16.3 m

3 A circular kitchen table, diameter 90 cm, has a plastic strip around the edge. How long is the strip?

4 The diameter of a 10p coin is 28 mm.
Find its circumference.

5 The diameters of three different sizes of plates in a dinner service are 16 cm, 21 cm and 27 cm. Find the circumference of each.

6 Insulation tape is wound on a cardboard ring. The inside diameter of this ring is 3.2 cm and the outside diameter is 3.9 cm.

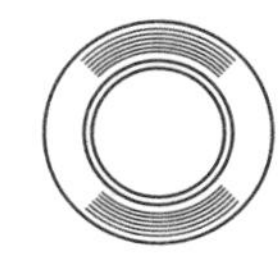

(a) How thick is the cardboard from which the ring is made?
(b) The overall diameter of the roll of tape is 6.8 cm. What depth of tape is there on the roll?

7

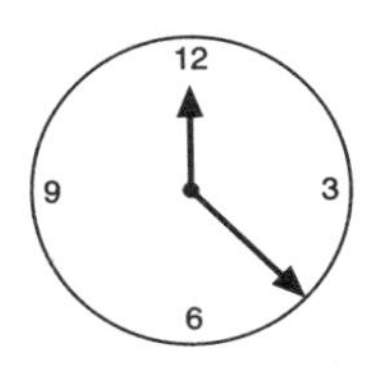

The minute hand of the town clock is 1.4 m long, while the hour hand is 0.91 m long. How far does the tip of each hand move in one hour?

8

The sketch shows a stand which is used for displaying china figures in a department store. The top is circular with a diameter of 14 cm and the bottom is a circle of diameter 17 cm.

(a) Find the circumference of each circle.

(b) The stand is to be decorated with a metal band around the top and bottom edges. What length of strip is needed?

(c) The strip is available to the nearest 5 cm. How much strip must be bought? How much is left over?

9 A cylinder lawn mower is 35 cm wide and has wheels of diameter 21 cm. Assuming that there is no slipping when the mower moves forward, find
(a) the distance moved forward for each revolution (i.e. complete turn), of the wheels
(b) the number of revolutions required to mow a straight run of 99 m.

10 An artist in a china factory paints a gold line, 0.5 cm from the edge, on saucers of diameter 12 cm, on plates of diameter 15 cm, and also on the tops of cylindrical cups of diameter 7 cm. Calculate the total length of gold line painted on a half-dozen teaset.

QUESTION

The distance round a circular running track is 400 m. What is the diameter of the track?

ANSWER

Circumference $= \pi \times$ diameter
i.e. $C = \pi \times D$
$\therefore$ $400 = \pi \times D$
i.e. $\frac{400}{\pi} = D$ (4 0 0 ÷ π =)
$\therefore$ $D = 127.32\ldots$
i.e. diameter of track is 127 m (3 s.f.)

11 Find the diameter of a circle whose circumference is

(a) 12.85 cm (b) 68.49 m (c) 734 mm.

12 Find the radius of a circle whose circumference is

(a) 18.47 cm (b) 168.39 m (c) 324 mm.

13 Findley has a 2.4 metre length of plastic edging. What is the diameter of the largest circular table that can be edged with this length of plastic?

14

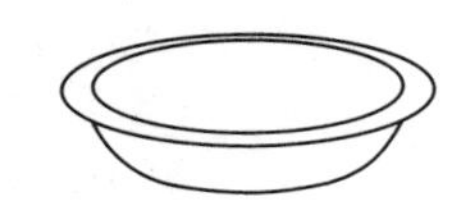

The distance round the outer edge of a soup dish is 120 cm and the distance round the inner edge of the rim is 104 cm. Find (a) the diameter of the outer edge (b) the diameter of the inner edge (c) the width of the rim.

15 A British Gas official uses a trundle wheel to check the length of a trench in which a new gas main has been laid. He pushes the wheel over the tarmacadamed surface after the job has been completed.

(a) If the radius of the wheel is 4 inches find its circumference.

(b) The wheel rotates 125 times. How long, in yards, is the trench?

(c) He wishes to mark out the next 100 yard section of gas main to be laid. How many rotations of his trundle wheel must he count to measure this distance?

16

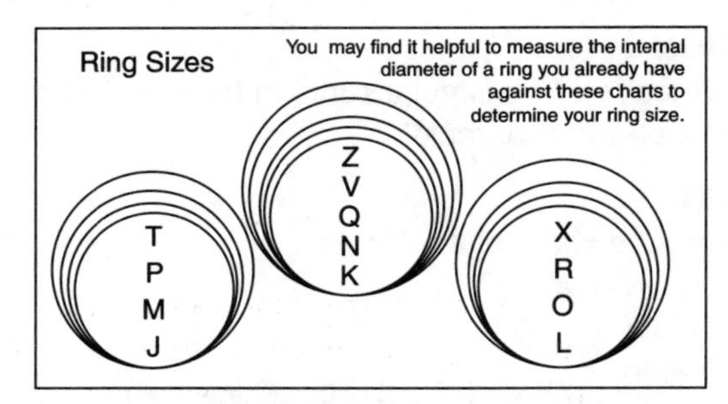

Ring sizes are referred to by the capital letters J to Z with the exception of letters S, U, W and Y. The exact size for each letter is shown on the diagram.

Use this information to find

(a) the number of different standard ring sizes;

(b) the diameter of
(i) the largest ring (ii) the smallest ring;

(c) the diameter of
(i) an M ring (ii) a V ring (iii) an L ring.

(d) A jeweller has a complete set of gold rings in a particular style. Is the difference between the diameter of one ring in the set and the next one up in size always the same? Justify your answer.

(e) If a ring is halfway between size L and size M it is referred to as size L + $\frac{1}{2}$. What is the diameter of a ring whose size is (i) Q + $\frac{1}{2}$ (ii) X + $\frac{1}{2}$?

17 Find the perimeter (the distance all the way round) of each shape. The curved lines represents half, a quarter or three-quarters of a circle.

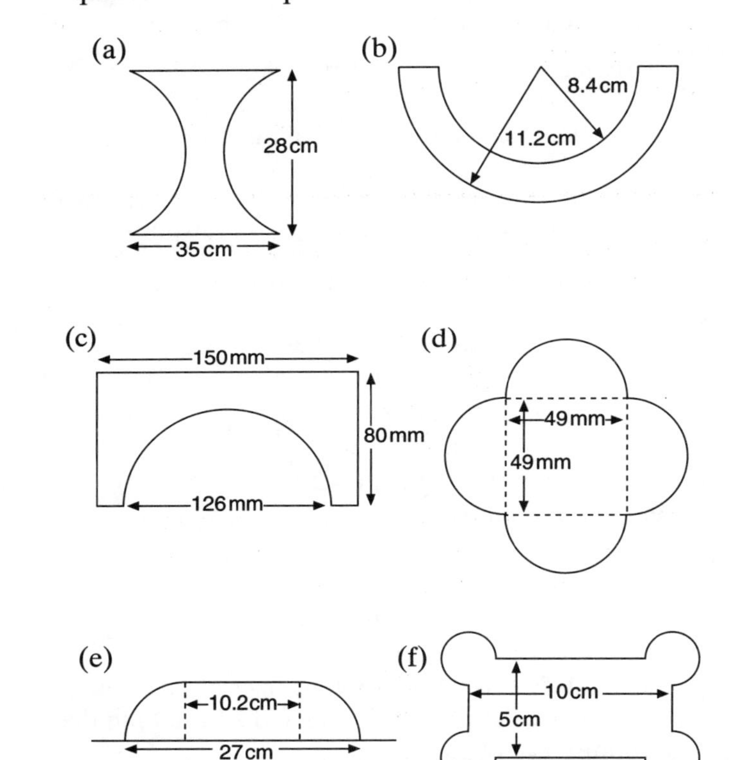

Parts of a circle

Half a circle is called a *semicircle.*
One quarter of a circle is called a *quadrant.*
Part of the circumference of a circle is called an *arc.*
The length of a semicircular arc is half the length of the circumference of the circle.
The length of a quadrant arc is one quarter the circumference of the whole circle.

EXERCISE 16c

QUESTION

A semicircular protractor has a radius of 5 cm. Find the distance round the curved edge.

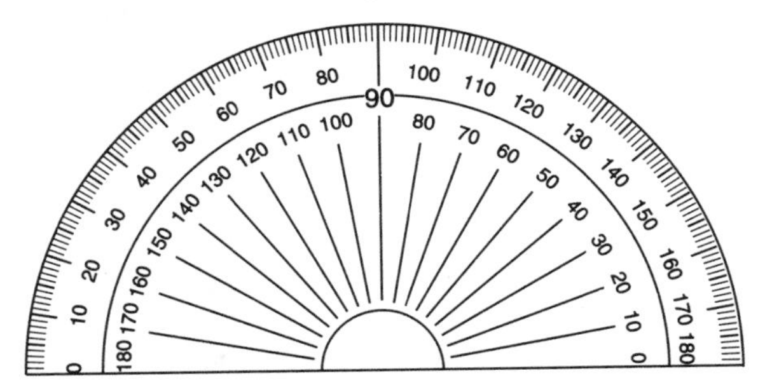

ANSWER

Circumference of whole circle = $2\pi r$.

Distance round the curved edge is half the distance around the whole circle.

$\therefore$ Distance round curved edge = $\pi \times 5$ cm
= 15.707... cm
= 15.7 (3 s.f.)

1 A flower bed is in the shape of a semicircle of radius 5.6 metres. Find the length of its curved edge.

2

The diameter of a paper doily to put on a plate under a cake is 22 cm. Find the distance round the curved edge when it has been folded (a) once (b) twice.

3

A fan is in the shape of a quadrant of a circle of radius 30 cm. Find the length of the curved edge.

QUESTION

The sketch shows a shelf, in the form of a quadrant of a circle of radius 24 cm, which fits into a corner of the room and can be used for holding an ornament. Find the perimeter of the shelf.

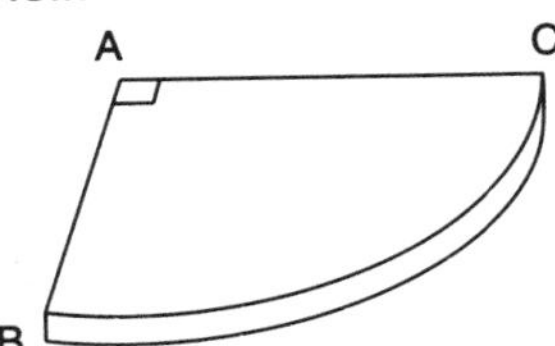

ANSWER

The diagram shows the shelf when viewed from above.

AB and AC are each of length 24 cm – they are both radii of the circle.

The arc BC is $\frac{1}{4}$ the circumference of a circle of radius 24 cm.

Circumference of whole circle = $2\pi r$
= $2 \times \pi \times 24$ cm
= 150.796... cm

$\therefore$ length of arc BC = 150.796... $\div$ 4 cm
= 37.69 cm

Perimeter of shelf = AB + arc BC + AC
= (24 + 37.69 + 24) cm
= 85.69 cm
= 85.7 cm (3 s.f.)

4

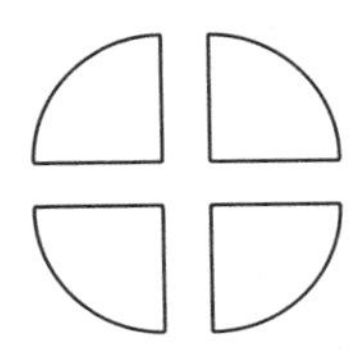

A metal disc, diameter 17 cm, is cut into four identical pieces. Find the distance round the edge of one of these pieces.

5

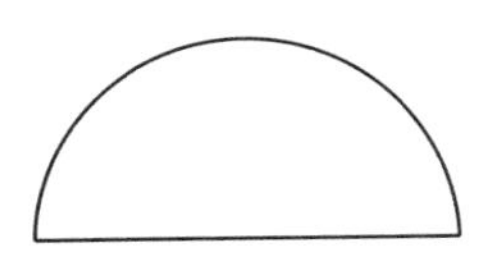

The diameter of a semicircular fire side rug is 170 cm. Find (a) the radius of the semicircle (b) the length of the curved edge (c) the total distance round the edge of the rug.

6

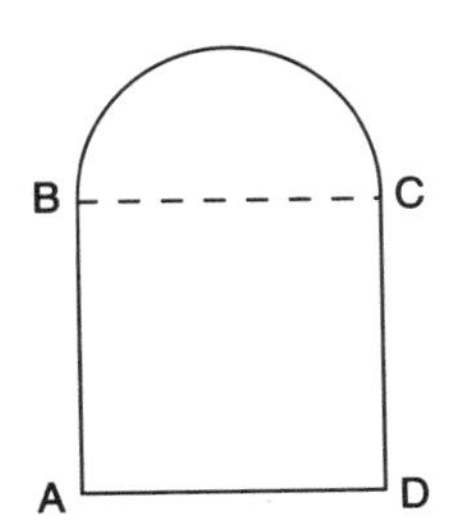

The sketch shows one of the windows in the town hall. Its shape is a square, of side 140 cm, with a semicircle on the top. (a) Write down the lengths of AB, AD and CD. (b) Find (i) the radius of the semicircle (ii) the length of the arc BC.
(c) What is the distance round the outside of the window?

7

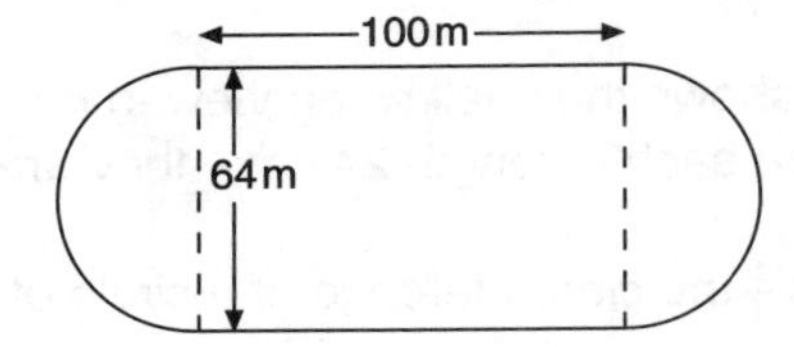

The diagram shows the inside edge of a running track which has semicircular ends. Use the dimensions on the diagram to find (a) the radius of each semicircle (b) the length of each semicircular arc (c) the distance once round the track (d) the distance run by an athlete who completes 20 laps of the track. Give your answer in kilometres.

Area of a circle

It can be shown that

area of a circle = $\pi \times (\text{radius})^2$

As a formula we write $A = \pi r^2$

EXERCISE 16d

QUESTION

A circular table has a diameter of 75 cm. Find its area.

ANSWER

Diameter = 75 cm

∴ radius = 37.5 cm

area = πr^2

= $\pi \times 37.5^2$ cm²   π × 3 7 . 5 x² =

= 4417.8... cm²

Area of table top is 4420 cm² (3 s.f.).

1 The diameter of the circular top of a tin of soup is 8 cm. Find its area.

2 The radius of a circular flower bed is 22 metres. Find its area.

3 The diameter of a circular cameo brooch is 38 mm. Find its area.

4 The diameter of a 10p coin is 2.4 cm. Find the total area of both sides.

5 In soccer the diameter of the centre circle is 10 yards. Find its area.

QUESTION

Find the area of a semicircular rose bed whose radius is 4.8 metres.

ANSWER

(The area of a semicircle is half the area of the whole circle.)

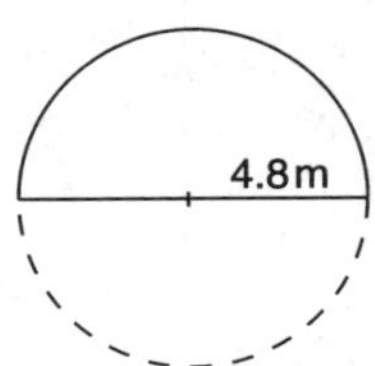

Area of whole circle = πr^2

= $\pi \times (4.8)^2$ m²

= 72.382... m²

area of rose bed = (72.382... ÷ 2) m²

= 36.191... m²

Area of rose bed is 36.2 m² (3 s.f.).

6

The sketch shows a Pembroke table which has two semicircular leaves that hang vertically when the table is not wholly opened out. Find

(a) the area of the rectangular top

(b) the area of one semicircular leaf

(c) the total surface area of the table when it is opened out.

7

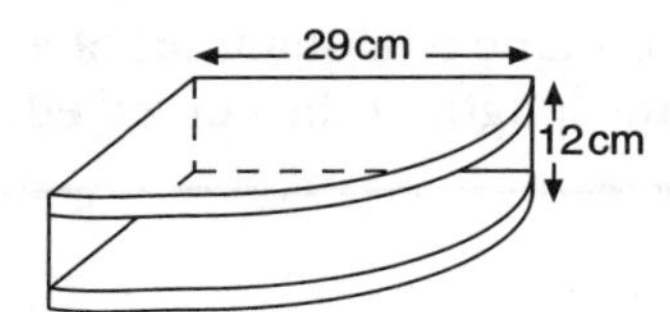

Sam makes a telephone shelf that fits into a corner in the hall. It consists of two quadrants of plywood supported by two rectangular pieces, each of which can be screwed to the wall. The telephone rests on the top and directories can be kept on the shelf. Use the dimensions given on the diagram to find (a) the area of one quadrant (b) the total area of plywood used to make the shelf.

8

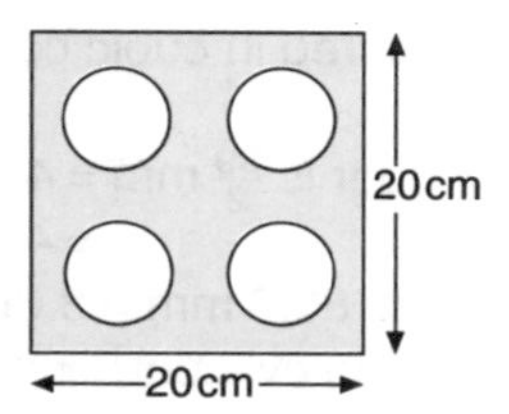

The shaded area shows the waste metal when four circular discs, each of radius 4.6 cm, are pressed from a flat steel sheet. Find the area of this piece of waste.

9

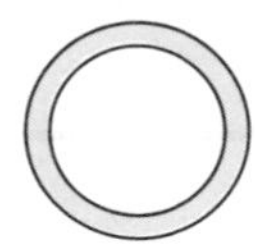

A copper pipe has a bore of 21 mm and an external diameter of 25 mm. Find the area of its cross-section.

10

A piece of lace is to be crocheted to the edge of a plain white circular tablecloth with a radius of 56 cm. If the edging is to be 7 cm wide all the way round, find the area of lace to be crocheted.

Cylinders

Curved surface area

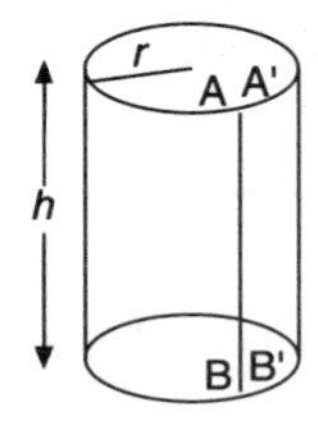

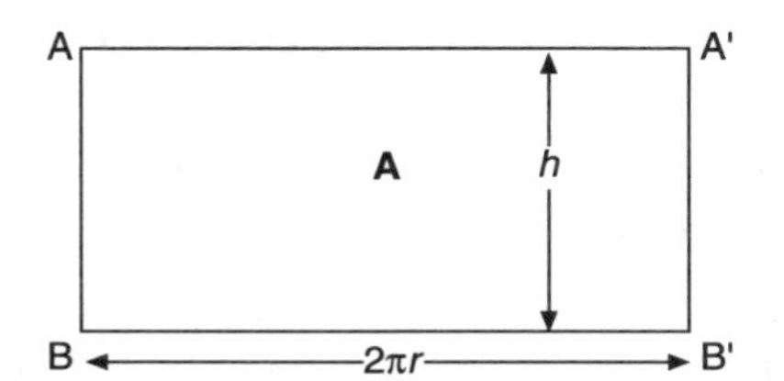

The curved surface of a cylinder, when opened out flat, gives a rectangle.
The length of the rectangle is equal to the circumference of the cylinder, and the width of the rectangle is equal to the height of the cylinder.
Since the area of a rectangle is equal to its length times its width, the curved surface area of a cylinder, A, of height h and base radius r, is given by

$$A = 2\pi rh$$

The area of each circular end is πr^2

Volume

A solid cylinder has a constant cross-section and is therefore a circular prism.

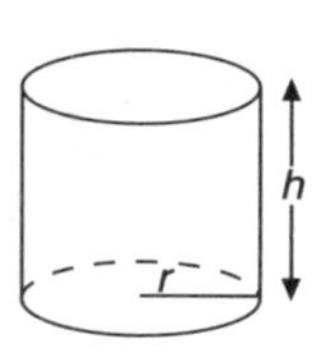

The volume V of a cylinder of height h and base radius r is

$$\pi \times (\text{radius})^2 \times \text{height}$$

(Height means 'width' when, for example, it is a garden roller, and 'thickness' when it is a coin.)
i.e. in letter symbols,

$$V = \pi r^2 h$$

EXERCISE 16e

QUESTION

A cylindrical water tank is 1.24 m high and has a radius of 54 cm. Find (a) the curved surface area of the tank
(b) the total surface area of the tank.

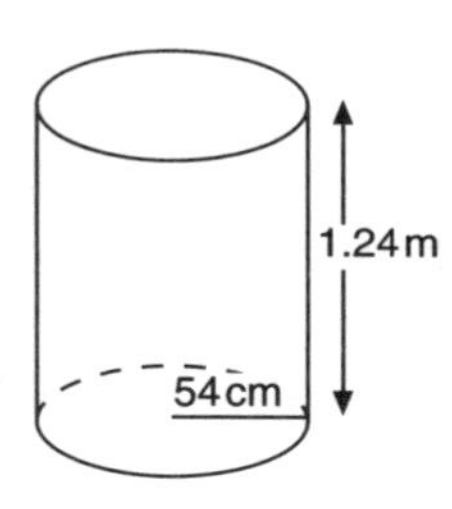

ANSWER

(Both dimensions must be in the same unit. We shall use centimetres.)

(a) Height of cylinder = 1.24 m
= 124 cm
curved surface area = $2\pi rh$
= $2 \times \pi \times 54 \times 124$ cm^2
= 42 072.2. . . cm^2
= 42 100 cm^2 (3 s.f.)

(b) Area of one end = πr^2
= $\pi \times 54^2$ cm^2
= 9160.8. . . cm^2
total surface area = 9160.8. . . + 9160.8. . . + 42 072 cm^2
= 60 393.6 cm^2
$\therefore$ total surface area is 60 400 cm^2 (3 s.f.).

1

A garden roller has a radius of 35 cm and is 60 cm wide.

(a) Find, in square metres, the area rolled by (i) one complete turn of the roller (ii) 100 complete turns of the roller.

(a) How many revolutions are needed to roll an area of 800 square metres? Give your answer correct to the nearest whole number.

2

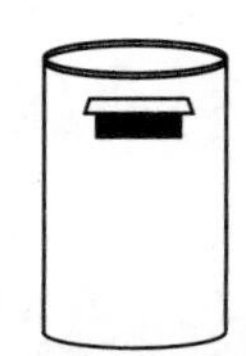

A cylindrical post box is 1.5 m high and has a diameter of 63 cm. Find, in square metres, the area that requires painting.

3

A cylindrical breakfast cup has a radius of 4 cm and is 8 cm deep. Find the surface area of the cup in contact with tea when it is filled to a distance of 0.5 cm from the top. Neglect the thickness of the cup.

4

A coin is 1.5 mm thick and has a diameter of 2.5 cm. Find the total surface area of the coin. (Take care with units.)

QUESTION

A 4-cylinder diesel engine has a bore (the diameter of each cylinder) of 89 mm and a stroke (the length of each piston stroke) of 86.6 mm. Find, correct to 4 significant figures, the capacity of the engine in cubic centimetres.

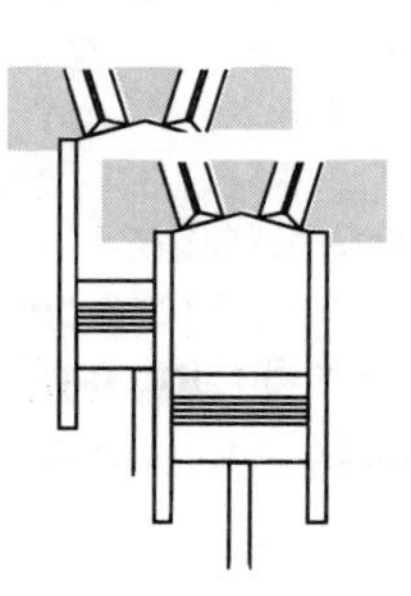

ANSWER

(Since the answer is required in cubic centimetres we work in centimetres.)

The radius of each cylinder is $\frac{89}{2}$ mm = 44.5 mm = 4.45 cm

Length of each cylinder is 86.6 mm = 8.66 cm

Volume, or capacity, of one cylinder $= \pi r^2 h$

$= \pi \times 4.45^2 \times 8.66$ cm^3

$\therefore$ capacity of 4 cylinders is $4 \times \pi \times 4.45^2 \times 8.66$ cm^3

(**4** **×** **π** **×** **4** **.** **4** **5** **x^2** **×** **8** **.** **6** **6** **=**)

= 2155 cm^3 (to 4 s.f.)

(For an engine, cm^3 is often written as cc, i.e. the capacity of this engine is 2155 cc.)

5 A hole, 30 mm in diameter, is drilled in a metal plate 25 mm thick. What volume of metal is removed from the plate?

6 Copper wire is circular in cross-section with a radius of 0.4 mm. Find, in cubic centimetres, the volume of copper in a 100 m length of this wire.

7 Find the capacity of a 4-cylinder petrol engine which has a bore of 84 mm and a stroke of 75 mm. Give your answer correct to 4 s.f.

8 Wooden dowel, with a diameter of 1 cm, is made from lengths of timber with a square cross-section of side 1.2 cm. Find (a) the area of cross-section of the original timber (b) the area of cross-section of the dowel (c) correct to the nearest whole number, the percentage of the wood wasted.

QUESTION

A cylindrical milk bottle has a capacity of 568 cm^3. If the diameter of the bottle is 8 cm find its height.

ANSWER

The radius of the bottle is 4 cm. If the capacity of the bottle is C cm^3 and the height is h cm

then, using $C = \pi r^2 h$ $\quad 568 = \pi \times 4^2 \times h$

$568 = 50.27 \times h.$

Dividing both sides by 50.27 $\dfrac{568}{50.27} = h$

$\therefore h = 11.29$

$\therefore$ the height is 11.3 cm (3 s.f.).

9 A cylindrical petrol can has a capacity of 5 litres. If the height is equal to the diameter of its base find its dimensions.

10

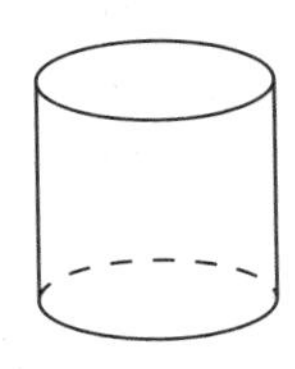

The capacity of a drum, which is 55 cm high, is 75 litres. Find (a) the capacity of the drum in cubic centimetres (b) the area of a circular end in square centimetres (c) the radius of one of the ends, in centimetres.

11 The capacity of a 4-cylinder petrol engine is 1799 cm^3. If the bore of the engine is 85.3 mm, find its stroke. Give your answer in mm correct to 3 s.f.

QUESTION
The dimensions of a pipe are shown in the diagram. Calculate the volume of material used to make it.

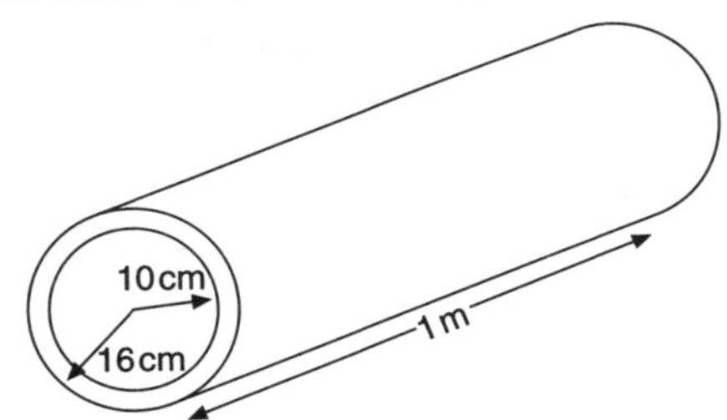

ANSWER

Area of cross-section $= (\pi \times 16^2 - \pi \times 10^2)$ cm^2
$= 804.2 - 314.1$ cm^2
(π × 1 6 x^2 =)(π × 1 0 x^2 =)
$= 490.1$ cm^2

Volume of material used $= 490.1 \times 100$ cm^3
$= 49\,010$ cm^3
$= 49\,000$ cm^3 (3 s.f.)

12

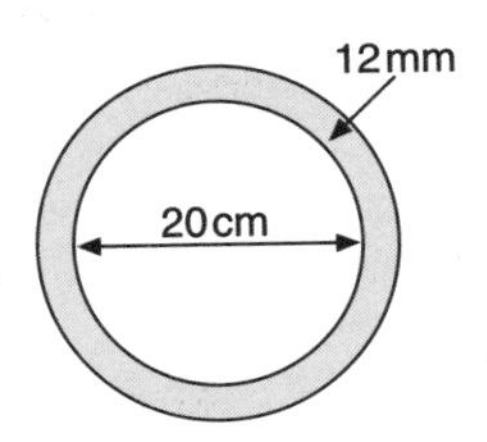

The diagram shows the section through a pipe. The bore of the pipe is 20 cm and the wall of the pipe is 12 mm thick. Find (a) the area of cross-section of the bore of the pipe (b) the cross-sectional area of the material from which the pipe is made. (This is shown shaded in the diagram.)

13

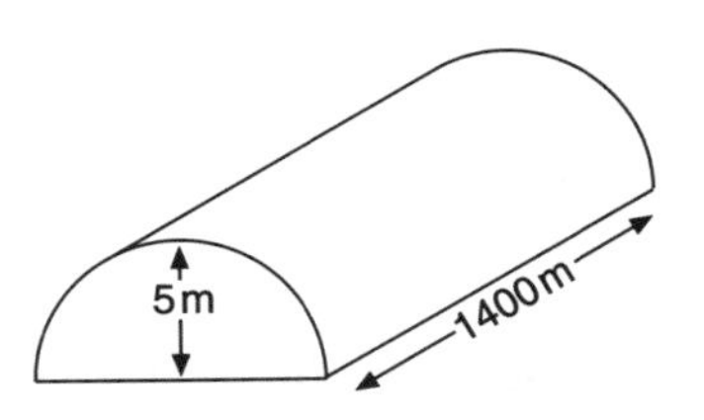

The diagram shows a semicircular railway tunnel 1400 m long, which has been driven through a mountain side. The height of the tunnel is 5 m. Find, in cubic metres, the volume of material that has been removed to construct the tunnel.

14

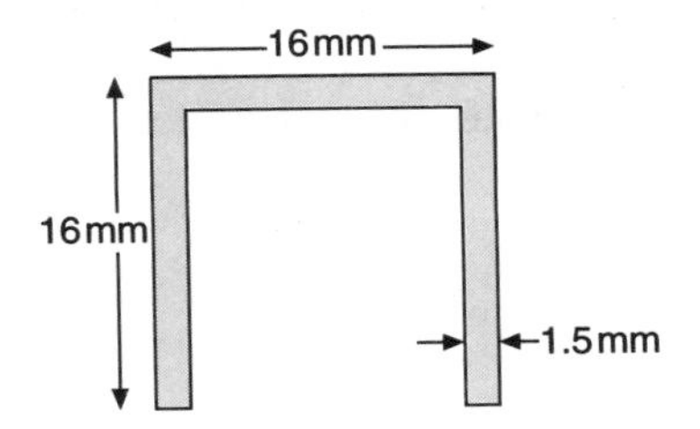

The diagram shows the section through a cylindrical bottle top which is everywhere 1.5 mm thick. If the external diameter is 16 mm and the external height is 16 mm, find the volume of material used to make it.

Multiple-choice questions 16

In this exercise several alternative answers are given. Write down the letter that corresponds to the correct answer.

1 The diameter of the wheel of a car is 70 cm. Correct to 3 s.f., the distance the car will move forward for each complete turn of the wheel is

A 220 cm **B** 219.9 cm
C 219.911 cm **D** 230.0 cm

2 The circumference of a coin is 75 mm. Its radius, correct to 1 d.p., is

A 12.0 mm **B** 1.1 cm
C 11.9 mm **D** 1.2 cm

3 A circular wine coaster is 90 mm in diameter. Correct to 3 s.f., its surface area is

A 6362 mm^2 **B** 25 400 mm^2
C 1590 mm^2 **D** 6360 mm^2

4 A cylindrical can has a diameter of 7 cm and is 9.5 cm high. Its total surface area, correct to 3 s.f., is

A 286 cm^2 **B** 247 cm^2
C 181 cm^2 **D** 726 cm^2

5 A circular hole, radius 4 mm, depth 1.2 cm, is drilled out of a solid piece of steel. The volume of metal removed, correct to 3 s.f., is

A 60.3 cm^3 **B** 60.3 mm^3
C 603 mm^3 **D** 60.3 cm^3

Self-assessment test 16

1 Find, correct to 3 s.f., the perimeter of this shape.

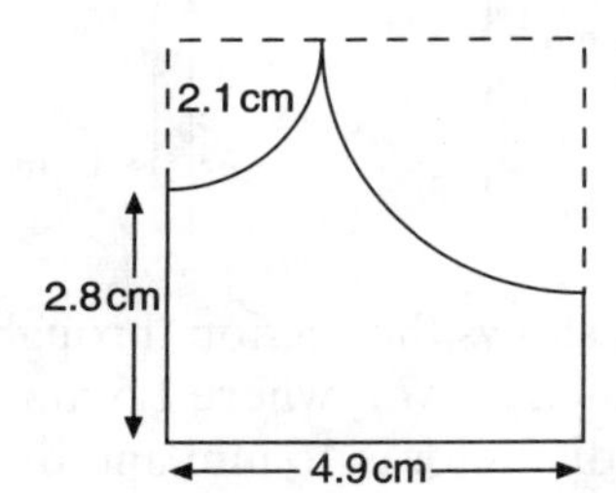

2

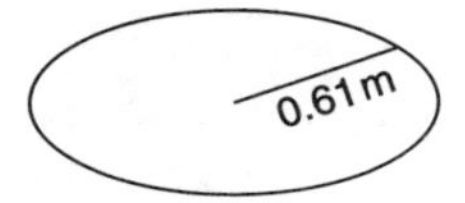

The radius of a circular rug is 0.61 m. Find (a) its diameter, in centimetres (b) the distance round its edge, in metres (c) its area in (i) square metres (ii) square centimetres.

3 A woman's cloak is made from a semicircular piece of material, the diameter of which is 90 cm. Find the area of the outside of the cloak.

4

A cylindrical china tankard has an internal diameter of 8.4 cm and is 12.8 cm deep. Find (a) the distance round the lip of the tankard (b) its total internal surface area (c) the capacity of the tankard in (i) cm^3 (ii) litres.

5

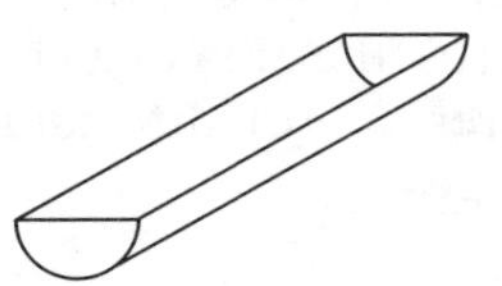

An 8 m length of guttering along the front of a house has a semicircular cross-section of diameter 11.5 cm. If there are stoppers at the ends, calculate, in cubic metres, the maximum volume of water that the guttering will hold at any one time.

6

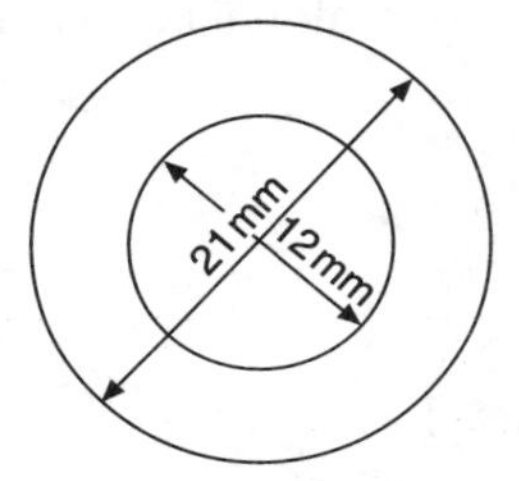

A circular washer is formed by removing a circular piece of diameter 12 mm from a disc of diameter 21 mm. Find (a) the surface area of the original disc (b) the area of the circular piece that is removed (c) the surface area of one side of the washer (d) the volume of the washer if it is 2 mm thick. (Volume of washer = area of one side × thickness.)

CHAPTER 17

Coordinates

Positive coordinates

In mathematics we fix the position of a point using two numbers called *coordinates*. To give the position of a point on a grid we draw two fixed lines that cut at right angles. One line, called the x-axis, is drawn across the grid. The other line, called the y-axis, is drawn up the grid. The point where the x and y axes cut is called the origin and is labelled O.

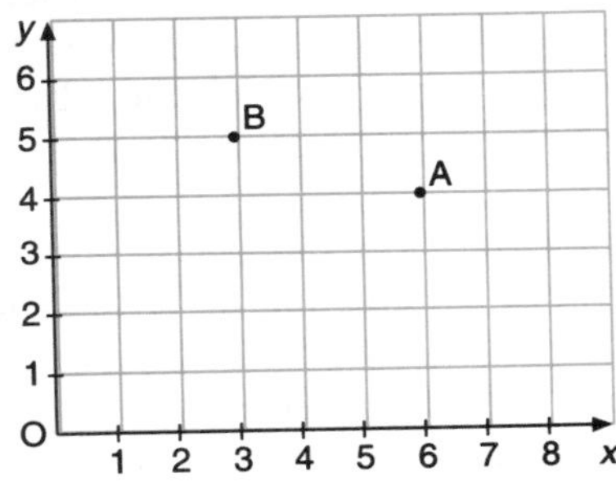

If we start at O, move 6 units across the grid, then 4 units up the grid we get to the point which is marked A. We say that the position of A is (6, 4) and we call these numbers the coordinates of A. The first figure or coordinate always tells us how many units to move across. This is the x-coordinate. The second number tells us how many units to move up and is the y-coordinate.

Similarly, for the point B, the x-coordinate is 3 and the y-coordinate is 5, i.e. B is the point (3, 5).

EXERCISE 17a

1

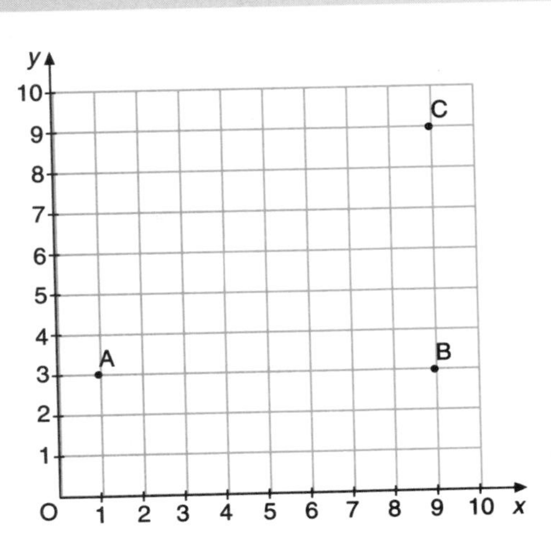

(a) Write down the coordinates of A, B and C.

(b) Write down the coordinates of D so that ABCD is a rectangle.

(c) Write down the coordinates of the point E on AB so that AE = AD.

(d) If F is on DC and AEFD is a square, write down the coordinates of F.

(e) What are the coordinates of the point that is exactly halfway between (i) A and B (ii) A and D (iii) B and D?

2

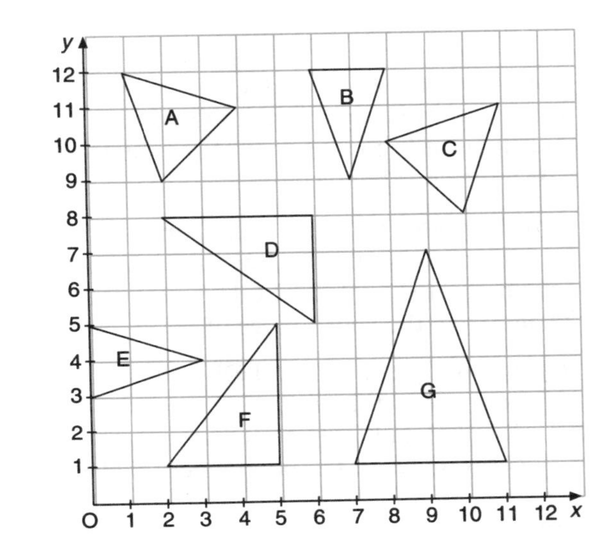

Write down the coordinates of the vertices (corners) of

(a) the largest triangle

(b) the right-angled triangle which has two x-coordinates equal to 6

(c) the triangle marked E

(d) the triangle that is identical with E in size and shape

(e) the triangle that has one y-coordinate equal to 10.

3 On a sheet of 1-cm squared paper, draw x and y axes as shown in question 2. Mark each axis from O to 10.

(a) Plot the points A(1, 3) and B(7, 1) and join AB.

(b) Plot the point C(8, 4) and join BC.

(c) Mark the point D so that ABCD is a rectangle. Join AD and CD. Write down the coordinates of D.

(d) Write down the coordinates of M, the middle point of AB, and N, the middle point of DC.

(e) Estimate the coordinates of the point where AC and DB cross.

4 Draw x and y axes and scale both axes from O to 14. Mark the following points, labelling each point with its own letter.

A(3, 0), B(3, 1), C(2, 4), D(2, 10), E(4, 14), F(8, 14), G(11, 12), H(11, 10), I(10, 9), J(10, 8), K(12, 5), L(10, 5), M(10, 4), N(9, 3), P(10, 3), Q(10, 1), R(7, 1), S(7, 0).

Join your points together in alphabetical order. What shape do you have?

5 On a sheet of 5-mm squared paper, draw x and y axes. Scale the x-axis from O to 14 and the y-axis from O to 16.

(a) Plot the points A(3, 1), B(11, 3) and C(9, 11). Join them by straight lines in that order. Mark a fourth point D so that ABCD is a square. Write down the coordinates of D.

(b) Plot the points E(3, 13), F(4, 7) and G(13, 7) and join them in order with straight lines. Find a fourth point H so that EFGH is a parallelogram. Write down the coordinates of H.

(c) (i) Join BD, DE, EG and GB. What name do you give to this shape?
(ii) Join EB and DG. Write down the coordinates of the point where they cross.

6 The graph shows the outline and important features of Stefan Island drawn on x and y axes.

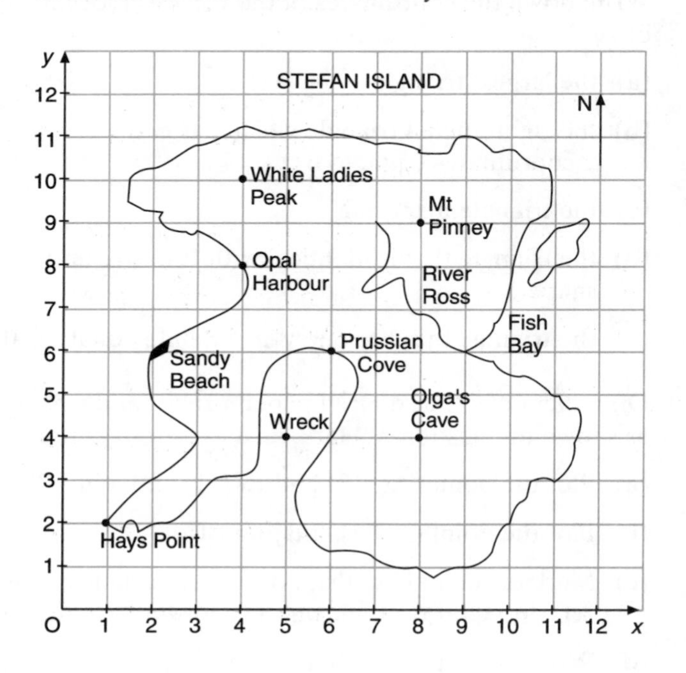

(a) Give the coordinates of (i) Hays Point (ii) Opal Harbour (iii) Mt Pinney.

(b) Give the coordinates of (i) the source of the River Ross (ii) the point where the River Ross enters the sea.

(c) Which places on the map have coordinates (i) (2, 6) (ii) (4, 10) (iii) (5, 4)?

7 It is recorded that during the middle of the last century the prisoners in Russian gaols found a simple way of passing messages from one prisoner to another by tapping.

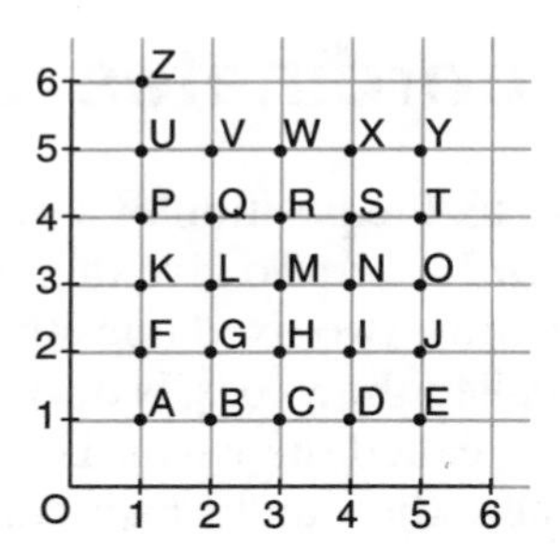

Each letter had a position on a grid which was indicated by a number of taps. The first group of taps referred to the column in which the letter was found. Then, after a short pause, the second group referred to the row.

For example, tap, tap, tap, pause, tap, tap meant 'go across to the 3rd column and up to the 2nd row'. When making notes the prisoner wrote down (3, 2) which stood for the letter H.

Use the grid given above to answer the questions that follow.

(a) What letter was indicated by (i) tap, pause, tap, tap, tap, tap (ii) tap, tap, pause, tap, tap?

(b) What letter was being sent if the receiver wrote down (i) (4, 3) (ii) (3, 4) (iii) (1, 5)?

(c) Decode the message
(i) (3, 5), (5, 1), (2, 3), (2, 3) long pause (4, 1), (5, 3), (4, 3), (5, 1)
(ii) (2, 1), (3, 4), (4, 2), (4, 3), (2, 2) long pause (2, 1), (3, 4), (5, 1), (1, 1), (4, 1).

(d) Code the message
(i) Joe got out (ii) tonight.

Negative coordinates

Suppose A(1, 0), B(3, 4) and C(7, 2) are three corners of a square ABCD. The fourth corner, D, is below the x-axis and needs a negative y-coordinate to locate its position. The coordinates of D are (5, −2).

For any point to the left of the y-axis its x-coordinate must be negative. The coordinates of E are (−2, 3) and the coordinates of F are (−4, −3).

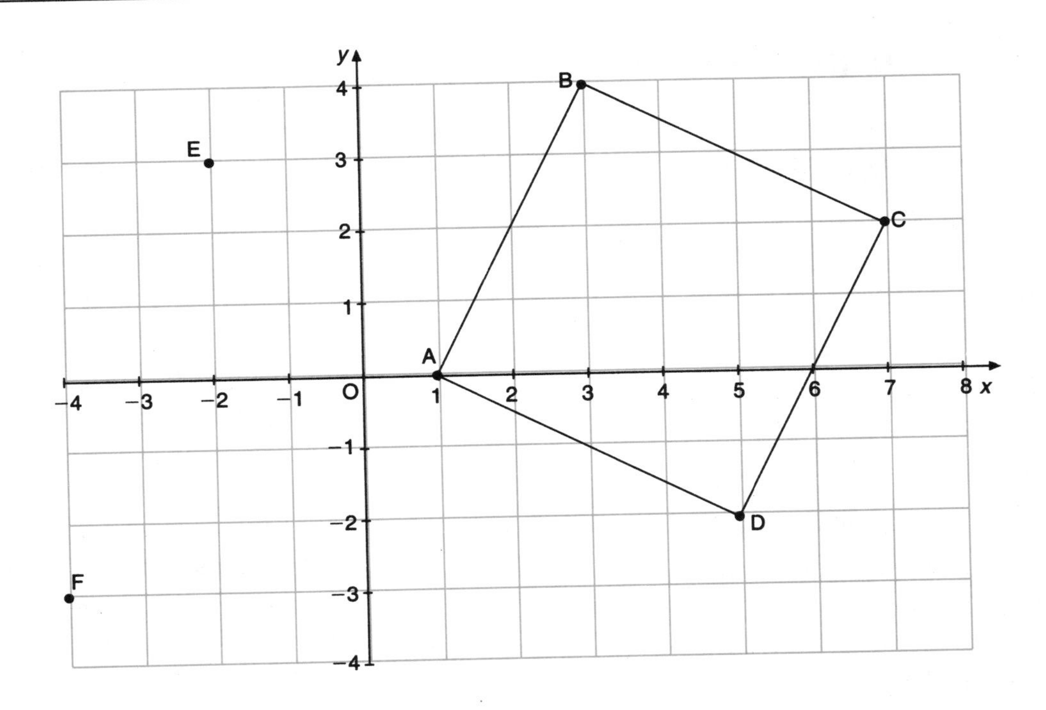

EXERCISE 17b

Questions 1 to 5 refer to the following diagram:

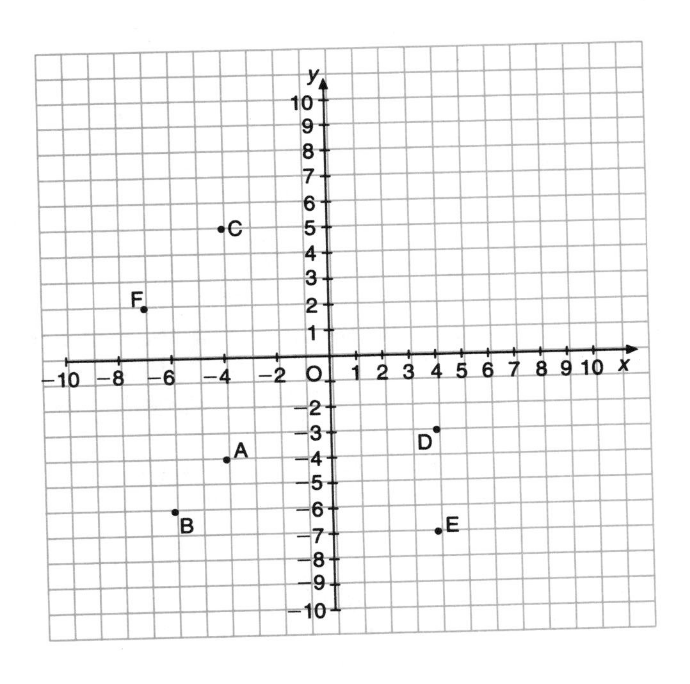

1 Write down the x-coordinate of (a) A (b) C.

2 Write down the y-coordinate of (a) B (b) D.

3 Write down the coordinates of (a) E (b) F.

4 Write down the y-coordinate of the point that is
(a) 3 squares below A (b) 5 squares below F.

5 Write down the x-coordinate of the point that is
(a) 5 squares to the left of E
(b) 8 squares to the left of D.

For the remainder of this exercise draw your own axes and scale each one from -10 to $+10$.

6 Mark the points A$(-4, 1)$, B$(6, 5)$, C$(4, -1)$ and D$(-6, -5)$ and join them in alphabetical order. What name do you give to this shape?

7 Mark the points P$(-7, -4)$, Q$(8, -4)$ and R$(4, 3)$. Now mark the point S so that PS is perpendicular to RS and PQRS is a trapezium with SR parallel to PQ. Write down the coordinates of S.

8 Mark the points A$(-9, -3)$, B$(-1, 1)$ and C$(2, -5)$.

(a) Mark D so that ABCD is a rectangle, and write down the coordinates of D.

(b) If E is the middle point of AB write down the coordinates of E.

(c) Write down the coordinates of F, the midpoint of DC.

(d) What is the difference between the y-coordinates of (i) A and D (ii) E and F.

(e) What is the y-coordinate of the midpoint of AC?

Multiple-choice questions 17

In this exercise several alternative answers are given. Write down the letter that corresponds to the correct answer.

1

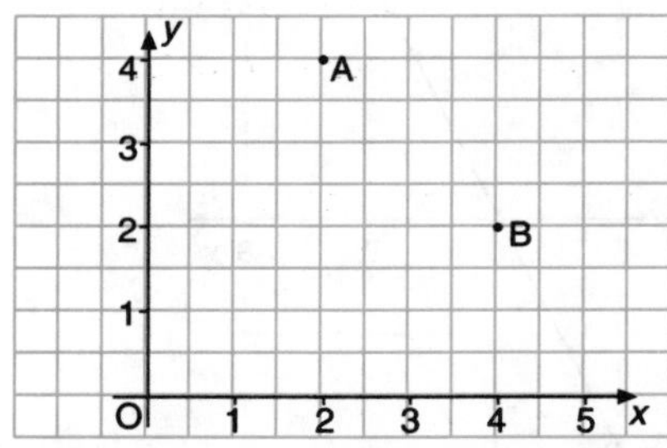

The coordinates of A and B are respectively

A (2, 4) and (4, 2) **B** (4, 2) and (2, 4)
C (5, 3) and (4, 2) **D** (3, 5) and (4, 2)

2

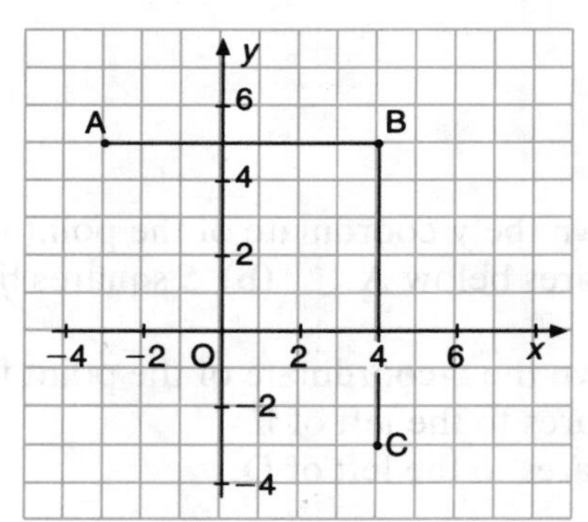

ABCD is a rectangle. The coordinates of three of its vertices are A(-3, 5), B(4, 5) and C(4, -3). The coordinates of the fourth vertex D are

A (8, -3) **B** (-3, 5)
C (4, -3) **D** (-3, -3)

3 ABCD is a square. The coordinates of three of the vertices are A(2, 1), B(8, 3) and C(6, 9). The coordinates of the fourth vertex D are

A (0, 6) **B** (0, 7) **C** (1, 9) **D** (8, -5)

4

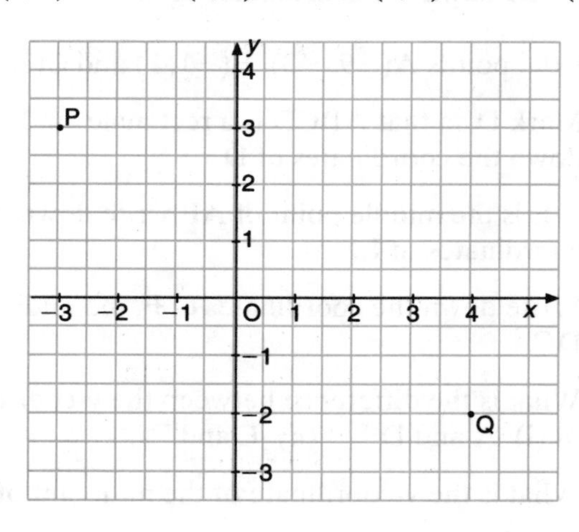

Which of the following statements are true and which are false?

A The x-coordinate of P is 7 bigger than the x-coordinate of Q.

B The y-coordinate of Q is 5 less than the y-coordinate of P.

C The difference in the y-coordinates is the same as the difference in the x-coordinates.

D If M is the middle point of PQ the coordinates of M are both positive.

Self-assessment test 17

Copy this diagram on squared paper and use it to answer the following questions.

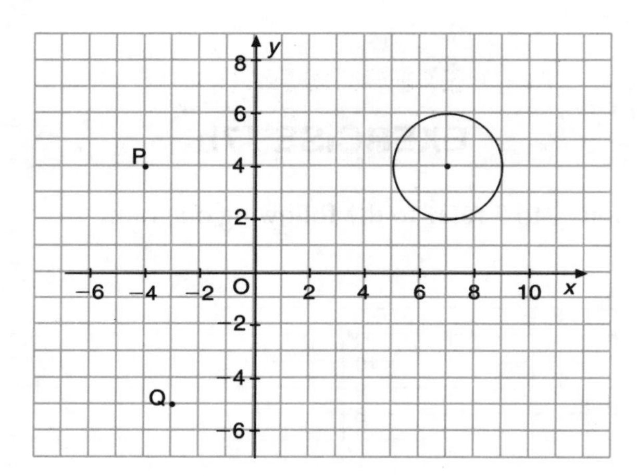

1 Write down the coordinates of (a) P (b) Q.

2 (a) Write down the coordinates of (i) the centre of the circle (ii) the point on the circle with the highest y-coordinate (iii) the point on the circle with the lowest x-coordinate.
(b) What is (i) the diameter of the circle (ii) the radius of the circle?

3 (a) Plot the points A(-5, 2), B(-4, -3) and C(3, -1). Mark the position of D so that ABCD is a parallelogram and write down its coordinates. (b) What is the distance from D to the centre of the circle?

4 (a) Find the coordinates of E if the x-coordinates of C and E are the same, and BCE is an isosceles triangle with BC = BE. (b) If CE is the base of this triangle, find its height.

CHAPTER 18

Graphs

Getting information from graphs

A graph shows how two changing quantities are related. If we have a value for one quantity then we can read from the graph the corresponding value for the other quantity. Drawing guide lines frequently helps us to read information from graphs more accurately.

EXERCISE 18a

1

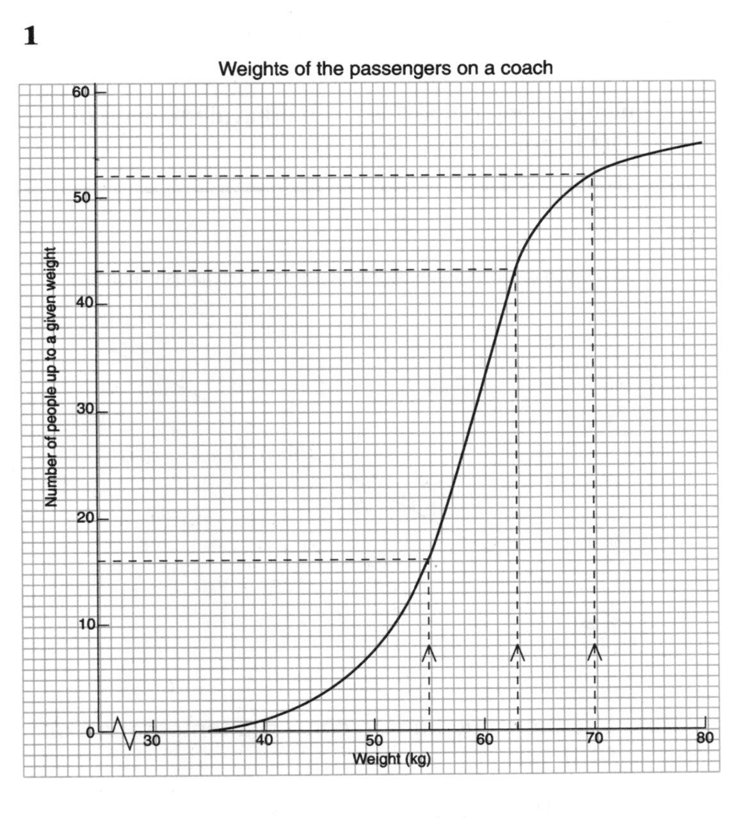

This graph was obtained by weighing all the passengers on a coach. It shows the number of passengers below a certain weight. For example, 10 passengers weighed less than 52 kg.

(a) How many passengers are there on the coach?

(b) How many passengers weigh (i) 55 kg or less (ii) 70 kg or less (iii) 63 kg or less?

(c) Use your answers to part (b) to find the number of passengers who are heavier than
(i) 55 kg (ii) 70 kg (iii) 63 kg.

(d) How many passengers are there that are heavier than 55 kg but not more than 63 kg?

2

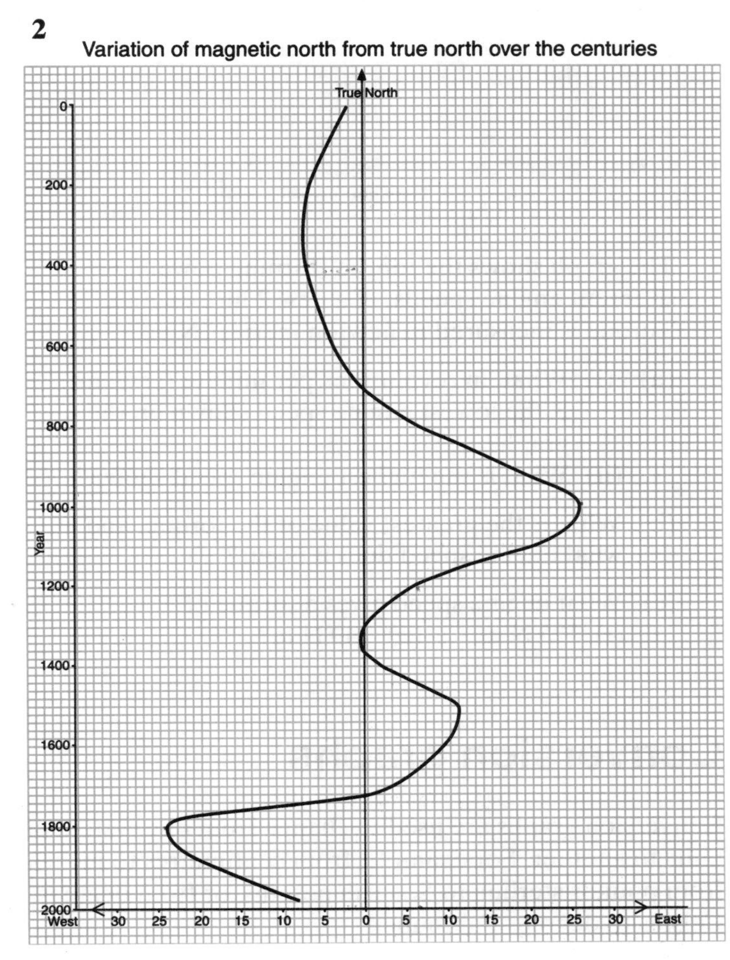

This graph shows the variation of magnetic north compared with true north throughout the centuries. For example, in the year 1600 the direction of magnetic north was about 10 ° east of true north.

(a) Use the graph to find the approximate direction of magnetic north in the year
(i) 1200 (ii) 400.

(b) In which period was the direction of magnetic north (i) most to the east of true north
(ii) most to the west of true north?

(c) As we approach the year 2000 what appears to be happening to the direction of magnetic north?

3

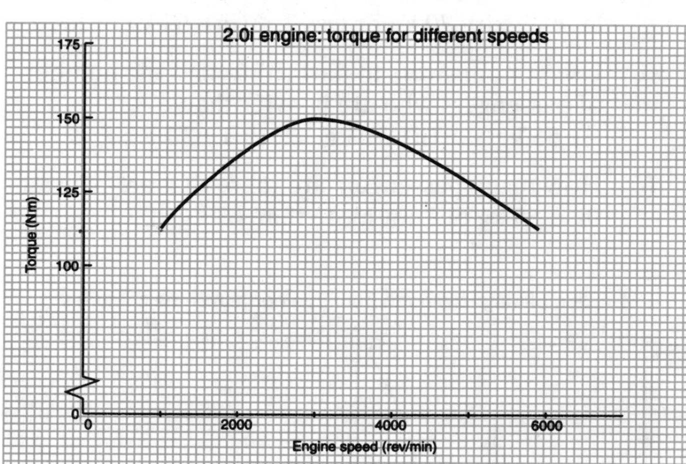

The graph shows the torque (turning power), for different engine speeds, of a new 2 litre engine. Torque is measured in newton metres (N m).

(a) (i) What, in revolutions per minute (rev/min), is the lowest engine speed shown on the graph?
  (ii) What is the highest engine speed shown?

(b) What is the greatest value of the torque, and at what engine speed does it occur?

(c) What engine speed gives a torque of
  (i) 125 N m (ii) 140 N m?

Conversion graphs

Conversion graphs are used to change from one system of units to another. For example, from centimetres to inches, from pounds sterling to Spanish pesetas, or from degrees Celsius to degrees Fahrenheit.

EXERCISE 18b

QUESTION

Use the conversion graph at the top of the next column to find (a) the equivalent, in Deutschmarks, of £47 (b) the cost, in pounds sterling, of a bottle of Benédictine liqueur priced 44 DM in a supermarket in Berlin.

ANSWER

(a) Draw a guide line up from £47 on the horizontal axis to meet the graph. At this point draw a guide line across to strike the vertical axis. This line strikes the vertical at 114 DM.
Hence, from the graph £47 is equivalent to 114 DM.

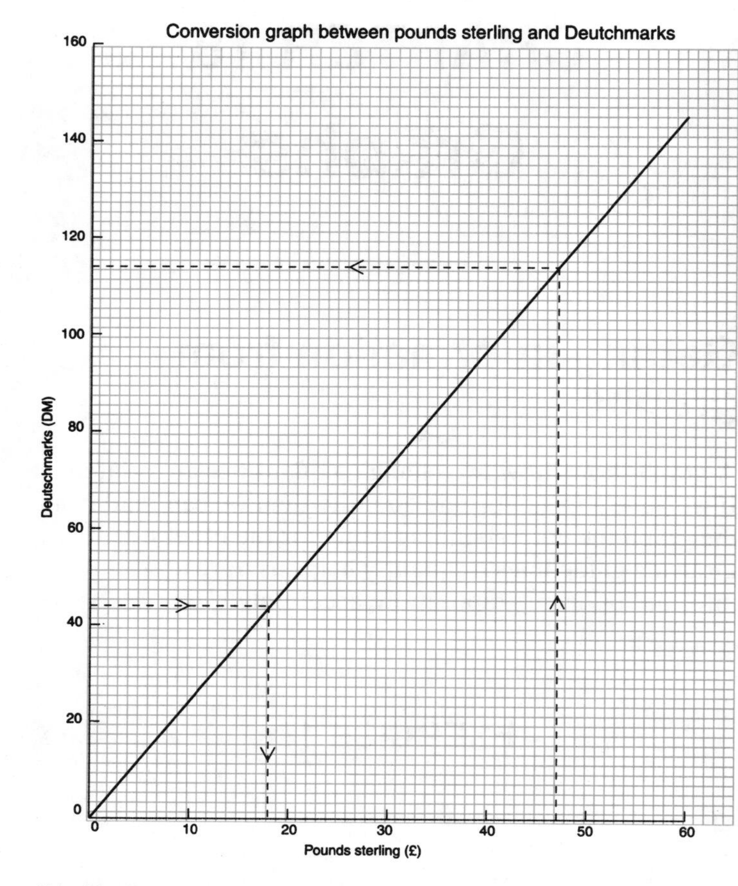

(b) Similarly, using guide lines, the equivalent value of 44 DM in pounds is £18.

1

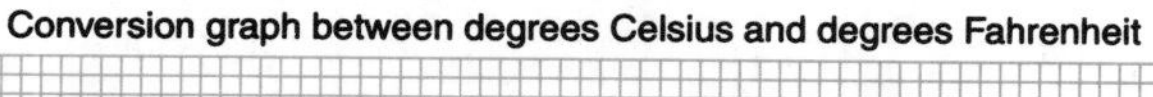

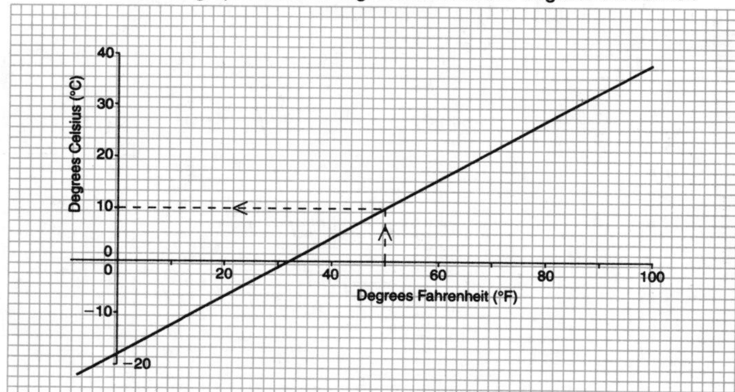

(a) Use the guide lines to convert a temperature of 50 °F into °C.

(b) With the help of a ruler to draw guide lines use the graph to convert a temperature of (i) 90 °F into °C (ii) 20 °C into °F (iii) −10 °C into °F.

(c) Convert (i) a temperature of 12 °C into °F
  (ii) a temperature of 0 °F into °C.

2

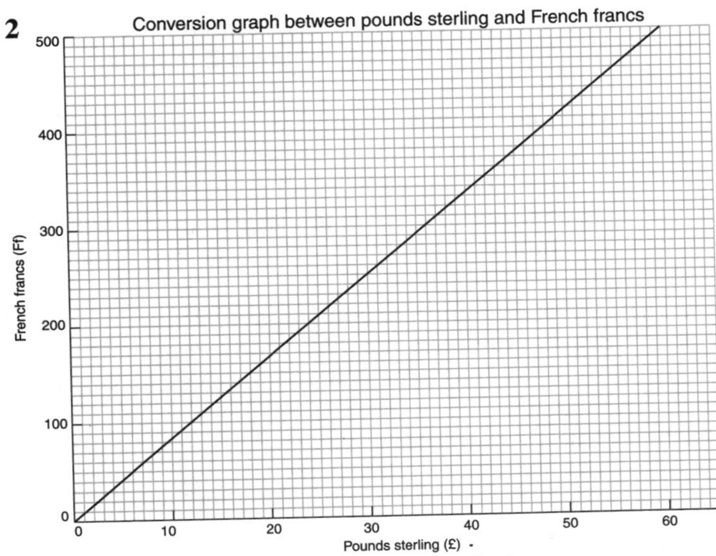

(a) Use this conversion graph to find
   (i) the cost in pounds of a meal costing 80 francs in France
   (ii) the equivalent, in French francs, of £35
   (iii) the cost, in pounds, of a bottle of wine sold in France for 25 Ff.

(b) How can you use the information from this graph to change (i) £500 into French francs
   (ii) 1200 French francs into pounds?

3

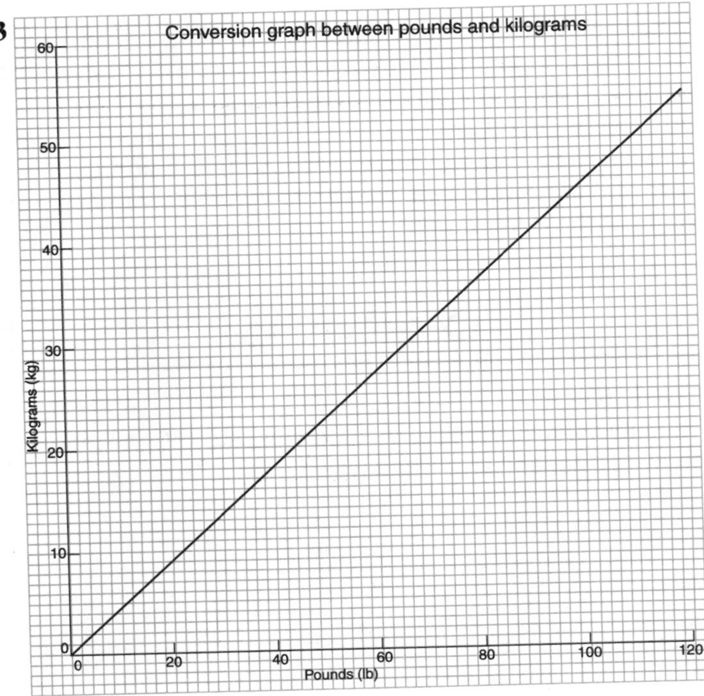

Use the conversion graph to answer the following questions.

(a) Jim Went buys a 50 kg bag of Arran Pilot potatoes. How many pounds is this?

(b) Sarah Middleton buys a 25 lb bag of swedes. How many kilograms is this?

Drawing conversion graphs

In this section we learn how to draw a conversion graph similar to those given in the previous section.

EXERCISE 18c

QUESTION

(a) Given that 1 cm^2 = 0.155 in^2, draw a conversion graph between square inches (in^2) and square centimetres (cm^2) for values up to 400 cm^2.

(b) Use your graph to convert
   (i) 240 cm^2 into in^2 (ii) 27 in^2 into cm^2.

ANSWER

(a) (Aim to plot two points apart from the origin.)

Given that 1 cm^2 = 0.155 in^2

then 100 cm^2 = 15.5 in^2

and 400 cm^2 = 4 × 15.5 in^2
 = 62 in^2

Draw the cm^2 axis horizontally and scale it from 0 to 400. A suitable scale is 4 cm = 100 cm^2.

Put square inches on the vertical axis and scale it from 0 to 70. A suitable scale is 2 cm = 10 in^2.

Plot the three points on these axes and draw a straight line through them. (If the points do not lie on a straight line, check your working – you have made a mistake!)

Finally, give your graph a title.

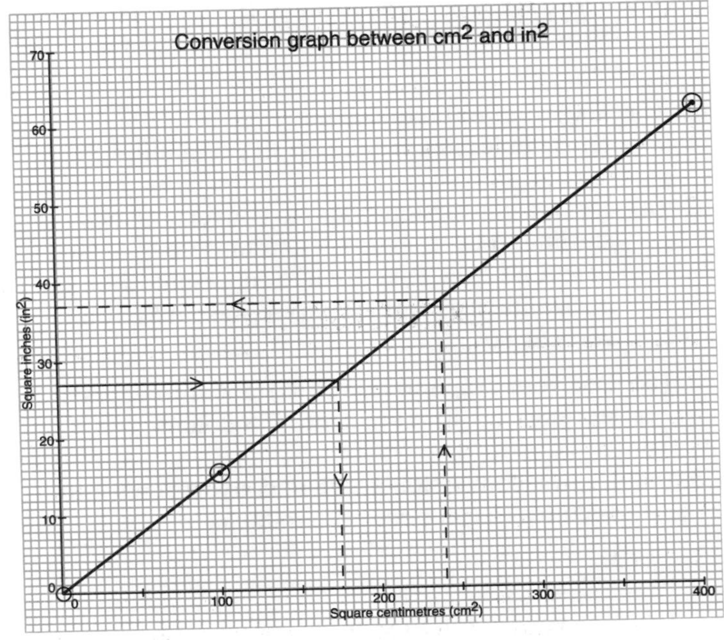

(b) From the graph (i) 240 cm^2 = 37 in^2
and (ii) 27 in^2 = 175 cm^2

1

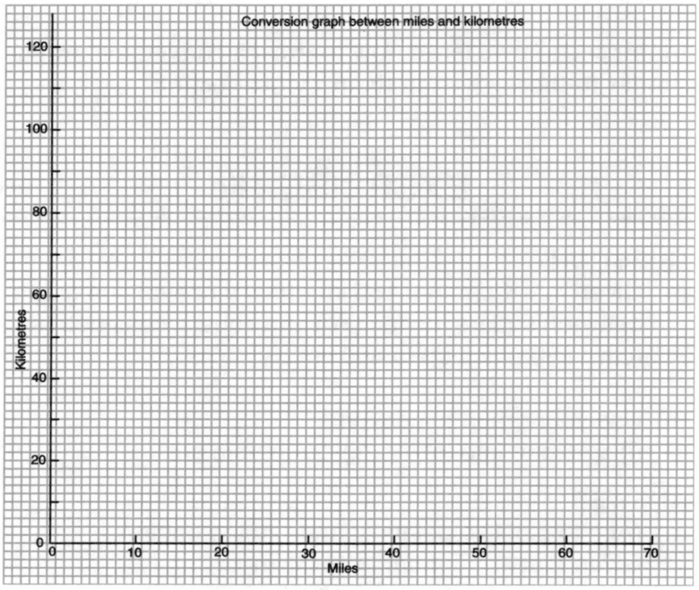

Conversion graph between miles and kilometres

1 mile = 1.6093 km.

(a) Copy this diagram on graph paper.

(b) Find 30 miles in kilometres. Give your value correct to the nearest whole number. Plot this point.

(c) Find 70 miles in kilometres. Give your value correct to the nearest whole number. Plot this point.

(d) Mark the origin (0 miles = 0 km).

(e) Draw a straight line through the three points. If they do not lie on a straight line, check your working.

(f) Use your graph to express
(i) 54 miles in km (ii) 36 km in miles.

2 (a) Draw a conversion graph to convert pounds sterling to US dollars for amounts up to $100 if £1 = US$2.46. Take 2 cm to represent £5 on the horizontal axis and 2 cm to represent $10 on the vertical axis.

(b) Use your graph to change (i) $56 into pounds sterling (ii) £14.50 into US dollars.

3 (a) Draw a conversion graph to convert acres into hectares (ha) for areas up to 80 ha (10 ha = 24.71 acres).
Take 2 cm = 10 ha and 2 cm = 25 acres.

(b) Use your graph to answer the following questions.
(i) The area of a farm in the United Kingdom is 163 acres. Convert this area into hectares so that you can give the information to a Frenchman who is interested in buying it.
(ii) Dick Younger owns two vineyards. His vineyard in Germany has an area of 37.5 ha and the one in Britain has an area of 56 acres. Which is the larger, and by how much?

4 (a) If 10 fluid ounces is equivalent to 284 millilitres draw a conversion graph to convert millilitres (ml) into fluid ounces (fl oz) for capacities up to 35 fl oz.
(Choose your own scales.)

(b) Use your graph to answer the following questions.
(i) A recipe instructs that 12 fl oz of warm water is added to the dry ingredients. How many millilitres is this?
(ii) Another recipe requires 100 ml of milk. About how many fluid ounces is this?

Drawing graphs from tables of values

When the values of two related quantities are given in a table, these values can be plotted on a graph. If the points lie on a straight line we use a ruler to draw the line through them, otherwise we draw a smooth curve to pass through them. We can then use the graph to find the corresponding values of one of the variables for any given value of the other one.

EXERCISE 18d

QUESTION

The table shows the time that the sun sets in Birmingham on twelve consecutive Sundays.

Month	April			
Date	9	16	23	30
Sunset	7.42	7.55	8.08	8.22
Month	May			
Date	7	14	21	28
Sunset	8.32	8.44	8.54	9.04
Month	June			
Date	4	11	18	25
Sunset	9.12	9.18	9.20	9.18

Plot these points on a graph. Put the dates along the bottom of your graph paper using 2 mm to represent one day, and the times of sunset along the vertical axis using 1 cm to represent 10 minutes. Scale the vertical axis from 7 p.m. to 9.30 p.m.

Draw a smooth curve to pass through the points.

(a) Use the graph to estimate the time that the sun sets on
  (i) 27 April (ii) 1 June.

(b) How much later is the sun setting on 8 June than on 15 of April?

(c) Is the difference in the time that the sun sets from one day to the next always the same? If it is not, when is the difference (i) greatest (ii) least?

ANSWER

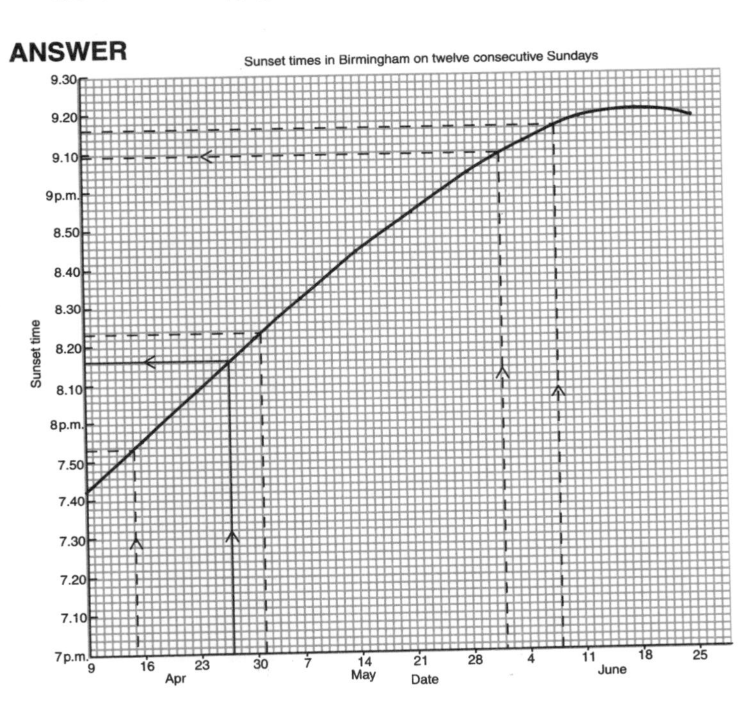

(a) (i) Sunset time on 27 April is 8.16 p.m.
  (ii) Sunset time on 1 June is 9.09 p.m.

(b) On 15 April the sun sets at 7.53 p.m. and on 8 June it sets at 9.16 p.m., so the sun sets 83 minutes later on 8 June than it does on 15 April.

(c) No. (i) At the beginning of the period under review. (ii) At the time when the sun sets latest.

---

1 A liquid is heated and left to cool. The temperature of the liquid at different times is given in the table.

Time (minutes)	0	2	4	6	8	10	12	14	16
Temperature (°C)	152	117	94	76	63	50	39	30	24

On graph paper draw axes, taking 1 cm = 1 min on the horizontal axis and 1 cm = 10° C on the vertical axis.

Plot the points given in the table and join them with a smooth curve. Use your graph to find

(a) the temperature of the liquid after
  (i) 1 minute (ii) 7 minutes.

(b) the time the liquid takes to cool to 100 °C.

(c) the time it takes for the liquid to cool from 120 °C to 60 °C.

2 A factory manufactures vases with different capacities but always with the same shape. The table gives the capacities, in pints, for vases of different heights.

Height (inches)	3.1	4.0	5.0	5.7	6.0	6.3	7.2
Capacity (pints)	0.25	0.5	1	1.5	1.75	2	3

(a) Draw a graph to represent this data using 2 cm to represent 1 in on the horizontal axis and 4 cm to represent 1 pint on the vertical axis.

(b) From your graph find
  (i) the capacity of a vase that is 4.5 in high
  (ii) the height of a vase that has a capacity of 2.5 pints.

3 The table below shows the temperature, in degrees Celsius, at 2-hourly intervals, in an Eastern European city during one complete day in the summer.

Time	Midnight	2.00	4.00	6.00	8.00	10.00	
Temp. (°C)	12	14	18.5	25	29.5	33	
Time	12.00	14.00	16.00	18.00	20.00	22.00	24.00
Temp. (°C)	36.1	37.5	37	34.5	29.5	21.5	11

Plot this data on a graph. Turn your graph paper longways. Use 1 cm = 1 hour on the horizontal axis and 4 cm = 10 degrees on the vertical axis.

Join the points with a smooth curve and use your graph to find

(a) the temperature at (i) 3 a.m. (ii) 3 p.m.

(b) the approximate times at which the temperature was 30 °C

(c) the period of time for which the temperature was above 35 °C

(d) the increase in temperature from midnight to midday

(e) the length of time for which the temperature is rising.

Self-assessment test 18

1 Given that 1 square yard is equivalent to 0.8361 square metres, draw a conversion graph to convert square yards into square metres for areas up to 18 square yards.
Take 1 cm ≡ 1 square yard on the horizontal axis and 1 cm ≡ 1 square metre on the vertical axis.

(a) Use your graph to find the equivalent of
(i) $11\frac{1}{2}$ square yards in square metres
(ii) 13.6 square metres in square yards.

(c) A carpet with an area of 10.2 square yards cost £356. How much is this a square metre?

2 In the United Kingdom the petrol consumption for a car is measured in miles per gallon (mpg), but on the Continent it is measured in litres per 100 kilometres (litres/100 km). The table gives the relationship between these measurements for different petrol consumptions.

Miles per gallon	20	27	34	38	42	47.9	58.8	64
Litres/100 km	14.2	10.5	8.4	7.4	6.8	5.9	4.8	4.4

Draw a graph to represent this data. Use 1 cm = 10 mpg on the horizontal axis and 1 cm = 1 litre/100 km on the vertical axis.
Use your graph to express (a) 45 mpg in litres/100 km (b) 5 litres/100 km in mpg.

CHAPTER 19

Scale drawings and maps

Scale drawings

A scale drawing is a smaller (or larger) drawing of an original object showing all the measurements in the same proportions.

Scales are given in one of two ways. A scale of 1 cm ≡ 1 m means that 1 cm on the drawing represents 1 metre on the actual object,
and a scale of 1 : 10 (or $\frac{1}{10}$) means that the drawing is $\frac{1}{10}$ the size of the actual object.

EXERCISE 19a

QUESTION

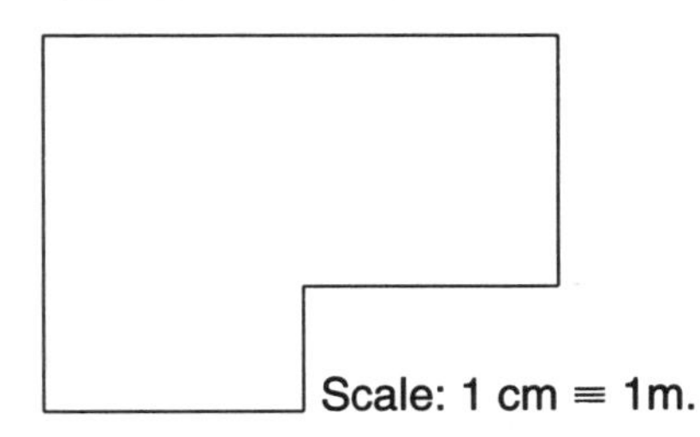

Scale: 1 cm ≡ 1m.

This is a scale drawing of Karen's kitchen.

(a) How long, in centimetres, is the drawing of the kitchen?

(b) How long is the actual kitchen?

(c) How wide, in centimetres, is the drawing of the kitchen at its widest point?

(d) How wide is the actual kitchen?

ANSWER

(a) The length of the drawing of the kitchen is 4 cm.

(b) Since 1 cm represents 1 m, the length of the actual kitchen is 4 × 1 m, i.e. 4 m.

(c) The width of the kitchen at its widest point is 3 cm.

(d) The width of the kitchen is 3 m.

1

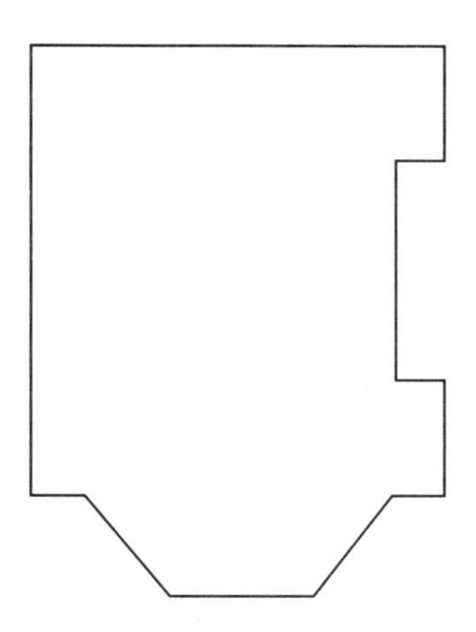

Scale: 1 cm ≡ 1 m.

This is a scale drawing of Nell's bedsitter.

(a) On the drawing, how long is the room, in centimetres, from the back wall to the front of the bay window?

(b) How far is it from the back wall to the front of the bay window?

(c) How wide is the room on the drawing at its widest point?

(d) What is the actual width of the room?

2

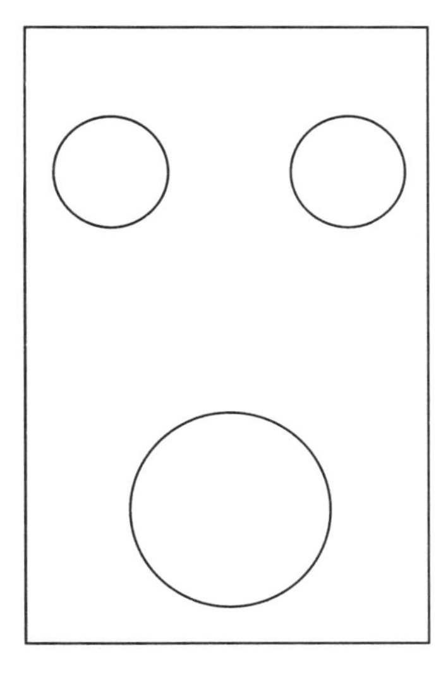

Scale: 1 cm ≡ 5 cm.

This is a scale drawing of one of the set of metal plates needed to manufacture an HK160 earthmoving machine. What is the actual measurement of
(a) the length of the plate (b) the diameter of one of the small holes (c) the radius of the large hole?

3

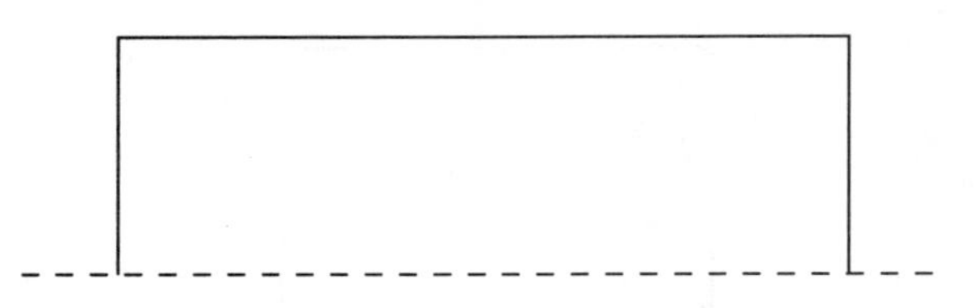

Scale: 1 cm ≡ 4 ft.

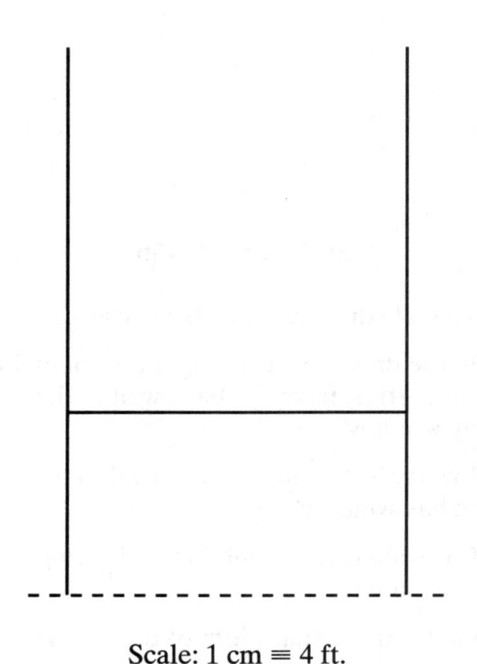

Scale: 1 cm ≡ 4 ft.

These are scale drawings for the goalposts on the soccer and rugby pitches at Windford Recreation Ground.

(a) On the drawing, how wide, in centimetres, are the goalposts for (i) soccer (ii) rugby?

(b) How far apart are the actual goalposts for (i) soccer (ii) rugby?

(c) How high is each crossbar above the ground?

(d) How high is one of the rugby posts?

4

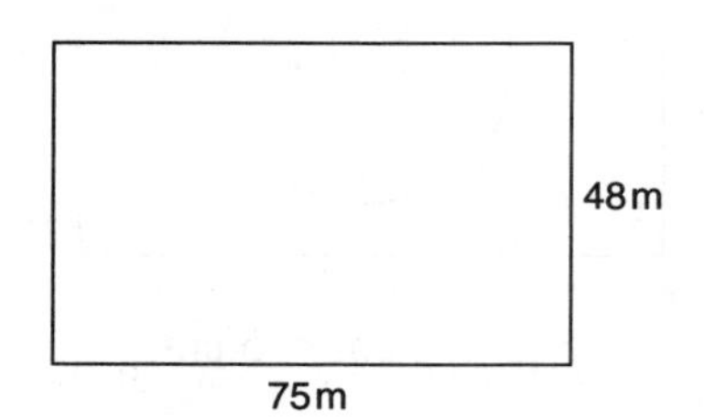

This is a sketch of an area of ground that is to be laid with tarmac. It is required to make a scale drawing of the area using a scale of 1 cm to represent 5 m.

(a) How long should the rectangle be in the drawing? (b) How wide should it be?

5 Given below is a scale drawing of the ground floor of a terraced house. Each square of the grid has a side of 1 cm and represents 1 m.

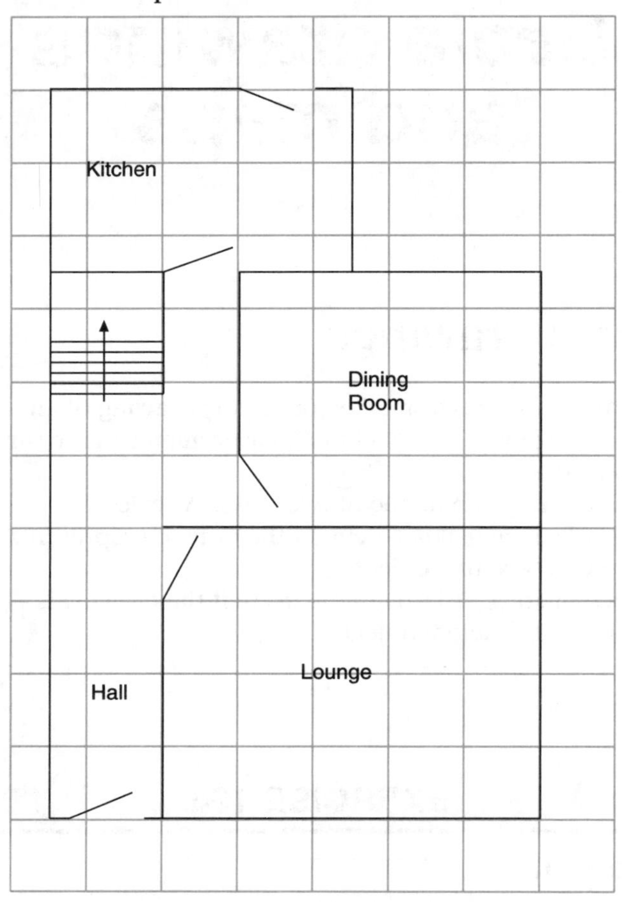

(a) Find the length and breadth of (i) the lounge (ii) the dining room.

(b) How wide is the hall at its widest part?

(c) What is the area of the lounge? How much would it cost to carpet at £20 a square metre?

6 See Figure on p. 173.
This is an accurate drawing, drawn half-size, of the cross-section of part of a domestic staircase.

(a) Use the drawing to find the actual length of
(i) the tread (ii) the rise
(iii) the going (iv) the nosing.

(b) What thickness of timber has been used for
(i) the tread (ii) the riser?

(c) A safety regulation states that the sum of the going plus twice the rise must be more than 500 mm but less than 700 mm. Do these stairs satisfy this regulation?

(d) The maximum permitted pitch of a stairs is 42 °. Use your protractor to check whether or not this staircase complies with the regulation.

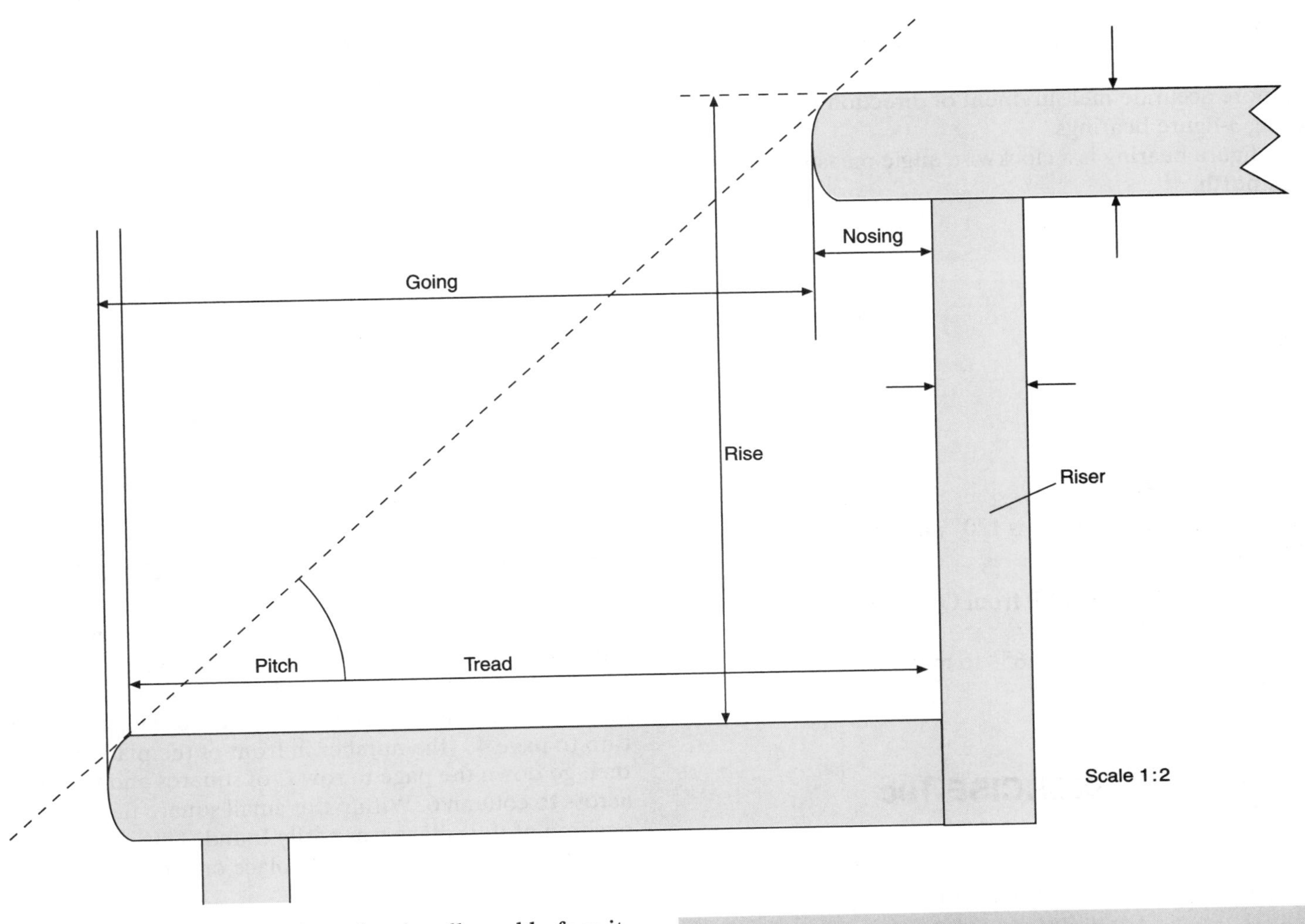

(e) The maximum number of stairs allowed before it is necessary to include a flat waiting area is 16.
  (i) If the next floor is level with the top of the 16th stair, how far is it vertically from one floor to the next?
  (ii) How many stairs are needed if the height of one floor above the other is 2.63 m?

(f) Each stair is 1.05 m wide. How much timber is used to make 12 risers?

Points of the compass

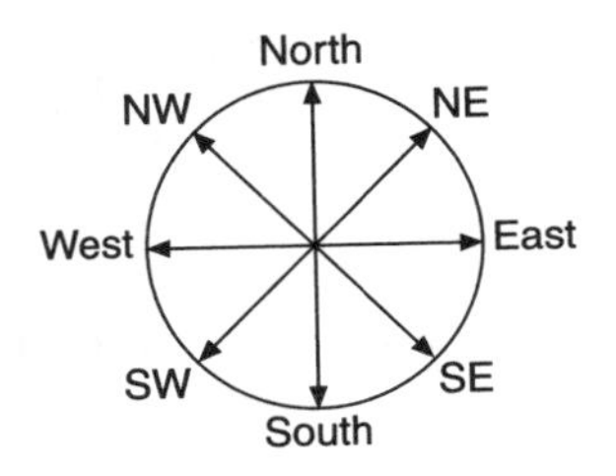

The eight points of the compass are enough to give a rough idea of the direction of one place from another.

EXERCISE 19b

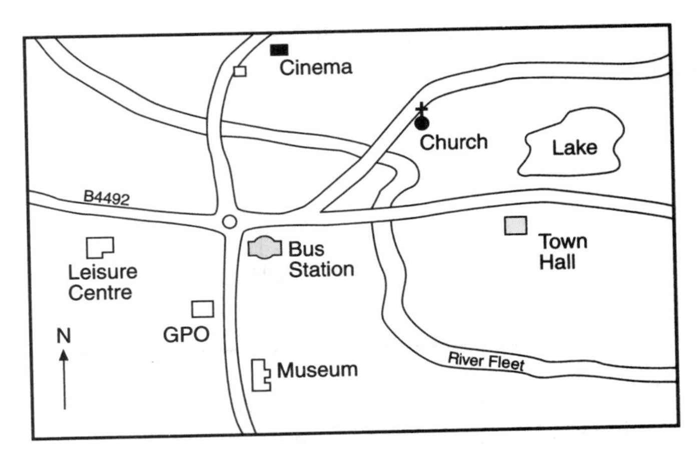

Use this map to give the approximate direction of

1 the town hall from the leisure centre

2 the bus station from the church

3 the museum from the cinema

4 the cinema from the town hall.

Three-figure bearings

A more accurate measurement of direction is found by using 3-figure bearings.
A 3-figure bearing is a clockwise angle measured from due north.

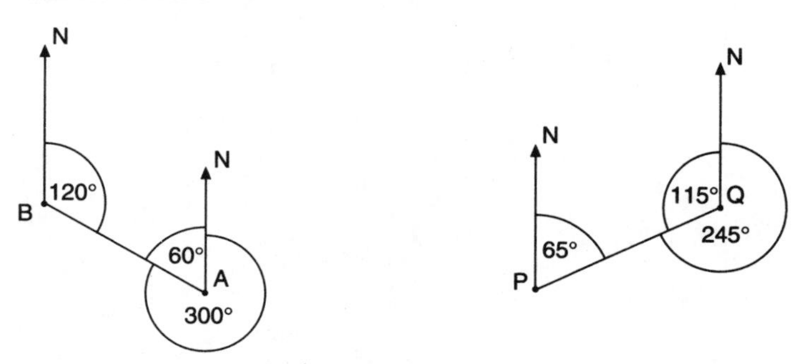

The bearing of A from B is 120° and the bearing of B from A is 300°.

Similarly, the bearing of P from Q is 245° and the bearing of Q from P is 0.65°.
(We put a zero in front of 65° to make it a 3-figure bearing.)

EXERCISE 19c

1 Give the 3-figure bearing for each of the directions
(a) east (b) west (c) north-east (d) south-west.

QUESTION
From a lighthouse, L, the bearing of a ship, S, is 285°.
Draw a rough sketch and mark the angle.

ANSWER

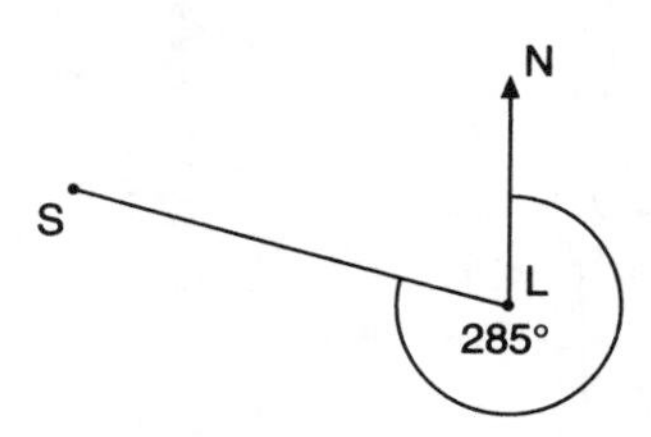

2 Draw a rough sketch to illustrate each of the following bearings. Mark the angle in each sketch.

(a) From a church, C, the bearing of the manor house, M, is 165°.

(b) From a tree, T, the bearing of the boat-house, B, is 305°.

(c) From a house, H, the bearing of a well, W, is 210°.

3 Use a protractor to give the 3-figure bearing of A from B.

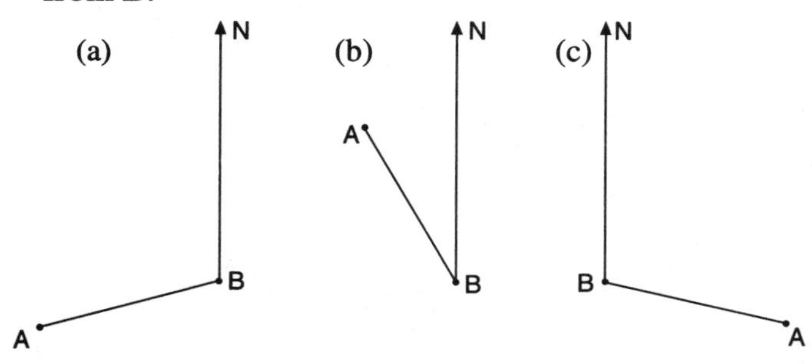

4 Eltham is 8 km from Minchester on a bearing of 080°. Vinckley is 6 km from Minchester on a bearing of 310 °. Draw a diagram to represent this information. What, roughly, is the bearing of Eltham from Vinckley?

Position of a place on a map

Suppose a motorist wishes to find out exactly where the village of Steeple Claydon is. A first step would be to look it up in the index of a good road atlas. When I did this the entry I found was 48 Steeple Claydon C6. This told me to turn to page 48 (the number in front of the place name), then go down the page to row C of squares and finally across to column 6. Within this small square the exact position of the village was easily found. This is a simple and effective way of locating a place on a map.

EXERCISE 19d

Use the map opposite to describe what you find

1 in the centre of square E5

2 just over halfway down the right-hand edge of H3

3 a town that is equally in D3 and E3

4 the place that is in the middle of J6

5 cutting through the middle of H5.

It is far more difficult to find the position of a place if all you know is the name of that place. This is why it will probably take you much longer to do questions 6 to 10 than it did to do 1 to 5.

What references would you expect to find in the index for the following places?

6 Didcot **7** Shabbington **8** Chetwode
9 Great Bedwyn **10** Thame

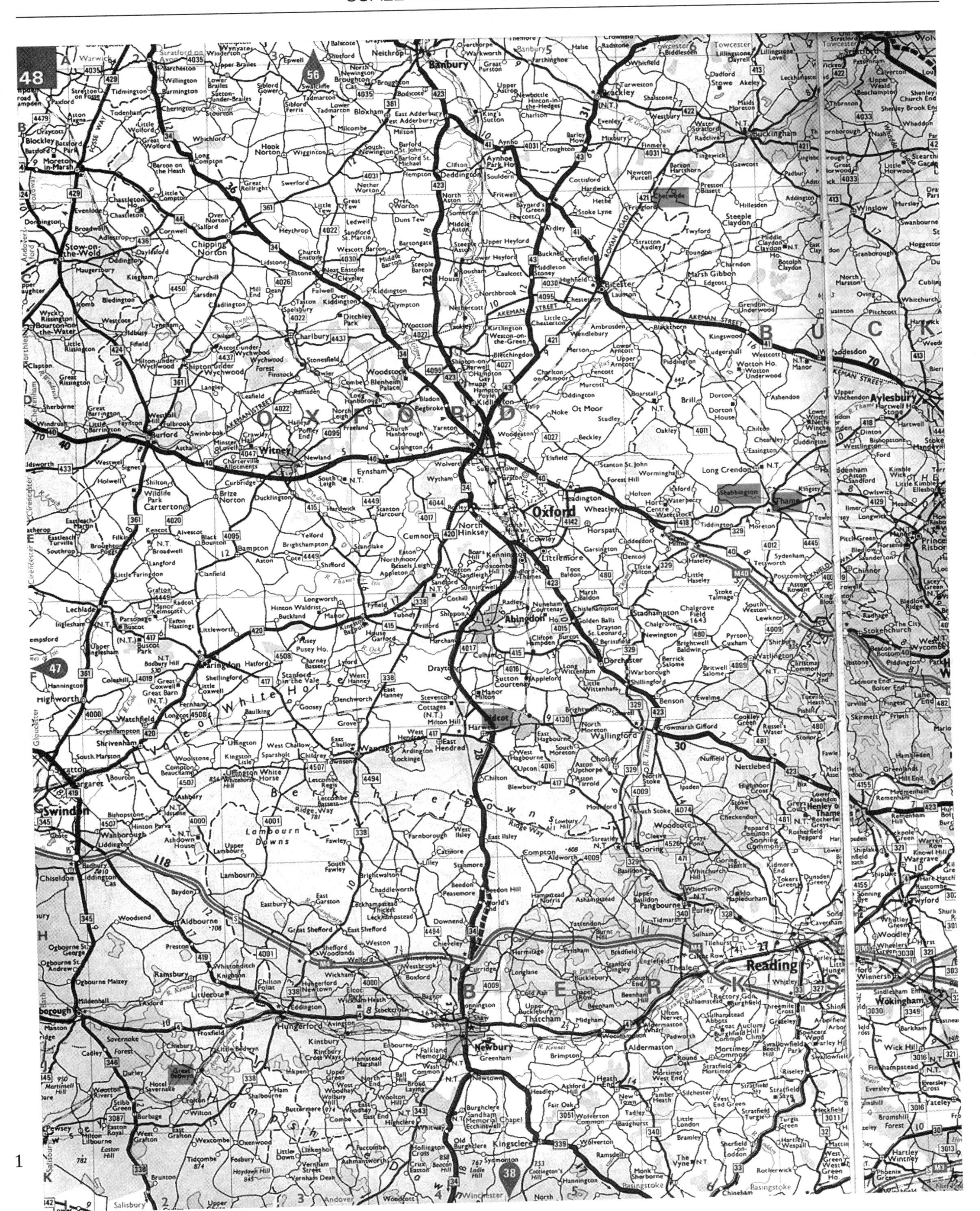
Banbury
Brackley
Buckingham
Deddington
Bicester
Chipping Norton
Stow-on-the-Wold
Woodstock
Witney
Burford
Kidlington
Oxford
Abingdon
Aylesbury
Thame
Wallingford
Didcot
Wantage
Faringdon
Swindon
Reading
Newbury
Hungerford
Thatcham
Wokingham
Kingsclere
Basingstoke
Lambourn Downs
Vale of White Horse
Berkshire Downs
OXFORD
BERKS
BUCK

Ordnance Survey maps

On the opposite page is a section from an Ordnance Survey map – called an OS map for short. On these maps the lines that form the grid are numbered. On this map those that go horizontally are numbered from 51 to 60 and are called *eastings*. When an OS reference is given the eastings must always be written first. The other set of numbers increase from 13 to 25 as we move up the page. If the 4-figure reference of a place is 56 15 it means that it is the square which is to the right of the vertical grid line numbered 56 and above the horizontal grid line numbered 15. In the middle of that square you will find Upcott Barton. The 4-figure reference of Upcott Barton is therefore 56 15.

To locate a place more accurately on an OS map a 6-figure reference number is used. The first three figures refer to the eastings and the other three to the vertical position. On the map, the first, second, fourth and fifth digits of the 6-figure reference 564 185, i.e. 56 18, are taken as the 4-figure reference to give the correct square. Within this square go across the square for $\frac{4}{10}$ of the side (4 is the third figure) and $\frac{5}{10}$ of a side up (5 is the sixth figure. The 6-figure reference 564 185 takes us to Ebberly House.

EXERCISE 19e

What village or point of interest has a 4-figure OS reference of

1 53 16 **2** 59 15 **3** 58 18

4 54 19 **5** 52 14?

Give the 4-figure reference of

6 Dolton Beacon, roughly north-east of Dolton

7 Down Farm, north of Dolton

8 Castle Hill just off the B3220

9 the church at St Giles in the Wood

10 the telephone on the B3227 at High Bullen.

What do you find at the following 6-figure references?

11 576 138 **12** 562 169 **13** 533 189

14 591 181 **15** 584 186

Give the 6-figure reference of

16 the church at Beaford

17 the camping site just off the B3227 near High Bullen

18 Beaford Bridge over the River Torridge

19 the junction of the B3220 with the B3217

20 the telephone on the main road (A386) near Potheridge Gate.

Multiple-choice questions 19

In questions 1 to 4 several alternative answers are given. Write down the letter that corresponds to the correct answer.

1 The scale of a map is 1 : 10 000. This means that if two villages are 4.7 km apart then the distance between them on the map is

A 4.7 mm **B** 47 mm **C** 47 cm **D** 470 cm

2

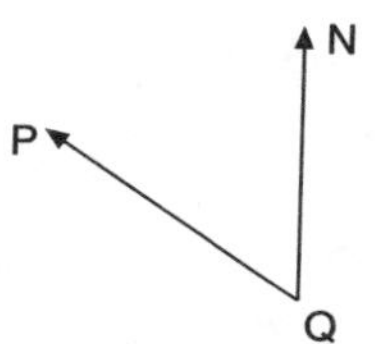

Of the four given directions the most accurate description for the direction of P from Q is

A south-east **B** north-west **C** north **D** south

3

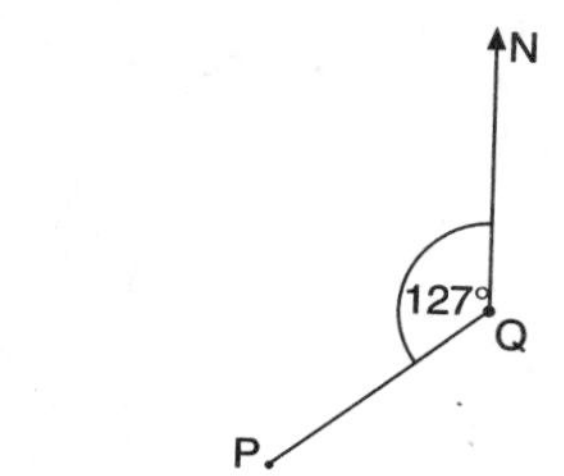

The 3-figure bearing of P from Q is

A 307° **B** 233° **C** 127° **D** 53°

4 The 6-figure Ordnance Survey reference for Menton is 434 173 and the corresponding reference for Newbold is 459 109. Which of the following statements are true and which are false?

A Menton is north of Newbold

B Menton is south of Newbold

C Newbold is west of Menton

D Newbold is east of Menton

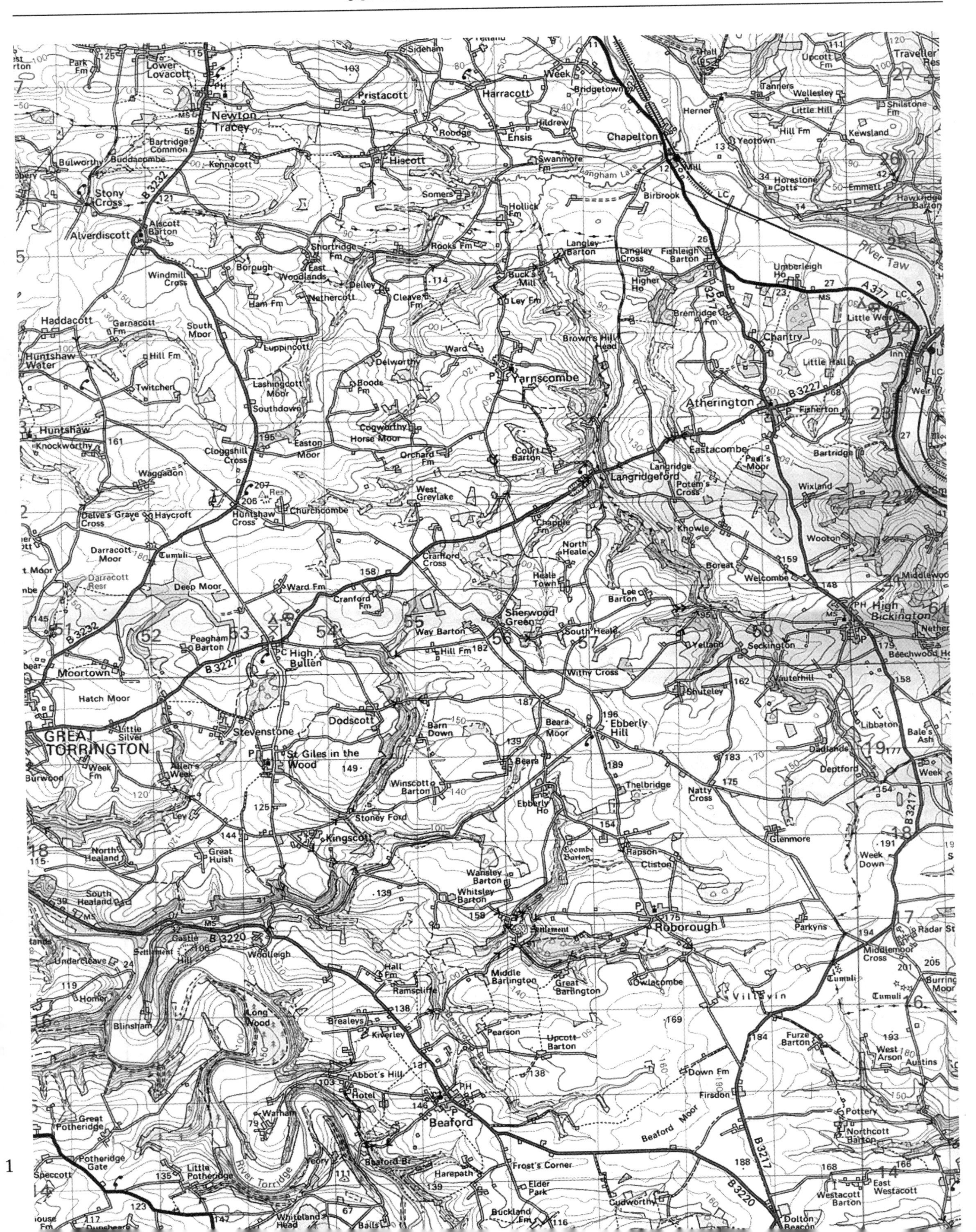
Lower Lovacott
Newton Tracey
Pristacott
Harracott
Week
Bridgetown
Chapelton
Hiscott
Kennacott
Ensis
Roodge
Swanmore Fm
Bulworthy
Buddacombe
Bartridge Common
Stony Cross
Alverdiscott
Alscott Barton
Somers
Hollick Fm
Birbrook
Yeotown
Herner
Tanners
Wellesley
Little Hill
Hill Fm
Kewsland
Shilstone Fm
Emmett
Horestone Cotts
Hawkridge Barton
River Taw
Umberleigh Ho
Shortridge Fm
East Woodlands
Rooks Fm
Langley Barton
Langley Cross
Fishleigh Barton
Borough
Windmill Cross
Ham Fm
Nethercott
Delley
Cleave Fm
Buck's Mill
Ley Fm
Higher Ho
Bremridge Fm
Chantry
Little Weir
Little Hall
Haddacott
Garnacott Fm
South Moor
Luppincott
Hill Fm
Huntshaw Water
Twitchen
Lashingcott Moor
Southdown
Delworthy
Ward
Boode Fm
Yarnscombe
Brown's Hill Head
Atherington
Fisherton
Huntshaw
Knockworthy
Cloggshill Cross
Easton Moor
Cogworthy Horse Moor
Orchard Fm
Court Barton
Eastacombe
Paul's Moor
Bartridge
Langridgeford
Langridge
Potem's Cross
Wixland
Waggadon
Huntshaw Cross
Churchcombe
West Greylake
Chapple Fm
Knowle
Delve's Grave Cross
Haycroft
Darracott Moor
Cumuli
Darracott Resr
Deep Moor
Ward Fm
Cranford Cross
Cranford Fm
North Heale
Heale Town
Boreat
Welcombe
Wooton
Middlewood
Lee Barton
Sherwood Green
South Heale
High Bickington
Moortown
Peagham Barton
High Bullen
Way Barton
Hill Fm
Yelland
Seckington
Beechwood
Withy Cross
Hatch Moor
Vauterhill
Shuteley
GREAT TORRINGTON
Little Silver
Stevenstone
Dodscott
Barn Down
Beara Moor
Ebberly Hill
Libbaton
Bale's Ash
St Giles in the Wood
Beara
Dadlands
Deptford
Week
Week Fm
Allen's Week
Burwood
Winscott Barton
Thelbridge
Natty Cross
Ebberly Ho
Ley
Stoney Ford
Kingscott
Glenmore
North Healand
Great Huish
Coombe Barton
Rapson
Cliston
Week Down
Wansley Barton
Whitsley Barton
South Healand
Castle Hill
Woolleigh
Settlement
Roborough
Parkyns
Radar St
Middlemoor Cross
Undercleave
Hall Fm
Ramscliffe
Middle Barlington
Great Barlington
Owlacombe
Villavin
Tumuli
Burrington Moor
Homer
Blinsham
Long Wood
Brealeys
Kiverley
Pearson
Upcott Barton
Furze Barton
West Arson
Austins
Abbot's Hill
Down Fm
Hotel
Firsdon
Great Potheridge
Warham
Beaford
Beaford Moor
Pottery
Northcott Barton
Potheridge Gate
Little Potheridge
River Torridge
Yeory
Beaford Br
Frost's Corner
Harepath
Elder Park
Speccott
Westacott Barton
East Westacott
Whiteland Head
Balls
Buckland Fm
Cudworthy
Dolton Beacon

Self-assessment test 19

Use the map below to answer the following questions.

1 What do you find in the square whose 4-figure reference is (a) 06 21 (b) 08 22?

2 What do you find in the square whose 6-figure reference is (a) 101 216 (b) 097 252?

3 Give the 4-figure reference for (a) the rugby ground (b) Bedlam College (c) the cemetery.

4 Give the 6-figure reference for (a) the General Post Office (b) the B.T. tower (c) the junction of Eastgate Street with Hinton Road.

5 The length of a side of each square on the map is 500 m. Estimate (a) the length of Salt Street (b) the distance, as the crow flies, from the railway station to the technical college.

6 What, roughly, is the bearing of (a) the GPO from the hospital (b) the Police Station from Pengam School?

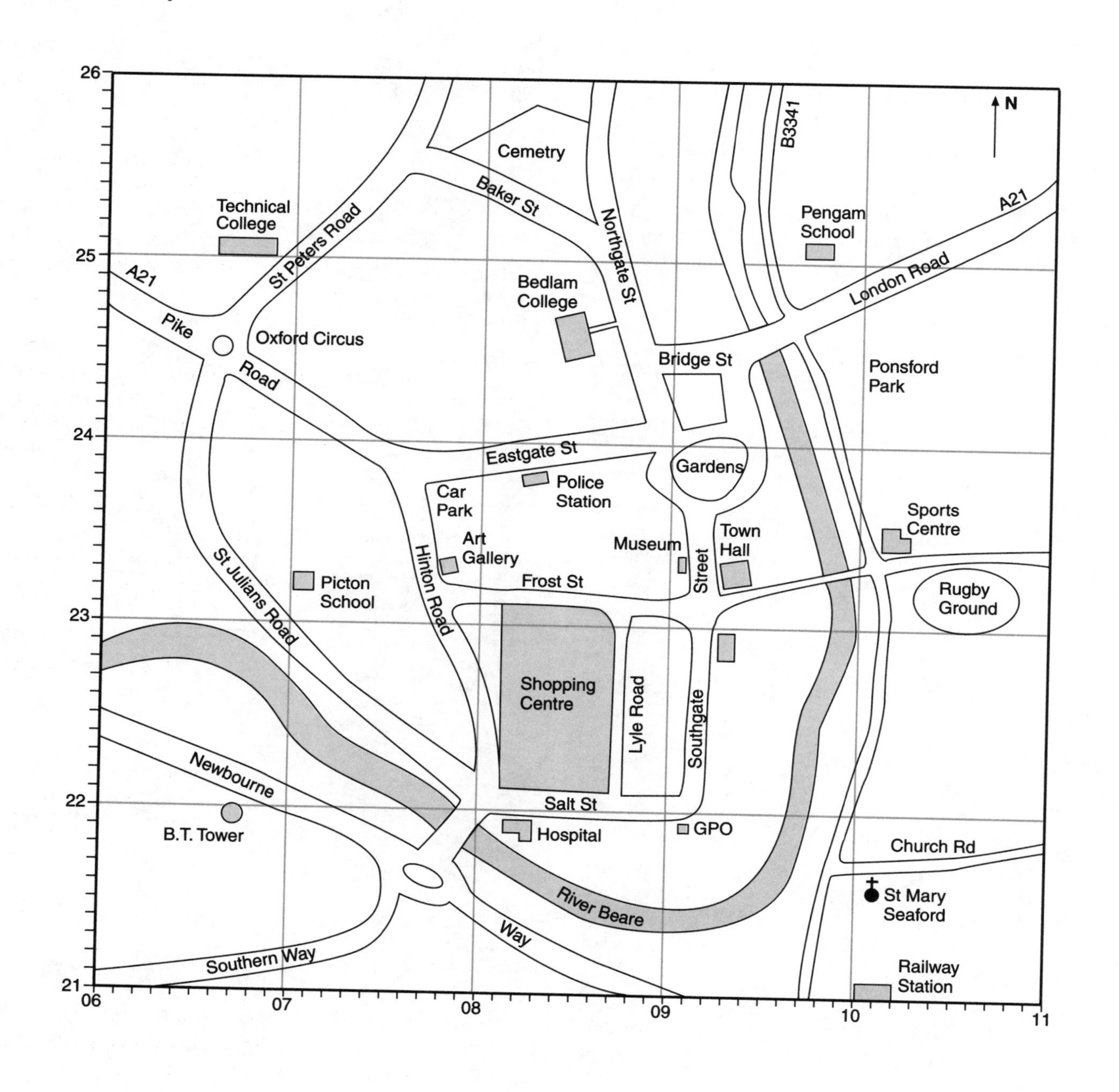

CHAPTER 20
Probability

Randomness

When we say that an event will happen at random, we mean that there is no certain way of predicting where and when it will happen. For example, it is fairly certain that at least one team in the football league will lose 2–0 at home on the last Saturday before next Christmas, but we cannot predict which team it will be. It is also fairly certain that every team in the league will lose 2–0 at home on some future occasion, but, once again, we cannot say when. If an event happens 'at random' then other possibilities are also implied. For example, if we toss a coin we know that it will come down either heads or tails.

When we say that a letter is chosen from a word *at random* we mean that each letter in the word is equally likely to be chosen, that is, it has the same chance of being chosen as any other letter. When you see the word random it means that all the possibilities are equally likely.

Probability is the study of unpredictable events, which may or may not happen. It is possible, though unlikely, that sometime in the next year you will receive a million pounds from someone in their will. On the other hand it is as certain as anything can be that the sun will rise tomorrow.

Equally likely events

How often have you heard people say 'It's an even chance – there are two possibilities; either we'll win or we won't'?

It is usually quite wrong to suppose that because there are two possibilities they are both equally likely. If you roll a dice it is certain that either you will roll a 6 or you will roll some value other than 6, but the two possibilities are not equally likely. The two chances are not the same. The face showing 6 is but one of six possible scores when the dice is rolled. You are just as likely to score 1, 2, 3, 4 or 5 as you are to score 6.

When you take a journey by road you also have two chances – you will either arrive safely or you will not. The chances are that you will arrive safely. When you go on a journey the chance that you will not arrive safely is quite small.

However, some events do have an even chance of happening. Suppose you toss an unbiased coin. It can land 'head' up or it can land 'tail' up. In this case there are two possible outcomes, each of which is equally likely.

Tossing a coin is called an *experiment*; the result is called an *outcome* or event.

EXERCISE 20a

1 Neale saved £100 and used the money to buy 100 Premium Bonds. Would he be equally likely to win a prize with any one of them?

2 Callum and Sandy decided to spend the evening playing darts. Callum won the first seven games. As Sandy stood to throw his first dart of the eighth game he said to himself 'I've lost the first seven games, so I'm bound to win this one.' Was he right? Give reasons for your answer.

3 Manchester United, who have won their last ten games, play Kidderminster United, who have also won their last ten games, in the FA Cup next weekend. Do you agree that each team is equally likely to win?

4 Before a test match between England and Australia a coin is tossed to decide which side can choose whether or not to bat. Is the captain who tosses the coin as likely to win as the captain who does not?

5 When someone is chosen from a group of boys and girls there is an even chance that the person is a girl. What does this tell you about the number of boys and the number of girls in the group?

6 Can you think of some events that have a 50–50 chance of happening? Discuss these events with a partner.

Probability

If you toss a coin, it will land head up or tail up. Landing head up is one of two equally likely events, so the chance of throwing a head is 1 out of 2, i.e. $\frac{1}{2}$.

Expressing the chance as a fraction is a way of

measuring that chance, but it is often more convenient to give this value as a decimal, e.g. the chance of getting a head when a coin is tossed is 0.5.

The word we use to measure chance is *probability*.

When a dice is rolled there are six equally likely possibilities so, the probability or chance of rolling a two is 1 out of 6, i.e. $\frac{1}{6}$.

EXERCISE 20b

In this exercise, assume that all the possible outcomes are equally likely.

1 What is the probability of rolling a dice and getting a 1?

2 What is the probability of tossing a coin and getting a tail?

3 If one letter is chosen at random from the letters in the word DASH, what is the probability that the letter is H?

4 If one letter is chosen at random from the letters in the word IRELAND, what is the probability that the letter is L?

5 One coin is chosen at random from the six different coins that were issued in a boxed set in 1970 in readiness for the introduction of decimal coinage on 15 February 1971. What is the probability that the value of the chosen coin is
(a) 50p (b) 10p (c) 5p?
(The coins in a 1970 boxed set are one each of 50p, 10p, 5p, 2p, 1p, $\frac{1}{2}$p.)

Events that can happen more than once

The word SPOON has 5 letters, including 2 Os.

There are 2 equally likely ways of choosing a letter O and there are 5 equally likely ways of choosing a letter.

2 out of these 5 equally likely ways give a letter O, so the probability that if one letter is chosen it is a letter O is $\frac{2}{5}$.

To take another example, look at the word SEPTEMBER. This word has 9 letters, 3 of which are E. If I choose a letter from this word the probability or chance that it will be a letter E is 3 out of 9, i.e. $\frac{3}{9}$, which simplifies to $\frac{1}{3}$.

In general, the probability that an event will happen is given by the fraction

$$\frac{\text{number of ways in which the event can happen}}{\text{total number of equally likely events}}.$$

EXERCISE 20c

QUESTION

Carl empties the coins in his pocket on to the counter of his local newsagent because he is not sure whether or not he has enough money to pay for some car magazines. He finds that he has five £1 coins, three 50p pieces, four 20p pieces and six 10p coins. One coin is picked up from the counter at random. What is the probability that it is
(a) a £1 coin (b) a 10p piece (c) a silver coin?

ANSWER

(a) He has $5 + 3 + 4 + 6$, i.e. 18, coins altogether, 5 of which are £1 coins.
Thus the probability of choosing a £1 coin is 5 out of 18, i.e. $\frac{5}{18}$.

(b) He has 18 coins altogether, 6 of which are 10p pieces.
Thus the probability of choosing a 10p piece is 6 out of 18, i.e. $\frac{6}{18} = \frac{1}{3}$.

(c) Of the 18 coins, 13 of them are silver, namely three 50ps, four 20ps and six 10ps.
Therefore the probability of choosing a silver coin is 13 out of 18 $= \frac{13}{18}$.

1 The china department of a large store sells crockery with a pattern called 'Summertime'. The present stock of plates in this pattern is given in the table.

Diameter (inches)	$6\frac{1}{2}$	7	8	9	10	$10\frac{1}{2}$
Number	5	12	10	4	3	2

A plate is chosen at random from this stock. What is the probability that the diameter of the chosen plate is (a) 7" (b) 10" (c) at least 8"?

2 At the end of a day a market trader has a wad of banknotes. He counts them and finds he has two at £50, twenty-eight at £20, thirteen at £10 and nine at £5. He takes one note at random from this wad to pay his assistant.

(a) Is the note more likely to be a £20 note than any other?

(b) What is the probability that the value of the note he gives is (i) £10 (ii) £50 (iii) not £20?

3

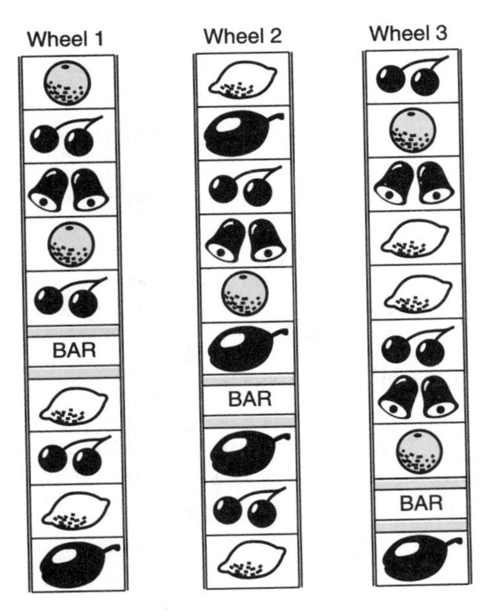

The sketch shows the pictures on the wheels of a fruit machine.

(a) Find the number of times each fruit appears on the display.

(b) Find the probability of getting (i) a bar on the first wheel (ii) a lemon on the second (iii) cherries on the third.

4 Thirty-eight old-age pensioners, 24 of whom are women, go on a day trip to London to see *Phantom of the Opera*. The tickets for the show are given out at random on the coach. What is the chance that the ticket for the best seat goes to a man?

5 The diagram shows the seating plan for a Boeing 767-300 Intercontinental. There are 42 rows altogether, some first class, some business class and the remainder coach class.

(a) How many seats are there for business-class passengers?

(b) Tim Stewart is allocated a seat at random in the business class section of the aircraft. What is the probability that (i) he has an aisle seat (ii) he has a window seat?

(c) Fiona Parker is travelling coach class. She asks to sit in row 31. She is given a seat in this row at random. What is the probability that her seat is (i) against a window (ii) on an aisle (iii) not on an aisle?

(d) In how many different ways can Meg and Peter Davies be seated in row 8 if (i) they sit together (ii) they sit apart? (Count sitting in seats across an aisle as sitting apart. Remember that if they are sitting with Meg on Peter's left it is different from sitting in the same two seats with Meg on Peter's right.)

Impossibility and certainty

Some events are impossible. For example, it is impossible to take a tin of beans from a kitchen cupboard if there are no tins of beans in the cupboard.

If an event is impossible then the probability that it happens is 0.

On the other hand, some events are certain. If you throw a javelin into the air it will come down again.

If an event is certain to happen then the probability that it happens is 1.

767
Boeing 767-300 Intercontinental

First Class Rows 2-4
Business Class Rows 7-12
Coach Rows 17-42

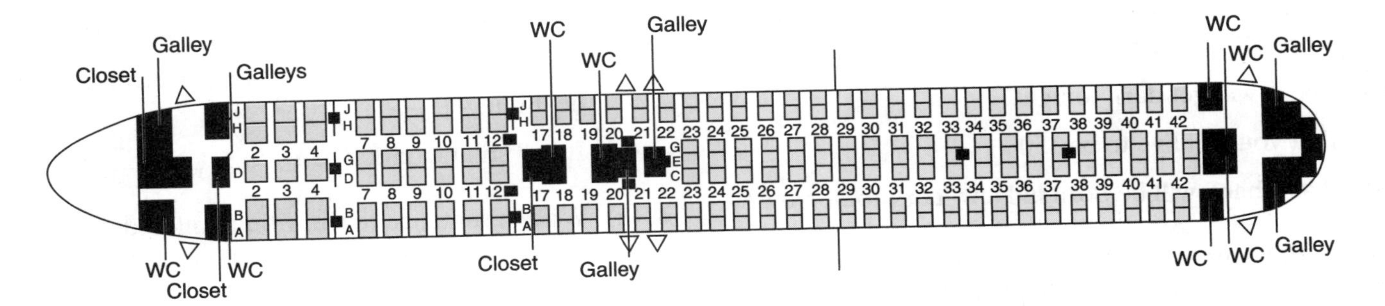

EXERCISE 20d

Questions 1 to 4 refer to the picture which shows some people waiting for a bus.

1 How many (a) women (b) men, are there in the queue?

2 What fraction of the people in this queue are
(a) female (b) male?

3 (a) How many boys are there in this queue?

(b) What fraction of the people in this queue are boys?

4 You choose a person at random from the queue. What is the probability that the chosen person is
(a) a male (b) a female (c) a boy
(d) a girl (e) either a male or a female?

5 What is the probability

(a) of choosing the letter H from the letters in the word OCTOBER

(b) that it will get dark tonight

(c) that you will live to be 150

(d) that a baby will be born in New York tomorrow?

If an event is impossible the probability that it happens is 0, but if an event is certain to happen the probability that it happens is 1.

For most events the probability that they occur lies between these two extremes.

The scale given below, which is given in fractions and in decimals, shows the complete range of possibilities.

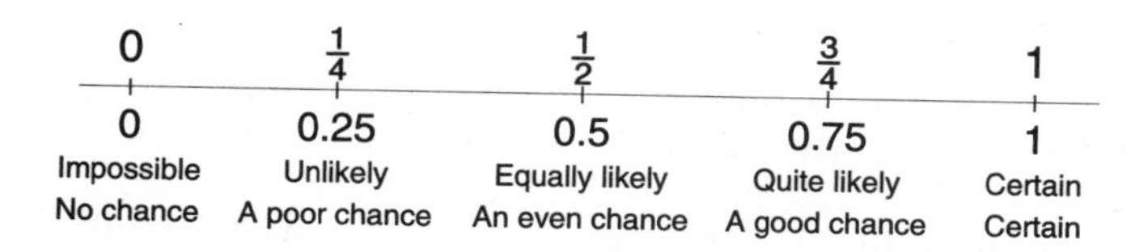

EXERCISE 20e

1 Use words such as 'unlikely', 'quite likely', etc. to describe the probability of the given events happening.

(a) The sun will rise tomorrow morning.

(b) You will live for 100 years.

(c) The first person I'll see when I switch the television set on will be a female.

(d) I get a head when I spin a coin.

(e) Next year will have at least 365 days.

(f) You will represent your country in a sport.

(g) Value added tax (VAT) will be reduced in the next budget.

(h) It will still be dark when you get up tomorrow.

2 (a) Write a sentence to show that you understand each of the following words/phrases: even chance, less than an even chance, no chance, a certainty, most unlikely, very likely.

(b) Which of the words/phrases given in (a) do you think best describes a probability of
(i) 0 (ii) 0.01 (iii) 0.45
(iv) 0.5 (v) 0.9 (vi) 1?

3 How many different possible outcomes are there if you

(a) choose a main course from a menu that has eight different main courses on it

(b) decide to buy a car from a secondhand car dealer who has 35 cars for sale

(c) telephone a friend at her home?

Probability that an event does not happen

If Tim promises he will give you a ring one day within the next week, with any day equally likely, the probability that he will ring tomorrow is $\frac{1}{7}$.

If he does not ring tomorrow the probability that he will ring on one of the other six days is $\frac{6}{7}$

$\therefore$ the probability of ringing tomorrow + the probability of ringing on some other day is $\frac{1}{7} + \frac{6}{7}$

$= \frac{7}{7} = 1$

i.e. the probability that he will ring tomorrow + the probability that he will not ring tomorrow = 1

In general terms,

$$\text{probability that an event will happen} + \text{probability that the event will not happen} = 1$$

i.e. probability that an event will happen

= 1 − probability that the event will not happen

and probability that an event will not happen

= 1 − probability that the event will happen

EXERCISE 20f

QUESTION

The sketch shows some brochures on the shelf in a travel agent's. A brochure is chosen at random. What is the probability that the selected brochure is

(a) for Turkey (b) is not for Turkey?

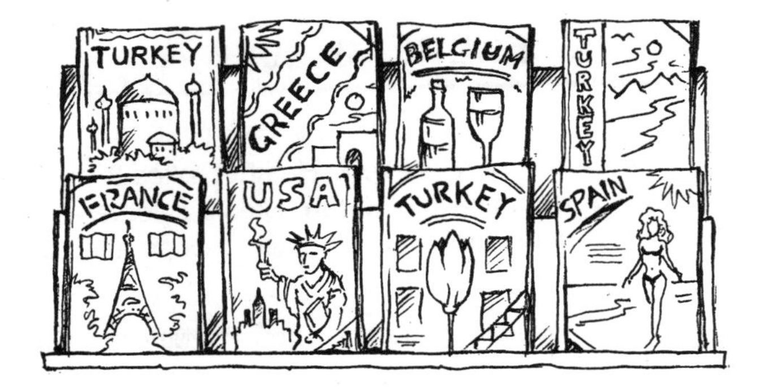

ANSWER

(a) There are 8 brochures on the shelf and 3 of them are for Turkey, so the probability that the selected brochure is for Turkey is $\frac{3}{8}$.

(b) The probability that the brochure is not for Turkey is $1 - \frac{3}{8} = \frac{5}{8}$.

1 On any day the probability that I will get up before 8 a.m. is $\frac{3}{4}$. What is the probability that tomorrow morning I will not get up before 8 a.m.?

2 The probability that it will rain tomorrow in Cairo is 0.008. What is the probability that it will not rain in Cairo tomorrow?

3 The probability that Marie will pass her driving test is 0.72. What is the probability that she will not pass?

4 A team is chosen at random from the 20 teams in the Premier League. What is the probability that it is

(a) Everton (b) a team other than Everton?

5 Recently the Blood Transfusion Service held a session at the Grenford Park Industrial Estate. The table shows how the donors were divided into different blood groups.

Blood group	Number of donors
O	56
A	44
B	15
AB	9

If a donor is chosen at random what is the probability that the donor's blood group is

(a) A (b) AB (c) not O?

6 A box contains a set of snooker balls. They consist of 15 reds and one each of white, yellow, green, brown, blue, pink and black. If one ball is removed at random from the box what is the probability that it is

(a) red (b) not red (c) blue
(d) neither red nor black?

Bookmakers' odds

If a horse is quoted at 10–1, it means that if you are prepared to stake £1, the bookmaker is willing to stake £10, i.e. the total stake is £11, the winner to take all. Odds of 10–1 therefore imply that you have 1 chance of winning and 10 chances of losing, i.e. the probability of winning is 1 out of 11 or $\frac{1}{11}$.

If Pink Panther is '2–1 on' it means that for every £2 you stake the bookmaker stakes £1, i.e. the chance of it winning is $\frac{2}{3}$. 'Evens', i.e. 1–1, implies a 50–50 chance of winning, i.e. the probability of winning is $\frac{1}{2}$.

EXERCISE 20g

1 What is the probability of winning if the starting price of a horse is
(a) 5–1 (b) 9–1 (c) 7–2 (d) 5–2?

2 A bookmaker quotes odds of 15–1 on Spurs winning the FA Cup next year. What does the bookmaker believe to be Spurs' probability of winning?

3 The odds that Billy's Boy will win the 3.30 at Doncaster are 3–2 on. Eddie puts £5 on the horse.
(a) What does the bookmaker think is the probability that Billy's Boy will win?
(b) How much will Eddie collect if it does win?

Possibility space for two events

Suppose Anju has 3 pairs of black shoes and 1 pair of brown shoes, while Sima has 2 pairs of black shoes and 2 pairs of brown shoes. If each of them chooses a pair of shoes at random then we can set out all the different possibilities in a table. This table is called a *possibility* space.

		Anju			
		Bl	Bl	Bl	Br
Sima	Bl	Bl, Bl	Bl, Bl	Bl, Bl	Br, Bl
	Bl	Bl, Bl	Bl, Bl	Bl, Bl	Br, Bl
	Br	Bl, Br	Bl, Br	Bl, Br	Br, Br
	Br	Bl, Br	Bl, Br	Bl, Br	Br, Br

Note that the first entry of each pair refers to Anju's choice, which is listed along the top, while the second entry refers to Sima's choice, which is listed down the side. From this table it is easy to see that there are 6 ways in which both of them can choose black shoes, 2 ways in which they can both choose brown shoes and 8 ways in which they can choose shoes of a different colour.

EXERCISE 20h

1 Nicki and Phil each have a bag with 3 compact discs and 2 cassettes. Liz chooses 1 item from Nicki's bag and 1 from Phil's. Complete the following possibility space to show the possible combinations of 2 items. A compact disc is denoted by D and a cassette by C.

		First bag				
		D	D	D	C	C
Second bag	D	D, D	D, D	D, D	C, D	
	D					
	D					
	C	D, C				
	C				C, C	

2 Lindsay and Vicki look into their purses. Lindsay's purse contains three £1 coins and two 20p coins, whereas Vicki's purse contains one £1 coin and one 20p coin. A coin is removed at random from each purse.

(a) Complete the following possibility space:

		Lindsay's purse				
		£1	£1	£1	20p	20p
Vicki's purse	£1				20p, £1	
	20p					

(b) How many different possible outcomes are there?

(c) How many of these outcomes give one £1 coin and one 20p coin?

(d) How many of these outcomes give two coins of the same value?

Using a possibility space

We can use a possibility space to find a probability, since we can count all the possible outcomes and we can count the number that satisfy the particular condition we are interested in.

EXERCISE 20i

QUESTION

When they go away for a weekend Heather takes 3 sweaters and 2 T-shirts, while Sarah takes 2 sweaters and 3 T-shirts. On the first morning they each choose a top at random.

(a) Construct a possibility space to show the different ways in which they can make their choices.

(b) What is the probability that (i) the two tops they choose are both sweaters (ii) one top is a sweater and the other a T-shirt (iii) at least one of the tops is a sweater?

ANSWER

(a) In the possibility space given below S denotes a sweater and T a T-shirt. The first letter in each box refers to Heather's tops.

		Heather's tops				
		S	S	S	T	T
Sarah's tops	S	S, S	S, S	S, S	T, S	T, S
	S	S, S	S, S	S, S	T, S	T, S
	T	S, T	S, T	S, T	T, T	T, T
	T	S, T	S, T	S, T	T, T	T, T
	T	S, T	S, T	S, T	T, T	T, T

(b) (i) The table shows that there are 25 different ways in which they can make their choice. In 6 of these, both wear sweaters.
∴ the probability that they both wear sweaters is $\frac{6}{25}$.

(ii) There are 13 possibilities with 1 S and 1 T.
∴ the probability that between them they choose one top of each type is $\frac{13}{25}$.

(iii) There are 19 possibilities with either one S or two.
∴ the probability that they choose at least one sweater is $\frac{19}{25}$.

In the questions that follow assume that all the possible outcomes are equally likely. Give probabilities as fractions or as decimals correct to 2 decimal places.

1 Use the possibility space in the worked example to find the probability that (a) Heather wears a sweater and Sarah wears a T-shirt (b) both wear T-shirts (c) at least one of them wears a T-shirt.

2 Use the possibility space for question 2 of Exercise 20h to find the probability that the two coins selected (a) are both £1 coins (b) are of different denominations (c) include at least one 20p coin.

3 Copy and complete the following possibility space which shows the total score when two dice are rolled together.

		First dice					
		1	2	3	4	5	6
Second dice	1	2	3	4	5	6	7
	2	3					8
	3	4					9
	4	5					10
	5	6					11
	6	7	8	9	10	11	12

(a) How many entries are there altogether?

(b) Which score is most likely? How many times does it occur?

(c) How many times is the score
(i) greater than 10 (ii) less than 10?

(d) Use your possibility space to find the probability that the score (i) is greater than 10 (ii) is less than 10 (iii) is 6 or more.

4 Damien keeps poodles. He has 3 dogs and 2 bitches. Mel also keeps poodles. He has 1 dog and 4 bitches. One poodle is chosen at random from each owner. Draw a possibility space to show the different combinations possible.
What is the probability that

(a) both poodles are dogs

(b) the poodles are of different sexes

(c) at least one of the poodles is a bitch?

Experimental probability

The probability that some events may happen can be found by calculation. For example, the probability that you will get two 6s when you roll two dice together is $\frac{1}{36}$. On the other hand, the probability that the next car that passes you will have three passengers can be found only by observation.

We can also check some calculated probabilities by experiment.

EXERCISE 20j

In this exercise give all probabilities in decimals correct to 2 decimal places.

1 (a) Throw a dice 10 times and count the number of times the score is 6. Work out the fraction

$$\frac{\text{total number of 6s}}{\text{total number of throws}}$$

Repeat the experiment again and again until the total number of throws is 120. Copy the following table and record your results in it.

Number of throws	10	20	30	40	50	60
Total number of 6s						
$\frac{\text{Total number of 6s}}{\text{Total number of throws}}$						
Number of throws	70	80	90	100	110	120
Total number of 6s						
$\frac{\text{Total number of 6s}}{\text{Total number of throws}}$						

Plot these values on the following graph.

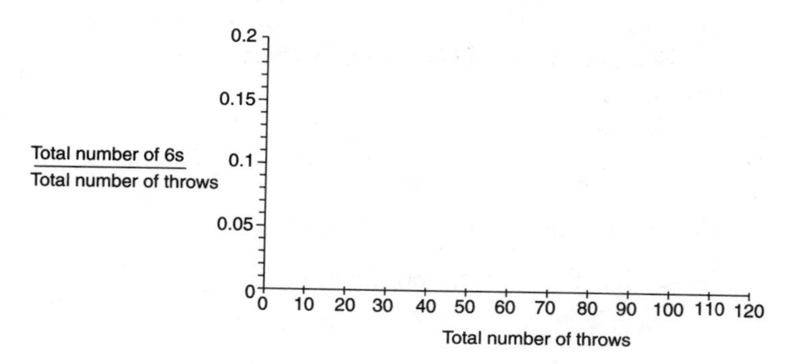

As the number of throws gets larger does the fraction

$$\frac{\text{total number of 6s}}{\text{total number of throws}}$$

settle down around a particular value?

(b) What is the theoretical probability of getting a 6 when a dice is thrown? How does this value compare with the value you got in part (a)?

2 (a) Toss a coin 100 times and count the total number of heads after every 10. Copy and complete the table.

Plot the decimal values you get for the fraction

$$\frac{\text{total number of heads}}{\text{total number of throws}}$$

against the total number of tosses, on a graph like the one you drew in question 1.

Number of tosses	10	20	30	40	50
Number of heads					
$\frac{\text{Number of heads}}{\text{Number of tosses}}$ (to 2 d.p.)					
Number of tosses	60	70	80	90	100
Number of heads					
$\frac{\text{Number of heads}}{\text{Number of tosses}}$ (to 2 d.p.)					

(b) What is the calculated probability of getting a head when a coin is tossed? Does your experimental value agree with this?

3 (a) If you choose a card at random from an ordinary pack of playing cards what is the probability of getting a heart?

(b) Shuffle an ordinary pack of 52 playing cards. Cut the pack, and note the suit of the card. Do this 40 times. Find the fraction

$$\frac{\text{number of times a heart is cut}}{\text{total number of times the pack is cut}}$$

How does this value compare with the value you got in part (a)?

(c) Repeat part (b) two or three times again.

4 For which of the following events can you calculate the probability that the event happens? Which must be found by experiment?

(a) Scoring 3 when a dice is rolled.

(b) Dropping a drawing pin to land point up.

(c) Getting the higher score when you play darts with a friend.

(d) Picking up exactly 10 sweets when you select a handful of sweets in a supermarket.

Expected values

We can use probability to estimate the expected number of times an event is likely to happen.

If I toss a tenpenny coin the probability of getting a head is $\frac{1}{2}$. On 1000 tosses I can therefore expect to get $1000 \times \frac{1}{2}$ heads, i.e. 500 heads.

If a student is chosen at random out of a class of 3 male students and 6 female students the probability of choosing a male student is $\frac{3}{9}$, i.e. $\frac{1}{3}$.

Suppose that on every one of the 180 days of the college year a student is chosen at random from these nine. The number of times a male student can be expected to be chosen is $180 \times \frac{1}{3}$, i.e. 60 times.

EXERCISE 20k

1 At Conley the probability of passing your driving test at the first attempt is $\frac{5}{8}$. Next week, 160 learner drivers are booked in to take their test. How many of them would you expect to pass? How many are likely to fail?

2 A car manufacturer knows from experience that the probability that the electrical system on any car they manufacture will fail during the first three years is 0.002. This year the company has produced 527 000 cars. How many of these are likely to have an electrical breakdown at some time during the next three years?

3 At Hurran's Nursery the probability that a cutting will become a saleable plant the following season is 0.9.

(a) How many saleable plants can be expected if 1200 cuttings are taken?

(b) How many cuttings should prove unsatisfactory?

4 A firm of motor insurers knows from experience that 5% of its policyholders will make a claim during a year's driving. At present it has 145 500 policyholders. How many claims does the firm expect will be made on these policies during the forthcoming year?

5 The probability that I will have to wait for a game when I go to the skittle alley is 0.6. I intend going to play skittles twice a week for the next 30 weeks. On how many occasions should I be able to play straight away?

6 If I post a first-class letter at my local post office, the probability that it will arrive at its destination the following morning is 0.95. The firm I work for sends out about 150 first-class letters every week. In a year how many of these letters would my firm expect to fail to be delivered the next morning?

7 The probability that the occupants of a house fitted with a smoke alarm will escape unharmed in the event of a fire is 0.96, whereas the probability that the occupants of a house not fitted with a smoke alarm will escape unharmed is one sixth of this.

(a) What is the probability that, Geoff, who lives in a house in which a smoke alarm has not been fitted, will escape unharmed in the event of a fire?

(b) During the next year in the county of Redfordshire it is estimated that there will be 650 fires in homes fitted with smoke alarms. In how many of these is it anticipated that the occupants
(i) will escape unharmed (ii) will suffer some kind of injury?

(c) During the same period it is estimated that the number of fires in houses not fitted with smoke alarms will be 1250. In how many of these fires is it estimated that the occupants will be injured?

Multiple-choice questions 20

In questions 1 to 3 several alternative answers are given. Write down the letter that corresponds to the correct answer.

1 If one letter is chosen at random from the letters in the word MANCHESTER, the probability that it is the letter E is

A $\frac{1}{10}$ **B** $\frac{1}{5}$ **C** $\frac{3}{10}$ **D** $\frac{2}{5}$

2 When Norman plays darts the probability that he will score a treble 20 with any dart is $\frac{1}{15}$. He throws a single dart 300 times. The number of times he does not expect to score treble 20 is

A 20 **B** 250 **C** 270 **D** 280

3 A taxi company, which has 3 red cabs and 2 yellow cabs, employs 2 female drivers and 3 male drivers. When a call comes in it is answered at random by any one of the 5 drivers. The colour of the cab that the driver takes is also selected at random. Ashok rings for a taxi. The probability that the cab he gets is yellow and driven by a female is

A $\frac{6}{25}$ **B** $\frac{9}{25}$ **C** $\frac{4}{25}$ **D** $\frac{3}{25}$

4 On a coach trip 250 tickets are sold in a raffle. Each person, including Jane, buys 5 tickets. Which of the following statements are true and which are false?

A Every person has exactly the same chance of winning and that chance is $\frac{1}{50}$.

B If every person had bought 1 ticket then Jane would have had exactly the same chance of winning as when everybody bought 5 tickets.

C There were fewer than 50 people on the coach.

D If Jane had bought 10 tickets but everybody else bought 5, Jane's chance of winning would have increased from $\frac{1}{50}$ to $\frac{1}{25}$.

5 Manora put £5 on Golden Wonder, a horse that was running in the 3.30 at York. Manora had a good day because the horse won at odds of 10–1. The following statements have been made:
Statement 1. The chance of winning is $\frac{1}{11}$ and since the horse wins Manora makes a profit of £50.
Statement 2. Manora wins £50, so she is £55 better off than if the horse had lost. How are these statements best described?

A True, True **B** True, False
C False, True **D** False, False

Self-assessment test 20

1 A letter is chosen at random from the word INTERNATIONAL. What is the probability that the letter is (a) R (b) N (c) A (d) B?

2 Bruce has ten CDs. Seven of them include hit songs by Aswad, while the remaining three include hit songs by Haddaway but none by Aswad. Hank chooses a CD from Bruce's collection. What is the probability that the CD he chooses includes a hit song by
(a) Aswad (b) Haddaway?

3 Estimate the probability that

(a) you will score 12 if you roll together 2 ordinary 6-sided dice

(b) it will get dark tonight

(c) you will get a head or a tail if you toss a coin

(d) you will get a diamond if you cut a card from a pack of 52 playing cards.

4 On any working day the probability that I will get stuck in a traffic jam on the way to work is 0.2.

(a) What is the probability that the next time I go to work I will not get stuck in a traffic jam?

(b) At present I work a 5-day week for 46 weeks a year. How many times in a year do I expect to get to work without getting stuck in a traffic jam?

5 In Wendy's kitchen cupboard she has 4 mugs and 2 cups on the upper shelf, and 2 mugs and 3 cups on the lower shelf. Copy and complete the following possibility space to show all the different possible combinations if 1 drinking vessel is chosen at random from each shelf. M stands for mug and C for cup. For each combination the first entry refers to the upper shelf and the second entry refers to the lower shelf.

		Upper shelf					
		M	M	M	M	C	C
Lower shelf	M	M, M	M, M	M, M			
	M						
	C						
	C						
	C	M, C	M, C				C, C

Use your possibility space to find the probability that (a) 2 mugs are chosen (b) 1 mug and 1 cup are chosen.

6 Yanumishi Electronics make television sets. The probability that a particular set will break down within three years is 0.001. Last year the company made 350 000 sets. How many of these does the company expect to break down during the first three years?

7

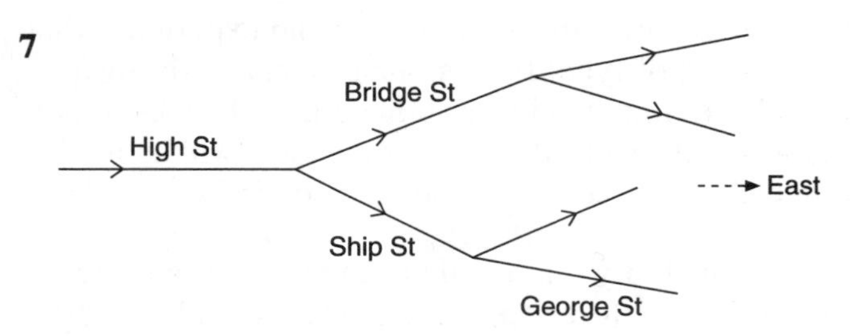

The diagram shows part of the one-way road system in Brickley. At each junction a vehicle must bear left or right. Experience shows that a vehicle travelling along High Street has a probability of $\frac{3}{4}$ of bearing left. On Ship Street there is a probability of $\frac{2}{3}$ that a vehicle bears left and on Bridge Street there is a probability of $\frac{2}{5}$ that a vehicle bears right.

(a) What percentage of the vehicles travelling along Bridge Street are expected to
(i) bear left (ii) bear right?

(b) Between 8 a.m. and 12 noon 3600 vehicles are predicted to enter High Street travelling east. How many of these vehicles are expected (i) to bear right along Ship Street (ii) to bear left twice (iii) to leave the system via George Street?

CHAPTER 21

Ratio and proportion

Ratio

A factory that assembles motorcars needs, among other things, roadwheels and front headlamp units. If they assemble 5 cars they need 25 wheels and 10 headlamp units. If they assemble 50 cars they need 250 wheels and 100 headlamp units. In all cases the number of wheels compared with the number of headlamp units is the same as 5 compared with 2. We say that the ratio of wheels to headlamps is 5 compared with 2 and we write this 5 : 2.

A ratio can be simplified by dividing each part by the same number. Thus, for example, when 6 buckets of sand are mixed with 2 buckets of cement, the ratio of sand to cement is 6 : 2. This ratio is the same as 3 : 1 because both 6 and 2 can be divided by 2.

Similarly, 12 : 3 is the same as 4 : 1 and 18 : 27 is the same as 2 : 3.

EXERCISE 21a

In questions 1 to 8 simplify the ratio.

1 40 : 20 **2** 49 : 35 **3** 12 : 18 **4** 56 : 72

5 7 : 21 **6** 150 : 100 **7** 24 : 40 **8** 45 : 81

9 Arrange the numbers 42, 6, 38, 75, 50, 9, 57 and 28 in pairs, so that in each pair the ratio of the first number to the second is 2 : 3.

QUESTION
At Vale Insurance there are 9 male staff and 15 female staff. What is the ratio of males to females?

ANSWER
Ratio of males to females is 9 : 15 = 3 : 5 (dividing by 3).

---

10 In a residential home there are 35 women and 14 men. What is the ratio of
(a) women to men (b) men to women?

11 Find the ratio of the length of the River Seine, which is 768 km long, to the length of the River Loire, which is 972 km long.

12 Dylan is 12 years old while his father is 42. Find
(a) the ratio of their present ages
(b) the ratio of their ages in 3 years' time.

13 This week at Holiday Travel they have taken 60 bookings for holidays in America and 210 bookings for holidays in Europe. What is the ratio of the number of holiday bookings for America to the number of holiday bookings for Europe?

14 It is expected that by the year 2011 the population of Wales will be 3 000 000 and the population of Scotland will be 5 000 000. What is the expected ratio in 2011 of the population of Scotland to the population of Wales?

15 On a farm of 371 acres, 106 acres are used to grow cereals and the remainder is devoted to grass. Find the ratio of (a) the acreage used for cereals to the acreage used for grass (b) the acreage used for grass to the acreage used for cereals.

Comparing the sizes of quantities

EXERCISE 21b

QUESTION
35 m compared with 15 m is the same as 7 compared with 3. Use the symbol : to write this sentence as an equation.

ANSWER
35 m : 15 m = 7 : 3.

---

1 Using the symbol : write each sentence as an equation.

(a) 25 lorries compared with 10 vans is the same as 5 compared with 2.

(b) 675 red posters compared with 540 yellow posters is the same as 5 compared with 4.

(c) 4344 seated spectators compared with 543 standing spectators is the same as 8 compared with 1.

2 Write each equation as a statement.
(a) 42p : 105p = 2 : 5.
(b) 80 CDs : 440 cassettes = 2 : 11.

QUESTION
Kelly has £4 and Stella has 75p. What is the ratio of the amount of money Kelly has to the amount of money Stella has?

ANSWER
(The units of money must be the same, so we change the larger unit to the smaller unit i.e. we change pounds to pence.)
£4 = 400p
Ratio of amount of money Kelly has to amount of money Stella has is £4 : 75p
= 400p : 75p
= 400 : 75
= 16 : 3 (dividing by 25).

3 A cheesecake costs £4.55 and a loaf of bread costs 85p. What is the ratio of the cost of a cheesecake to the cost of a loaf of bread?

4 One metal rod is 160 cm long and a second rod is 3 m long. Find the ratio of the length of the first rod to the length of the second.

5 To make sweet marrow wine Glenys uses 1 oz of whole ginger to every 4 lb of sugar. Find the ratio of the weight of whole ginger to the weight of sugar.

The ratios we have considered so far have been simplified by dividing by a common factor. To simplify ratios that include fractions we multiply both parts by the same number.

QUESTION
Simplify (a) $3 : \frac{2}{3}$ (b) $\frac{3}{4} : \frac{2}{5}$.

ANSWER
(a) $3 : \frac{2}{3} = 9 : 2$ (multiplying by 3)
(b) $\frac{3}{4} : \frac{2}{5} = 15 : 8$ (multiplying by 20, the common denominator of 4 and 5)

6 Express each ratio in its simplest form.

(a) $2 : \frac{3}{4}$ (b) $4 : \frac{5}{8}$ (c) $\frac{2}{3} : \frac{3}{4}$ (d) $3 : 3\frac{1}{2}$
(e) $1\frac{1}{2} : \frac{3}{4}$ (f) $\frac{1}{2} : 5\frac{1}{2}$ (g) $1\frac{2}{3} : 2\frac{1}{5}$ (h) $1\frac{1}{4} : 2\frac{3}{4}$

7 A recipe for raspberry jam includes $3\frac{1}{2}$ lb of raspberries and 2 lb of sugar. Find the ratio of the weight of raspberries to the weight of sugar.

8 Out of his working day of $9\frac{1}{2}$ hours, a salesman spends $3\frac{1}{2}$ hours driving. Find the ratio of
(a) the time he is driving to the length of his working day
(b) the time he is driving to the time he is not driving
(c) the time he is not driving to the time he is driving.

QUESTION

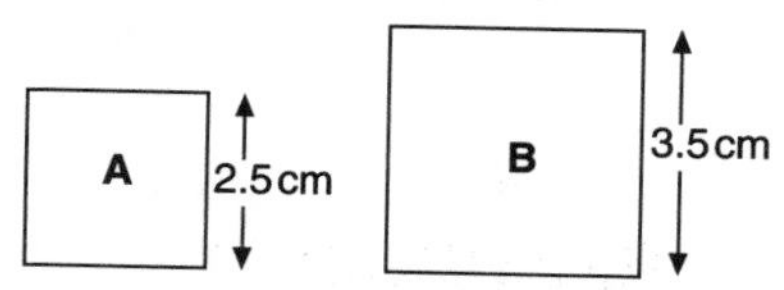

The lengths of the sides of two square metal plates, A and B, are respectively 2.5 cm and 3.5 cm. Find the ratio of
(a) the length of a side of A to the length of a side of B
(b) the area of A to the area of B.

ANSWER
(a) Ratio of length of a side of A to length of a side of B is
2.5 cm : 3.5 cm
= 2.5 : 3.5
= 25 : 35 (multiply by 10)
= 5 : 7 (dividing by 5)

(b) Area of A = 2.5×2.5 cm^2
and area of B = 3.5×3.5 cm^2
Ratio of area of A to area of B is
2.5×2.5 cm^2 : 3.5×3.5 cm^2
= 6.25 : 12.25
= 625 : 1225
= 25 : 49 (dividing by 25)
(Note that the ratio of the areas is the same as the ratio of the squares of the sides.)

Simplify each ratio:

9 (a) 1.2 : 4.4 (b) 13 : 7.8
(c) 1.19 : 0.56 (d) 44.8 : 39.2

10 (a) 4 kg : 2.5 kg (b) 18 m : 4.8 m
(c) 5.4 kg : 7.2 kg (d) 2.75 litres : 3.5 litres

11

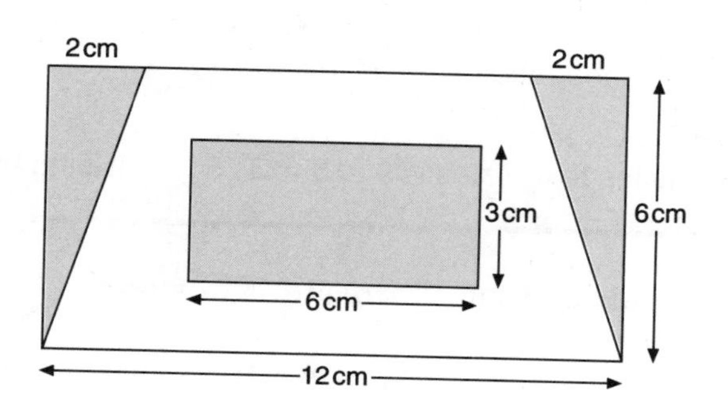

The diagram shows a component for a machine. It has been made from a rectangular plate by cutting off two triangular corners and stamping out a rectangular hole. Use the dimensions given on the diagram to find the ratio of

(a) the width of the original rectangular plate to its length,

(b) the area of one of the triangular pieces to the area of the original plate,

(c) the area of the finished component to the area of the original rectangle.

EXERCISE 21c

QUESTION

A recipe for 24 tea cakes needs the following ingredients:
8 oz margarine
3 tablespoons cream
8 oz plain flour
1 egg
2 tablespoons crushed walnuts
2 tablespoons sugar
3 oz raspberry jam
If a larger number of tea cakes is made:

(a) How much margarine would be required to mix with 24 oz plain flour?

(b) How many tablespoons of crushed walnuts would be required to mix with 6 eggs?

(c) How many tablespoons of sugar would be required to mix with 12 oz raspberry jam?

ANSWER

(a) The ratio of the weight of plain flour to the weight of margarine is 8 oz : 8 oz, i.e. 1 : 1, so if 24 oz plain flour is used then the required weight of margarine is also 24 oz.

(b) The ratio of the number of eggs to the number of tablespoons of crushed walnuts is 1 : 2, so 6 eggs require 12 tablespoons crushed walnuts.

(c) The ratio of the number of ounces of raspberry jam to the number of tablespoons of sugar is 3 : 2, so 12 oz raspberry jam requires 8 tablespoons of sugar.

---

1 A recipe for 4 servings of beef stew includes the following ingredients:
1 lb stewing beef
3 tablespoons lard
2 medium onions
$\frac{3}{4}$ pint water
4 carrots
one 8 oz packet frozen peas.

If a larger quantity of beef stew is made,

(a) how many onions would be needed to go with 6 carrots?

(b) How much beef would be needed to go with 3 pints of water?

(c) what weight of frozen peas would be needed to go with $3\frac{1}{2}$ lb stewing beef?

2 Gunmetal is made by mixing copper and tin in the ratio 9 : 1.

(a) How much copper is required to mix with 4 kg tin?

(b) How much tin is required to mix with 720 g copper?

3 The ratio of males to females at a factory is 2 : 3.

(a) If there are 120 male employees, how many females are there?

(b) If there are 120 female employees, how many males are there?

4 A shopkeeper visits the bank for change. He needs 20p coins and 50p coins in the ratio 5 : 1. If he collects £60 in 20p coins,

(a) how many 20p coins does he collect,

(b) how many 50p coins does he collect,

(c) what is the total value of the 50p coins?

5 The scale of an Ordnance Survey map is 1 : 50 000.

(a) What distance, in metres, is represented by 1 mm?

(b) What distance, in kilometres, is represented by 1 cm?

(c) The distance between Cross Ash and Eckford on a map is 5.5 cm. What is the actual distance?

QUESTION

In a soccer squad the ratio of attackers to defenders is 8 : 7. What fraction of the squad consists of
(a) attackers (b) defenders?

ANSWER

For every 15 players (8 + 7) there are 8 attackers and 7 defenders.

(a) $\therefore$ fraction that are attackers is $\frac{8}{15}$

(b) Fraction that are defenders is $\frac{7}{15}$

---

6 The ratio of boys to girls in a brass band is 4 : 3. What fraction of the players are girls?

7 In Jason's pay the ratio of £10 notes to £20 notes is 2 : 3. What fraction of the notes he receives are £10 notes?

8 Pat O'Connell is an artist. He works in watercolours and in oils. If $\frac{3}{10}$ of his pictures are watercolours and the remainder are oils find the ratio of watercolours to oils.

9 Seven-ninths of the mileage driven by a commercial traveller is for business purposes and the remainder is for pleasure. Find the ratio of the distance driven for work to the distance driven for pleasure.

Division in a given ratio

EXERCISE 21d

QUESTION
Share £350 between Kate and Jonathan in the ratio 3 : 4.

ANSWER
(One share is made up of 3 portions and the other share is made up of 4 portions. There are therefore 7 portions altogether.)

1 portion is £$\frac{350}{7}$, i.e. £50

Kate's share is 3 × £50, i.e. £150, and Jonathan's share is 4 × £50, i.e. £200.
(Check: £150 + £200 = £350.)

1 Share 36 chocolates between Phil and Meg in the ratio 4 : 5.

2 Share £84 between Paul and Amanda in the ratio 4 : 3.

3 Two sisters, Carol and Diane, are given £50 between them by an aunt for Christmas. They are to share the money in the ratio of their ages. Carol is 11 years and Diane is 14 years. How much does Carol get?

4 A 48 acre field is to be divided into two parts in the ratio 7 : 5. What is the area of the smaller part?

5 An alloy consists of copper and zinc in the ratio 5 : 7. How much copper is needed to make 276 kg of this alloy?

6 A national housebuilder builds houses and bungalows in the ratio 7 : 2. Last year they built 12 500 properties. How many houses did they build? Give your answer correct to the nearest 10.

Direct proportion

Proportion is another word for comparison. We say that two quantities are in proportion if they are always in the same ratio, e.g. if one quantity is doubled, so is the other.

When we buy breadrolls the total cost is proportional to the number of rolls we buy, e.g. if we treble the number of rolls we treble the cost.

EXERCISE 21e

1 If 5 cups of tea cost £3.50 what is the cost of
(a) 1 cup (b) 3 cups?

2 It costs £3.30 to buy 3 cups of coffee. How much does it cost to buy (a) 1 cup (b) 4 cups?

QUESTION
It costs £115 for 5 adults to take the coach from their home town to Heathrow Airport. What does it cost for 7 adults to make the same trip?

ANSWER
5 fares cost £115
∴ 1 fare costs £$\frac{115}{5}$ = £23
∴ 7 fares cost 7 × £23 = £161

3 Three copies of the magazine *Good Housekeeping* cost £5.85. Find the price of 5 copies.

4 The amount of plain flour required to make 24 biscuits is 8 oz. How much plain flour is required to make 42 biscuits?

5 Five coaches can carry 235 passengers. How many passengers can 13 similar coaches carry?

6 A car travels 171 km on 15 litres of petrol. How many litres are required for a journey of 285 km?

7 An invoice from a computer centre lists the total cost of 8 boxes of $3\frac{1}{2}$ in diskettes as £41.76. This was an error, as the requested order was for 18 boxes. How much do 18 cost?

8 A motorcyclist uses 14 litres of petrol to ride 308 km. How many litres should he use for a journey of 341 km?

9 The fare for a 1350 mile flight is £303.75. At the same cost per mile what should be the fare for a flight of 3440 miles?

10 In an Olympic swimming pool there is seating all the way round. Section A has 30 rows, with 12 seats in each row.

(a) How many seats are there in this section?

(b) Section B has the same number of seats but they are arranged in 24 rows. How many seats are there in each row?

(c) In Section C there are the same number of seats as in each of the other two sections. There are 18 seats in each row. How many rows are there?

Inverse proportion

In the previous section we considered quantities that were in direct proportion, i.e. quantities where, if one increases so does the other. This is not always the case. Sometimes when one quantity is increased the other decreases.

For example, suppose we have £5 to spend on oranges. If they are 20p each we can buy 25, but if the price is raised to 25p each we can buy only 20.

The number of oranges × the cost of one orange is a constant.

The result of multiplying together two inversely proportional quantities is a constant.

EXERCISE 21f

QUESTION

The manager at a cattery has sufficient food to feed 12 cats for 15 days. If she takes in another 6 cats today how long will the food last?

ANSWER

12 cats can be fed for 15 days

1 cat can be fed for 15 × 12 days

18 cats can be fed for $\frac{15 \times 12}{18}$ days

i.e. for 10 days

1 When a box of chocolates is divided among 5 children they get 8 chocolates each. How many chocolates would each child get if the chocolates were divided among 4 children?

2 A fruit farmer employs 34 men for 9 days to harvest his apples. How many men should he employ to pick the apples in 6 days?

3 The average waiting time at a supermarket checkout when there are 12 checkout points is 8 minutes. How many checkouts are required to reduce the average waiting time to 3 minutes?

4 A brass band and a theatre group receive equal grants from the local authority. The band has 44 members and receives the equivalent of £7 for each member, while the theatre group receives the equivalent of only £4 a member.

(a) How much does the local authority give the brass band?

(b) How many members are there in the theatre group?

5 A borough council agrees to supply, free of charge, 'wheelie' bins to all the properties from which it collects refuse. It is far too expensive to make the change immediately, so they agree to set aside a fixed amount each year until the changeover has been completed. If they choose a bin that costs £34 they can buy 1900 bins in the first year.

(a) How much money do they set aside for wheelie bins each year?

(b) How many bins can they buy for the same sum of money if they go for more expensive bins costing £38 each?

Multiple-choice questions 21

In questions 1 to 3 several alternative answers are given. Write down the letter that corresponds to the correct answer.

1 The air fare between two American cities is \$545 during the high season and \$436 during the low season. The ratio, in its lowest terms, of the fare during the high season to the fare during the low season is

A 545 : 436 **B** $1 : 1\frac{1}{4}$ **C** 5 : 4 **D** 4 : 5

2 A lorry is 8.64 metres long and a model of the same lorry is 12 cm long. The ratio of the length of the model to the length of the actual lorry is

A 1 : 72 **B** 72 : 1 **C** 1 : 0.72 **D** 1 : 36

3 If 4 jars of bramble jelly cost £3.44 then the cost of 7 similar jars is

A £6.88 **B** £6.02 **C** £5.95 **D** £6.08

4 A cog wheel with 60 teeth is revolving at 84 revolutions a minute and meshes with a cog wheel with 35 teeth. Which of these statements are true and which are false?

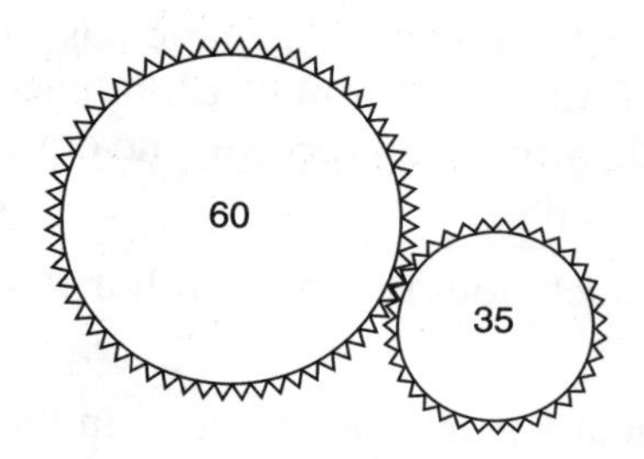

A The wheel with 60 teeth turns faster than the wheel with 35 teeth.

B The wheel with 60 teeth turns slower than the wheel with 35 teeth.

C The wheel with 35 teeth makes 49 revolutions per minute.

D The wheel with 35 teeth makes 144 revolutions per minute.

5 A recipe that will make 12 tarts includes 4 oz sugar, 1 tablespoon flour, 1 egg and 6 oz raisins. Eve has half a dozen eggs.

The following statements have been made.
Statement 1. If Eve uses half the eggs she has she will also need 18 oz raisins, 12 oz sugar and 2 tablespoons flour.
Statement 2. If Eve has enough ingredients to use all the eggs she can make 72 tarts and has 12 oz of raisins left after opening a 3 lb bag.
How are these statements best described?

A True, True **B** True, False **C** False, True
D False, False

Self-assessment test 21

1 In a small factory there are 35 employees, 21 of whom are female. What is the ratio of
(a) females to males (b) males to females?

2 A ship is 350 m long and a model of it is 1750 cm long. Find the ratio of the length of the model to the length of the ship.

3 The ingredients required for 7 lb marmalade are: 2 kg oranges, 4 kg sugar, 1 lemon, 1 litre water. What quantities are needed to make 63 kg marmalade?

4 At a bank the ratio of the number of customers having to wait less than 4 minutes to the number of customers having to wait 4 minutes or more is 7 : 2. During one day there were 747 customers. How many had to wait at least 4 minutes?

5 A factory needs 45 sewing machines to satisfy an order for a given number of dresses in 22 days.
(a) How many dresses are ordered?
(b) How many machines are needed to produce the same number of dresses in 18 days?

CHAPTER 22

Basic algebra

Formulas in words

Many people regularly use formulas that are expressed in words rather than in letters.

EXERCISE 22a

QUESTION
An electricity bill is calculated using the formula

amount to pay (excluding VAT) = standing charge + number of units used × price of each unit

How much is there to pay if the standing charge is £12.36 and 1645 units have been used at a cost of 7.96p each?

ANSWER
Amount to pay (excluding VAT) = £12.36 + 1645 × 7.96p
= £12.36 + 13094.2p
= £12.36 + £130.94 (to the nearest penny)
= £143.30

1 Local time in New York is found by subtracting 5 hours from the time in London. What is the time in New York when the time in London is
(a) 8 p.m. (b) 4 p.m. (c) 2 a.m.?

2 The area of a rectangle, in square metres, is found by multiplying its length, measured in metres, by its width, also measured in metres. Find the area of a rectangular tennis court that is 72 metres long and 33 metres wide.

3 The average speed of a coach journey is calculated by dividing the number of miles travelled by the number of hours the journey takes.

(a) For the first part of a journey a coach takes 4 hours to travel 160 miles. Find its average speed.

(b) For the second part of the journey it takes $2\frac{1}{4}$ hours to drive 81 miles. What is the average speed for the second part of the journey?

4 The annual birth rate of a population is defined as

$$\frac{\text{registered number of births}}{\text{total population}} \times 1000$$

and the annual death rate as

$$\frac{\text{registered number of deaths}}{\text{total population}} \times 1000$$

Find (a) the birth rate (b) the death rate, for a population of 68.5 million for which there were 895 536 registered births and 767 983 registered deaths.

5 The amount of value added tax included in the purchase price of an article is given by

$$\frac{\text{sale price including VAT} \times \text{rate of VAT as a percentage}}{100\% + \text{rate of VAT as a percentage}}$$

How much value added tax is included in the price of

(a) a chair costing £156 when the VAT rate is 20%

(b) an album costing £18.80 when the VAT rate is $17\frac{1}{2}\%$

(c) a car costing £17 580 when the VAT rate is 20%

(d) a motorbike costing £564 when the VAT rate is $17\frac{1}{2}\%$

6 The 'density' of a cruise ship is the gross registered tonnage divided by the number of passenger berths. Find the density of

(a) the cruise ship *QE2* which has a gross tonnage of 66 450 tons and can carry 1877 passengers

(b) the cruise ship *Canberra* which has a gross tonnage of 43 975 tons and can carry 1706 passengers

(c) the yacht *Ocean Islander* which has a gross tonnage of 5000 tons and can carry 260 passengers.

7 The annual sales growth of a company is defined as

$$\frac{\text{increase in sales}}{\text{previous year's sales}} \times 100\%$$

(a) Find the annual sales growth over the last 5 years for a company whose sales figures are those given in the table:

Year	1991	1992	1993	1994	1995
Sales (000s)	145	167	190	214	240

(b) Comment on what is happening to (i) the annual sales growth (ii) the annual sales.

8 A person's mean blood pressure is calculated according to a formula that uses both the diastolic blood pressure (when the heart is expanding) and the systolic blood pressure (when it is contracting):

$$\text{mean blood pressure} = \text{diastolic pressure} + \frac{(\text{systolic pressure} - \text{diastolic pressure})}{3}$$

The unit in which it is measured is the millimetre of mercury, which is the pressure required to raise a column of mercury by 1 mm. The symbol for this unit is mmHg.

Use the information given in the table to find the mean blood pressure for each person:

	Systolic pressure mmHg	Diastolic pressure mmHg
Mel	140	80
Wendy	160	86
Bina	176	90
Hank	120	75

9 The displacement of an engine is given by the formula

$$\text{displacement (cm}^3\text{)} = \text{number of cylinders} \times \pi \times \left(\frac{\text{bore (cm)}}{2}\right)^2 \times \text{stroke (cm)}$$

(a) Find the displacement of 4-cylinder diesel engine that has a bore of 87.0 mm and a stroke of 84.0 mm.

(b) Find the displacement of a 6-cylinder petrol engine that has a bore of 89.9 mm and a stroke of 86.6 mm.

Equations involving words

A market trader started the day with a certain number of pairs of trainers. Of these, two pairs were badly damaged so had to be thrown away, and of the good ones he sold 19 pairs. At the end of the day he still had 9 pairs left. How many did he start with?

From this information we can form an equation:
number he began with
− 2 (those he had to throw away)
− 19 (the number he sold)
= 9 (the number he had left)

More simply,

number he began with − 2 − 19 = 9

i.e. number he began with − 21 = 9

Add 21 to each side number he began with = 9 + 21
= 30

We were able to form a simple equation from which we found that he had 30 pairs of trainers to start with.

Many problems can be expressed as a simple equation, involving numbers and words, which can then be solved.

EXERCISE 22b

QUESTION
Paul bought a pack of second-hand cassette tapes in a car boot sale. He went through the tapes carefully and decided to keep 8 of them. The remainder he divided equally among his 3 sons. If each son received 7 tapes how many tapes were there in the pack?

ANSWER
The number he had to divide between his 3 sons was: the number in the pack, minus 8.
But each son received 7 tapes, i.e. the sons had $7 \times 3 = 21$ altogether between them.

∴ number in pack − 8 = 21

Adding 8 to each side gives:

number in pack = 21 + 8
= 29

There were 29 tapes in the pack.

1 Any product that is manufactured needs components such as screws, nuts, bolts or washers. Inevitably some of the components are faulty so cannot be used. The following equations have arisen in calculating the number of components needed in different situations. In each case find that number.

(a) Number of components − 5 = 245.

(b) (Number of components − 3) ÷ 4 = 63.

(c) (Number of components + 7) ÷ 3 = 146.

(d) Number of components × 2 − 7 = 159.

2 In this question study each set of statements carefully and then write down an equation similar to those given in question 1. Once you are satisfied that your equation is correct solve it to answer the question asked.

(a) Nicki started with a box of components. After using 512 of them she had 27 left. How many did she have to start with?

(b) Cliff began the shift with a basket of components. He used 387 of them but had 13 left over at the end of the shift. How many were in the basket to start with?

(c) Alan needed another 5 bolts to complete the assembly of 65 electric motors. If each motor required 4 bolts how many bolts did Alan need to assemble that batch of motors?

(d) Each of the units Sharon assembled required 7 washers. She started with a box of washers that was sufficient to assemble 54 units, with 4 washers left over. How many washers did she have at the beginning?

3 An operator on the production line for front disc brakes was given a basket containing a quantity of identical components. He used the components, 2 to a brake, until all that remained in the basket were 5 faulty components. A check showed that he had assembled 43 front disc brakes. Form a suitable equation and use it to find the number of components in the basket when he started.

In the questions that follow form an equation and solve it to answer the question asked.

4 A fuse box takes 8 identical fuses. How many fuses does Madge need to draw from the stores if she completes an order for 144 fuse boxes and in the process comes across 3 faulty fuses?

5 Six bolts are needed to assemble an electric light fitting. How many bolts did Tim start with if he was able to assemble 176 light fittings and had 27 bolts left over?

6 A washing machine needs 12 of a particular size of Phillips screw. Dave starts with a box of 288 screws, 3 of which he finds to be faulty. How many washing machines can he complete from his stock of screws? How many usable screws remain?

7 Sid has a stock of 514 self-tapping screws which can be used with plastics. Each unit he assembles requires 8 screws. When he has completed the order 146 screws remain. How many plastic units were there in the order?

Using letters in equations

Frequently it is convenient to use a single letter to stand for a word or descriptive phrase. For example, instead of writing

(number of bolts $-$ 5) $\div$ 3 $=$ 52

we could write $(n-5)\div 3=52$

where n stands for 'the number of bolts'.

We can then proceed as we did in the questions in the previous exercise using n (or any other letter we care to choose) instead of the words that it represents.

Then $(n-5)\div 3=52$ (Multiply both sides by 3)

$n-5=52\times 3$

$n-5=156$ (Add 5 to each side)

$n=161$

This shows that the number of bolts is 161.

The only rule that you need remember when solving equations of this type is

Whatever you do to one side you must do to the other.

We will now consider solving simple equations increasing the degree of difficulty as we progress. In any question, if it helps, you can think of the letter in the equation as standing for a word. Let it mean 'the number of screws, or people, or CDs, or whatever else the problem involves'.

Addition and subtraction

Some equations can be solved by **adding the same quantity to each side**. (Add 4 to each side)

For example, if $a-4=8$

then $a=4+8$

i.e. $a=12$

For other equations we **subtract the same quantity from each side.** (Subtract 6 from each side)

If $b+6=14$

then $b=14-6$

i.e. $b=8$

EXERCISE 22c

QUESTION

Solve $b-10=12$.

ANSWER

$b-10=12$ (Add 10 to each side)

$b=12+10$

i.e. $b=22$

Solve

1 $b-6=3$ **2** $a-2=9$ **3** $c-8=7$

4 $p-10=12$ **5** $q-17=24$ **6** $y-4=29$

7 $a-12=56$ **8** $b-26=78$ **9** $a-3=34$

10 $b-27=71$ **11** $c-47=59$ **12** $y-77=158$

QUESTION
Solve $a + 4 = 10$.

ANSWER

$a + 4 = 10$ (Subtract 4 from each side)

∴ $a = 10 - 4$

i.e. $a = 6$

Solve

13 $a + 7 = 21$ **14** $c + 11 = 14$ **15** $y + 6 = 23$

16 $q + 4 = 13$ **17** $9 + r = 36$ **18** $p + 21 = 44$

19 $a + 3 = 67$ **20** $b + 45 = 75$ **21** $p + 54 = 86$

22 $q + 47 = 83$ **23** $23 + z = 29$ **24** $136 + y = 243$

Multiplication and division

We can **divide** both sides by the same quantity.

For example, if $3a = 24$

then $a = 24 \div 3$ (Dividing both sides by 3)

i.e. $a = 8$

Or we can **multiply** both sides by the same quantity.

Thus, if $\frac{p}{4} = 7$

then $p = 7 \times 4$ (Multiplying both sides by 4)

i.e. $p = 28$

EXERCISE 22d

QUESTION
Solve $8c = 24$.

ANSWER

$8c = 24$ (Divide both sides by 8)

∴ $c = 24 \div 8$

i.e. $c = 3$

Solve

1 $4b = 16$ **2** $5d = 75$ **3** $7e = 42$

4 $8f = 72$ **5** $12p = 96$ **6** $7p = 56$

7 $9y = 72$ **8** $6z = 36$

QUESTION

Solve $\frac{p}{4} = 5$

ANSWER

$\frac{p}{4} = 5$ (Multiply both sides by 4)

∴ $p = 5 \times 4$

i.e. $p = 20$

Solve

9 $\frac{a}{3} = 3$ **10** $\frac{b}{5} = 8$ **11** $\frac{y}{6} = 13$

12 $\frac{z}{9} = 23$ **13** $\frac{w}{12} = 7$ **14** $\frac{a}{3} = 45$

15 $\frac{b}{6} = 73$ **16** $\frac{c}{7} = 39$

Choosing the operation

In Exercises 22c and 22d the worked example has suggested what you needed to do to solve the questions that followed. The next exercise revises the four operations – but you have to decide which one to use.

EXERCISE 22e

Solve the following equations. In each case say what you have done.

1 $7x = 49$ **2** $\frac{1}{2}b = 24$ **3** $q - 10 = 12$

4 $a + 6 = 58$ **5** $\frac{1}{4}c = 23$ **6** $b - 19 = 34$

7 $3b = 24$ **8** $x + 11 = 21$ **9** $2a = 16$

10 $b + 8 = 25$ **11** $p - 5 = 21$ **12** $4y = 48$

13 $\frac{1}{3}x = 15$ **14** $y - 7 = 2$ **15** $x - 16 = 4$

16 $\frac{1}{10}p = 4$

Inexact answers

Sometimes the answers are not whole numbers.

EXERCISE 22f

QUESTION

Solve $3x = 7$

ANSWER

$3x = 7$ (Divide both sides by 3)

$\therefore$ $x = 7 \div 3$

i.e. $x = 2\frac{1}{3}$ or 2.33 (Correct to 2 d.p.)

Solve

1 $a + 3.5 = 5$ 2 $p + \frac{1}{3} = 3$ 3 $\frac{p}{2} = 2.8$

4 $\frac{x}{4} = \frac{1}{2}$ 5 $b - 2.7 = 7.9$ 6 $q - \frac{2}{3} = 7\frac{1}{3}$

7 $\frac{q}{3} = 3.1$ 8 $\frac{a}{2} = \frac{1}{4}$ 9 $z + \frac{1}{4} = \frac{3}{4}$

10 $4c = 6$ 11 $\frac{x}{5} = 14.2$ 12 $\frac{b}{3} = \frac{2}{3}$

13 $w - \frac{1}{2} = 2\frac{3}{4}$ 14 $5p = 12$ 15 $\frac{y}{7} = 6.7$

16 $\frac{c}{5} = \frac{3}{10}$

Equations that require two operations

Sometimes we need to perform two operations on an equation before it can be solved.

If $2p + 3 = 23$

then $2p = 20$ (Subtracting 3 from each side)

i.e. $p = 10$ (Dividing both sides by 2)

Also, if $\frac{q}{5} - 6 = 3$

then $\frac{q}{5} = 9$ (Adding 6 to each side)

i.e. $q = 45$ (Multiplying both sides by 5)

If $2p + 3 = 23$

then $2p = 20$ (Subtracting 3 from each side)

i.e. $p = 10$ (Dividing both sides by 2)

Also, if $\frac{q}{5} + 5 = 11$

then $\frac{q}{5} = 6$ (Subtracting 5 from each side)

i.e. $q = 30$ (Multiplying both sides by 5)

EXERCISE 22g

QUESTION

Solve $5x + 7 = 42$

ANSWER

$5x + 7 = 42$ (Subtract 7 from each side)

$5x = 42 - 7$

$5x = 35$ (Divide both sides by 5)

i.e. $x = 7$

Solve

1 $2a - 7 = 13$ 2 $9q + 1 = 10$ 3 $6x - 5 = 15$

4 $5x - 9 = 6$ 5 $4y + 3 = 15$ 6 $12z + 3 = 13$

7 $7p - 11 = 17$ 8 $2x + 7 = 10$ 9 $3a + 9 = 11$

10 $3a + 7 = 16$ 11 $5b - 6 = 14$ 12 $8 + 7d = 36$

QUESTION

Solve $\frac{b}{3} - 5 = 7$

ANSWER

$\frac{b}{3} - 5 = 7$

$\frac{b}{3} = 7 + 5$ (Adding 5 to each side)

$\frac{b}{3} = 12$

$b = 36$ (Multiplying both sides by 3)

Solve

13 $\frac{y}{2} - 4 = 5$ 14 $\frac{a}{3} + 4 = 9$

15 $5 + \frac{z}{3} = 13$ 16 $\frac{b}{5} - 7 = 9$

17 $\frac{3x}{5} - 2 = 7$ 18 $\frac{2c}{7} - 9 = 5$

19 $\frac{7y}{2} + 4 = 25$ 20 $\frac{5a}{3} + 3 = 11$

Like and unlike terms

Four cars plus three cars can be added together to give seven cars, but four cars and three motorbikes cannot be added together because they are quite different things.

Similarly, $3a$ and $5a$ are examples of like terms. They can be added together to give $8a$, but $3a$ and $5b$ are unlike terms. They cannot be simplified in any way.

EXERCISE 22h

QUESTION
Simplify where possible
(a) $2a + 3 + 7a - 4$ (b) $2b + 4c - 5$.

ANSWER
(a) $2a + 3 + 7a - 4 = 2a + 7a + 3 - 4$
$= 9a - 1$
(b) $2b + 4c - 5$ are unlike terms and so cannot be simplified.

Simplify where possible

1 $a + a + a + 6$ **2** $5b - 3b$

3 $9c + 4c$ **4** $11y - 7y$

5 $2a + 3a + 4a$ **6** $8p + 2q - 5p + 3q$

7 $5k - 4k + 9k - 3k$ **8** $2a + 4c$

9 $5a - 2 + 7a - 4$ **10** $9p - 3p - 2p - p$

11 $16a - 8a - 4a - 2a$ **12** $8a + 6b - 3a - 4b$

13 $5a + 7 + 2b - 5$ **14** $9q + 5q - 14q$

15 $p + q + r + 5q - 2r$ **16** $8m - 2n + 6m - 7$

17 $9y - 3z - 6y + 4z$ **18** $5p + 3q + 8 - 5p - 3q$

Equations that need simplifying before they can be solved

Many equations need to be simplified before they can be solved. This usually means collecting like terms together.

EXERCISE 22i

QUESTION
Simplify the equation $3p + 2p = 25$ and hence solve it.

ANSWER
$3p + 2p = 25$
$5p = 25$
i.e. $p = 5$

Simplify and hence solve

1 $a + 3a = 24$ **2** $3b + 5b = 48$

3 $7c - 3c = 36$ **4** $p + 2p + 3p = 30$

5 $10q - 6q + 3q = 56$ **6** $6y - 3y + 8y = 99$

7 $b + 2b = 12$ **8** $a + 2a + 3a = 24$

9 $8p - 3p + p = 36$ **10** $5q + 2q - q = 27$

11 $3y - y = 7$ **12** $8x - 4x + x = 5$

QUESTION
Solve the equation $7p - 2 + 5p - 7 = 27$

ANSWER
$7p - 2 + 5p - 7 = 27$ (Collect like terms)
$7p + 5p - 2 - 7 = 27$
$12p - 9 = 27$ (Add 9 to each side)
$12p = 27 + 9$
$12p = 36$ (Divide both sides by 12)
$p = 36 \div 12$
i.e. $p = 3$

Solve

13 $3b + 2b + 8 - 3 = 15$ **14** $4c + 3 - 2c - 5 = 4$

15 $p + 2p + 5p - 7 = 1$ **16** $5q - 2q + 4 = 10$

17 $7x - 2 + x + 6 = 36$ **18** $a + 7 + 2a = 25$

Sometimes the unknown quantity appears on both sides of the equation.

If the unknown quantity appears on both sides of an equation we must collect the terms in the unknown on one side and the number terms on the other side.

QUESTION
Solve $3b - 5 = b + 7$

ANSWER
$3b - 5 = b + 7$
$3b = b + 7 + 5$ (Adding 5 to each side)
$3b - b = 12$ (Subtracting b from each side)
$2b = 12$
$b = 6$ (Dividing both sides by 2)

Solve

19 $3b + 6 = 14 - b$

20 $3d - 5 = d + 9$

21 $6c + 7 = c + 27$

22 $8p - 11 = 5p + 10$

23 $5y - 4 = 2y - 1$

24 $14a - 8 = 9a + 17$

QUESTION
Solve $3p + 14 = 6p - 1$

ANSWER
Although this equation looks more difficult it is quite simple if we interchange the two sides:

$$6p - 1 = 3p + 14$$
$$6p = 3p + 14 + 1 \quad \text{(Adding 1 to each side)}$$
$$6p - 3p = 15 \quad \text{(Subtracting } 3p \text{ from each side)}$$
$$3p = 15$$
$$p = 5 \quad \text{(Dividing both sides by 3)}$$

Solve

25 $x + 18 = 4x + 3$

26 $13 - 3z = 1 + z$

27 $3q + 5 = 7q - 3$

28 $2y + 7 = 5y + 4$

29 $2p + 15 = 5p - 6$

30 $6b + 59 = 13b + 17$

Using equations to solve problems

Many problems can be solved by forming an equation. The equation can then be solved by using the methods we have just practised.

EXERCISE 22j

QUESTION
The Peacock family take 2 pints of milk a day and an extra pint on Saturday and on Sunday. They pay every Monday when they get 4p change from a £5 note. If the price of one pint of milk is q pence, form an equation in q and solve it to find the price of a pint of milk.

ANSWER
The Peacock family take 2 pints of milk a day, Monday to Friday, plus 3 pints on Saturday and 3 pints on Sunday.
Altogether they take $5 \times 2 + 3 + 3$ pints, i.e. 16 pints.
If 1 pint costs q pence, 16 pints cost $16 \times q$ pence, i.e. $16q$ pence.
The amount they pay is £5 − 4 pence
= 500 pence − 4 pence
= 496 pence

We now know how much they pay in two different ways, namely $16q$ pence and 496 pence.
These two quantities must be equal,
so $16q = 496$

i.e. $q = \frac{496}{16}$

$= 31$

The cost of a pint of milk is therefore 31 pence.

1 A fishing rod, consisting of three pieces, is 450 cm long. Measuring from one end the first piece is h cm long, the second piece is 15 cm longer than the first piece, and the third piece is 15 cm longer than the second piece. Form an equation in h and solve it to find
(a) the length of the shortest piece
(b) the lengths of the other two pieces.
As a check the sum of your three lengths should be 450 cm.

2 A Chelsea bun costs x pence and a cream doughnut costs $2x$ pence. Find, in terms of x, the cost of (a) 3 Chelsea buns (b) 4 cream doughnuts. If the total cost of these 7 cakes is £2.75 form an equation in x and solve it to find the cost of (c) a Chelsea bun (d) a cream doughnut.

3 Sandra orders a cup of coffee, costing n pence, and a jacket potato, costing $4n$ pence. She pays with a £5 note and receives £2 change. Form an equation in n and solve it. Hence find the price of (a) a cup of coffee (b) a jacket potato.

4 On a 420-acre farm there are five times as many acres of wheat as there are acres of barley; there are three times as many acres of grassland as there are acres of barley and as many acres is unused due to 'set aside' as are used to grow barley. Assuming that there are x acres of barley form an equation in x and solve it to find the number of acres (a) put to 'set aside' (b) of wheat (c) of grassland.

Note: In an attempt to prevent surplus food production the European Parliament has decreed that a certain percentage of farm land must not be used for producing food. This land is called 'set aside'.

5 For a concert at the village hall the Amberley Operatic Society are able to sell 70 tickets at £a each and 148 tickets at £$2a$ each. If the total receipts are £1464 form an equation in a and solve it to find the price of each ticket.

6 An artist sells three sizes of prints – small, medium and large. She charges £10 for the small size, £25 for the medium size and £75 for the large. Last year, of the 133 prints she sold, twice as many were medium compared with large and twice as many were small compared with medium.

(a) Form an equation and solve it to find how many of each size of print were sold.

(b) What was the total income from the sale of the 133 prints?

Simplifying, including the removal of brackets

When a bracket has a number immediately in front of it, that number multiplies everything inside the bracket.

For example, $7(4a - 3) = 7 \times 4a - 7 \times 3$
$= 28a - 21$

EXERCISE 22k

QUESTION

(a) Simplify $5 \times 4p$.

(b) Remove the brackets in the expression $3(2q + 5)$.

ANSWER

(a) $5 \times 4p = 20p$

(b) $3(2q + 5) = 3 \times 2q + 3 \times 5$
$= 6q + 15$

1 Simplify

(a) $2 \times 3x$ (b) $5 \times 2p$ (c) $3 \times 8q$
(d) $12 \times 5y$

2 Write without brackets

(a) $4(3p - 4)$ (b) $5(6 - 3b)$
(c) $7(p + 2)$ (d) $3(2x + 7)$

QUESTION

Write the equation $5(x - 2) = 25$ without brackets and hence solve it.

ANSWER

$5(x - 2) = 25$ (Remove the brackets)
$5x - 10 = 25$ (Add 10 to each side)
$5x = 35$ (Divide both sides by 5)
$x = 7$

In each question from 3 to 8 remove the brackets and hence solve the equation.

3 $2(a + 5) = 14$ **4** $3(x - 2) = 42$ **5** $4(p + 6) = 44$

6 $5(q - 3) = 25$ **7** $2(3 + a) = 25$ **8** $3(5 + b) = 18$

QUESTION

Solve $5(2p - 1) - 11 = 14$.

ANSWER

$5(2p - 1) - 11 = 14$ (Collect up like terms)
$10p - 5 - 11 = 14$ (Add 16 to each side)
$10p - 16 = 14$ (Divide both sides by 10)
$10p = 30$
$p = 3$

Solve

9 $2(2a - 7) = 6$ **10** $5(b - 1) + 3 = 8$

11 $2(3c - 1) - 3 = 13$ **12** $3 + 2(3p + 4) = 41$

13 $3(4y + 7) - 17 = 28$ **14** $6(4y - 5) + 9 = 51$

QUESTION

Solve $2(q + 4) = 3(2q + 1)$

ANSWER

$2(q + 4) = 3(2q + 1)$
(Multiply out the brackets)
$2q + 8 = 6q + 3$
$2q + 8 - 3 = 6q$ (Take 3 from both sides)
(Simplify $8 - 3$ and take $2q$ from both sides)
$5 = 6q - 2q$ (Simplify $6q - 2q$)
$5 = 4q$ (Divide both sides by 4)
$\frac{5}{4} = q$, i.e. $q = \frac{5}{4}$

Solve

15 $5(x - 1) = 2(x + 8)$ **16** $4(3 - q) = 3(q + 4)$

17 $3(y - 4) = y + 12$ **18** $7(5 - p) = 2(3p - 2)$

19 $5(x + 7) = 3(4x + 3)$ **20** $5(p + 2) - 4 = 2(p + 5)$

Inequalities

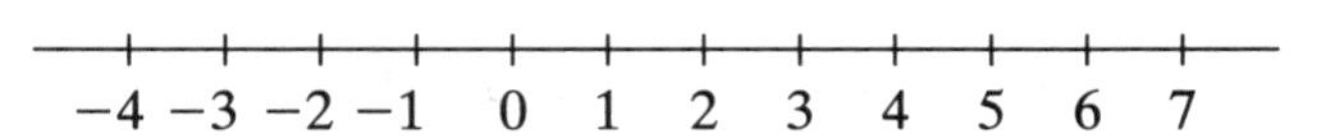

$4 > 3$ is an example of an inequality, as is $5 < 7$.

The first inequality tells us that 4 is greater than 3 (> means 'is greater than') and the second that 5 is less than 7 (< means 'is less than').

Consider the inequality $x + 3 > 8$
If we subtract 3 from both sides $x > 5$
i.e. the solution of the inequality $x + 3 > 8$ is that x can have any value provided it is greater than 5. For example, x can be 6 or 12 or 100.

EXERCISE 22l

QUESTION
Solve the inequalities (a) $x - 4 < 5$, (b) $2x + 1 > 11$.
Give two values that satisfy each inequality.

ANSWER
(a) $x - 4 < 5$
$x < 9$ (Adding 4 to each side)
Two possible values for x are 1 and 6
(b) $2x + 1 > 11$
$2x > 10$ (Subtracting 1 from each side)
$x > 5$ (Dividing each side by 2)
Possible values for x are 6 and 7

Solve the following inequalities and give two whole number values of x that satisfy each one.

1 $x - 6 > 8$ **2** $x - 4 > 9$ **3** $x - 3 > 2$

4 $x - 2 < 4$ **5** $x - 5 < 7$ **6** $x + 2 > 4$

7 $x + 6 > 9$ **8** $x + 3 > 10$ **9** $x + 4 < 8$

10 $x + 5 < 12$ **11** $3x - 1 > 8$ **12** $4x + 7 > 23$

13 $3x - 5 < 10$ **14** $5x - 7 < 8$

Simultaneous equations

Sometimes a problem arises involving two unknown quantities that gives more than one equation in the two unknowns.

For example, Pam was solving a problem about the price of a cup of coffee and the price of a cup of tea. The two equations she got were

$$a + b = 150$$
$$a - b = 30$$

She was able to solve these equations and found that $a = 90$ and $b = 60$. This told her that coffee cost 90p a cup and tea 60p a cup.

These two equations form a pair of simultaneous equations, i.e, they are both true for particular values of a and b.

EXERCISE 22m

QUESTION
Solve the simultaneous equations $a + b = 5$ and $a - b = 1$

ANSWER
$a + b = 5$ (1)
$a - b = 1$ (2)

Adding (1) and (2) gives $2a = 6$
i.e. $a = 3$ (Dividing both sides by 2)
Substituting $a = 3$ in (1)
gives $3 + b = 5$
i.e. $b = 2$
Check. Put $a = 3$ and $b = 2$ in (2)
LHS $= 3 - 2 = 1 =$ RHS
Therefore $a = 3$ and $b = 2$.

Solve the simultaneous equations

1 $a + b = 7$
$a - b = 1$

2 $2a + b = 8$
$a - b = 1$

3 $3a + b = 17$
$a - b = 3$

4 $5a + b = 28$
$2a - b = 7$

As well as adding equations we can subtract one from the other.

QUESTION
Solve the equations $4a + b = 24$ and $a + b = 9$

ANSWER
$4a + b = 24$ (1)
$a + b = 9$ (2)

Subtract (2) from (1) $3a = 15$
$a = 5$ (Dividing both sides by 3)
Substitute $a = 5$ in (2) $5 + b = 9$
i.e. $b = 4$
Check. Put $a = 5$ and $b = 4$ in (1)
LHS $= 4 \times 5 + 4 = 20 + 4 = 24 =$ RHS
Therefore $a = 5$ and $b = 4$.

Solve the simultaneous equations

5 $5a + b = 17$, $3a + b = 11$ **6** $3a + b = 7$, $a + b = 5$ **7** $7p + 2q = 67$, $3p + 2q = 31$

8 $5p + 3q = 41$, $4p + 3q = 37$ **9** $2a + 3b = 30$, $2a + b = 14$ **10** $5a - b = 7$, $3a - b = 3$

11 $4p + 5q = 31$, $4p + 2q = 22$ **12** $3x + 7y = 19$, $3x + 2y = 14$

Standard form

If you find the square of 600 000 on your calculator you may find that the display shows **3.6 11**. This gives the answer in scientific notation, which is a shorthand way of giving the number in standard form. It is short for 3.6×10^{11}.

Written fully $3.6 \times 10^{11} = 3.6 \times 100\,000\,000\,000$
$= 360\,000\,000\,000$

Any number written as $a \times 10^n$, where a, which is a number between 1 and 10, is multiplied by a power of 10, is a number written in standard form.

For example $4 \times 10^3 = 4 \times 1000 = 4000$
and $8.25 \times 10^5 = 8.25 \times 100\,000 = 825\,000$

Also, 79 000 in standard form is 7.9×1000
$= 7.9 \times 10^3$

i.e. 79 000 in standard form is 7.9×10^3.

Powers

In algebra we write $a \times a$ as a^2 and read it as 'a squared', or sometimes 'a to the power 2'. Similarly, the short way of writing $b \times b \times b$ is b^3 ('b cubed' or 'b to the power 3') and the short way of writing $p \times p \times p \times p$ is p^4 ('p to the 4' or 'p to the power 4').

EXERCISE 22n

1 What is the shorthand way of writing

(a) $a \times a \times a \times a$ (b) $p \times p$ (c) $q \times q \times q$
(d) $r \times r \times r \times r \times r$?

2 What is each of the following expressions short for?

(a) y^3 (b) a^5 (c) m^2 (d) $4q^4$

3 Write the following numbers as ordinary numbers.

(a) 5×10^2 (b) 6×10^4 (c) 1.2×10^5
(d) 8.3×10^3 (e) 7.21×10^6 (f) 4.9×10^7

4 Write each number in standard form.

(a) 900 (b) 7500 (c) 800 000
(d) 6420 (e) 34 900 (f) 126 400

Substituting

A: Into an expression

Frequently we need to substitute a particular value, or values, into an expression.
For example, if we know that the temperature is 20 ° Celsius we can find this temperature in degrees Fahrenheit by substituting $C = 20$ in the expression

$$\frac{9C}{5} + 32.$$

i.e. if $C = 20$, then
$$\frac{9C}{5} + 32 = \frac{9 \times 20}{5} + 32$$
$$= 36 + 32$$
$$= 68$$

i.e. a temperature of 20 °C is equivalent to 68 °F.

EXERCISE 22p

QUESTION
If $p = 5$ and $q = 4$, find the value of
(a) $2p + 6q$ (b) $5p - 3q$.

ANSWER
If $p = 5$ and $q = 4$, then:
(a) $2p + 6q = 2 \times 5 + 6 \times 4$
$= 10 + 24$
$= 34$
(b) $5p - 3q = 5 \times 5 - 3 \times 4$
$= 25 - 12$
$= 13$

In questions 1 to 12 find the value of the given expression if $a = 2$, $b = 3$ and $c = 5$.

1 $a + b$ **2** $a + 2b$ **3** $a + b + c$

4 $c - a - b$ **5** $3a - b$ **6** $b + c - 3a$

7 $3a - 2b$ **8** $10a - 2c$ **9** $a + 2b + 3c$

10 $4a - 2b + c$ **11** $3a + 2b - c$ **12** $b - a - c$

QUESTION

If $p = 10$ and $q = 5$ find the value of

(a) $3pq$ (b) $p^2 + q^2$ (c) $\frac{p^2 - 2q^2}{25}$.

ANSWER

If $p = 10$ and $q = 5$, then:

(a) $3pq = 3 \times 10 \times 5 = 150$

(b) $p^2 + q^2 = 10 \times 10 + 5 \times 5$
$= 100 + 25$
$= 125$

(c) $$\frac{p^2 - 2q^2}{25} = \frac{10 \times 10 - 2 \times 5 \times 5}{25} = \frac{100 - 50}{25} = \frac{50}{25} = 2$$

In questions 13 to 24 find the value of the given expression if $a = 6$, $b = 3$ and $c = 4$.

13 $a^2 + b^2$ **14** $b^2 + c^2$ **15** $a^2 + b^2 - c^2$

16 $2a^2 + c^2$ **17** abc **18** $3ab + 2c$

19 $a^3 + 3bc$ **20** $ab + bc + ca$ **21** $\frac{a^2 - b^2}{9}$

22 $\frac{2ab + 3c}{12}$ **23** $\frac{8a - 3bc}{6}$ **24** $\frac{a^2 + 2b^2 + c^2}{10}$

B: Into a formula

Formulas are often given using letters rather than words because they are much shorter. Rather than saying
the area of a triangle = half the base × the perpendicular height,
it is easier to use the formula $A = \frac{1}{2}bh$, where A represents the area, b the length of the base and h the perpendicular height.

Note that in algebra, when there is no sign between two letters it is assumed that the quantities are multiplied together. For example, if $A = bh$ then it is assumed that the value of b is multiplied by the value of h to give the value of A.

We often use formulas when we find the areas of shapes, the volumes of solids, the amount of simple interest or various quantities in science.

EXERCISE 22q

QUESTION

The formula used to calculate the simple interest (£I) when a sum of money (£P) is invested for a certain time (T years) at a given rate of interest (R per cent) is $I = \frac{PRT}{100}$. Find the simple interest when £850 is invested for 5 years at 8%.

ANSWER

$I = \frac{PRT}{100}$

∴ if P 850, $R = 8$ and $T = 5$

then $I = \frac{850 \times 8 \times 5}{100}$

i.e. $I = 340$

∴ the simple interest earned is £340.

1 If $s = \frac{a + b + c}{2}$, find s when $a = 12$, $b = 17$ and $c = 23$.

2 If $A = \frac{(a + b)}{2}h$, find A when $a = 13$, $b = 9$ and $h = 8$.

3 Use the formula $A = lb$ to find A when $l = 4$ and $b = 7$. What is this a formula for?

4 Use the formula $A = \frac{1}{2}bh$ to find A when $b = 17$ and $h = 12$.

5 Given that $C = 90 - \frac{1}{2}A$, find C when A is
(a) 60 (b) 90 (c) 0.

6 Given the formula $V = lbh$, find V when $l = 6$, $b = 7$ and $h = 8$.

7 Use the formula $I = \frac{PRT}{100}$ to find I when $P = 600$, $R = 10$ and $T = 4$.

8 Use the formula $C = 2\pi r$ to find the circumference (C) for a circle with a radius (r) of 45 cm. (Use the value of π on your calculator.)

9 Use the formula $C = \frac{5}{9}(F - 32)$ to find C when F is
(a) 113 (b) 212 (c) 32.

10 Use the formula $S = \frac{n(n + 1)}{2}$ to find S when
(a) $n = 12$ (b) $n = 21$.

11 Find S if $S = \dfrac{v^2 - u^2}{2a}$ and $u = 6$, $v = 10$ and $a = 16$.

12 Given that $\dfrac{1}{u} + \dfrac{1}{v} = \dfrac{1}{f}$, find f when $u = 3$ and $v = 4$.

13 If $v = \dfrac{40}{p}$, find v when p is (a) 4 (b) 8 (c) 80.

14 Find V when $r = 2.5$, given that $V = \frac{4}{3}\pi r^3$. (Use the value of π on your calculator.)

15 If $C = \dfrac{nE}{R + nr}$, find C when $n = 9$, $E = 5$, $R = 7$ and $r = 2$.

Dimensions of formulas

If r is a number of units of length then

$2\pi r$ is one-dimensional, i.e. a length.
2 and π are numbers, and a number multiplied by a length gives a length.

πr^2 is two-dimensional, i.e. an area.
A length × a length gives an area and an area multiplied by a number is still an area.

$4r^3$ is three-dimensional, i.e. a volume.
A length × a length × a length gives a volume and a volume multiplied by a number is still a volume.

A length must be 1-dimensional, an area 2-dimensional and a volume 3-dimensional. We can use these facts to decide whether or not some formulas must be wrong.

EXERCISE 22r

1 Which of the following quantities is
(a) a length (b) an area (c) a volume
(d) neither a length nor an area nor a volume?
44 cm², 16 m³, 32 mm, 9.2 ft², 8 cm³,
12 in, 2π, 60 mm³

2 Which of these quantities should be measured in units of (a) length (b) area (c) volume:
the space inside a room,
the distance round the edge of a door,
the amount of surface on the top of a table,
the region inside a circle,
the distance from my home to the post office,
the amount of milk a jug will hold?

3 The letters, a, b and c each represent a number of metres. Write down the unit for

(a) $8c$ (b) $\dfrac{d^2}{4}$ (c) $3bc$ (d) $\dfrac{abc}{8}$

(e) $2\pi b$ (f) $3ab^2$ (g) $\dfrac{5b^2c}{a}$

4 Given that a, b, c, and L represent units of length, A represents units of area and V represents units of volume, decide which of the following formulas must be wrong:

(a) $A = ab + bc$ (b) $V = 4bc$ (c) $L = a + b + c$

(d) $V = 6a^2b$ (e) $A = \dfrac{3ab}{c}$ (f) $L = a + bc$

5 Four students were asked to find the surface area (A cm²) of a solid, certain dimensions of which are p cm, q cm and r cm. Jane worked out the value of A as $4pq + r$, Paul got $4pqr$, Madge $4pg + r^2$ and Sim $4p + qr$. Which expressions are definitely wrong?

The equation of a straight line

Lines parallel to an axis

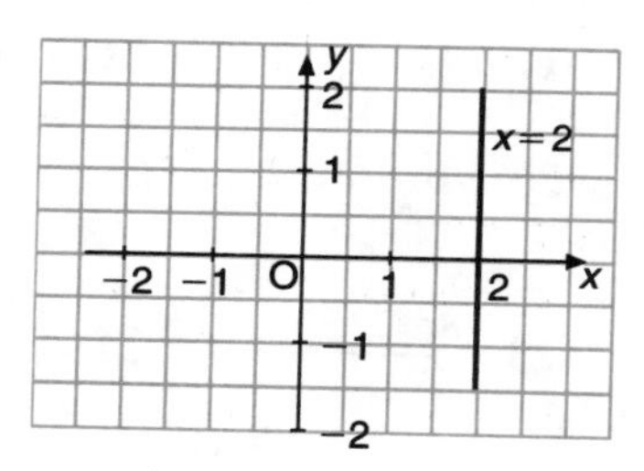

For every point on this line the x-coordinate is 2, whatever the y-coordinate.
The equation of this line is $x = 2$

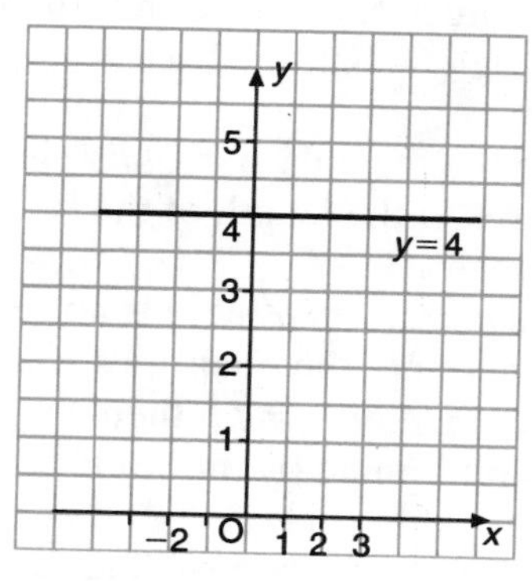

Similarly, for every point on this line the y-coordinate is 4, i.e. the equation of the line is $y = 4$.

If a and b are whole numbers, $x = a$ is the equation of a straight line parallel to the y-axis, and $y = b$ is the equation of a straight line parallel to the x-axis.

The equation $y = ax + b$

If the equation of a straight line is $y = 3x$, the y-coordinate of every point on the line is three times the x-coordinate.

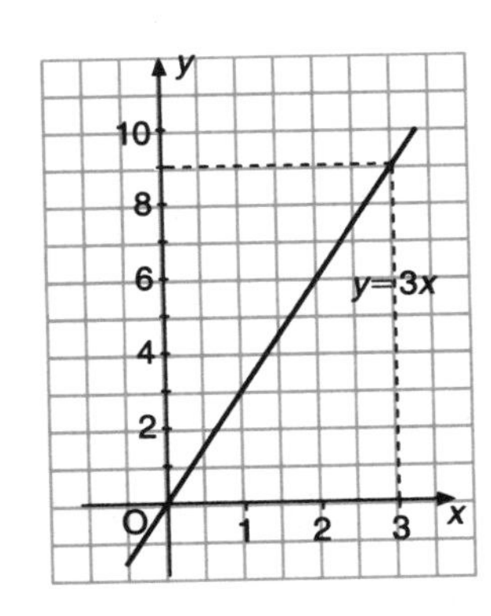

The equation $y = ax$ represents a straight line through the origin. The value of a can be positive or negative, small or large. If a is positive, the line slopes up to the right; if a is negative, the line slopes up to the left.

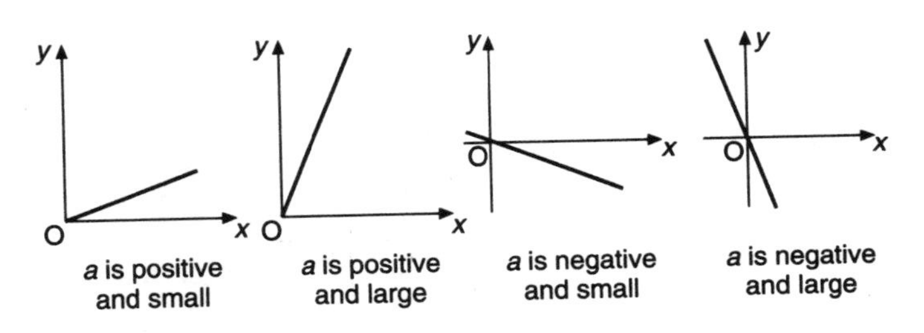

The equation $y = 3x + 2$ gives a straight line parallel to the line $y = 3x$ but everywhere 2 units above it, and the equation $y = 3x - 3$ gives a line parallel to the line $y = 3x$ but 3 units below it.

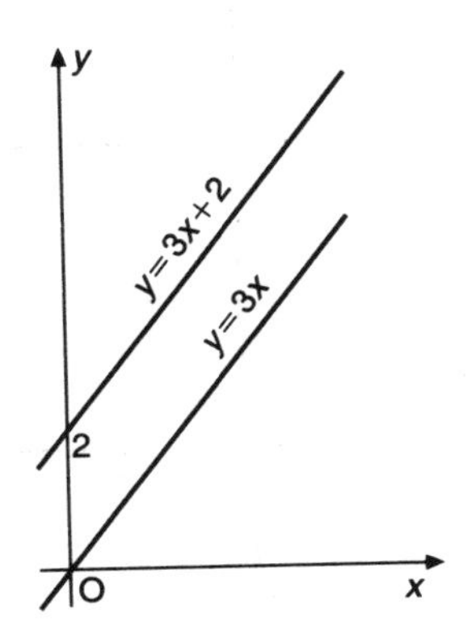

EXERCISE 22s

On squared paper sketch the line with the given equation. Give the coordinates of a least two points on each line.

1 $y = 3$ **2** $x = 3$ **3** $x = -4$

4 $y = -2$ **5** $y = 2x$ **6** $y = 4x$

7 $y = x$ **8** $y = -2x$ **9** $y = -x$

10 $y = -3x$ **11** $y = x + 1$ **12** $y = 2x + 3$

13 $y = x - 1$ **14** $y = 2x + 1$ **15** $y = 2x - 4$

Curved graphs

A sketch of the graph of the equation $y = x^2$ is given below.

If $x = 2$, $y = 2 \times 2 = 4$

and if $x = -2$, $y = (-2) \times (-2) = 4$,

i.e. two different values of x give the same value of y.

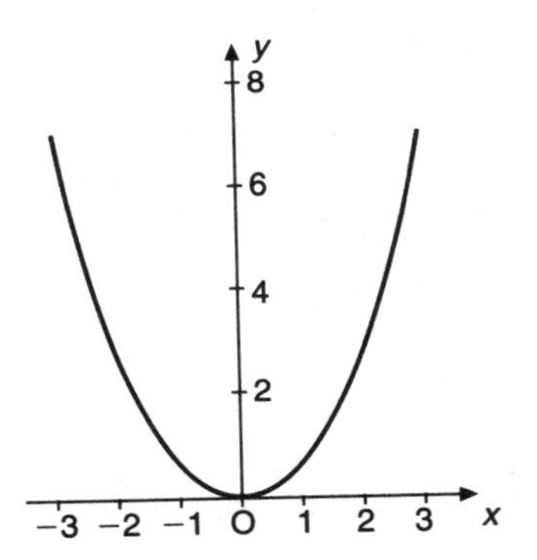

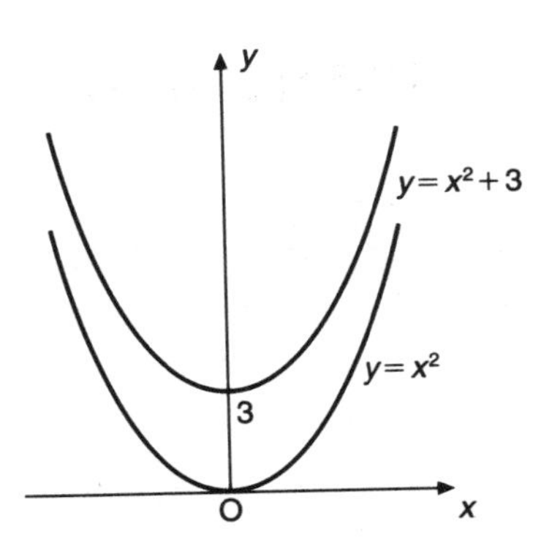

For any value of x the value of $x^2 + 3$ is 3 more than the value of x^2.

The graph of the equation $y = x^2 + 3$ can therefore be found by sketching the graph of $y = x^2$ and then moving it 3 units up the page.

EXERCISE 22t

1

(a) Copy and complete the following table which gives values of x^2 for whole number values of x from -4 to 4

x	-4	-3	-2	-1	0	1	2	3	4
x^2	16		4		0	1			

(b) Draw the x- and y-axes. Scale the x-axis from -4 to 4 and the y-axis from 0 to 16. Use 1 cm to represent 1 unit on each axis.

(c) Use the values in your table to plot points that lie on the curve with equation $y = x^2$. For example, the first point has an x-coordinate of -4 and a y-coordinate of 16.

(d) Join the points with a smooth curve. Your graph should look like the sketch of $y = x^2$ shown on page 207.

2 Sketch the graph of $y = x^2$ and use it to sketch the graphs of
(a) $y = x^2 + 4$ (b) $y = x^2 - 2$
Show clearly where each graph crosses the y-axis.

Solving equations by trial and improvement

Sometimes, a real-life problem leads to an equation that we cannot solve easily. When this happens we guess the solution, and then substitute the guess into the equation to see how well it fits. This should enable us to make a better guess second time than we did first time.

EXERCISE 22u

QUESTION

The area of a small metal plate, which is used in the assembly of a lawnmower, is 19 cm^2. This plate is 1 cm longer than it is wide. The width of the plate can be found by finding the value of x that satisfies the equation $x^2 + x = 19$. Find, correct to 1 decimal place, two positive values, between which the width of the plate lies.

ANSWER

x^2, $2x$ and 19 are unlike terms, so the equation cannot be simplified.

Try $x = 3$ in the left-hand side of the equation:

$$x^2 + 2x = 3^2 + 2 \times 3 = 9 + 6 = 15$$

(Too small i.e. less than 19)

Try $x = 4$:

$$x^2 + 2x = 4^2 + 2 \times 4 = 16 + 8 = 24$$

(Too big i.e. bigger than 19)

Try $x = 3.5$:

$$x^2 + 2x = 3.5^2 + 2 \times 3.5 = 12.25 + 7 = 19.25$$

(A little too big – larger than 19)

Try $x = 3.4$:

$$x^2 + 2x = 3.4^2 + 2 \times 3.4 = 11.56 + 6.8 = 18.36$$

(A little too small – less than 19)

$\therefore$ x lies between 3.4 and 3.5.

The equations that follow have arisen in solving the problems that are referred to in brackets. Find, correct to 1 decimal place, two positive numbers between which the solution of the given equation lies.

1 $x^2 = 30$. (x cm is the side of a square that has an area of 30 cm^2.)

2 $6a^2 = 330$. (a m is the length of the edge of a cube that has a total surface area of 330 m^2.)

3 $\pi r^2 = 20$. (r cm is the radius of a circle which has an area of 20 square centimetres. Use the value of π on your calculator.)

4 $x^2 + x = 60$. (x m is the shorter side of a rectangular flower bed that has an area of 60 m^2.)

5 $y^2 - y = 21$. (y cm is the length of the longer edge of an oblong piece of metal that has an area of 21 cm^2.)

6 $h^2 + 4h = 100$. (h cm is the height of a triangle that has an area of 100 cm^2.)

7 $b^2 + 4b = 105$. (b cm is the distance between two parallel sides of a parallelogram that has an area of 105 square centimetres.)

8 $x^3 = 100$. (x cm is the length of the side of a small cubical metal block that has a volume of 100 cubic centimetres.)

9 $x^3 = 65$. (x cm is the length of an edge of a cubical wooden box that has a capacity of 65 cubic centimetres.)

10 $\frac{1}{3}h^3 = 12\,000$. (h m is the height of an Egyptian pyramid that takes up 12 000 cubic metres of space.)

Multiple-choice questions 22

In questions 1 to 4 several alternative answers are given. Write down the letter that corresponds to the correct answer.

1 The solution of the equation $5x = 15$ is

A $x = 10$ **B** $x = 3$ **C** $x = 5$ **D** $x = 18$

2 If $b - \frac{1}{2} = 2\frac{3}{4}$ it follows that the value of p is

A $2\frac{1}{4}$ **B** $3\frac{1}{4}$ **C** $2\frac{3}{8}$ **D** $2\frac{2}{3}$

3 When $3c + 4c + 5c$ is simplified the answer is

A $12c$ **B** $12c \times c \times c$
C $60c$ **D** $60 \times c \times c \times c$

4 A rectangular lawn, which has an area of 65 m^2, is 3 m longer than it is wide. If the lawn is p metres wide the value of p can be found by solving the equation $p^2 + 3p = 65$. Trial and improvement methods show that the value of p lies between

A 6.6 m and 6.7 m **B** 6.7 m and 6.8 m
C 6.8 m and 6.9 m **D** 6.9 m and 7.0 m

5 George is p years old and his father, Sid, is four times as old as George. In 16 years' time Sid will be twice as old as George.

Which of the following statements are true and which are false?

A Sid's present age is $p + 4$ years

B In 16 years' time George will be $p + 16$ years old and Sid will be $4p + 16$ years old.

C The equation we can form from the given information is $4p + 16 = 2p + 32$.

D In 5 years' time George will be 13 and Sid will be 35.

6 Silchester Electrics make a 1 for 5 rights issue of their ordinary shares. This means that for every 5 shares each investor owns, 1 new share will be offered at a favourable price. Fractions of a share are discounted. Sam Cule has 523 ordinary shares in Gilchester Electrics.

The following statements have been made:
Statement 1. If he takes up the rights issue Sam will have exactly 20% more shares than he had to start with.
Statement 2. If Sam does not take up the rights issue he will have 104 fewer shares than if he had taken them up.

How are these statements best described?

A True, True **B** True, False
C False, True **D** False, False

Self-assessment test 22

1 The body mass index (BMI) for a person is $\dfrac{\text{weight in kilograms}}{(\text{height in metres})^2}$.

(a) Find the BMI for the four brothers whose heights and weights are listed below.

	Height (m)	Weight (kg)
Bob	1.71	84
Dennis	1.92	92.5
Oliver	1.83	75.2
Reg	1.58	96.8

(b) Find Eddy's body mass index if he is 5 ft 4 in tall and weighs 13 st 12 lb. (2.2 lb = 1 kg and 1 inch = 2.54 cm.)

2 A small component for a washing machine requires 4 rubber washers. How many washers must be taken out of stock to manufacture 195 components if 14 washers are broken during assembly and have to be replaced?

3 Solve the equations

(a) $a + 7 = 25$ (b) $b - 8 = 16$
(c) $8c = 48$ (d) $\frac{1}{3}d = 4$

4 Solve the equations

(a) $3p - 7 = 20$ (b) $2q + 9 = 18$

(c) $\dfrac{x}{10} = \dfrac{9}{5}$ (d) $y + \frac{1}{4} = 3\frac{1}{2}$

5 Simplify the following equations and hence solve them:

(a) $6x - 5x + 7x = 48$ (b) $8y + 3 - 3y + 9 = 27$

6 (a) Simplify (i) $5(3p + 9)$ (ii) $4(5q - 3)$.
(b) Solve the equation $3(2m - 5) = 42$.

7 If $p = 5$, $q = 3$ and $r = 7$ find the value of
(a) $5p + 3q - 4r$ (b) $7pqr$ (c) $2p^2 + q^2 - r^2$.

8 Richard has two wooden boxes, one of which is four times as heavy as the other. 3 kg of oranges are put into the heavier box and 12 kg of apples into the other box. When the partially filled boxes are put on the opposite sides of a scales they balance. (a) If the weight of the lighter box is x kg, how heavy, in terms of x, is the other box? (b) Form an equation in x and solve it to find the weight of each box.

CHAPTER 23

Statistics

Statistics is the subject that tries to make sense of a large amount of information, called data, which is given in the form of numbers.

Most data is collected by observing what happens, by interviewing people or by filling in forms.

Observation

Direct observation is used to gather information on, for example, the number of vehicles passing along a street at different times of the day and on different days of the week, or the number of packets of biscuits of different kinds sold each day in a supermarket. This information can be found by counting and can be classified and tabulated as it is gathered provided adequate preparation has been made in advance.

For example, in collecting information about the different makes of cars using a public car park on different days of the week, a table like the one given here would be useful.

	Make of car						
Day/Date	Ford	Vauxhall	Mercedes	BMW	Rover	Toyota	...
Mon 20 July							
Tue 21 July							
Wed 22 July							
...							

EXERCISE 23a

Draw up an observation sheet that would help you to collect data to solve the following problems.

1 A doctor wishes to find out how many of his patients smoke, what they smoke (a pipe, cigarettes, cigars) and how often they smoke.

2 A local bus company wants to buy some new buses, but is uncertain whether to order 12-seater, 15-seater, 24-seater or 35-seaters to replace the existing 35-seaters on the route from Leefold to Bampton.

3 Yvette's Boutique needs to order dresses from Osmond Fashions for next season. They have records of their sales for the last five years.

4 A market gardener wants to run trials this year to decide which type of kidney bean plant he will grow on a commercial basis next year.

Questionnaires

Information about people and their opinions that cannot be observed directly, or cannot be measured, can often be found by asking questions. You can either ask people questions in a face-to-face interview or you can get them to fill in a form.

An **interview** is an example of a questionnaire. It can be formal or informal. In a formal interview only agreed, previously prepared questions are asked. In an informal interview, such as a job interview, the first few questions asked can lead to other questions which will vary from person to person.

The answers to the questions asked during an interview must be easily available. A woman interviewed on the street will know which daily newspaper she reads, but she is unlikely to know exactly how many building societies there are in the local high street. When a person is interviewed he is far more likely to think carefully about his answer if he thinks that his opinion is valued or will influence events.

A **questionnaire** is a list of questions intended to discover particular information. A questionnaire is relatively easy to construct, and is comparatively cheap to produce. An advantage of handing out a questionnaire is that people have time to think about their answers before they give them; a disadvantage is that many people put off replying to them unless there is some incentive.

The questions in a questionnaire must be worded so that they

- are short and easy to understand
- do not suggest a particular answer
- are likely to be answered truthfully
- allow for all possible answers
- preferably can be answered 'yes' or 'no' or by ticking one of several suggested answers.

A short questionnaire on travelling to school is given on the next page.

Travelling to school

1 How do you come to school?

Bus ☐ Car ☐ Walk ☐ Cycle ☐ Other ☐

2 How far do you have to travel to school?

less than 1 mile ☐ 1 mile – less than 2 miles ☐ 2 miles – less than 3 miles ☐ 3 miles – less than 5 miles ☐ 5 miles or over ☐

3 How long does it take you to get to school?

less than 15 min ☐ 15 min – less than 30 min ☐ 30 min – less than 45 min ☐ 45 min – less than 60 min ☐ 1 hour or more ☐

The easiest way to gather information expressing people's opinions about some matter is to make a statement and measure the reaction to it. The person interviewed is asked to tick the box that is nearest to his or her opinion. For example:

1 Footballers are paid too much.

Strongly agree ☐ Agree ☐
Neither agree nor disagree ☐ Disagree ☐
Strongly disagree ☐

2 British troops should get out of Ireland.

Strongly agree ☐ Agree ☐
Don't know ☐ Disagree ☐
Strongly disagree ☐

3 Everybody should be taught to read and write.

Strongly agree ☐ Agree ☐
Don't know ☐ Disagree ☐
Strongly disagree ☐

EXERCISE 23b

Comment on each of the following questions which have been extracted from some actual questionnaires.

1 How do you rate this airline's meals?

Excellent ☐ Good ☐ Average ☐ Poor ☐
Very poor ☐ (Please tick one box.)

(A question taken from an airline questionnaire to be filled in by passengers on their journey home.)

2 How much do you spend each week on travelling? (Taken from a student's survey on spending.)

3 Which political party do you think would be best for Britain?
(Taken from a newspaper questionnaire two weeks before a general election.)

4 At your local supermarket, how long, on average, do you have to wait at the checkout?
Less than 1 minute ☐ 1–2 min ☐ 2–3 min ☐
3–5 min ☐ Over 5 min ☐
(Please tick one box.)
(Included in a supermarket questionnaire.)

5 Which of these questions are likely to get honest answers?

(a) Are you generous to your friends?
Yes ☐ No ☐

(b) How old are you? Under 18 □ 18–21 □ 22–40 □ Over 40 □

(c) Do you always listen carefully when someone is talking to you? Yes □ No □

(d) You have been given too much change. Do you point this out to the cashier? Yes □ No □

(e) Do you care enough about your family to take adequate insurance cover when you go on holiday? Yes □ No □.

6 What's wrong with these questions?

(a) Would you prefer not to eat in a non-smoking restaurant?

(b) What do you think about the size and shape of this container?

7 Design a short questionnaire to find out

(a) how many times a week the students in your group read newspapers, which newspapers they read, how long they spend reading them.

(b) how often the teenagers in your street have an alcoholic drink, where they drink, how much they drink and how much they spend on drink.

Frequency tables

The list of numbers given below shows the number of occupants, including the driver, in each car entering a car park between 8 a.m. and 8.30 a.m. one morning.

2 3 1 4 2 3 2 2 2 1 2 4 1 6 2

1 2 3 2 1 3 5 1 2 2 1 3 1 2 1

2 1 3 2 1 2 2 2 2 1 3 1 4 2 3

This is raw data and needs to be sorted into categories. To do this we draw up a table, first of all entering tally marks (///) and then finding the total or frequency for each category.

Number of occupants per car	1	2	3	4	5	6
Tally	~~////~~ ~~////~~ ///	~~////~~ ~~////~~ ~~////~~ ////	~~////~~ ///	///	/	/
Frequency	13	19	8	3	1	1

This is called a **frequency table**. It would have saved time if the table had been prepared previously so that the data could have been entered as the cars entered the car park.

Discrete and continuous data

The data given above was collected by counting. It is an example of **discrete data**. Discrete data can take particular values only. We cannot have $\frac{1}{2}$ or $\frac{1}{3}$ of a person in a car!

Discrete data values are usually whole numbers but do not have to be; for example $3\frac{1}{2}$ and $8\frac{1}{2}$ are shoe sizes.

While discrete data is obtained by counting, other data can be found by measuring. For example, the heights and weights of a group of people can be found by measuring. Such values can lie anywhere between certain limits. This kind of data is called **continuous data**.

Grouping

When discrete data, such as the number of people queueing at a cash machine, is being collected, it is quite clear that if the data is to be put in groups, 0–4, 5–9, 10–14, . . . will do. The next possible value after 4 is 5, so the fact that there is a gap between the end of one group and the beginning of the next group does not matter.

For continuous data, however, we must consider all the possible values from the lowest to the highest, leaving no gaps between.

If we have a list of the weights of a group of adults that vary from 51 kg to 96 kg, suitable groups or **class-intervals** would be* $50 \leqslant w < 60$, $60 \leqslant w < 70$, and so on up to $90 \leqslant w < 100$, where the weight of a given adult is w kg.

In this way there is no doubt about which group a given weight belongs to.

For the group $50 \leqslant w < 60$, 50 is called the lower boundary and 60 the upper boundary. The difference between these two values is the width of the group. In this case the group width is 10.

In our work all groups, or class intervals, in the same question have the same width. When you have to choose the number of groups yourself do not choose too many or too few. Between 5 and 8 is usually satisfactory.

*The symbol $\leqslant$ means 'is less than or equal to' and $<$ means 'is less than', so $50 \leqslant w < 60$ means that 50 is less than or equal to the values of w (i.e. w is greater than or equal to 50, but w is less than 60).

EXERCISE 23c

In questions 1 to 10 state whether the data is discrete or continuous.

1 The number of telephone calls made by an office in a day.

2 The length of a telephone call.

3 The weight of coffee in a jar as it leaves the factory.

4 The length of beans picked on an allotment.

5 The number of cans of tomatoes produced by a factory in one week.

6 The number of letters in a postman's bag.

7 The weight of the letters in a postman's bag.

8 The number of miles a tyre can be run before it reaches the legal limit.

9 The number of compact discs in a music store.

10 The time that patients have to wait before they are seen by the doctor.

In questions 11 to 14 the first two groups to be used for a set of data are given. Suggest the next three groups.

11 The number of rejects per 100 in a manufacturing process:
0–9, 10–19, . . .

12 The number of passengers on an InterCity train between stations:
0–49, 50–99, . . .

13 The height, h cm, of the adults in a cinema:
$150 \leqslant h < 155, 155 \leqslant h < 160, \ldots$

14 The weight, w g, of the nails produced by a machine:
$8.85 \leqslant w < 8.90, 8.90 \leqslant w < 8.95.$

15 The groups for the heights, h cm, of some plants after 12 weeks are
$0 \leqslant h < 10, 10 \leqslant h < 20, 20 \leqslant h < 30, 30 \leqslant h < 40$
Into which class interval would you put a plant whose measured height after 10 weeks is

(a) 8.7 cm (b) 21.4 cm (c) 29.8 cm (d) 15.3 cm?

16 The number of letters in a postman's bag can be anything up to 400. Suggest 5 groups that would be suitable for grouping this data.

17 A sample of 100 bottles of milk were checked by measuring the amount of milk, v ml, in each bottle. The contents ranged from 562 ml up to, but not including, 592 ml. Suggest 6 equal groupings, or class intervals, that would be suitable to group this data.

Pictograms

Pictograms use simple pictures to represent data. They are often used in advertising material when it is important to attract attention. A pictogram should always have a key to explain any symbols used and should represent different things by pictures of the same size.

For example, it would be better to use the symbols

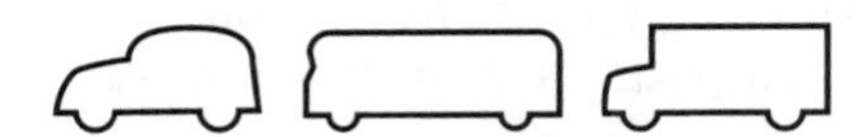

to represent cars, buses and lorries, rather than the symbols

An example of a simple pictogram, from which it is easy to extract useful information, is given below.

Pictogram showing the choice of main course at Martha's Café one lunchtime.

Chicken	
Steak and kidney pie	
Beef casserole	
Ham and salad	

Key: = 5 servings

From this pictogram we see that

(a) steak and kidney pie was the most popular main course dish and ham salad was the least popular.

(b) there were 20 servings of the chicken dish and between 30 and 35 servings of the beef casserole.

Bar charts

The following frequency table shows the number of new jobs created at Farley Electronics in 1995.

Month	Jan	Feb	Mar	April	May	June
Number of new jobs	8	12	16	22	16	25
Month	July	Aug	Sept	Oct	Nov	Dec
Number of new jobs	14	8	6	4	6	6

Data can be illustrated very clearly on a bar chart. The bar chart for the given data is shown here.

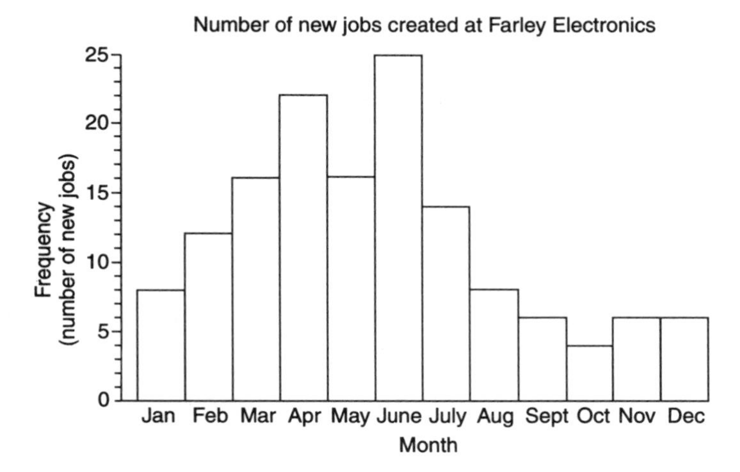

We mark the months of the year along the horizontal axis and frequency along the vertical axis.

Each bar gives the number for one month; all the bars are the same width. The height of the bar shows the frequency, i.e. the number of new jobs, for that month.

There could be gaps between the bars and there is no reason why bars could not be arranged horizontally.

EXERCISE 23d

QUESTION

The number of children, by age, that have had their first birthday and live on the Broadway Housing Estate is given below.

Age	Number
1–4	140
5–8	125
9–12	65
13–16	50

Show this information on a bar chart.

ANSWER

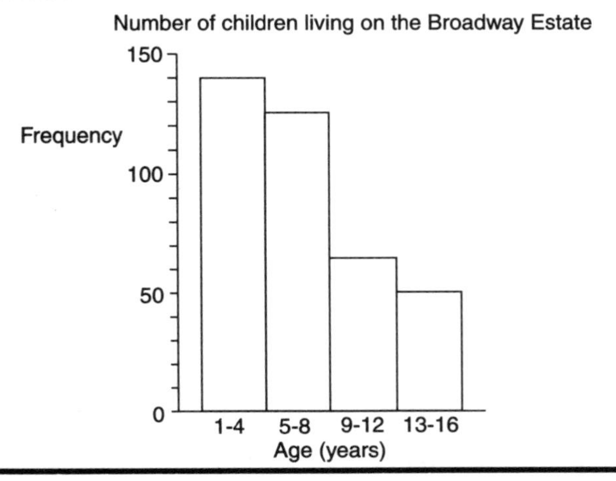

1 In a store sales are put into one of four types: electrical (E), floor coverings (C), fabrics (F) and bedding (B). The list given below records each sale one morning.

F C B C E B E E F C E F E C B E

C B C E F F E C B C E E F C B F

B E C E F B F F E E E C E F B B

(a) Copy and complete this frequency table:

Type of sale	Electrical (E)	Floor coverings (C)	Fabric (F)	Bedding (B)
Tally				
Frequency				

(b) Draw a bar chart to illustrate this data.

(c) How many more electrical sales than bedding sales were there?

(d) How many more sales were there for fabrics than for floor coverings?

(e) How many sales were there altogether?

2 A machine makes 6-inch screws and puts them in packs of five. A small number of packs are selected at random and the number of defective screws in each pack noted. The results for one morning shift are shown in the bar chart.

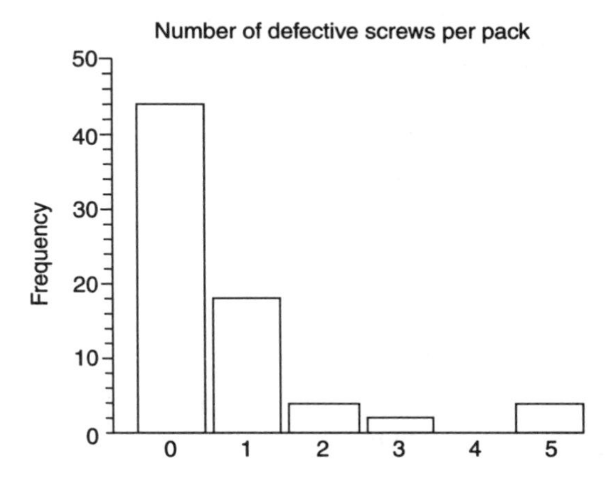

(a) How many packs contained
(i) no defective screws
(ii) 2 defective screws?

(b) How many packs were checked?

(c) How many defective screws were there altogether?

(d) What percentage of the screws checked were defective?

3 The following list gives the age, in years, in 100 people taken into residential care by a local authority:

99 82 87 85 81 87 83 73 82 77 83 90 72 84 78 92 84 87 83 92

84 74 80 65 93 84 89 87 81 94 84 67 85 80 94 84 74 78 80 81

82 87 83 77 89 80 88 66 72 77 91 98 77 88 87 83 94 88 94 85

86 75 72 80 94 82 95 70 92 81 89 78 87 76 72 86 77 68 86 83

87 92 84 67 89 91 76 84 78 93 74 68 71 75 96 72 83 79 74 88

(a) What is the age of (i) the youngest (ii) the oldest person in this list?

(b) Copy and complete the following frequency table:

(c) Draw a bar chart to represent this data.

(d) How many of the new residents were at least 80?

(e) Which age group has the largest number of people?

Age	65 to 69	70 to 74	75 to 79	80 to 84	85 to 89	90 to 94	95 to 99
Tally							
Frequency							

Continuous data

The number of employees in a factory is a whole number but their heights are likely to be anywhere between 140 cm and 200 cm. Because height can be anywhere on a continuous scale, the heights of the employees are an example of continuous data.

167 172 185 175 174 174 188 178 179 172

173 169 175 172 169 147 147 172 188 179

182 174 184 168 153 176 172 197 173 189

172 179 165 145 174 193 165 187 146 172

165 172 151 176 186 167 171 176 152 179

This is a list of the heights of 50 employees. It was found using a computer database and gives the heights in ascending order. Each height has been rounded down to the nearest whole centimetre, so that a height of 152 cm means any value, h cm, that is in the range $152 \leqslant h < 153$. This data shows a shortest height of 145 cm and a tallest height of 197 cm. We can sort the data into six class intervals as follows:

Height, h (cm)	Frequency
$140 \leqslant h < 150$	4
$150 \leqslant h < 160$	3
$160 \leqslant h < 170$	8
$170 \leqslant h < 180$	25
$180 \leqslant h < 190$	8
$190 \leqslant h < 200$	2

Another way of giving this information in a table is:

Height, h (cm)	140–	150–	160–	170–	180–	190–200
Frequency	4	3	8	25	8	2

Note: 140– means 'all values from 140 cm up to but not including 150 cm'.
In each case the width of the class interval is 10 cm.
The bar chart for this data is shown below.

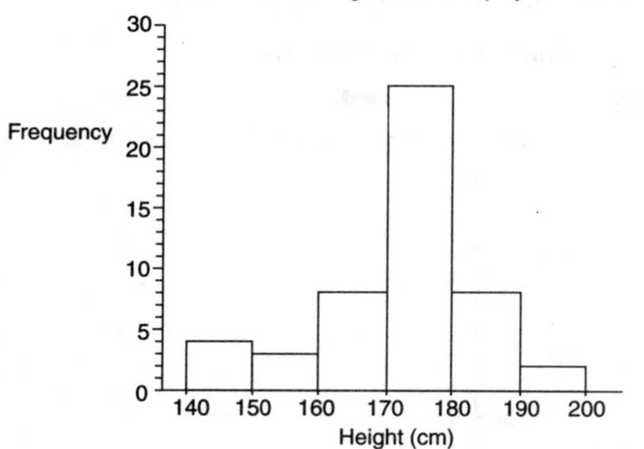

The horizontal axis gives the height on a continuous scale. No gaps are allowed between the bars.

EXERCISE 23e

1 In a factory making radios a sample of 100 radios is selected at random each day to test for defects. The number with defects found on 60 consecutive days is listed below.

2	0	8	10	7	3	6	4	7	11	8	12	7	9	0
7	13	11	14	3	10	8	7	13	6	4	5	16	14	6
3	17	8	5	16	1	11	7	0	10	0	7	7	3	10
7	6	4	13	11	4	9	11	15	2	5	6	9	8	11

(a) Is this data discrete or continuous?

(b) Copy and complete the following frequency table.

Number of defects	Tally	Frequency
0 to 2		
3 to 5		
6 to 8		
9 to 11		
12 to 14		
15 to 17		
	18 to 20	

(c) On how many days were there more than 11 radios with defects?

(d) Draw a bar chart to illustrate this data. For the heights of the bars use 1 cm to represent 2 defective radios.

2 The frequency table shows the time, in minutes, taken by the passengers going on a package tour to Crete, to travel from home to the airport.

Time, t (min)	$0 \leqslant t < 20$	$20 \leqslant t < 40$	$40 \leqslant t < 60$
Frequency	19	34	58
Time, t (min)	$60 \leqslant t < 80$	$80 \leqslant t < 100$	
Frequency	41	16	

(a) Copy and complete this bar chart.

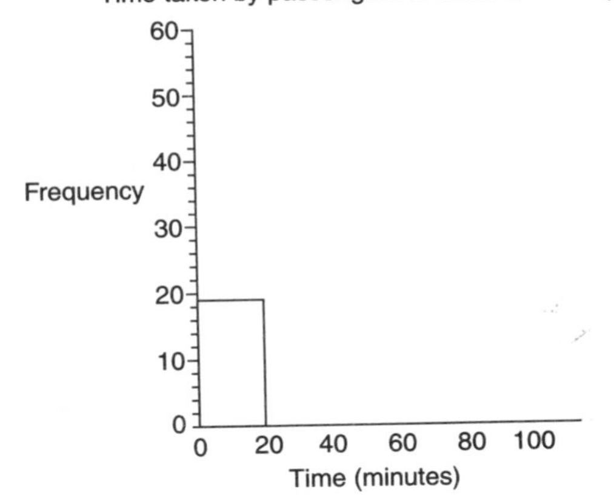

(b) How many passengers travelled on the aircraft?

(c) How many passengers had a journey to the airport that took less than an hour?

3 Given below is a list of the amount, each correct to the nearest millilitre, of engine oil in a batch of containers delivered to a garage shop. Each container is said to contain 500 ml. The quantities are given in ascending order.

487	489	490	491	491	492	492	492	493	495
495	496	496	496	496	497	497	498	498	498
498	498	498	499	499	500	500	500	501	501
501	501	501	502	502	503	503	503	503	504
504	504	504	504	504	504	504	504	504	504
505	505	505	505	506	506	506	507	507	507
508	508	508	508	508	508	508	509	509	509
510	510	511	511	512	512	512	513	514	514

(a) What is the smallest quantity recorded?

(b) If the recorded amount is 498 ml, what is the range within which the actual amount lies?

(c) Copy and complete the following frequency table.

Amount, v (ml)	Tally	Frequency
$484.5 \leqslant v < 489.5$		
$489.5 \leqslant v < 494.5$		
$494.5 \leqslant v < 499.5$		
$499.5 \leqslant v < 504.5$		
$504.5 \leqslant v < 509.5$		
$509.5 \leqslant v < 514.5$		
$514.5 \leqslant v < 519.5$		

(d) How many of the sample contain 499.5 ml or more?

(e) Explain why it is not possible to find out from the table the number of bottles containing more than 500 ml.

Line graphs

Line graphs are drawn by plotting points, then joining the points in order with straight lines.

EXERCISE 23f

QUESTION

Pirie was admitted to hospital as an emergency. Her temperature was taken at 4-hourly intervals and a record kept on a chart. The chart is shown below.

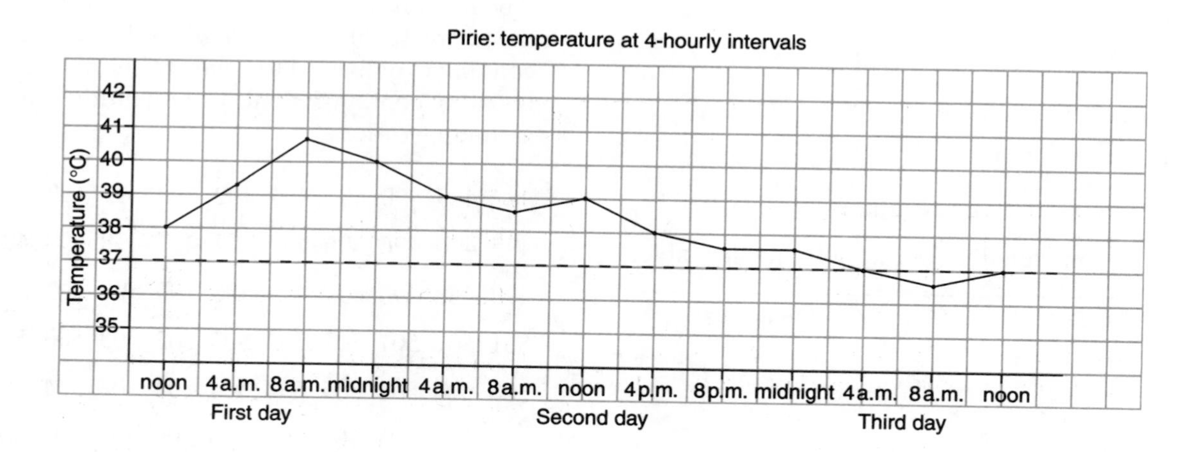

(a) What was Pirie's
(i) lowest temperature (ii) highest temperature?

(b) Was her highest recorded temperature necessarily her highest temperature?

(c) By the third day Pirie was feeling much better. What do you think the dashed line represents?

ANSWER

(a) (i) Her lowest recorded temperature was 36.5 °C at 8 a.m. on the third day.
(ii) Her highest temperature was 40.5 °C at 8 p.m. on the first day.

(b) No. Her temperature could have been higher at some time between 4 p.m. and midnight.

(c) Since Pirie was feeling much better it is probably the normal temperature.

1 Norman measured the height of a plant at the end of each week for 8 weeks. His values are shown on the graph opposite.

(a) How high was the plant after
(i) 2 weeks (ii) 3 weeks?

(b) How much did the plant grow (i) in the 3rd week (ii) from the end of the 2nd week to the end of the 7th week?

(c) During which week did the plant grow
(i) most (ii) least?

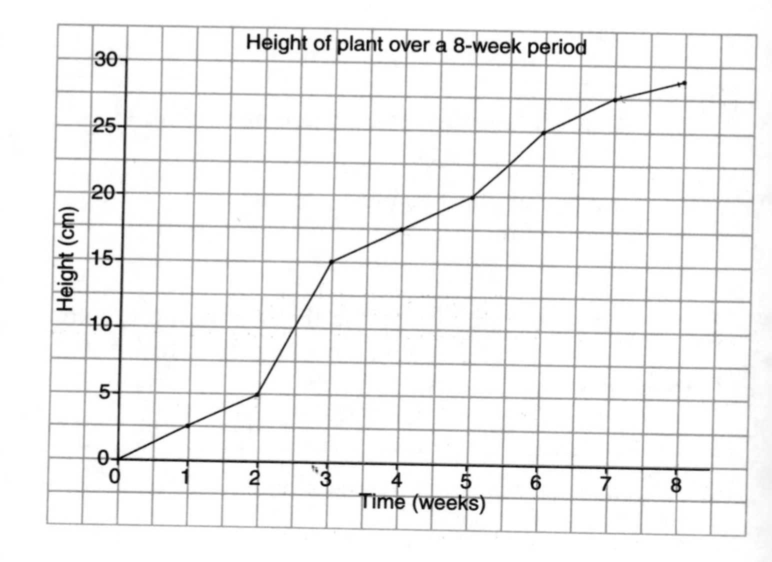

2 The line graph given on page 219 – sometimes called a time series – shows the quarterly sales figures for a manufacturing company.

(a) What were the first-quarter sales in
(i) 1992 (ii) 1994?

(b) What were the third-quarter sales in
(i) 1991 (ii) 1993?

(c) Find the difference between the second-quarter sales and the fourth-quarter sales in
(i) 1991 (ii) 1994.

(d) In which year was there the greatest difference between the poorest quarter and the best quarter?

(e) Is there a sales pattern in these figures? If you were the boss would you be satisfied?

(f) Can you think of a product that could give a sales pattern like this?

(g) Sketch a similar graph for (i) an ice cream seller at a seaside resort (ii) the sales of a company distributing school and college textbooks (iii) the sales of sugar in a supermarket.

Pie charts

When we want to show the fraction of the whole that each part takes we use a pie chart.

EXERCISE 23g

QUESTION

The pie chart shows the breakdown of a bill of £54 for servicing my washing machine.

(a) What fraction of the bill was for labour?

(b) How much was the charge for VAT?

(c) What percentage of the bill was to pay for parts?

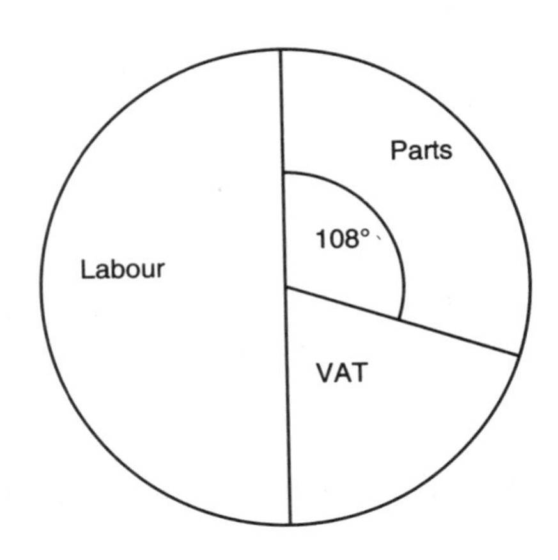

ANSWER

(a) Angle in the slice for labour is 180°

$\therefore$ fraction of bill for labour is $\frac{180°}{360°} = \frac{1}{2}$

(Remember that 1 revolution is 360°.)

(b) Angle in the slice for VAT is $360° - 180° - 108° = 72°$

$\therefore$ cost of VAT is $\frac{72}{360}$ of the total cost

i.e. cost of VAT is $\frac{72}{360} \times £54 = £10.80$

(c) Proportion spent on parts is $\frac{108}{360}$ of the total

$\therefore$ percentage spent on parts is $\frac{108}{360} \times 100\%$

$= 30\%$

1 120 people were asked to name their favourite fruit. Their answers are shown in the pie chart.

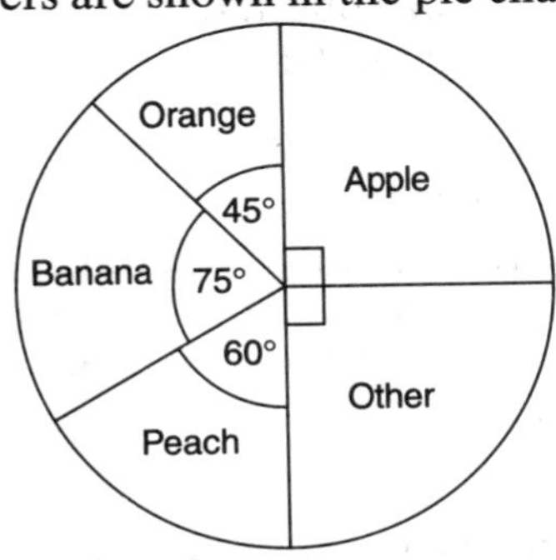

(a) What fraction chose
(i) an apple (ii) a banana?

(b) What fraction did not choose an orange or a peach?

(c) How many chose
(i) an apple (ii) a peach (iii) an apple or a banana?

2

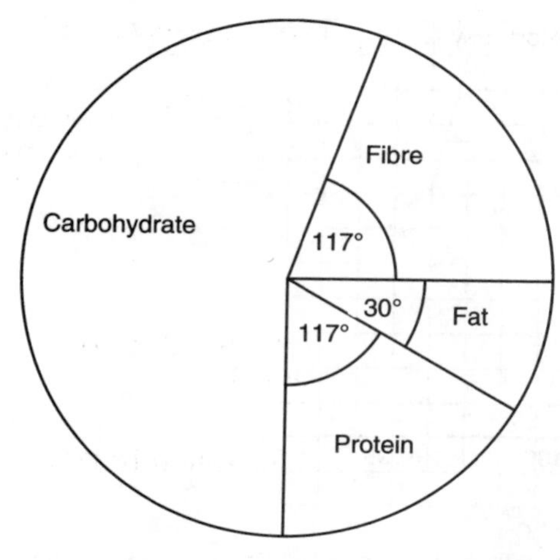

This pie chart shows the proportion, by weight, of various nutrients in a packet of oat cereal.

(a) What fraction of the nutrients is
(i) fat (ii) fibre (iii) carbohydrate?

(b) How many grams of protein are there in a serving of (i) 100 g (ii) 36 g?

(g) How many grams of carbohydrate are there in a serving of (i) 100 g (ii) 36 g?

3

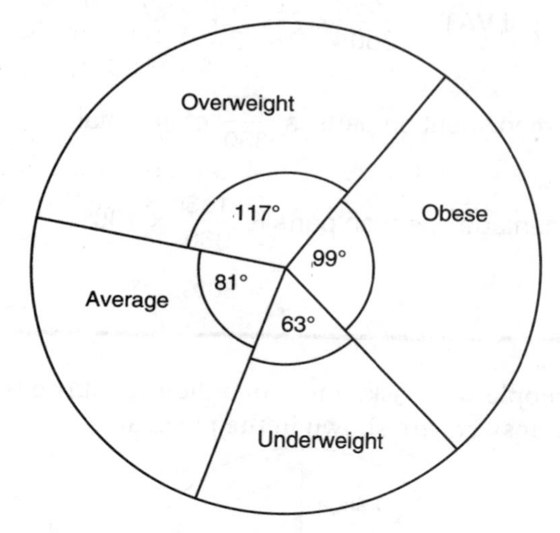

1080 adults were weighed and placed into one of four categories: underweight, average, overweight, obese (i.e. grossly overweight). The pie chart shows the proportion of adults falling into each category.

(a) What fraction of the group were
(i) overweight (ii) obese (iii) above average?

(b) How many of these adults were
(i) underweight (ii) either above average weight or below average weight?

(c) What percentage of the group were
(i) obese (ii) not above average weight?

Constructing a pie chart

EXERCISE 23h

QUESTION

The profits from five shops in a chain are shown in the table.

Location of shop	Menton	Northsea	Wayland	Perlo	Benham
Profit (£000)	85	30	120	130	30

Construct a pie diagram to illustrate this data.

ANSWER

The total sales, in thousands of pounds, is
$85 + 30 + 120 + 130 + 35 = 400$.
The total angle of 360° at the centre of the pie chart must be divided according to the proportion of the profits for each shop.
The angle representing the profit at Menton is given by
$\frac{85}{400} \times 360° = 77°$ (to the nearest whole number)

The value for the other shops are given in the table.

Location of shop	Angle at centre
Northsea	$\frac{30}{400} \times 360° = 27°$
Wayland	$\frac{120}{400} \times 360° = 108°$
Perlo	$\frac{130}{400} \times 360° = 117°$
Benham	$\frac{35}{400} \times 360° = 31°$ (rounded down so that the total is 360°)

The resulting pie chart is given below.

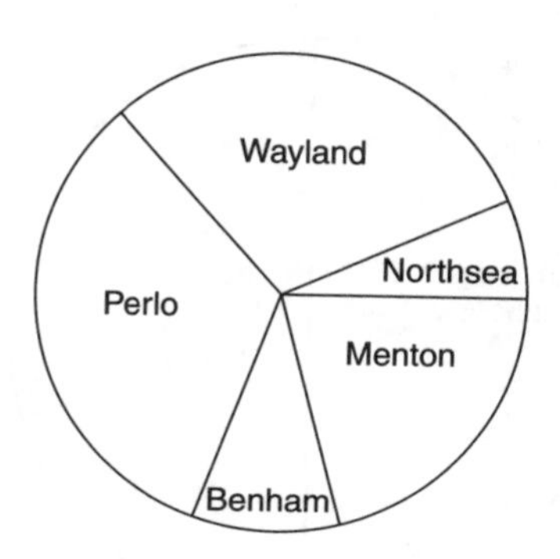

1 120 people were asked which fuel they used at home for heating. The results were: gas 48, electric 24, coal 28, oil 20.

(a) (i) What fraction of the people asked used electricity to heat their homes?
(ii) In a pie chart what size should the angle for electricity be at the centre for this slice?

(b) Construct a pie chart to illustrate this data.

2 Each £1 received from sales at Hyton Plastics is divided as follows: raw materials 28p, wages 33p, plant and machinery 8p, advertising 9p, the remainder being profit.
(a) How much in each £ is profit? (b) Construct a pie chart to illustrate this information.

3 The populations, in millions, of India, China and the USA in 1991 are given as: India 844, China 1116 and the USA 253.

(a) Draw a pie chart to illustrate this data.

(b) During the decade to the year 2001 it is anticipated that the population of India will grow by 170 m, the population of China will grow by 100 m and the population of the USA will grow by 20 m. Draw a pie chart to illustrate the populations of the three countries in the year 2001.

4 The table shows the known oil reserves in 1993.

Region	Number of barrels (thousand million)
America (North and South)	160
Middle East	660
Former Soviet Union	60
Africa	60
Asia (except Former Soviet Union) and Australasia	50
Europe (except Former Soviet Union)	10

Construct a pie chart to illustrate this data.

Scatter diagrams

Often we suspect that two quantities may be related. For example, we may think that a person's weight is related to that person's height. To test whether or not these thoughts are true we record the two values for a group of people and plot them on a graph called a scatter diagram. If the two quantities are related they will lie roughly on a straight line. When the points are very close to a straight line we say that the quantities are strongly correlated. Sometimes they are so widely scattered that there is no correlation whatsoever. For example, this graph shows the heights and weights of a group of secondary school girls.

We can see that the taller girls tend to be heavier than the shorter girls but the relationship is not strong enough to say that there is a high correlation between the two.

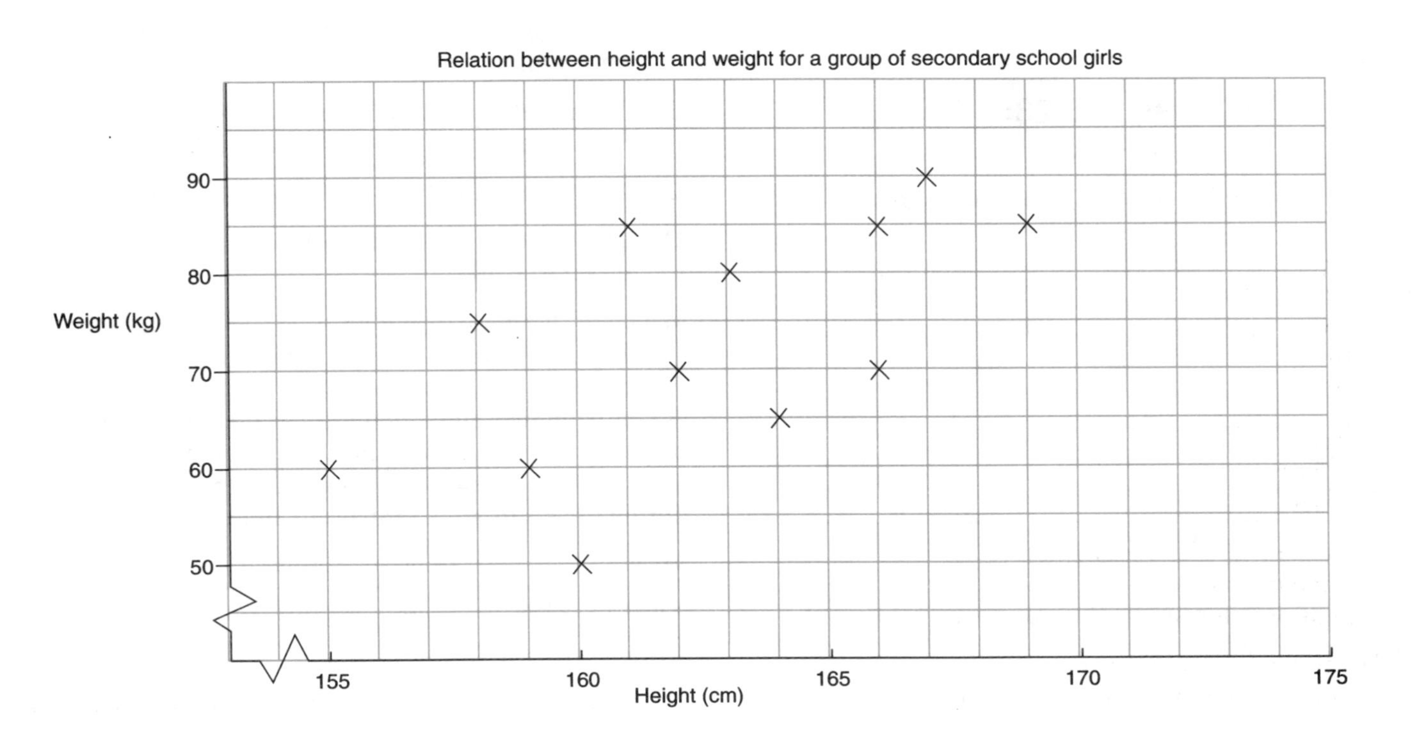

Correlation

In the example given above, the two quantities tend to increase together, i.e. the taller a person is the heavier that person is likely to be. This is an example of *positive* correlation. As another example, the area of a circular rug correlates positively and exactly with its radius.

On the other hand, for a particular model of car, the value tends to decrease as the age of the car increases.

This is an example of *negative* correlation. Another example of negative correlation is the number of people attending an open-air fête and the number of millimetres of rain falling on the day of the fête.

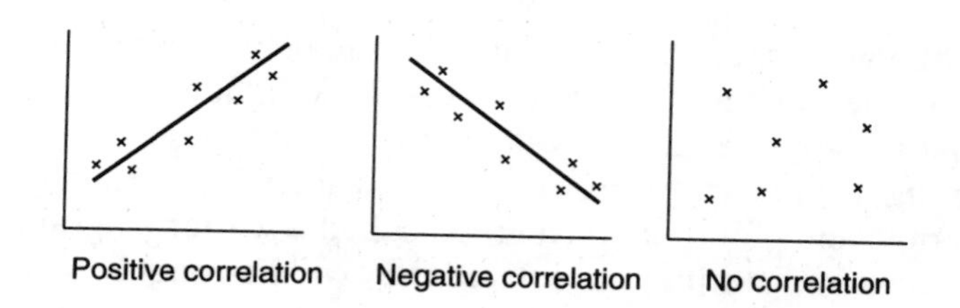

Positive correlation   Negative correlation   No correlation

The less scatter there is, the more highly correlated are two quantities:

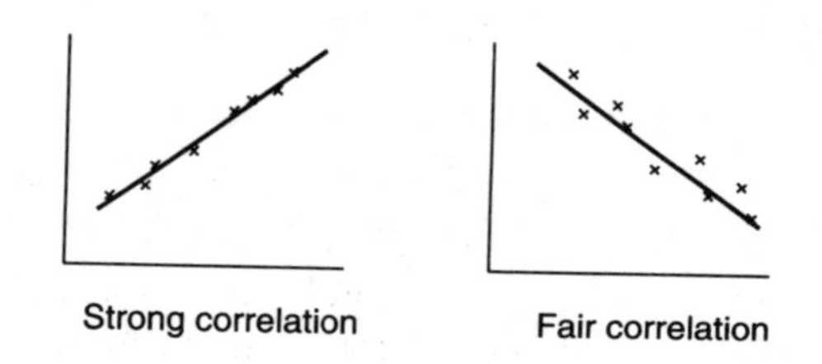

Strong correlation   Fair correlation

EXERCISE 23i

1

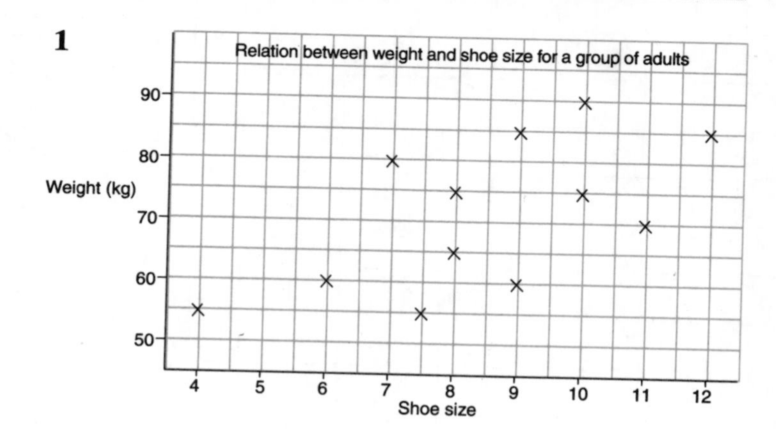

This scatter diagram shows the weights and shoe sizes of a group of adults.

(a) How many adults are there in a group?

(b) How heavy is
(i) the heaviest adult (ii) the lightest adult?

(c) Does the scatter diagram suggest that there is a correlation between a person's weight and their shoe size?

2 A teacher wanted to see if there was a correlation between the mark a pupil got in the mock exam in maths and the mark that pupil got in the final exam. She recorded the marks of 12 pupils and these are given in the table.

Mock mark	72	84	85	41	46	57
Final exam mark	84	73	77	53	62	54
Mock mark	44	43	56	80	52	38
Final exam mark	55	56	48	66	72	50

(a) Draw a scatter diagram to show this data on a graph. Use 1 cm to represent 5 marks on both axes. Mark each axis from 35 to 90.

(b) Does your scatter diagram support the belief that results in the mock exam gave a good idea of the mark a pupil was likely to get in the final exam?

(c) Esther got 66 in the mock exam but failed to take the final exam. Use the scatter diagram to estimate what she might have scored in the final exam.

Self-assessment test 23

1 Listed below are several different types of data:

A The weights of the potatoes I harvested this year on my allotment.

B The number of cards Kim received last Christmas.

C The shoe sizes of the students in my group.

D The distances that the workforce at a factory travel to work.

Which of these are examples of
(a) discrete data (b) continuous data?

2 A company that manufactures washing machines produces three models – the Mondial, the Diamond and the Giro. The table shows the sales of each model during the six months January to June.

Model	Mondial	Diamond	Giro
Number of sales	12	22	7

Represent this information on
(a) a bar chart (b) a pie chart.

3 The table shows the weights, in kilograms, of the bags of carrots loaded on a lorry. Each bag is supposed to contain at least 20 kg.

Weight (w kg)	Frequency
$19 \leqslant w < 19.5$	12
$19.5 \leqslant w < 20$	13
$20 \leqslant w < 20.5$	120
$20.5 \leqslant w < 21$	55

(a) How many bags are there on the lorry?

(b) What fraction of the bags are underweight?

(c) Illustrate this data on a bar chart.

4

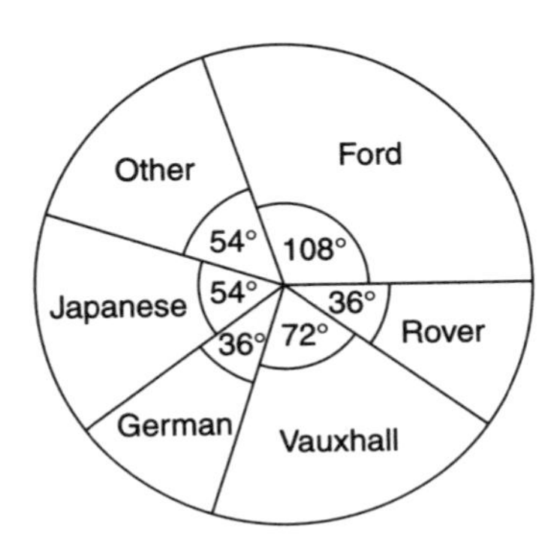

The cars that pass through Midland Car Auctions are placed in one of six categories for record purposes. The pie chart shows the number of cars in each category for sales that took place in 1985.

(a) What fraction of the cars sold were
(i) Fords (ii) Japanese (iii) German?

(b) If 340 German cars went through these auction rooms how many of the cars auctioned were
(i) Vauxhalls (ii) Japanese?

(c) By 1995 the total number of cars passing through the auction rooms had increased to 4420 and the percentage in each category had changed to: Rover 15%, Ford 25%, Vauxhall 20%, German 12% and Japanese 20%. What percentage were there in the 'other' category? Draw a pie chart to represent this data.

(d) Comparing 1995 with 1985, which category had
(i) held its market share steady
(ii) increased its market share?

(e) in which category had the number of cars sold increased even though the market share had decreased?

5 The number of people sitting in the lounge of a residential home was counted at hourly intervals one Sunday and the results recorded on a line graph. A copy of this graph is given below.

(a) How many people were sitting in the lounge at
(i) 10 a.m. (ii) 11 p.m.?

(b) Can you say how many there were at
(i) 11.30 a.m. (ii) 3.35 p.m.?

(c) Can you explain the pattern?

(d) Would you expect to find a similar pattern
(i) in this lounge on the following day
(ii) for a lounge in an hotel that has a similar number of beds to the residential home?

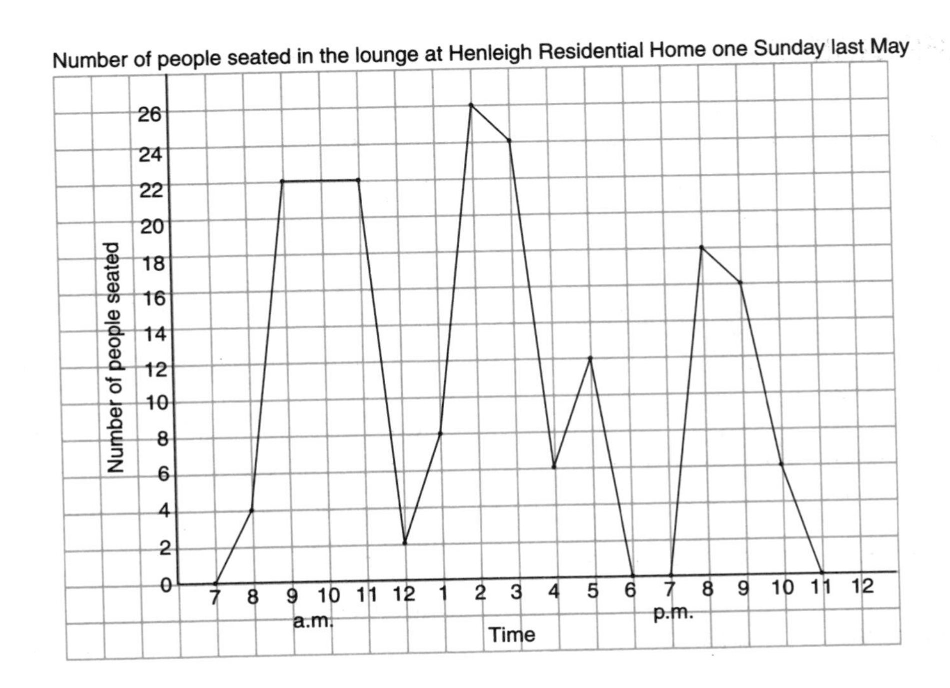

CHAPTER 24
Averages

It is often useful to compare data. For example, the marks that two students get in a series of tests, or the wages in one factory compared with another, or the number of miles I can expect to travel on 1 gallon of petrol if I use one car compared with the number of miles I can expect to travel if I use another car. One of the simplest ways to compare two sets of numbers is to compare their averages. The most commonly used average is the mean, closely followed by the median and the mode. Each of these three different ways of representing a set of numbers by a single number is now considered in detail.

Mean

The **mean** of a set of numbers is found by adding all the numbers together and dividing by the number of numbers.

For example the mean of 6, 6, 2 and 10 is

$$\frac{6+6+2+10}{4} = \frac{24}{4} = 6$$

and the mean of 3.2, 1.7, 10.3, 15.2 and 7.25 is

$$\frac{3.2+1.7+10.3+15.2+7.25}{5}$$

$$= \frac{37.65}{5}$$

$$= 7.53$$

EXERCISE 24a

QUESTION

Find the mean of the numbers 16, 28, 0, 22, 13, 25, 22 and 20.

ANSWER

$$\text{Mean} = \frac{16+28+0+22+13+25+22+20}{8}$$

$$= \frac{146}{8}$$

$$= 18.25$$

Find the mean of the following sets of numbers.

1 5, 8, 8, 8, 7, 9, 11

2 13, 18, 30, 24, 35, 25, 17, 30

3 1.9, 1.6, 2.7, 2.8, 1.8, 1.9, 2.7

4 8.2, 7.5, 10.1, 11.2, 12, 10.1, 9.5

5 70, 75, 83, 86, 74, 70, 85, 70, 71

6 12, 83, 31, 92, 12, 62, 15, 27, 44

Find the mean for the following sets of numbers, giving your answers correct to 2 decimal places.

7 5.2, 2.9, 6.5, 18.3

8 3.82, 2.97, 4.15, 3.52, 8.05

9 0.45, 1.08, 0.93, 4.26, 0.76, 2.28

10 14.8, 7.7, 13.9, 21.3, 1.5, 4.6, 9.1

Mode and median

The **mode** of a set of numbers is the number that occurs most often.

For example, the mode of 3, 7, 8, 8, 12, 12, 12, 14, 14, 21 is 12, since 12 occurs three times and the most any other number occurs is twice.

A set of numbers can have more than one mode. For example, the set of numbers 1, 1, 2, 2, 2, 3, 4, 5, 5, 6, 6, 6, 7, 9 has two modes, namely 2 and 6.

The **median** of a set of numbers is the middle number when the numbers have been arranged in order of size.

For example, the median of 1, 9, 14, 20, 29, 48 and 57 is 20.
There are seven numbers. The middle number of seven is four, and the fourth number is 20.

To find the median the numbers are usually placed in increasing order, but they do not have to be. If they are placed in decreasing order the median is still in the middle number.
For example, the median of 25, 20, 19, 18 and 5 is 19.

If there is no middle number the median is the average of the two middle numbers.
For example, the median of 5, 9, 12 and 16 is

$$\frac{9+12}{2} = \frac{21}{2} = 10.5$$

EXERCISE 24b

QUESTION
Find (a) the mode (b) the median, of the numbers 45, 39, 28, 35, 36, 42, 35, 57, 35, 45.

ANSWER
(a) The number that occurs most often is 35 (it occurs 3 times).
The mode is therefore 35.

(b) Putting these numbers in order, 28, 35, 35, 35, 36, 39, 42, 45, 45, 57, there are ten numbers, so the median is found by finding the average of the fifth and sixth numbers.

i.e. median = $\frac{36 + 39}{2} = \frac{75}{2} = 37.5$

Find (a) the mode (b) the median, of the following sets of numbers:

1 28, 24, 19, 24, 22, 35, 30

2 51, 55, 53, 66, 54, 50, 65, 50, 51

3 23, 23, 23, 23, 24, 24, 24, 25, 26

4 2, 3, 3, 3, 3, 4, 4, 4, 5, 5, 5, 5, 5, 6, 6

5 32, 43, 23, 32, 43, 32, 45, 23, 45, 43, 24, 43

6 15, 14, 12, 14, 15, 18, 18, 14, 12, 15, 9

7 2.1, 2.6, 2.3, 2.2, 2.1, 2.4, 2.6, 2.1, 2.3, 2.6, 2.2, 2.6, 2.2

Range

The **range** of a set of data is the difference between the highest value and the lowest value.

For example, the range of the numbers 5, 3, 8, 40, 48, 32, 31, 17 and 28 is 48 − 3, i.e. 45.

Similarly if, over a period of ten years the largest profit a company makes is £546 000 and the smallest profit it makes is £65 000 the range is £546 000 − £65 000 i.e. £481 000.

EXERCISE 24c

QUESTION
The heights, in centimetres, of the girls in a hockey squad are
168, 165, 164, 168, 169, 175, 186, 154, 152, 178, 183, 166, 141, 168

Find the range.

ANSWER
The height of the shortest girl is 141 cm and the height of the tallest girl 186 cm.
Range = 186 cm − 141 cm = 45 cm.

Find the range of the following sets of numbers:

1 34, 45, 23, 14, 56, 23, 45, 36, 53

2 45, 56, 45, 44, 43, 47, 48, 49, 54

3 2.3, 5.4, 6.4, 3.7, 5.3, 2.5, 4.4, 3.9

4 4, 0, 3, 5, 3, 4, 2, 5, 6, 4, 3, 5, 6, 3, 4

5 82, 45, 87, 34, 56, 87, 97, 56, 43, 56, 66

Problems involving the mean, mode, median and range

EXERCISE 24d

QUESTION

The girls at one table in a factory canteen are asked to turn out their purses and count the number of coins in them. The results are

14, 10, 10, 18, 26, 0, 5 and 11

For this data find (a) the mean (b) the mode (c) the median (d) the range.

ANSWER

(a) Mean $= \dfrac{14+10+10+18+26+0+5+11}{8}$

$= \dfrac{94}{8}$

$= 11.75$

(b) The only number that occurs more than once is 10. The mode is therefore 10.

(c) First arrange the numbers in order. We will choose ascending order:

0, 5, 10, 10, 11, 14, 18, 26

There are 8 numbers, so there is no middle number. The two middle numbers of eight numbers are the fourth and the fifth.
The median is therefore the average of 10 and 11, i.e. 10.5.

(d) The range of this data is 26 − 0, i.e. 24.

(*Note:* In this question the mean, mode and median are all different.)

---

1 Find the mean, mode, median and range, of seven successive rounds of golf for a golfer whose scores were: 71, 84, 70, 70, 85, 70, 75.

2 Dave watches his fellow workmates arriving by car one morning as they enter the car park. He counts the number of occupants in each car and obtains the following list:
1, 2, 2, 2, 1, 1, 4, 3, 2, 1, 2, 1, 1, 5, 2, 1, 2, 3, 1, 1

(a) How many cars are there in the survey?

(b) How many workmates does he count altogether?

(c) What is the mean number of occupants per car?

(d) What is the modal number of occupants per car?

(e) What is the median number of occupants per car?

(f) Find the range.

3 The heights (to the nearest centimetre) of a group of boys are
160, 164, 162, 158, 160, 156, 165, 155, 157, 163
What is (a) the mean height (b) the median height (c) the modal height (d) the range?

4 The hourly rates of pay for a group of workers are
£4.10, £4.65, £3.85, £4.05, £4.10,
£4.43, £4.16, £4.10, £4.10, £4.16
Find (a) the mean hourly rate (b) the median hourly rate (c) the modal hourly rate.

5 The recorded daily rainfall, in millimetres, falling on Birmingham during a particular week was
34, 18, 0, 0, 21, 22, 24
Find (a) the mean daily rainfall for the week (b) the median rainfall for the week.

6 Over the space of one year the days off sick taken by the staff in a shop were
4, 23, 0, 1, 0, 10, 0, 3, 18, 35

(a) (i) How many staff are employed at the shop?
(ii) Find the total number of days lost.

(b) Find (i) the mean (ii) the modal (iii) the median, number of days off sick taken by the staff of this shop.

7 Some of the patients who attend a doctor's surgery one morning have their diastolic blood pressure taken. The diastolic blood pressures recorded are
82, 88, 69, 76, 84, 90, 75, 62, 80, 84, 93, 79 and 88

(a) How many patients have their blood pressure taken?

(b) Find, correct to the nearest whole number, the mean diastolic blood pressure for the group.

(c) What is the modal diastolic blood pressure?

(d) What percentage of the group have a diastolic blood pressure greater than 80?

(e) Find the median diastolic blood pressure.

(f) Find the range.

Harder problems

EXERCISE 24e

QUESTION
The mean weight of the 15 players in a rugby team, i.e. the forwards and the backs, is 84 kg. If the mean weight of the 8 forwards is 91 kg, find

(a) the total weight of the 15 players

(b) the total weight of the forwards

(c) the total weight of the backs

(d) the mean weight of the backs.

ANSWER
(a) Total weight of the 15 players is 84×15 kg = 1260 kg.

(b) Total weight of the 8 forwards is 91×8 kg = 728 kg.

(c) If there are 15 players, 8 of whom are forwards, there are 7 backs.
Total weight of the 7 backs is 1260 kg − 728 kg
= 532 kg.

(d) Mean weight of the 7 backs is $\frac{532}{7}$ kg = 76 kg.

---

1 The mean weight of the 13 players in a Rugby League side is 84 kg. If the mean weight of the 6 forwards is 91 kg, find

(a) the total weight of the 13 players

(b) the total weight of the forwards

(c) the total weight of the backs

(d) the mean weight of the backs.

2 Ray drives from Lenstow to Saston and on to Wormley. He drives the 80 km from Lenstow to Saston at an average speed of 40 km/h, and takes 3 hours, at an average speed of 50 km/h, to drive from Saston to Wormley.

(a) How long does he take to drive from Lenstow to Saston?

(b) How far is it from Saston to Wormley?

(c) How far is it from Lenstow to Wormley?

(d) How long does Ray take to drive from Lenstow to Wormley?

(e) What is his average speed for the whole journey?

(Distance travelled = average speed × time.)

3 In a game of darts, three throws make one turn. On 12 turns Sid has a mean score of 22. How many does he need to score on his next turn to raise his mean score to 26?

4 Over a four week period the mean number of rejects per day from an automatic lathe is 12. This is unsatisfactory, so the lathe is serviced ahead of schedule. As a result, during the next seven weeks, the mean number of daily rejects is reduced to 2.5.

(a) Find the total number of rejects during (i) the first four week period (ii) the next seven week period (iii) the full period of the study. (Assume that the lathe runs for 6 days each week.)

(b) What is the mean number of daily rejects for the period of the study?

(c) Estimate the number of potential rejects that have been 'saved' as a result of the service.

5 Every day at Brace Electronics, a sample of 1000 components is selected at random from the thousands produced by machine A on a production line. These are tested and it is found that the mean number of defective components is 5 and the range of defects 10. Similar figures for machine B give a mean of 3 and a range of 7.

(a) Which machine appears to be the more reliable?

(b) Is it possible that when the tests are run tomorrow there will be more defective items from machine B than machine A?

Weighted averages

A professional golfer's scores for the first five competitions he played in during the early part of last season are given in the table.

Score	68	69	70	71	72
Number of times the score is recorded	2	2	5	7	4

This table shows that the golfer scored 68 on 2 occasions, 69 on 2 occasions, and so on. To find his mean score we must find the total of all his scores and divide this total by the number of rounds he played.
Total number of rounds = 2 + 2 + 5 + 7 + 4 = 20.
Total score for the 20 rounds is

$$68 \times 2 + 69 \times 2 + 70 \times 5 + 71 \times 7 + 72 \times 4$$
$$= 136 + 138 + 350 + 497 + 288$$
$$= 1409$$

$$\text{Mean score} = \frac{\text{total score}}{\text{number of rounds}}$$
$$= \frac{1409}{20}$$
$$= 70.45$$

EXERCISE 24f

QUESTION

A group of students sat a maths test. Their results are given in the table.

Mark	0	1	2	3	4	5	6	7	8	9	10
Number of pupils	0	0	3	1	1	8	8	7	2	2	2

Find, for this group
(a) the mean mark (b) the median mark.

ANSWER

(a) The total number of students is
$3 + 1 + 1 + 8 + 8 + 7 + 2 + 2 + 2 = 34.$
Total marks scored by all the students is
$2 \times 3 + 3 \times 1 + 4 \times 1 + 5 \times 8 + 6 \times 8 + 7 \times 7 + 8 \times 2 + 9 \times 2 + 10 \times 2$
$= 6 + 3 + 4 + 40 + 48 + 49 + 16 + 18 + 20$
$= 204$

$$\text{Mean mark} = \frac{\text{total marks}}{\text{number of students}} = \frac{204}{34} = 6$$

(b) The middle mark of 34 marks is the average of the 17th and 18th marks.
Up to and including a score of 5 the total number of students $= 3 + 1 + 1 + 8$, i.e. 13.
Up to and including a score of 6 the total number of students $= 3 + 1 + 1 + 8 + 8$, i.e. 21.
The 18th and 19th marks are both 6.
The median mark is therefore 6.

Give any answers that are not exact correct to 2 decimal places.

1 The record of goals scored by Manston Athletic in the Attica League last season is shown in the table.

Number of goals	0	1	2	3	4	5	6	7
Number of matches	6	7	8	4	2	0	2	1

(a) How many matches did Manston Athletic play in the league last season?

(b) How many goals did they score altogether?

(c) What was the mean number of goals per match? (Give your answer correct to 2 d.p.)

2 The number of days lost last week by the workforce at a small factory is shown in the table.

Number of days lost	0	1	2	3	4	5
Number of employees	34	4	2	0	0	2

(a) How many people are employed at the factory?

(b) How many days work were lost in the week?

(c) What was the mean number of days lost per employee?

(d) What was the median number of days lost per employee?

3 During 1994 the number of recorded births each month in Besterham were:

Number of births	5	6	7	8	9	12
Number of months	5	0	3	2	1	1

(a) What should the numbers in the bottom line add to? Do they?

(b) Find, for Besterham, the mean, median and modal numbers of births per month in 1994.

In your own work you may well have to decide which of the averages – mean, mode or median – to use. To help you to make this decision some of the advantages and disadvantages of each average are listed below.

Type of average	Advantages	Disadvantages
Mean	The best-known average. Uses all the data and can be found exactly. Used a great deal in further work.	Can give impossible values for discrete data, e.g. a shoe size of 5.13, and is affected too much by extreme values.
Median	Not affected by extreme values. Can be an actual value from the given data.	May not be a good representative of the given data when the number of items is small.
Mode	Usually quick and easy to find. Unaffected by extreme values.	There may be no mode or even more than one.

Multiple-choice questions 24

In questions 1 to 4 several alternative answers are given. Write down the letter that corresponds to the correct answer.

1 A shoe manufacturer exporting to Malaysia needs to know the size of the 'average' person's feet. The most useful single average is

A the mean **B** the mode
C the median **D** none of these

2 For the numbers 21, 24, 32, 24, 22, 23, 31, 32, 26 the mode is

A 24 **B** 32 **C** 28 **D** 24 and 32

3 The median of the numbers 42, 40, 41, 42, 43, 43, 44, 42, 40, 42 is

A 42 **B** 41.5 **C** 42.5 **D** 41.9

4 In a rugby team the mean weight of the 8 forwards is 87.20 kg and the mean weight of the 7 backs is 74.30 kg. It follows that the mean weight of the 15 players in the team is

A 82.35 kg **B** 81.05 kg **C** 80.34 kg **D** 81.18 kg

5 The weights, correct to the nearest kilogram, of 8 girls are 56 kg, 48 kg, 58 kg, 54 kg, 53 kg, 61 kg, 58 kg and 55 kg. Which of the following statements are true and which are false?

A The mean weight is larger than the modal weight.

B The median weight is larger than the mean weight.

C The range is 13 kg.

D The modal weight and the mean weight are the same.

Self-assessment test 24

1 The numbers of pupils on the school bus from Kingston on 8 consecutive days were:
24, 25, 24, 26, 25, 26, 24 and 26.
What was the mean number of pupils travelling to school on the bus from Kingston?

2 Find (a) the mode (b) the median of the numbers 16, 18, 15, 14, 15, 16, 18, 19, 15, 21, 14.

3 Find (a) the range (b) the mean, of the numbers 9.5, 8.2, 7.7, 9.3, 8.8, 6.4, 7.5.

4 At Carlton Heights Residential Home they keep a record of the number of times each resident is taken out by friends or relatives for the day. Last quarter the recorded numbers of times were: 20, 8, 3, 5, 0, 12, 0, 5, 3, 6, 3, 0, 18, 0, 2, 0, 6, 0, 3, 5, 14, 10, 5, 2, 0, 3, 0, 4, 5, 1, 11.

(a) How many residents lived in the home?

(b) Find the mean, mode, median and range of the number of day trips taken.

5 A gardener planted 6 seeds in each pot and after 4 weeks counted the number of seedlings in each pot. The results are given in the table:

Number of seedlings	0	1	2	3	4	5	6
Number of pots	0	1	5	13	14	13	4

(a) How many pots did he plant seeds in?

(b) How many seeds germinated?

(c) Find the mean number of seedlings per pot.

(d) Find the median number of seedlings per pot.

INVESTIGATIONS, PUZZLES AND PROBLEMS

1 A farmer is going to erect 66 ft of fencing. He puts a post every 6 ft. How many posts does he need?

2

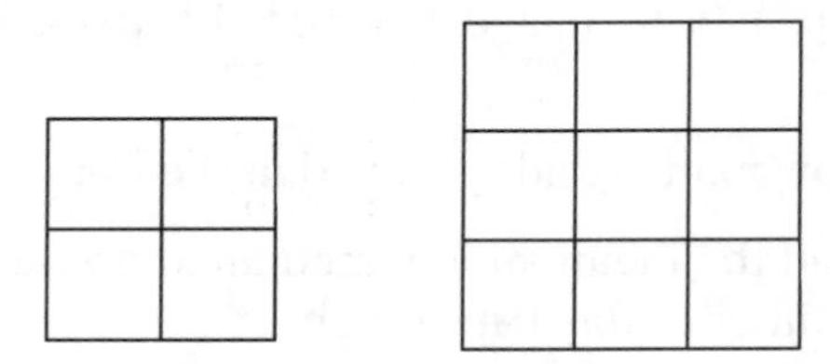

There are 5 squares in the first diagram – 4 small squares and 1 large one. How many squares can you find in the second diagram?

3 Put +, −, ×, or ÷ in each space so that the calculations are correct.

(a) 3 □ 4 □6 = 18 (b) 10 □ 3 □ 2 □ 5 = 9
(c) 12 □ 2 □ 3 □ 5 = 4 (d) 5 □ 4 □ 3 □ 2 = 14

4

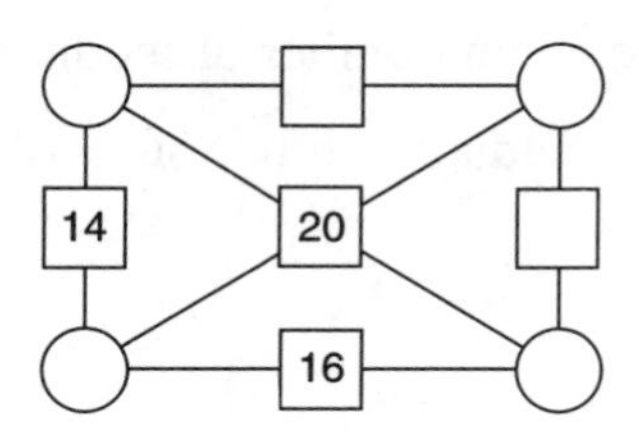

Complete the diagram so that the number in each square is the sum of the two numbers in the adjacent circles.

5 An electricity worker has to check the bulbs in all the lamp standards along a road. The lamp standards are numbered consecutively from 181 to 284. How many lamp standards are there?

6 A farmer has 90 m of fencing and wishes to enclose a rectangular plot of ground with an area of 500 m^2. What are the measurements of the rectangle?

7 The sketch shows the layout of the runways at an airport. Two runways cross at right angles. How many rectangles can you find in the layout?

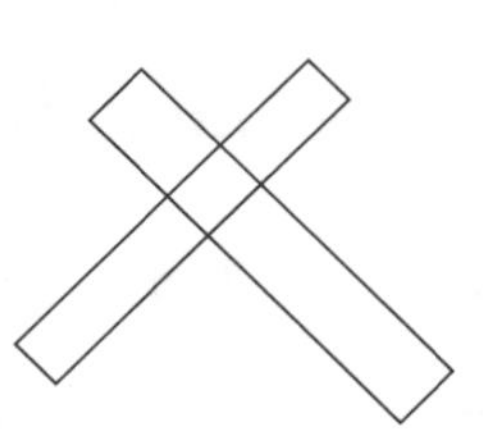

8 A coin dealer is offered 27 gold coins. He is told that 26 of them are of equal weight but one is slightly lighter than the others because it is counterfeit. He has a balance scales so that he can weigh some on one side against some on the other side. He cannot find the exact weight of any one coin. By using the scales three times, how can he tell which coin is counterfeit?

9 Over the first 50 miles of a journey a motorist averages 25 m.p.h. Is it possible for the motorist to increase her speed over the next 50 miles so that her average speed for the whole journey of 100 miles is raised to 50 m.p.h..? If your answer is 'yes', what speed is necessary for the second 50 miles? If your answer is 'no', justify it.

10

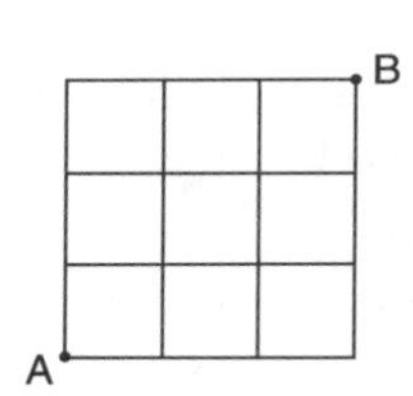

The sketch shows the layout of 8 intersecting streets. How many different routes can Meg take to go from A to B if she is always walking away from A and towards B?

11 How many pieces of card shaped like this do you need to arrange to make a square?

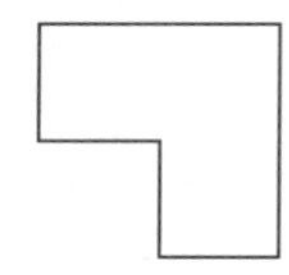

12 Three squares are marked with the numbers 1, 2 and 3. They can be arranged in two rows so that the difference between the numbers in the top row equals the number in the bottom row, for example

3	2		or		3	1
	1				2	

When 6 squares are marked from 1 to 6 there are several ways of arranging them in three rows so that similar rules apply, that is so that each number placed below the gap between two numbers is the difference between those two numbers. For example,

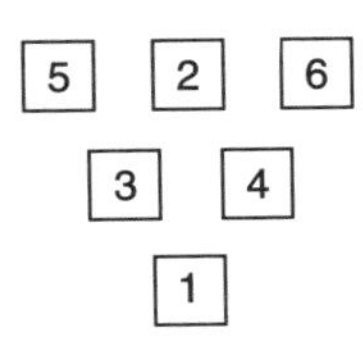

Can you find other ways of doing this?

13

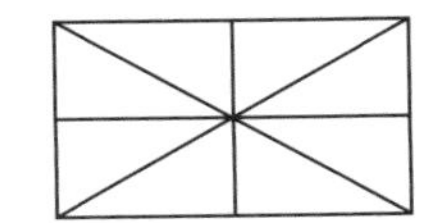

How many different triangles can you find in each of these figures?

14 A secondhand car dealer buys a car for £1400, sells it for £1800, buys it back a short time later for £2200 and finally sells it for £2600. How much profit (loss) does he make?

15 Sid's calculator has developed a fault. When he presses **+** the calculator multiplies and when he presses **×** the calculator adds. He presses **1** **8** **×** **2** **3**. What answer does he get? What answer should he get?

He can press the buttons **1** **8** **2** **3** **×** **+** in any order but each button can be pressed once and only once. What is the largest answer he can get in the display?

16 The improper fraction $\frac{14\,865}{2973}$ simplifies to 5. To write the fraction, each digit from 1 to 9 has been used once and only once. Can you use each of the digits from 1 to 9 once each to write a fraction that simplifies to give 3?

17 In how many different ways can 4 stamps be bought from the Post Office if they are all taken from the same sheet and remain attached? One possible way is shown here:

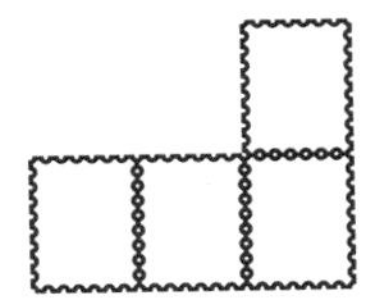

Solve the same problem if you buy 5 stamps.

18 A coachload of pensioners went on an outing. One of the pensioners bought a cup of tea for everybody. The total bill came to £28.09. How many pensioners were there?

19 Dawn has made some cakes and wants to put them in plastic bags to place them in the freezer. If she puts 12 cakes in each bag she has 2 bags left over, but if she puts 8 cakes in each bag there are 4 cakes left over with no bag to put them in. How many cakes does she have? How many bags does she have?

20 Find the value of 13×13 and the value of 31×31. What do you notice when you compare your answers? Can you find other numbers that gives similar results?

21

$$\begin{matrix} \cdot & \cdot & \cdot \\ \cdot & \cdot & \cdot \\ \cdot & \cdot & \cdot \end{matrix}$$

How many different straight lines can be drawn on this grid by joining two dots? If the length of each line is measured how many different answers can you get?

22

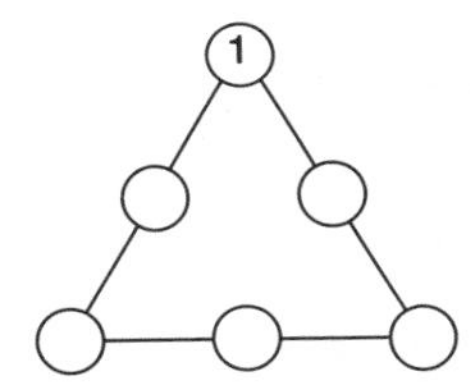

Using the first six whole numbers, complete the diagram so that the sum of the three numbers on each side of the triangle is nine. Each number can be used once and only once.

23

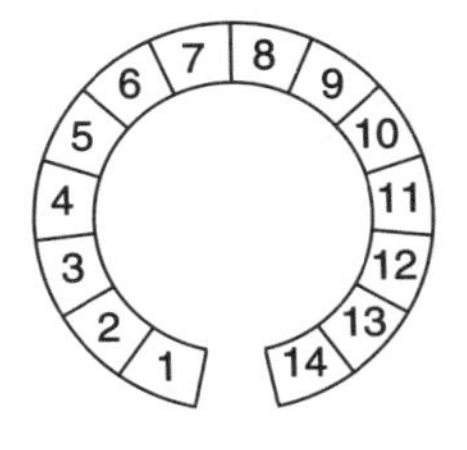

The sketch shows 14 sheep pens with gates that open into a ring that is used when the animals are sold by auction. The 14 pens are filled with sheep and all the gates locked. An hour before the auction, one of the auctioneer's employees enters the ring and, moving clockwise around the edge of the ring, unlocks every other pen beginning with the first. A short time later a second employee goes around in the same direction. She goes to every third pen, starting with the first. If the pen is locked she unlocks it, if it is unlocked she locks it. When the auction is about to start which pens are locked and which are unlocked?

24

□ − □ = □
                    ×
□ ÷ □ = □
                    =
□ + □ = □

Use each of the digits 1 to 9 once and only once, so that all four of the above calculations are correct.

25 There are 15 teams in the local darts league. Each team plays every other team twice – once at home and once away. Games are played midweek and at weekends. How many games should be played altogether?

What is the shortest possible length of the season?

If another two teams join the league, how many more games will there be? By how much must the season be extended?

26

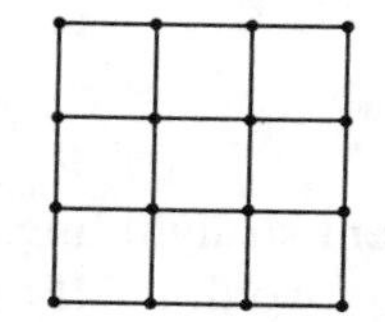

A square is drawn on a grid so that it encloses 9 smaller squares. Each grid intersection is marked by a dot. By joining dots with straight lines, show how the large square can be divided into two identical shapes. There are 13 different ways of doing this, of which 3 are given below. Can you find the other 10?

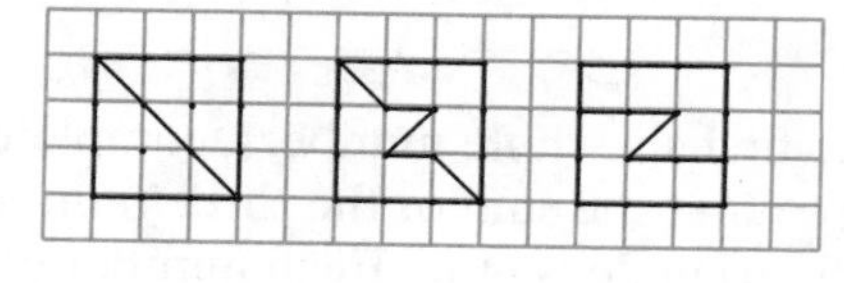

27

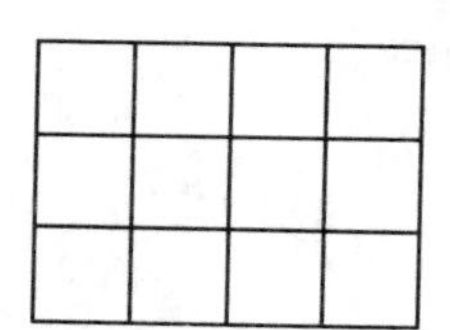

Wines and spirits are often delivered in cartons containing 12, 16, 18 or 24 bottles. The sketch shows a carton for 12 bottles. Can you arrange 8 bottles in this carton so that there are an even number of bottles in each row and in each column? (Assume that 0 is even.) If you can, try to arrange 12 bottles in a 4×4 carton so that there are an even number of bottles in every row and in every column. Is there more than one way of doing this?

28

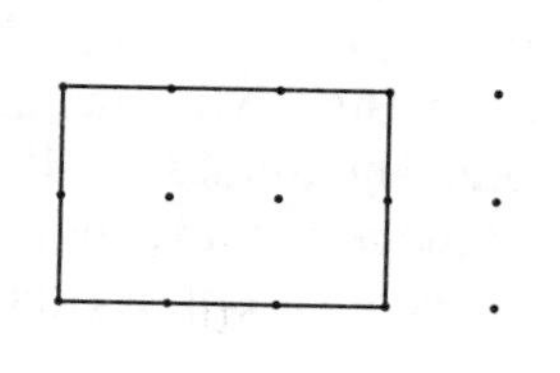

A rectangle measuring 3 cm by 2 cm is drawn on 1 cm square dotted paper. The rectangle can be divided into identical shapes by joining the dots by straight lines in different ways. Two such ways are shown below. How many more can you find?

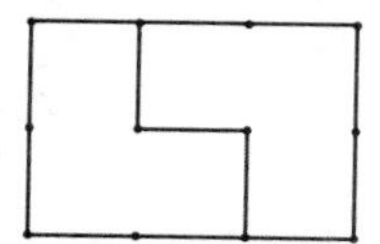

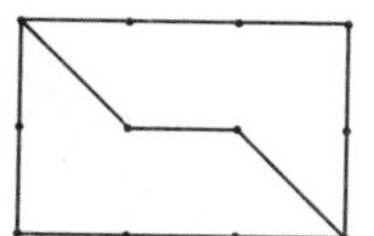

29 Most whole numbers can be written as the sum of two or more consecutive whole numbers. For example, $13 = 6 + 7$. Some numbers can be expressed in more than one way, for example

$31 = 15 + 16$ or $31 = 10 + 11 + 12$.

Can you write every number from 90 to 130 as the sum of consecutive whole numbers?

Which numbers can be expressed in more than one way? Which number can be expressed in the greatest number of ways?

30 A frog fell into a well 15 ft deep. It managed to climb up the side at the rate of 3 ft each day, but it slipped back 2 ft every night. How long did it take to get out?

31 From midnight tonight to midnight tomorrow how many times will the minute hand of a clock pass the hour hand?

32 If the town clock takes 12 seconds to strike 6, how long does it take to strike 12?

33 Norman thinks his watch is 5 minutes fast, whereas it is 7 minutes slow. Relying on his watch he arrives at the bus stop 3 minutes before the bus is due. The bus arrives on time. Will Norman be waiting to get on?

34 By dividing only along the grid lines show how you can divide this Swiss cross into four identical pieces.

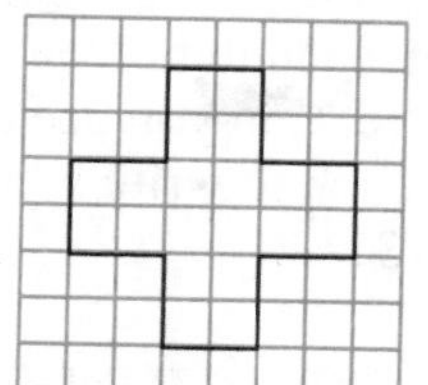

35 Using the signs +, −, × and ÷, arrange four 3s as an expression that simplifies to give each of the whole numbers from 1 to 10.

For example, $3 + 3 + 3 \div 3 = 7$ and $3 \times 3 - 3 \div 3 = 8$.

36

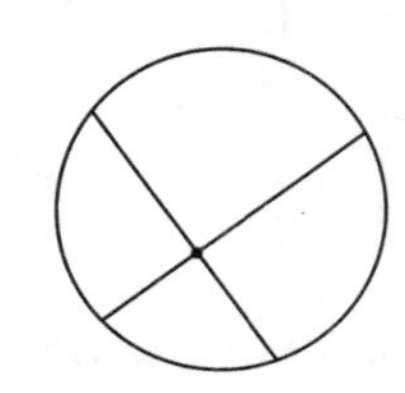

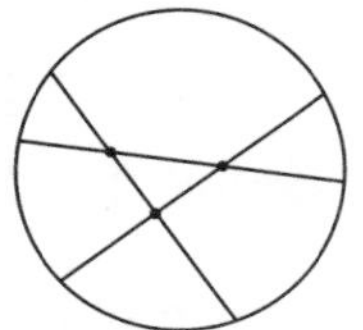

If two chords are drawn in a circle they can cross in one point. If three chords are drawn the greatest number of possible intersections is three.

What is the greatest number of intersections if four chords are drawn in a circle? (Draw a circle that has a radius of at least 5 cm. Check that each chord you draw crosses all the chords already in the circle.)

Draw a fifth chord and count the number of intersections. Copy the table and enter your results.

Number of chords	Number of intersections	Increase in number of points of intersection
1	0	
2	1	1
3	3	2
4		
5		
6		
7		
8		
9		
10		

37 In the previous investigation we counted the number of intersections as we added more chords to the diagram. In this investigation we turn our attention to the number of regions formed.

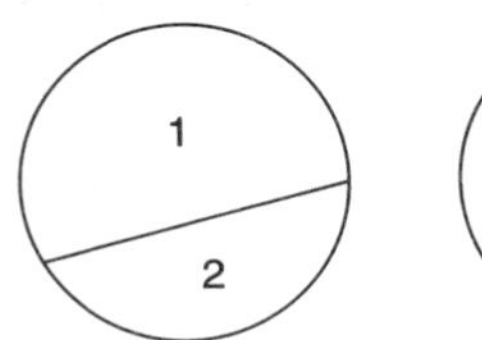

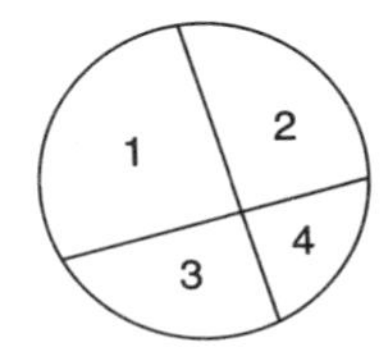

One chord in a circle divides it into 2 regions. When a second chord is drawn the number of regions is increased to 4. Draw a third chord that does not pass through the point of intersection of the first 2. How many regions are there now?

Add a fourth chord, then a fifth and a sixth. No new chord should go through the point of intersection of 2 previous chords. As each chord is added count the total number of regions. Copy the table and enter your results.

Number of chords	Number of regions	Increase in the number of regions compared with the last number
1	2	
2	4	2
3		
4		
5		
6		
7		
8		
9		
10		

Is there a pattern in the numbers in the third column? Can you use this pattern to find the greatest number of regions you can get if you draw more chords – 15 or 20 for example?

38 If 6 men can make 12 machines in 6 days, how long should it take 12 men to make 24 machines?

39 Fred has to saw an 8 ft plank of timber into four 2 feet lengths. It takes him 2 minutes to cut off 1 length. How many minutes should it take to cut the four lengths he wants?

40 A farmer has an L-shaped field similar to the one

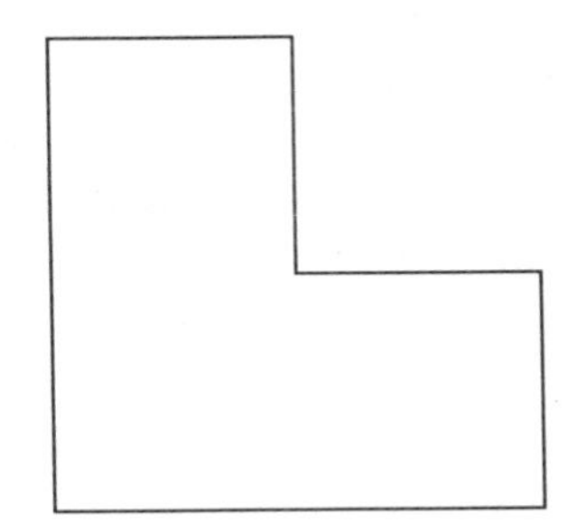

shown in the sketch. He wishes to divide the field into four identical plots such that all the edges of all the fields are straight lines. How does he do it?

41 In Mirrorland the only coins they have in circulation are 5ps and 7ps. To pay for something costing 2p they give a 7p coin and get a 5p as change. We can write this as $7 - 5 = 2$. To pay for something costing 6p they offer three 7p coins and receive three 5p coins as change, that is $3 \times 7 - 3 \times 5 = 6$. How do they pay for something costing 1p or something costing 9p? Can they pay for articles costing any whole number of pence up to 10p? If your answer is 'yes', does it follow that they can make a payment of any whole number of pence up to 100p?

42 Using each of the digits from 1 to 6 once several different multiplications are possible. For example $12\,345 \times 6 = 74\,070$, $623 \times 541 = 337\,043$ and $61 \times 52 \times 43 = 136\,393$. Find the multiplication that gives the largest answer. You must include every digit once and only once. You can use the multiplication sign as many times as you wish.

43 Following a few simple rules, arrange four 4s in different ways to make all the whole numbers up to 10. The rules are: you must use all the 4s each time. You can use the signs +, −, × and ÷. You can use brackets and the square-root symbol.

For example,

$$\frac{4+4}{4+4} = \frac{8}{8} = 1 \quad \text{and} \quad 4 + 4 - 4 \div 4 = 8 - 1 = 7$$

44 A photographer is going to take some photographs. He can arrange Alyson (A) and Ben (B) on two chairs side by side in two different ways, that is either AB or BA. When Colin (C) joins them there are six different ways in which they can be arranged in a row. Two of these arrangements are ABC and ACB. Can you write down the other four ways?

When Derek (D) joins the other three things become far more complicated. There are now twenty-four possible arrangements of the four of them sitting in a row. Can you write down all of these?

Esther (E) joins them. How many different ways are there of arranging five people in a row? Can you give your answer without writing down all the possibilities? Can you see a pattern developing?

What if a sixth person joins them? How many different arrangements are possible then? What if there are any number of people?

45 Robin has a bag full of red tokens and blue tokens. He takes out two tokens, one after the other, and lays them down in a line on the table in front of him. Four different arrangements are possible, namely RR RB BR BB.

If he takes out three tokens and lays them in a row in front of him, eight different arrangements are possible. Three of those possible are RRR, RRB and RBR. Can you write down the other five ways? You should find that you can get two red and one blue (i.e. 2R + 1B) in three different ways. In how many different ways can you get one red and two blue?

Now copy and fill in this table, which shows the number of different ways of getting each particular combination:

	3R	2R + 1B	1R + 2B	3B	Total
Number	1				8

If 4 tokens are taken from the bag one after the other, 16 different arrangements are possible. For example we could have RRRB or RBBB or BBRR, i.e. 3R + 1B or 1R + 3B or 2R + 2B. Can you write down the other 12 possibilities? Collect your results together and then copy and fill in the table.

	4R	3R + 1B	2R + 2B	1R + 3B	4B	Total
Number						16

Can you see a pattern? What if 5 tokens are taken from the bag?

What happens if there are red, blue and white tokens in the bag?

46

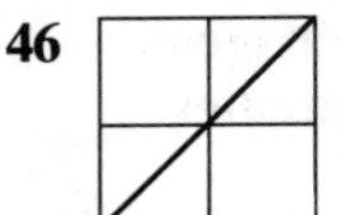

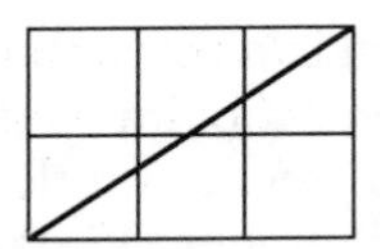

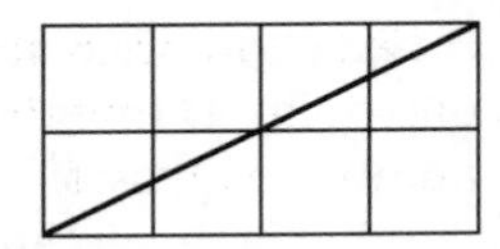

Paul draws several rectangles of different lengths but all 2 cm wide. The length of each rectangle is a whole number of centimetres. Each rectangle is divided into centimetre squares.

The diagonal of a square measuring 2 cm by 2 cm crosses 2 of these squares.

The diagonal of a rectangle measuring 2 cm by 3 cm crosses 4 of these squares.

The diagonal of a rectangle measuring 2 cm by 4 cm also crosses 4 of these squares.

Copy and complete the following table for rectangles 2 cm wide:

Length of rectangle	Number of squares a diagonal crosses
2 cm	
3 cm	
4 cm	
5 cm	
6 cm	

Can you see a pattern in the numbers in the second column? If you can, continue the pattern to decide how many squares are crossed by the diagonals of other rectangles that are 2 cm wide but have lengths greater than 6 cm.

What happens if we consider rectangles that are 3 cm wide?

47

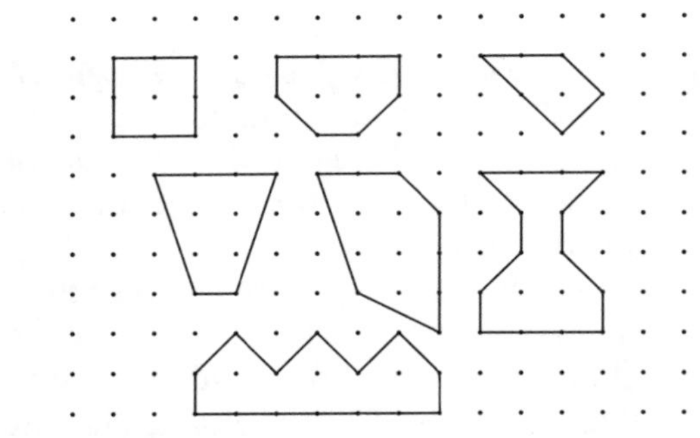

Each grid intersection is marked with a dot. Several polygons are drawn that surround one dot or more dots. Copy and complete the following table:

Polygon	Number of grid line intersections on the perimeter of the polygon (N)	Number of grid line intersections within the polygon (I)	Area of polygon by counting squares (A)
A			
B			
C			
D			
E			
F			
G			

Pick's theorem states that the area of a polygon drawn by joining the points of intersection of grid lines is given by the formula

$$A = \frac{N}{2} + I - 1$$

where N is the number of grid intersections on the boundary of the polygon, I is the number of grid lines intersections inside the polygon and A is the number of grid squares that represents the area of the polygon.

Do your results confirm that Pick's theorem is true?

Draw some polygons of your choice. Does Pick's theorem give the area of each?

48

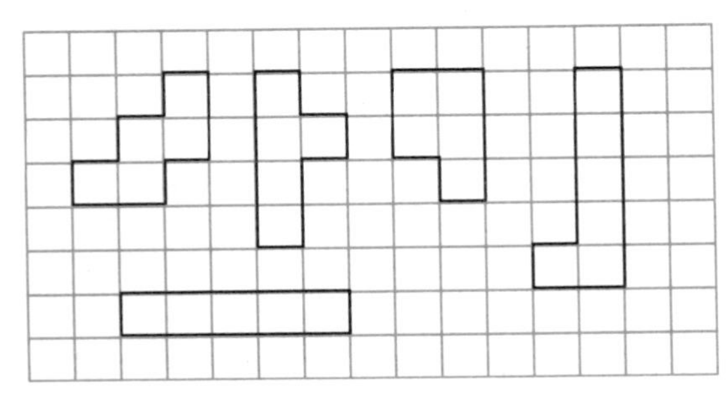

Fit these five shapes together to form a square?

49 Signposts are placed at 1-mile intervals along the road joining Aston and Barryton, which are 23 miles apart. Each signpost shows the distance to each town. The signpost that is 10 miles from Aston shows Aston 11 miles, Barryton 12 miles. This signpost uses the digit 1 three times and the digit 2 once, i.e. it uses two digits only.

How many signposts are there altogether? (Don't forget the one in Aston and the one in Barryton.)

How many signposts between the two towns use exactly two digits? (0 counts as a digit.)

How many signposts use exactly three digits?

Which digit is used most? How many times is this?

50 What digit does each letter stand for, if when *abcde* is multiplied by 4 the answer is *edcba*?

$$\begin{array}{r} abcde \\ \times \quad\quad 4 \\ \hline edcba \end{array}$$

Answers

EXERCISE 1a

1 72 **2** 308 **3** 737 **4** 5600
5 4706 **6** 16 050 **7** 200 000 **8** 850 600
9 2 500 000 **10** 5 014 060
11 eighty-seven
12 three hundred and seventy
13 five hundred and ninety-two
14 six thousand seven hundred
15 four thousand four hundred and thirty-nine
16 forty-seven thousand
17 fifty thousand seven hundred and fifty
18 six hundred and seventy-five thousand
19 four hundred and twenty thousand three hundred and fifty
20 sixty-five million
21 44 **22** 1200 **23** 527 **24** 27 317 **25** 248 554

EXERCISE 1b

1 (a) £15 000 (b) £13 000 (c) £23 000 (d) £28 000
2 £13 000 000 **3** £15 000 000 **4** £896 000 000 000
5 (a) nineteen ninety-five (b) one thousand nine hundred and ninety-five

EXERCISE 1c

1 3924 **2** 5072 **3** 4005 **4** 80 **5** 56 000
6 40 706 **7** 480 309 **8** 7 hundreds, 4 tens
9 6 tens of thousands, 3 thousands
10 3 thousands, 1 hundred thousand
11 4 hundreds of thousands, 8 thousands
12 5 hundreds of thousands, 7 tens of millions

EXERCISE 1d

1 (a) 843 (b) 476
2 (a) 442 (b) 484
3 (a) 999 (b) 435 (c) 874
4 (a) 352 (b) 794 (c) 3301
5 (a) 973 (b) 2904
6 (a) 78, 152, 289, 362 (b) 94, 172, 325, 533
(c) 627, 672, 762, 767 (d) 756, 777, 988, 1567, 2009
7 (a) 744, 532, 423, 384 (b) 1643, 974, 264, 78
(c) 576, 564, 476, 467 (d) 745, 742, 709, 707

EXERCISE 1e

1 100 **2** 275 **3** 431 **4** 680 **5** 1085
6 3084 **7** 577 **8** 2810 **9** 4496 **10** 15 242
11 799 **12** 994 **13** 2647 **14** 4083 **15** 3956
16 673 **17** 2613 **18** 9455 **19** 1721 **20** 11 274
21 16 032 **22** 16 220 **23** 22 711 **24** 17 239 **25** 4821
26 5709 **27** 12 525 **28** 27 810 **29** 48 993

EXERCISE 1f

1 15 **2** 31 **3** 22 **4** 113 **5** 218
6 538 **7** 136 **8** 3779 **9** 1114 **10** 4974
11 179 **12** 488 **13** 346 **14** 1581 **15** 1136
16 218 **17** 322 **18** 544 **19** 406 **20** 308
21 698 **22** 4818 **23** 1077 **24** 565 **25** 4570
26 976

EXERCISE 1g

1 23 **2** 2957 **3** (a) 21st (b) 65th
4 60 500 **5** (a) 68 (b) 58 **6** 2318
7 (a) 1453 (b) 1283 **8** 270

EXERCISE 1h

1 3520 **2** 7000 **3** 12 300 **4** 567 000 **5** 71 000
6 43 000 **7** 70 000 **8** 520 000 **9** 3 970 000
10 59 000 000 **11** 410 **12** 228 **13** 546
14 747 **15** 536 **16** 11 050 **17** 49 628 **18** 68 224
19 49 623 **20** 21 518 **21** 15 397 **22** 36 314 **23** 18 759
24 4158 **25** 137 602 **26** 275 058 **27** 117 576 **28** 433 755

EXERCISE 1i

1 830 **2** 362 **3** 7900 **4** 920 **5** 440
6 134 **7** 159 **8** 153 **9** 129 **10** 245
11 561 **12** 81 **13** 56 **14** 96 **15** 73
16 56 **17** 56 **18** 36 **19** 112 **20** 113, r. 11
21 26, r. 2 **22** 26, r. 13 **23** 80, r. 25 **24** 48, r. 2
25 132, r. 49 **26** 53, r. 12 **27** 62, r. 46 **28** 145, r. 23
29 134, r. 5 **30** 226, r. 30

EXERCISE 1j

1 (a) 48 (b) 288 (c) 16 128 **2** 1384 **3** 560 miles
4 £840 **5** (a) 675 000 000 (b) 1 116 000 000
6 (a) 301 000 000 (b) 644 000 000 **7** India, 293 000 000
8 (a) 275 (b) 11 **9** 25 **10** (a) no (b) yes
11 (a) (i) Middle East (ii) Europe (b) yes
(c) 10 000 000 000 (d) 1 000 000 000 000 **12** 25, 47
13 (a) 18 (b) 86 (c) £14 849 (d) £2447

EXERCISE 1k

1 44 **2** 34 **3** 26 **4** 1 **5** 2
6 34 **7** 30 **8** 1 **9** 6 **10** 12
11 2 **12** 10

EXERCISE 1l

1 3600 **2** 8000 **3** 35 000 **4** 20 000 **5** 18
6 6.25 **7** 70 **8** 14

EXERCISE 1m

1 31 **2** (a) 9 (b) 12 **3** (a) 72 (b) 5
4 51 **5** 405 **6** 858 (smallest whole number above)
7 (a) 135 (b) 75 **8** 32 **9** 38
10 (a) 16 (b) 15 **11** 14, 1492

EXERCISE 1n

1 (a) 1800 (b) 1800 (c) 2000
2 (a) 7890 (b) 7900 (c) 8000
3 (a) 7350 (b) 7400 (c) 7000
4 (a) 8890 (b) 8900 (c) 9000
5 (a) 21 640 (b) 21 600 (c) 22 000
6 (a) 35 730 (b) 35 700 (c) 36 000
7 (a) 9290 (b) 9300 (c) 9000

8 (a) 36 670 (b) 36 700 (c) 37 000
9 (a) 5840 (b) 5800
10 (a) (i) thousands (ii) hundreds (b) (i) 29 700 sq ft (ii) 30 000 sq ft
11 (a) 300 (b) 250 **12** (a) 1 876 000 (b) 1 900 000

EXERCISE 1p

1 (a) 450 (b) 1250 (c) 1750 (d) 57 350
2 (a) 549 (b) 1949 (c) 4449 (d) 13 949
3 (a) 205 (b) 1550 (c) 32 950 (d) 48 500
4 (a) 249 (b) 1654 (c) 83 049 (d) 47 499
5 (a) 45 499 (b) 44 500
6 (a) 23 499 999 (b) 22 500 000
7 (a) 9500 (b) 10 499
8 For example 55 400 is 55 000 to the nearest 1000, but 100 000 to the nearest hundred thousand.

EXERCISE 1q

1 (a) 4500 sq ft (b) 1400 sq ft (c) 4000 sq ft (d) 88 200 sq ft
2 (a) 4128 sq ft (b) 1608 sq ft (c) 3696 sq ft (d) 88 200 sq ft
3 (a) 400 000 m^2 (b) 120 000 m^2 (c) 780 000 m^2 (d) 5 400 000 m^2
4 (a) 436 506 m^2 (b) 106 590 m^2 (c) 831 402 m^2 (d) 5 681 175 m^2
5 (a) 1000 (b) 900 (c) 1050 (d) 10 200

Multiple-choice questions 1

1 B **2** D **3** D **4** B **5** A
6 A and C are true, B and D are false
7 C and D are true, A and B are false **8** B **9** D

Self-assessment test 1

1 (a) £65 000 (b) £5 000 000 000
2 (a) (i) 405 (ii) 482 (b) 339
3 136 **4** 72 900 (b) 73 000 (c) 72 850
5 (a) £16 499 (b) £15 500 **6** 741 **7** 1800
8 (a) 9 (b) 574 (c) 254

EXERCISE 2a

1 (a) 10, 24, 28, 36 (b) 24, 28, 36 (c) 24, 36
2 21, 28, 35 **3** 25, 30, 35, 40
4 (a) yes (b) no (c) yes
5 (a) 1, 2, 3, 4, 6, 12 (b) 1, 3, 5, 15
(c) 1, 2, 3, 4, 6, 9, 12, 18, 36
(d) 1, 2, 3, 4, 5, 6, 10, 12, 15, 20, 30, 60
6 (a) yes (b) yes (c) yes **7** 1, 3, 7, 21
8 2, 4, 8, 14, 28, 56 **9** 18 **10** 84

EXERCISE 2b

1
```
. . . . . . . . . . . .     . . . . . . . . .     . . . . . .
. . . . . . . . . . . .     . . . . . . . . .     . . . . . .
                            . . . . . . . . .     . . . . . .
                                                  . . . . . .
```

2 (a) 15, 16, 18, 20 (b) 17, 19 **3** 13, 17, 19
4 29, 31, 47, 67 **5** 37, 41, 43
6 (a) 25 (b) 49 (c) 121 **7** 36, 49, 64
8 81, 100 **9** 216 **10** 27, 64, 125
11 125, 216, 512, 729 **12** 64 **13** 5 **14** 64
15 6 and 7 **16** 4 and 5

17 (a) (i) 17 (ii) 15 (iii) 9, 16 (b) 7 and 16, 8 and 9, 8 and 15, 15 and 16 (c) 9 + 18 **18** 31

EXERCISE 2c

1 (a) go down 2 stairs (b) go down 5 stairs (c) go up 2 stairs
2 I have lost 5 kg **3** I am 3 m below the water line
4 (a) I am 2 m above the level of the guttering
(b) I am 6 m below the level of the guttering
5 (a) 3 m below normal (b) 4 m above normal (c) normal
6 (a) £250 in credit (b) £75 in debt (c) is neither in credit nor in debt
7 −20 °C
8 (a) −8 °C (b) −5 °C (c) 0 (d) 2 °C (e) 20 °C
9 (a) 5 °C (b) −4 °C (c) 2 °C
10 (a) −20 °C (b) −9 °C (c) −4 °C
11 (a) Thursday (b) Friday (c) Saturday
12 (a) fallen 10 °C (b) fallen 2 °C (c) risen 9 °C (d) risen 3 °C

EXERCISE 2d

1 $-4 < 3$ **2** $-5 < -4$ **3** $-4 < -2$ **4** $0 > -6$ **5** $6 > -2$
6 $-3 > -5$ **7** $-10 < -4$ **8** $6 > -3$ **9** $-2 < 0$ **10** $-4 > -5$
11 $10 > -6$ **12** $-8 > -12$

EXERCISE 2e

1 −4 **2** −7 **3** −1 **4** −8 **5** 13
6 −7 **7** −10 **8** 0 **9** 0 **10** −6
11 6 **12** −1 **13** 9 **14** 15 **15** 4
16 4 **17** −1 **18** 2 **19** −13 **20** −8
21 (a) (i) +3 (ii) −2 (iii) −15 (iv) −7
(b) (i) 18 °C (ii) 11 °C (iii) 5 °C (iv) 15 °C
22 (a) −4 (b) 8 (c) 12
23 (a) Mrs Peake (b) Mrs Peake, 22
(c) Mr Eaves (d) 16 (22–6) (e) (i) 30 (ii) −10

EXERCISE 2f

1 −15 **2** −15 **3** −20 **4** −35 **5** −14
6 −18 **7** −8 **8** −20

EXERCISE 2g

1 −2 **2** −4 **3** −3 **4** −3

EXERCISE 2h

1 −7 **2** 7 **3** −1 **4** 1 **5** 1
6 2 **7** −4 **8** 12 **9** −18 **10** 18
11 −2 **12** −2 **13** 4 **14** −28 **15** 18
16 −5 **17** −14 **18** 14 **19** 14 **20** −2
21 −2 **22** −2 **23** 2 **24** −5
25 $9 \times -2, -9 \times 2, 6 \times -3, -6 \times 3, 1 \times -18, -1 \times 18$; 6
26 $-12 \div 4$, as many ways as you wish

EXERCISE 2i

1 5, 6, 7 **2** 12, 14, 16 **3** 48, 55, 62 **4** 16, 32, 64
5 9, 11, 13 **6** 30, 35, 40 **7** 20, 30, 42 **8** 6, 3, 0
9 3, −1, −5 **10** 10, 5, −1 **11** −18, −25, −32
12 162, 486, 1458 **13** 81, 100 **14** 343, 512 **15** $5 \times 6, 6 \times 7$
16 $6 \times 6 - 5, 7 \times 7 - 6$ **17** 33, 65 **18** 720, 5040
19 (b) $4 \times 4 + 5 \times 5 = 21 \times 21 - 20 \times 20$
$5 \times 5 + 6 \times 6 = 31 \times 31 - 30 \times 30$
$6 \times 6 + 7 \times 7 = 43 \times 43 - 42 \times 42$

20 (a)

11
111
1111
11111
111111

(b) (i) 1 111 111
(ii) 11 111 111

21 $4n$, 48 **22** $2n + 3$, 27 **23** $5n - 2$, 58
24 $3n + 5$, 41 **25** $7n - 1$, 83 **26** $10n - 5$, 115

Multiple-choice questions 2

1 B **2** B **3** C **4** D **5** C
6 A and B are true; C and D are false **7** C

Self-assessment test 2

1 (a) 1, 2, 3, 4, 6, 8, 12, 16, 24, 48
(b) (i) all except 1 and 3 (ii) 2 and 3
2 (a) 53 (b) 12, 18, 24 (c) 36
3 (a) £300 (b) £50 (c) −£50, i.e. £50 overdraft
(d) £200
4 (a) −9 °C (b) 0 °C
5 (a) −20 (b) 15 (c) 2 (d) −2
6 (a) 17, 20, 23 (b) 45, 54, 63 (c) 28, −33, 38
(d) 21, 34, 55
7 (a) $9 \times 55 = 495$, $9 \times 66 = 594$ (b) $12345 \times 8 + 5 = 98765$, $123456 \times 8 + 6 = 987654$
8 (a) $6n + 3$ (b) (i) 51 (ii) 93

EXERCISE 3a

1 (a) $\frac{1}{4}$ **2** $\frac{3}{8}$ **3** $\frac{7}{8}$ **4** $\frac{5}{16}$ **5** $\frac{5}{6}$ **6** $\frac{5}{9}$
7(a) (b) (c) (d)

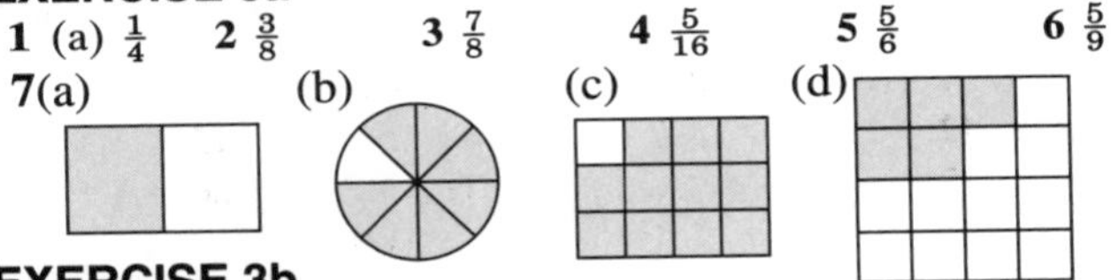

EXERCISE 3b

1 (a)

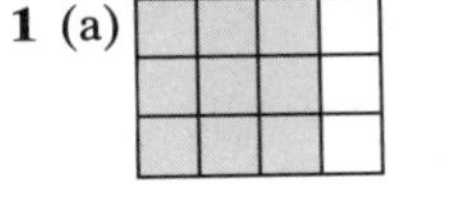

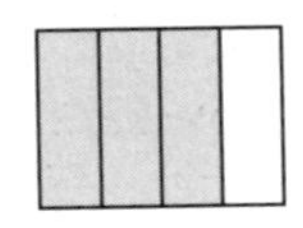

(b) yes (c) $\frac{12}{16}$
2 (a) $\frac{1}{5}$ (b) $\frac{1}{2}$ (c) $\frac{3}{4}$ (d) $\frac{1}{3}$ (e) $\frac{7}{9}$ (f) $\frac{2}{3}$
3 (a) $\frac{3}{5} = \frac{3 \times 5}{5 \times 5} = \frac{15}{24}$ (b) $\frac{4}{7} = \frac{4 \times 4}{7 \times 4} = \frac{16}{28}$
(c) $\frac{5}{9} = \frac{5 \times 6}{9 \times 6} = \frac{30}{54}$
4 (a) $\frac{4}{6}$ (b) $\frac{6}{21}$ (c) $\frac{20}{44}$ (d) $\frac{12}{15}$
5 (a) $\frac{2}{5} = \frac{4}{10} = \frac{6}{15}$ (b) $\frac{1}{4} = \frac{8}{32} = \frac{6}{24}$
(c) $\frac{1}{2} = \frac{9}{18} = \frac{21}{42}$ (d) $\frac{5}{6} = \frac{30}{36} = \frac{25}{30}$
6 (a) $\frac{6}{8}, \frac{9}{12}, \frac{15}{20}$ (b) $\frac{10}{14}, \frac{20}{28}, \frac{30}{42}$ (c) $\frac{14}{22}, \frac{21}{33}, \frac{49}{77}$
7 (a) $\frac{8}{16}$ (b) $\frac{15}{20}$ (c) $\frac{6}{10}$ (d) $\frac{25}{100}$
8 $\frac{5}{20}, \frac{6}{20}, \frac{10}{20}, \frac{12}{20}, \frac{16}{20}$

EXERCISE 3c

1 (a) $\frac{7}{12}$ (b) $\frac{3}{4}$ (c) $\frac{7}{12}$ (d) $\frac{5}{8}$ (e) $\frac{8}{9}$
2 (a) $\frac{1}{2}$ of a loaf of bread (b) $\frac{5}{8}$ kg
3 (a) $\frac{3}{8}$ mile (b) $\frac{5}{7}$ of the passengers in an aircraft
4 $\frac{7}{16}$ lb, $\frac{9}{16}$ lb, $\frac{11}{16}$ lb, $\frac{13}{16}$ lb
5 $\frac{13}{16}$ lb, $\frac{3}{4}$ lb, $\frac{5}{8}$ lb, $\frac{9}{16}$ lb, $\frac{1}{2}$ lb
6 (a) Mandy (b) Vera
7 $\frac{5}{14}$", $\frac{1}{2}$", $\frac{5}{7}$", $\frac{3}{4}$"

EXERCISE 3d

1 (a) $\frac{12}{5}, \frac{123}{33}$ (b) $\frac{36}{6}, \frac{39}{13}$ (c) $3\frac{2}{7}, 5\frac{9}{11}, 51\frac{1}{4}$ (d) $\frac{4}{5}, \frac{9}{10}, \frac{5}{9}$
2 (a) $\frac{16}{3}$ (b) $\frac{19}{4}$ (c) $\frac{47}{6}$ (d) $\frac{25}{7}$ (e) $\frac{43}{5}$
3 (a) $3\frac{3}{4}$ (b) $2\frac{2}{5}$ (c) $4\frac{6}{7}$ (d) $1\frac{7}{8}$ (e) $7\frac{1}{4}$

EXERCISE 3e

1 (a) $\frac{1}{2}$ (b) $\frac{1}{4}$ (c) $\frac{4}{5}$ (d) $\frac{13}{20}$
2 (a) $\frac{1}{2}$ (b) $\frac{3}{4}$ (c) $\frac{5}{12}$ (d) $\frac{1}{10}$
3 (a) $\frac{2}{5}$ (b) $\frac{3}{5}$ **4** $\frac{5}{8}$ **5** $\frac{3}{16}$
6 (a) $\frac{1}{28}$ (b) $\frac{1}{4}$ **7** $\frac{2}{3}$ **8** (a) $\frac{2}{5}$ (b) $\frac{1}{10}$
9 (a) $\frac{5}{12}$ (b) $\frac{7}{12}$ **10** (a) $\frac{3}{10}$ (b) $\frac{13}{20}$

EXERCISE 3f

1 (a) £25 (b) £35 **2** (a) 300 g (b) 2700 g
3 (a) 3 litres (b) 5 litres **4** (a) 30 (b) 4 (c) 6
5 £75 000

EXERCISE 3g

1 $\frac{5}{7}$ **2** $\frac{11}{15}$ **3** $\frac{3}{4}$ **4** $1\frac{4}{5}$ **5** $\frac{5}{12}$ **6** $1\frac{4}{15}$
7 $1\frac{5}{18}$ **8** $\frac{73}{99}$ **9** $1\frac{5}{12}$ **10** $1\frac{17}{30}$ **11** $1\frac{8}{9}$ **12** $1\frac{71}{72}$

EXERCISE 3h

1 $6\frac{5}{8}$ **2** $7\frac{1}{2}$ **3** $14\frac{1}{6}$ **4** $17\frac{13}{14}$ **5** $5\frac{1}{6}$ **6** $7\frac{5}{24}$
7 $14\frac{13}{16}$ **8** $10\frac{1}{16}$ **9** $16\frac{29}{60}$ **10** $14\frac{3}{10}$ **11** $6\frac{7}{8}$ **12** $13\frac{17}{40}$
13 $7\frac{2}{7}$ **14** $11\frac{11}{126}$

EXERCISE 3i

1 $\frac{1}{3}$ **2** $\frac{1}{12}$ **3** $\frac{1}{12}$ **4** $\frac{1}{12}$ **5** $\frac{1}{4}$ **6** $\frac{2}{9}$
7 $\frac{3}{35}$ **8** $\frac{9}{35}$ **9** $\frac{3}{10}$ **10** $\frac{1}{60}$ **11** $\frac{7}{36}$ **12** $\frac{11}{12}$
13 $2\frac{5}{8}$ **14** $4\frac{19}{24}$ **15** $2\frac{7}{8}$ **16** $\frac{11}{24}$

EXERCISE 3j

1 $1\frac{1}{4}$ **2** $1\frac{1}{6}$ **3** $3\frac{3}{8}$ **4** $4\frac{1}{6}$ **5** $2\frac{1}{8}$ **6** $1\frac{11}{40}$
7 $3\frac{1}{6}$ **8** $5\frac{3}{16}$ **9** $3\frac{5}{6}$ **10** $5\frac{5}{6}$ **11** $4\frac{5}{8}$ **12** $2\frac{5}{8}$

EXERCISE 3k

1 $2\frac{5}{12}$ **2** $\frac{1}{12}$ **3** $5\frac{19}{24}$ **4** $3\frac{29}{60}$ **5** $3\frac{37}{48}$ **6** $2\frac{5}{8}$
7 $1\frac{19}{30}$ **8** $6\frac{23}{84}$

EXERCISE 3l

1 (a) $\frac{1}{3}$ (b) $\frac{2}{15}$ **2** $26\frac{1}{8}$ lb **3** $\frac{3}{20}$ **4** 18 yd

EXERCISE 3m

1 $\frac{6}{35}$ **2** $\frac{10}{33}$ **3** $\frac{15}{28}$ **4** $\frac{49}{60}$ **5** $\frac{3}{16}$ **6** $\frac{4}{15}$
7 $1\frac{2}{3}$ **8** $\frac{1}{12}$ **9** $\frac{3}{20}$ **10** $\frac{4}{21}$ **11** $\frac{3}{16}$ **12** $\frac{2}{21}$

EXERCISE 3n

1 2 **2** $3\frac{1}{2}$ **3** $7\frac{1}{3}$ **4** $5\frac{3}{5}$ **5** $2\frac{1}{2}$ **6** $2\frac{7}{10}$
7 $28\frac{1}{2}$ **8** $11\frac{1}{3}$

EXERCISE 3p

1 $\frac{5}{3}$ **2** $1\frac{2}{7}$ **3** $\frac{5}{11}$ **4** $\frac{5}{11}$ **5** $\frac{7}{25}$ **6** $\frac{12}{41}$

EXERCISE 3q

1 8 **2** 18 **3** $8\frac{1}{3}$ **4** $5\frac{3}{5}$ **5** 3 **6** $1\frac{1}{4}$
7 $1\frac{1}{2}$ **8** $\frac{4}{5}$ **9** $\frac{2}{3}$ **10** $\frac{4}{9}$ **11** $4\frac{2}{3}$ **12** $1\frac{5}{7}$

EXERCISE 3r

1 (a) (i) $\frac{3}{4}$ (ii) $\frac{1}{4}$ (b) 12 000 (c) 4000
2 (a) $\frac{11}{20}$ (b) 720 **3** (a) $\frac{1}{10}$ (b) (i) £2m (ii) £$1\frac{3}{4}$ m
4 50 **5** 20 **6** (a) $4\frac{1}{2}$ s (b) $26\frac{1}{4}$ min
7 (a) 30 (b) yes; it should take 1 h 10 min **8** 38 m
9 (a) £300 (b) £360
10 (a) yes (£8000 sales, £7750 costs) (b) £4250
(c) £4200, no, £50 less

EXERCISE 3s

1 $\frac{3}{4}$ **2** $\frac{5}{6}$ **3** $2\frac{11}{12}$ **4** $4\frac{1}{2}$ **5** 2 **6** 5
7 $\frac{7}{27}$ **8** $2\frac{2}{5}$ **9** $16\frac{13}{24}$

Multiple-choice questions 3

1 C **2** A **3** B **4** D

Self-assessment test 3

1 $\frac{15}{20} = \frac{45}{60} = \frac{3}{4} = \frac{12}{16}$

2 $\frac{11}{18}$ of a mile **3** (a) $\frac{7}{16}$ (b) $\frac{9}{16}$
4 (a) $8\frac{5}{12}$ (b) $2\frac{11}{12}$ (c) $7\frac{39}{40}$ (d) $9\frac{1}{3}$ (e) $\frac{10}{21}$ (f) $1\frac{1}{3}$
5 (a) £2400 (b) (i) £600 (ii) £1500

EXERCISE 4a

1 (a) 0.7 (b) 0.09 (c) 0.17 (d) 0.001
2 (a) $\frac{27}{100}$ (b) $\frac{81}{100}$ (c) $\frac{9}{100}$ (d) $\frac{1}{100}$
3 (a) hundredths (b) tenths (c) units
(d) hundredths
4 (a) 3 tenths (b) 1 ten (c) 2 thousandths
(d) 4 hundredths
5 (a) (i) 7 (ii) 9 (iii) 7
(b) (i) 4 (ii) 4 (iii) 6 (c) (i) 8 (ii) 7 (iii) 3
6 (a) 31.83 (b) 9.25 (c) 460.34 (d) 6.543
(e) 300.219

7

	Hundreds	Tens	Units		Tenths	Hundredths	Thousandths
(a)		3	1	.	5		
(b)	7	5	5	.	8	1	
(c)			5	.		3	6
(d)	3	6	1	.		6	
(e)		3	7	.	2	2	8

8 (a) 0.35 (b) 0.735 (c) 0.804 (d) 0.064
9 (a) $\frac{4}{10} + \frac{4}{100} + \frac{7}{1000}$ (b) $\frac{8}{10} + \frac{3}{1000}$ (c) $\frac{9}{10} + \frac{7}{100} + \frac{1}{1000}$
(d) $\frac{2}{100} + \frac{8}{1000}$
10 (a) $\frac{3}{5}$ (b) $\frac{12}{25}$ (c) $\frac{16}{25}$ (d) $\frac{177}{1000}$ (e) $\frac{7}{8}$ (f) $\frac{1}{8}$
(g) $\frac{111}{250}$
11 (a) 3.7 (b) 0.48 (c) 12.05 (d) 6.1 (e) 12.37
(f) 5.07 (g) 0.3
12 10.3 cm **13** 5.8 cm **14** 7.7 cm **15** 9.2 cm

EXERCISE 4b

1 0.4 **2** 0.375 **3** 0.75 **4** 0.76 **5** 0.56 **6** 0.504
7 0.56 **8** 0.281 25 **9** 1.5 **10** 3.25 **11** 5.8 **12** 7.55
13 4.28 **14** 13.725 **15** 6.843 75 **16** 24.1875

EXERCISE 4c

1 7.83 **2** 9.2 **3** 3 **4** 2.587 **5** 4.92, 5.66, 6.99
6 7.17, 7.34, 7.43 **7** 0.998, 3.92, 10.35
8 7.005, 7.05, 7.15, 7.45 **9** 20.74, 20.87, 21.39, 21.48
10 8.33, 5.09, 4.27 **11** 3.27, 3.11, 3.09 **12** 67.3, 54.39, 50.37
13 9.444, 9.44, 9.4, 9.04 **14** 16.20, 16.02, 12.60, 10.62
15 (a) 1.55 (b) 12.6

EXERCISE 4d

1 (a) 46 (b) 7 (c) 14 (d) 124 (e) 1
2 (a) 8.9 (b) 0.6 (c) 73.7 (d) 0.1 (e) 0.3
3 (a) 37.35 (b) 9.29 (c) 63.59 (d) 0.08 (e) 0.34
4 (a) 2.558 (b) 0.948 (c) 14.667 (d) 7.333
(e) 8.707
5 (a) 7.58 cm (b) 7.6 cm **6** (a) 0.52 cm (b) 0.5 cm
7 (a) 13.22 cm (b) 13.2 cm **8** (a) 24.88 cm (b) 24.9 cm
9 (a) 2.9 g, 2.9 g, 3.0 g, 3.0 g, 3.0 g
(b) 2.94 g, 2.95 g, 3.01 g, 2.98 g, 3.02 g
10 (a) 5 m (b) 1.8 m (c) 1.41 m (d) 1.5 m
(e) 1.47 m (f) 2.76 m (g) 0.02 m

EXERCISE 4e

1 (a) 54 (b) 4.8 (c) 170 (d) 0.84 (e) 3.0
2 (a) 528 (b) 0.812 (c) 0.0645 (d) 3530 (e) 9.88
3 (a) 18.56 (b) 5.009 (c) 7.071 (d) 0.5051
(e) 435.9
4 (a) 47 (b) 47.10 (c) 47.1 (d) 47.0963
(e) 47.096
5 (a) 7.1 (b) 7.06 (c) 7.060 (d) 7.06 (e) 7.060

EXERCISE 4f

1 7.9 **2** 5.8 **3** 7.9 **4** 8.9 **5** 9.9 **6** 7.74
7 7.98 **8** 8.58 **9** 14.32 **10** 9.43 **11** 11.66 **12** 23.51
13 7.42 m
14 (a) (i) 269.3 cm (ii) 155.3 cm (b) 260 cm × 150 cm
15 294 mm × 208 mm **16** 28.3 cm **17** 78.195
18 53.36 **19** 11.871 **20** 16.399 **21** 40.519 **22** 80.676
23 151.69 **24** 934.347

EXERCISE 4g

1 32.4 **2** 6.04 **3** 15.8 **4** 6.93 **5** 49.35
6 6.17 **7** 16.78 **8** 61.43 **9** 18.3908 **10** 42.903
11 (a) 4.9 cm (b) 7.2 cm **12** 3.39 m **13** 13.5 cm
14 (a) 2.48 m (b) 4.13 m (c) 3.47 m

EXERCISE 4h

1 (a) 43.4 (b) 19.85 (c) 674.3 (d) 7.374 (e) 0.088
2 (a) 5.68 (b) 1.7445 (c) 0.469 (d) 0.0723
(e) 0.0008
3 (a) 264.9 (b) 4538 (c) 9530 (d) 4.45 (e) 61.74
4 (a) 7.672 (b) 0.076 (c) 0.1582 (d) 0.0078
(e) 0.000 437
5 87.2 **6** 3.94 **7** 0.372 **8** 44 **9** 64.6
10 0.648 **11** 0.092 **12** 3.4 **13** 36 **14** 0.012
15 42.7 **16** 0.03

EXERCISE 4i

1 38.1 2 41.09 3 30.72 4 34.902 5 236.44
6 28.4484 7 10.669 8 2.9336 9 0.3735 10 26.82
11 (a) 85.3 (b) 85.27 12 (a) 48.1 (b) 48.08
13 (a) 18.6 (b) 18.56 14 (a) 20.6 (b) 20.56
15 (a) 19.5 (b) 19.46 16 (a) 10.3 (b) 10.31

EXERCISE 4j

1 7.93 2 0.11 3 0.28 4 2.26 5 4.27
6 3.75 7 0.118 8 8.6 9 0.0216 10 3.95
11 1.225 12 5.64 13 3.33 14 10.2 15 1.29
16 1.02 17 0.451 18 2.46 19 70.5 20 0.446

EXERCISE 4k

1 960 g 2 10.8 cm 3 (a) 38.25 (b) £238.68
4 212.5 min 5 (a) 172.8 g (b) 188.5 g
6 (a) 1.14 t (b) 4.02 t 7 12.6 8 50 9 8
10 (a) 15 (b) 1.25 cm 11 12 12 £6.84
13 12.96 kg (12 960 g) 14 (a) 961 ℓ (b) 6730 ℓ
15 60 16 25.2 mm

EXERCISE 4l

1 £300 000, £291 152 2 £72, £71.10
3 12 000 g, 11 931 g (nearest g) 4 7 m, 6.89 m 5 £5, £5.87
6 (a) £21 (70 × 0.3) (b) £19.30
7 (a) 180 miles (300 × 0.6) (b) 174 miles

EXERCISE 4m

1 nearest mm 2 nearest mm 3 nearest metre
4 nearest 10 km 5 nearest km 6 nearest milligram
7 nearest $\frac{1}{10}$ of a litre 8 nearest hectare
9 nearest kg
10 (a) nearest 5 (b) nearest 1000 (c) nearest 100

Multiple-choice questions 4

1 B 2 D 3 B 4 D 5 C
6 A and D are true, B and C are false 7 B

Self-assessment test 4

1 (a) 491.895 (b) 68.0238 (c) 0.635 (d) 12.763
(e) 12
2 (a) 53.1 (b) 53.1 (c) 53
3 (a) 18.0 (b) 1.86 (c) 203
4 (a) 5.32 (b) 2.53 5 8.6 cm 6 0.0378 mm
7 (a) 10.09 m (b) 7.36 m
(c) (i) 5.21 m × 2.95 m (ii) 3.34 × 2.46 m
(d) (i) 29.9552 m^2 (ii) 30.0 m^2 (iii) 29.96 m^2
(e) 2.5 m
8 (a) 54 m^2 (b) 55.4 m^2

EXERCISE 5a

1 (a) 50 mm (b) 120 mm (c) 3420 mm (d) 82 mm
(e) 135 mm (f) 8 mm
2 (a) 800 cm (b) 1500 cm (c) 43 300 cm (d) 590 cm
(e) 1427 cm (f) 74 cm
3 (a) 2000 m (b) 11 000 m (c) 7500 m (d) 330 m
(e) 1490 m (f) 50 m
4 (a) 5 cm (b) 25 cm (c) 800 cm
5 (a) 35 m (b) 900 m (c) 4.52 m
6 (a) 10 km (b) 7.5 km (c) 0.45 km
7 (a) 190 cm (b) 1900 mm
8 (a) 130 cm (b) 950 mm
9 (a) 1670 m (b) 0.65 km
10 1.41 km
11 (a) 108 in (b) 180 in (c) 42 in (d) 57 in
12 (a) 12 ft (b) 36 ft (c) 19 ft (d) $24\frac{3}{4}$ ft
13 (a) 72 in (b) 324 in (c) 198 in (d) 297 in
14 (a) 8800 yd (b) 5720 yd (c) 7 miles (d) 21 120 ft
15 46 145 yd
16 3207 yd
17 (a) 3960 yd (b) $2\frac{1}{4}$ miles
18 (a) 71 yd, 12 yd, 7 yd (b) 2556 in, 432 in, 252 in

EXERCISE 5b

1 (a) 120 cm (b) 64 cm (c) 580 mm
2 (a) 480 cm (b) 4.5 m
3 18 m 4 495 m 5 42 in

EXERCISE 5c

1 (a) 25 squares (b) 33 squares (c) 10 squares
(d) 27 squares (e) 22 squares
2 (a) 42 (b) 25 (c) 31 (d) 23

EXERCISE 5d

1 (a) 81 cm^2 (b) 70.56 cm^2 (c) $12\frac{1}{4}$ in^2
2 (a) 135 cm^2 (b) 21 cm^2 (c) $13\frac{1}{2}$ cm^2 (d) 27.06 cm^2
3 (a) 16 000 cm^2 (b) 2 m high, 0.8 m wide (c) 1.6 m^2
4 (a) 210 ft, 2106 ft^2 (b) 228 ft, 2808 ft^2
5 (a) 648 mm (b) 24 480 mm^2 (c) 20.4 cm × 12 cm
(d) 245 cm^2
6 (a) (i) 60 in (ii) 5 ft (b) (i) 216 in^2 (ii) 1.5 ft^2
7 (a) 3 (b) (i) 16 × 1 (340 cm) (ii) 4 × 4 (160 cm)
(c) 180 cm
8 (a) 4 (18 × 2, 12 × 3, 9 × 4, 6 × 6) (b) 18 × 2 (40 in)
(c) 6 × 6 (24 in, a square)
9 (a) 7 (b) (i) 8 cm × 7 cm (ii) 14 cm × 1 cm

EXERCISE 5e

1 8 2 16 3 18 4 14 5 13
6 (a) 8, i.e. all of them (b) 0 7 1440
8 8 9 (a) 24 (b) 64 (c) 432
10 (a) 8 (b) 54 11 16
12 All dimensions of box A do not divide exactly by 2 cm or by 3 cm, so neither of these cubes will cover the base of the box without cutting.
13 (a) 2 cm × 2 cm × 2 cm, i.e. a cube, 8
(b) (i) yes, 2 cm × 2 cm × 3 cm (ii) no
(c) 2, 2 cm × 2 cm × 6 cm and 2 cm × 3 cm × 4 cm
14 240 in^3
15 Ted's 3 cm^3, Wendy's 3.36 cm^3; Wendy by 0.36 cm^3
16 (a) 60 cm^3 (b) 63 cm^3 (c) 72 cm^3 (d) 66 cm^3
(e) 72.9 cm^3 (f) 64 cm^3
(g) (i) the cuboid in (e) (ii) the cuboid in (a)
17 $3\frac{1}{3}$ yd 18 (a) 900 m^3 (b) 900 000 ℓ
19 (a) 1728 mm^3 (b) 1.728 cm^3
20 (a) 0.064 m^3 (b) £5.44
21 (a) 60.5 cm (b) 8 (c) (i) 33 (ii) 264
(d) (i) 1 353 600 mm^3 (ii) 1353.6 cm^3 (e) 50 000 cm^3
22 (a) (i) 1500 cm^3 (ii) 0.0015 m^3
(b) yes, in layers 7.5 cm thick; there will be 18 bricks in each layer (c) 12 (d) 216

EXERCISE 5f
1 (a) 9000 cm^3 (b) 9 ℓ **2** 1000 ℓ **3** 4000
4 (a) 40 (b) 80 lb
5 (a) 5832 cm^3 (36 cm × 18 cm × 9 cm) (b) 6264 cm^3
6 (a) 3 cm (b) 18 cm × 14 cm (c) 756 cm^3

EXERCISE 5g
1 500 g **2** 0.005 g **3** 1776 kg
4 (a) 7.5 t (b) 12 t
5 16 ℓ **6** 60 **7** 40
8 (a) 90 240 g (b) 90.24 kg

EXERCISE 5h
1 25p **2** (a) 9 (b) 12 gallons **3** 92 **4** 7
5 (a) 1.5 lb (b) 5 gallons **6** 630 **7** 36 **8** 2.5 m
9 (a) 500 cm^2 (b) 3000 mm^2
10 (a) 1.19 yd^2 (b) £16.50 per m^2

EXERCISE 5i
1 3.4 cm **2** 28.6 m **3** 162 mm **4** $47\frac{5}{8}$ in
5 12.7 cm **6** $6\frac{3}{16}$ in **7** 55 m.p.h. **8** 118 km/h
9 2.35 kg **10** 3 lb 6 oz **11** 10 st 5 lb **12** 67.6 kg
13 52 ℓ **14** 37.6 °C **15** 3.7 mm

Multiple-choice questions 5
1 B **2** A **3** D **4** B
5 A and D are true, B and C are false **6** A

Self-assessment test 5
1 (a) 925 cm (b) 1050 m (c) 0.426 m (d) 10 000 mm^2
(e) 3 000 000 m^2 (f) 4000 mm^3
2 53 squares **3** (a) 178 m (b) 1870 m^2
4 (a) 180 (b) (i) yes (ii) yes (iii) no; 2 and 3 will divide exactly into 18, 12 and 6 but 4 will not.
5 (a) 126 in (b) 10 ft 4 in (c) 12 yd^2 (d) 2 yd^3
6 (a) 24 cm by 15 cm, 360 cm^2 (b) (i) 180 (ii) 19 mm
(c) 6.48 m^2 (one side of each sheet only is counted)
(d) 330 g
7 (a) (i) 16 °C (ii) −7 °C (b) 23 °C

EXERCISE 6a
1 $\frac{1}{4}$ **2** $\frac{11}{20}$ **3** $\frac{3}{5}$ **4** $\frac{12}{25}$ **5** $\frac{7}{20}$
6 $\frac{24}{25}$ **7** $\frac{21}{25}$ **8** $\frac{69}{100}$ **9** $\frac{6}{5}$ **10** $\frac{13}{5}$
11 $\frac{49}{25}$ **12** $\frac{13}{4}$

EXERCISE 6b
1 40% **2** 34% **3** 65% **4** $66\frac{2}{3}$% **5** $8\frac{1}{3}$%
6 $162\frac{1}{2}$% **7** 108% **8** $38\frac{8}{9}$% **9** 240% **10** $271\frac{3}{7}$%

EXERCISE 6c
1 0.2 **2** 0.65 **3** 0.47 **4** 0.73 **5** 0.025
6 0.423 **7** 0.0225 **8** 0.125 **9** 1.28 **10** 3.33

EXERCISE 6d
1 2.4 **2** 3.7 **3** 9 **4** 55 **5** 13
6 3 **7** 637.5 **8** 16.2 **9** 375 **10** 165

EXERCISE 6e
1 0.65 **2** 0.74 **3** 0.34 **4** 1.35 **5** 2.3
6 $\frac{1}{10}$ **7** $\frac{1}{5}$ **8** $\frac{43}{100}, \frac{57}{100}$ **9** $\frac{7}{20}$ **10** 25%
11 65% **12** 68% **13** 28% **14** 32% **15** 41%
16 (a) 14% (b) $\frac{29}{50}$ **17** 37% **18** (a) 60% (b) 40%
19 (a) $\frac{11}{25}$ (b) no (c) $\frac{14}{25}$
20 (a) 140 000 ft^3 (b) (i) $\frac{23}{50}$ (ii) 64 400 ft^3
(iii) 716 ft^3 (3 sf) (c) $11\frac{2}{3}$%

EXERCISE 6f
1 $\frac{1}{2}$ **2** $\frac{3}{10}$ **3** $\frac{1}{8}$ **4** $\frac{2}{1}$ **5** $\frac{3}{10}$ **6** $\frac{1}{5}$
7 $\frac{3}{40}$ **8** $\frac{1}{10}$ **9** $\frac{7}{20}$ **10** $\frac{1}{4}$ **11** $\frac{1}{20}$ **12** $\frac{1}{5}$
13 (a) $\frac{7}{10}$ (b) $\frac{3}{10}$ **14** 80% **15** 48% **16** 40%
17 20% **18** 40% **19** 25% **20** 65% **21** 55%
22 (a) $16\frac{2}{3}$% (b) $83\frac{1}{3}$% **23** $101\frac{1}{4}$% **24** 58%

EXERCISE 6g
1 £8 **2** 2500 **3** 24 cm **4** 68
5 (a) 1320 (b) 1080 **6** 270 **7** £192 **8** 1.8 kg
9 (a) £77.45 (b) £15
10 (a) 12 kg (b) 120 (c) 40 kg

EXERCISE 6h
1 (a) £35 (b) £288 (c) £50 **2** £82.62 **3** £2880
4 £8.40 **5** 87.75 cm **6** 100 kg **7** £668.50
8 (a) 55 000 (b) 59 400
9 (a) £155.10 (b) 90p
10 (a) 46 412, 56 354 (b) (i) 10.7%, 9.72%, 1.5% (decrease), 11.7%
(c) (i) N. Ireland (an increase) (ii) Scotland (a decrease)
(d) (i) N. Ireland (ii) N. Ireland
(e) 56 000 000, 47 000 000, 3 000 000, 5 000 000, 2 000 000
(i) $\frac{47}{56}$ (ii) $\frac{3}{56}$

EXERCISE 6i
1 40% **2** (a) £210 000 (b) 44.7% (3 s.f.)
3 (a) £5.4 m (b) 63.0% (3 s.f.)
4 (a) £6.75 (b) £7.20 (c) £7.88 (d) £9
5 (a) 62% (b) (i) £9.90 (ii) £4.40 (iii) £13.64
(c) 120% (d) £20
6 (a) £7000 loss (b) 100% (c) share of fixed overheads
(d) (i) £24 000 (ii) yes, income exceeds fixed overheads by £6000 (iii) yes
7 £80

EXERCISE 6j
1 £141 **2** £79.90 **3** £9.99 **4** £98.11 **5** £41.71
6 (a) £940 (b) Walfords by £17.62
7 £34.68, £6.07, £40.75, £2.04 (a) £38.71 (b) £40.75
8 £74.55
9 £52.80 **10** £1.93 **11** £218.75
12 (a) £10 (b) £2.61 (c) £4.89 (d) 49%

EXERCISE 6k
1 £336 **2** £82.50 **3** (a) £864 (b) £865.28
4 £55 **5** (b) by £13.88 **6** £166.40
7 £124.86 **8** £339.08 **9** £1663.08 **10** £2852.92 **11** £5363.20

EXERCISE 6l
1 8930 (3 s.f.) **2** £126.20 **3** £2869.20 **4** 9 yr
5 (a) about 5030 (b) about 10 100
6 (a) 1156 (b) 1835

EXERCISE 6m

1 (a) (i) £330 (ii) £935 (b) £66 000
2 (a) £562.50 (b) £6750 (c) £202 500
3 (a) £72 000 (b) £8000 (c) (i) £882 (ii) £264 600
4 (a) £43 520 (b) £110 106
5 (a) £950 (b) £4430 (c) £630
6 (a) £243.20 (b) £290.06 (c) £46.86
7 bank loan by £33.40
8 (a) £18.73 (b) £8.90 (c) £355.13

Multiple-choice questions 6

1 C **2** B **3** D **4** A
5 A and C are true, B and D are false **6** A

Self-assessment test 6

1 (a) $\frac{1}{4}$ (b) 25% **2** 9% **3** 112% **4** £2353.40
5 £13.50 **6** Denhams by 25p **7** £75
8 (a) £21.84 (b) £10.37

EXERCISE 7a

1 (a) 31 (b) 28 **2** no **3** (a) November (b) July
4 13 **5** 5
6 (a) Saturday (b) 16 Sept (c) 4 Oct
7 (a) 10 Sept (b) 2 Sept (c) 11 Sept
8 22 Aug **9** 15
10 (a) 14 (b) 20 Sept (c) 10 weeks

EXERCISE 7b

1 (a) 14 h 45 min (b) 2 h 11 min (c) 32 h
2 7.25 a.m.
3 (a) 4 h 4 min (b) 12.22 p.m.
4 (a) (i) 3 h 15 min (ii) 5 h 10 min (b) (i) 25 (ii) 20
(c) Firefox by 25 min (d) 4 h 15 min

EXERCISE 7c

1 (a) 5.55 p.m. (b) 17.55
2 (a) 632 (b) 825 (c) 625
3 14 h 31 min (871 min)
4 (a) (i) 09.15 (ii) 12.48 (b) 14 min
(c) 38 min, 09.58, 37 min (d) 09.33

EXERCISE 7d

1 (a) 2 (b) 8 (c) 8 (d) 9
2 (a) 3 (b) 8 (c) 6 (d) 5
3 (a) 2 p.m. (b) 10 p.m. (c) 7 a.m. (d) 6 a.m.
4 (a) 4 p.m. (b) 11 p.m. (c) 10 a.m.
5 (a) 1 a.m. (b) 7 p.m. (c) 9 a.m.
6 (a) 7 a.m. (b) 5 a.m. next day
7 (a) 11 a.m. (b) 4 a.m.
8 (a) 9 h (b) 1.30 a.m. the next day
9 (a) 9 p.m. (b) 7 a.m.
10 (a) date moves back 1 day (b) date moves on 1 day

EXERCISE 7e

1 (a) 394 miles (b) 169 miles
2 (a) Cardiff and Bristol (b) Dover and Glasgow
3 (a) Liverpool (b) Dover **4** 57 miles
5 (a) 375 miles (b) 278 miles

EXERCISE 7f

1 75 m.p.h. **2** 14 km/h **3** 375 m/min **4** 1350 miles
5 $5\frac{1}{2}$ h **6** (a) 1.6 ($1\frac{3}{5}$) miles/min (b) 96 m.p.h.
7 (a) $8\frac{1}{3}$ m/s (b) 500 m/min (c) 30 000 m/h
(d) 30 km/h
8 (a) 1950 miles (b) 5 h (c) 390 m.p.h.
9 16.8 m.p.h. ($16\frac{4}{5}$ m.p.h.) **10** 60 km/h

EXERCISE 7g

1 (a) On the time axis 1 small square represents 15 min and on the distance axis 1 small square represents 5 miles. Shena starts from York at 8 a.m. and travels to a place that is 50 km from York, in 2 h, arriving there at 10 a.m. Here she stays for $\frac{1}{2}$ h before returning to York at 1 p.m. Derek starts 50 km from York at 8.45 a.m. and travels the 50 km to York without stopping, arriving there at 1.45 p.m.
(b) On the time axis 1 square $= \frac{1}{5}$ h i.e. 12 min and on the distance axis 1 square $= 2\frac{1}{2}$ miles. Liz leaves Belfast at 12.24 and travels to a place 20 miles away from Belfast arriving there at 13.24. She stays there for 1 h 12 min, before continuing to a place 30 miles from Belfast. She arrives there at 15.48. Charlie leaves Belfast at 13.48 and travels for 2 h, meeting Liz 30 miles away.
2 (a) 30 miles (b) 15 min
(c) they pass going in opposite directions, first at 10.30 a.m. 5 miles from Fletcham, and again at 12.15 p.m. 5 miles from Stokely. (d) (i) 20 m.p.h. (ii) 20 m.p.h.
3 (a) 1 p.m. (b) 137 km/h
(c) At 11.58 a.m., 97 km from Caxton (d) 100 km/h

EXERCISE 7h

1 July **2** (a) 20 °F (b) 5 **3** 56 (4 × 14)
4 (a) 3 (b) 93 (3 × 31)
5 (a) Sept (and July) (b) April
6 (a) £388 (b) £486.20 (c) £527.60
7 £1272.40 **8** £2103 **9** (a) 11 May (b) £56.40
10 (a) £1582 (b) £1862 **11** 4 h
12 Gatwick, Manchester or Glasgow
13 (a) £11 (b) £7 (c) £18 (d) £9
14 £48 **15** Between 7 and 21 July, £272
16 (a) £1160.80 (b) £18 (c) £1768.70

EXERCISE 7i

1 (a) 2050 Ff (b) £200
2 (a) 41 800 pta (b) £56
3 Wait until they get there, \$405 compared with \$432.
4 No, they were cheaper in Germany and in the UK.
5 £34.34
6 (a) £1 = \$1.55 (b) £1 = 185 pta (c) £1 = 2.40 DM
7 7.33 **8** (a) Germany (b) France

EXERCISE 7k

1 £61.25 **2** £85.75 **3** £168 **4** £448

Multiple-choice questions 7

1 B **2** C **3** D **4** A
5 B and C are true, A and D are false **6** D

Self-assessment test 7

1 (a) 9 h 45 min (b) 7 a.m.
2 (a) £1520 (b) £255.30, £1461.60 (c) £16.50
(d) £2490.40, £44.47

3 (a) 50 min (b) 16 h 35 min (c) 2 h 55 min (d) 7 h 25 min (e) (i) 9 h (ii) 8 h 10 min (f) $\frac{1}{2}$ h (g) 3 h 25 min (h) 4 h 40 min, excluding his break
4 7 July, 13 h 15 min, 452 m.p.h., 13 h 37 min, 0817
5 (a) Betty 9 miles, Doug 6 miles (b) Betty (c) (i) 8.10 (ii) 8.40, 30 min, 18 m.p.h. (d) (i) 8.10 (ii) 8.55, 45 min, 8 m.p.h. (e) 3.6 miles from Alcan at 8.28 (f) Betty – by car in heavy traffic; Doug – on a bicycle.

EXERCISE 8a

1 (a) £181.30 (b) £203.30
2 (a) 8.00 a.m. (b) 5.00 p.m. (c) 8 h (d) none (e) $5\frac{3}{4}$ h (f) $37\frac{1}{4}$ h (g) 183.27 (h) £35.36 (nearest p) (i) £218.63
3 (a) £6 (b) £182.40 (c) £230.40 **4** £329.40
5 (a) afternoons (b) (i) once (Thursday) (ii) once (Thursday) (c) 4 h (d) $37\frac{1}{2}$ h (e) £215
6 (a) £135 (b) £575 (c) £1100 **7** £129.25
8 £172.50 **9** £364 **10** £2050 **11** £224
12 (a) £1000 (b) £2450 (c) £1345
13 (a) £16 200 (b) £47 040 (c) £30 564
14 Grant by £2000 p.a.

EXERCISE 8b

1 (a) £13 800 (b) £10 270 (c) Tim £3900, Molly £0 (d) £4360
2 (a) £480 (b) £3497.50 (c) £2301 (d) £7456 (e) £21 200
3 (a) £4933 (b) £1093.25 (c) £21.02
4 £2350.75
5 (a) £2195 (b) £2375
6 (a) £20 000 (b) wife £3735, husband £2485 (c) no
7 (a) £722.50 (b) £446 **8** (a) £11 440 (b) £400

EXERCISE 8c

1 £41
2 (a) £99.50 (b) £1134 (c) £21.81
3 (a) £1580 (b) £124.70 **4** (a) £81.50 (b) £115.50

EXERCISE 8d

1 £51.36 **2** £68.30 **3** £73.32 **4** £63.92
5 £45.36 **6** £135.40 **7** £230.96 **8** £79.20
9 £10.24 **10** £11.16 **11** £10
12 £16.28 (nearest p) **13** (a) £30 360 (b) £10 120
14 (a) £21 577.50 (b) £7192.50

EXERCISE 8e

In questions 1 to 5 the missing values are:
1 £152.02 **2** £343 **3** £31.26 **4** £58.12 **5** £13.55
6 (a) £44 (b) £22.85 (c) £18 (d) £84.85 (e) £215.15
7 (a) 70% (b) (i) £1500 (ii) £18 000
8 (a) £195 (b) £7.80, $11\frac{1}{2}$ h (c) £89.70 (d) £284.70 (e) £43.94 (f) £17.08 (g) £203.84

9

Name	Wages	£20	£10	£5	£1	50p	20p	10p	5p	2p	1p
Norse	£187.86	180		5	2	50	20	10	5		1
Neale	£109.33	100		5	4		20	10		2	1
George	£215.92	200	10	5		50	40			2	
Cox	£266.79	260		5	1	50	20		5	4	

Multiple-choice questions 8

1 A **2** D **3** B **4** C

Self-assessment test 8

1 (a) $7\frac{1}{2}$ h (b) $37\frac{1}{2}$ h (c) £185.63
2 (a) £21 650 (b) £5262.50
3 Sally, by £173.56 (£526 − £352.44)

EXERCISE 9a

1 (a) 64p (b) 90p (c) £2.58 (d) 44p
2 (a) 96p (b) £2.24 (c) £1.56 (d) £2.40
3 (a) 36p (b) £1.13 (nearest p) (c) £1.12 (d) 95p

4	5	6
0.96	0.96	1.68
0.44	1.04	1.50
1.08	2.24	0.80
£2.48	£4.24	1.38
Change £7.52	Change £5.76	£5.36
		Change £4.64

7 (a) £2.10 (b) 70p (c) £1.32 (d) 90p

8	9	10
1.20	0.30	1.50
0.70	0.35	0.70
1.00	0.84	1.26
£2.90	0.30	1.50
Change £7.10	£1.79	£4.96
	Change £8.21	Change £5.04

11 correct **12** £22.57 **13** correct **14** £19.85
15 £19.52

EXERCISE 9b

1 £99.88 **2** £65.80 **3** £11.99 **4** £10.06 **5** £317.18
6 £75.55 **7** £29.36 **8** £450
9 (a) £8.50 (b) £10.20
10 (a) £24 (b) £27.60 (c) 60p

EXERCISE 9c

1

	Number of units used in quarter
first	1480
second	1224
third	715
fourth	562

2 (a) 1.5 (b) 16 (c) 0.15 (d) 3
3 (a) 10 (b) $83\frac{1}{3}$ (c) $\frac{1}{2}$ (d) 4 (e) $\frac{2}{5}$ (f) $6\frac{2}{3}$
4 (a) £5.66 (b) 57p (c) 15p (d) £1.21
5 (a) (i) 56.16 (ii) 7.5 (iii) 16.5 (b) 80.16 (c) £6.77
6 £135.23 **7** £107.72 **8** £236.96 **9** £435.25 **10** £329.54
11 £403.76

EXERCISE 9d

1 £217.05 **2** £186.01 **3** £254.23 **4** £200.47 **5** £237.40

EXERCISE 9e

1 (a) £89.10 (b) £145.20 (c) £224.40
2 (a) £36.75 (b) £43.40 (c) £65.45
3 £9.36 **4** (a) £182.50 (b) £3.51
5 (a) £179.05 (b) £3.44 **6** (a) £394.05 (b) £7.58

EXERCISE 9f

1 (a) F (b) D (c) G (d) B **2** £373
3 (a) £194.39 (b) £21.34 **4** (a) £279.75 (b) £93.25
5 (a) first payment £31.69 then 9 at £31.60
(b) first payment £28.80 then 9 at £28.76
(c) first payment £28.02 then 9 at £27.97

EXERCISE 9g

1 (a)

	Jan	Feb	Mar	Apr	May	June	July	Aug	Sept	Oct	Nov	Dec
Amount over	330		260	210		470	160			50	150	
Amount under		80			190			120	150			450

(b) £16 720 (c) £16 080 (d) yes (e) yes

2 (a) (i) £4200 (ii) £1920 (iii) £960

(b)

	Jan	Feb	Mar	Apr	May	June	July	Aug	Sept	Oct	Nov	Dec
Opening balance	0	210	420	585	200	450	535	1	251	456	706	506
Closing balance	210	420	585	200	450	535	1	251	456	706	506	711

(c) (i) £13 800 (ii) £13 089 (d) Apr, July and Nov (e) no (f) £840, 6.09%
(g) £14 500 (to nearest £10) (h) yes, expenditure less than £14 200 (i) 30.4%

Multiple-choice questions 9

1 A **2** C **3** D **4** B

Self-assessment test 9

1 (a)

	£
5 lb bananas at 54p per lb	2.70
3 lb apples at 38p per lb	1.14
$1\frac{1}{2}$ lb grapes at £1.80 per lb	2.70
8 oranges at 22p each	1.76
4 grapefruit at 35p each	1.40
	9.70

(b) 30p

2 £4166.55
3 (a) 1329 (b) £118.55 (c) £137.29 (d) £148.27
4 £261.25

EXERCISE 10a

1 (a) For £19.25 in the cheapest seats (b) £43.75
2 (a) £3 (b) £13.50 **3** (a) £9 (b) £21 (c) £7
4 (a) £21.90 (b) £138.70
5 (a) £135 (b) £125.80 (c) £138.60 (d) £338.40
(£6 − 5% − £1 per person per concert)

EXERCISE 10b

1 £9.70 **2** £4498 **3** £125
4 £2.50 a dozen + breakages **5** (a) £200.50 (b) yes
6 (a) £6.25 (b) £13

EXERCISE 11a

1 (a) £659.49 credit
(b) £99.33 credit
(c) £29.14 credit
2 yes, £27.78 for 1 day 29–30 Aug
3 (a) 30 Aug
(b) 29 Aug (in debt)
4 £6.86
5 £537.12
6 The cheques were not paid in and cleared in the same order as they were written.
7 Monthly – probably on the last working day.
8 £694.13 including bank charges
9 £940.08
10 (a) £132.77
(b) £3.96
11 (a) 48
(b) £599.64

12 (a) (i) £190 (ii) £37.04 (b) (i) 19 (ii) 17
(c) £41.72

	13	**14** (a)	(b)
Notes £50	100		900
Notes £20	360	240	180
Notes £10	150		
Notes £5		85	
coin £1			
50p	13.50	6.50	33.50
20p	6.80		8.80
silver	8.95		
bronze	14.56	7.34	
Total cash	£653.81	£338.84	£1122.30
Postal orders			
Cheques			
Total credit	£653.81	£338.84	£1122.30

EXERCISE 10c

1 0.57p per km for the four **2** 8p
3 (a) £487.20 (b) 11.0p
4 (a) (i) 214.5 km (ii) 11 154 km (b) £1259.60
5 (a) 100 gal (b) £280

EXERCISE 10d

1 (a) 75p (b) £1.14 **2** £1.07 **3** £2.18 **4** £1.52
5 £2.29 **6** (a) £6.50 (b) £13.50
7 £9 **8** (a) £3.25 (b) £4.45
9 (a) £2.65 (b) £2.05 (c) £1.45
10 £6.40; no – too heavy **11** 55p; letter post is usually quicker
12 £6.60 **13** £1440 **14** £1271.60 **15** £110.61

EXERCISE 10e

1 (a) 90p (b) £1.50 (c) £3 (d) £4 (e) £10.40
2 (a) (i) £79.50 (ii) £110.25 (iii) £168.75
(b) (i) 100 (ii) 200 (iii) 325
(c) 125, £66.25 (d) 175, £92.75
3 (a) (i) 43p (ii) 37p (iii) 32p
(b) (i) £77.40 (ii) £84.36 (iii) £337.50 (iv) £43
4 (a) (i) 60p (ii) £1.20 (iii) £1.75
(b) £1.68 (12 × 10p + 4 × 12p) (c) 90p

Multiple-choice questions 10

1 C **2** A **3** D **4** B

Self-assessment test 10

1 £143
2 (a) (i) £9.18 (ii) £15.34 (b) buying by £140.30
3 (a) £2.39 (b) £14
4 (a) (i) £2.79 (ii) £1.99 (b) (i) £99.50 (ii) £268.50

EXERCISE 11b

1 (a) £209.79 (b) £193.38 (c) £81.67
2 £100 3 £290.28 4 £322.18 5 none 6 £15.49
7 (a) £313.46 (b) £134.72
8 Her cheque for £234.84 has not been cleared. Without this there is insufficient in the account to meet a cheque for £51.77.

EXERCISE 11c

1 (a) (i) £330 (ii) £935 (b) £66 000
2 (a) £562.50 (b) £6750 (c) £202 500
3 (a) £72 000 (b) £8000
(c) (i) £882 (ii) £264 600
4 (a) £43 200 (b) £109 296

EXERCISE 11d

1 (a) £8.78 (b) £8.10 2 (a) £6.62 (b) £9.28
3 £15 860
4 Joan Cartwright £1356, George Helman £5022, Damon Southgate £4132.50, Penny Gates £8730

EXERCISE 11e

In questions 1 and 2 the missing values, in order, are
1 £84.00, £84.00, £109.45, £285.85, £50.02, £335.87
2 £14.40, £8.97, £23.96, £34.95, £82.28, £8.23, £74.05, £14.81, £88.86
3 Other relevant details are:

Quantity	Description	Unit price £	Amount £
15	ELQ computer ribbon	2.99	44.85
6	PQ diskettes	7.99	47.94
3	Surge adaptors	9.75	29.25
4	Printer labels	19.95	79.80
		Subtotal	201.84
		Add VAT at $17\frac{1}{2}$%	35.32
		Total	237.16

4

Quantity	Description	Unit price £	Amount £
15	ELQ computer ribbon	2.99	44.85
6	PQ diskettes	7.99	47.94
3	Surge adaptors	9.75	29.25
4	Printer labels	19.95	79.80
		Gross total	201.84
		less discount at 5%	10.09
		Subtotal	191.75
		Add VAT at $17\frac{1}{2}$%	33.56
		Total	225.31

Multiple-choice questions 11

1 D 2 C 3 B 4 B

Self-assessment test 11

1 The missing values in order are: £44.97, £43.98, £12.30, £23.95, £125.20, £12.52, £112.68, £19.72, £132.40
2 (a) £911.68 (b) £48 000
3 (a) £2267.84 (b) £482.84 more
4 (a) £455.96 (b) (i) £940.08 (ii) £788.03

EXERCISE 12a

1 (a) $\frac{1}{2}$ (b) $\frac{1}{4}$ (c) $\frac{3}{4}$ (d) $\frac{1}{12}$ (e) $\frac{1}{3}$
2 (a) 180° (b) 90° (c) 270° (d) 30° (e) 120°
3 (a) $\frac{1}{4}$ (b) $\frac{1}{2}$ (c) $\frac{3}{4}$ (d) $\frac{1}{6}$ (e) $\frac{2}{3}$
4 (a) $\frac{1}{2}$ (b) $\frac{3}{4}$ (c) $\frac{1}{12}$ (d) $\frac{1}{24}$ (e) $\frac{1}{144}$
5 (a) $\frac{1}{2}$ (b) $\frac{1}{12}$ (c) $\frac{3}{4}$ (d) $\frac{2}{1}$
6 (a) 150° (b) 210°
7 (a) 210° (b) 270° (c) 360°

EXERCISE 12b

1 obtuse 125° 2 reflex 335° 3 acute 45° 4 acute 85°
5 obtuse 125° 6 reflex 220°
7 (a) e, g, h and i are bigger than d (b) j is smaller than d
(c) f is equal to d

EXERCISE 12c

1 101° 2 63° 3 284° 4 142°

EXERCISE 12d

1 Any three from BE, GH, JI, PQ, AF, SR
2 Any three from BA, GS, HI, PS, QR, EF
3 HI or GJ 4 BA or EF
5 Any three from BA, GS HI, PS, QR, EF 6 BC or DE

EXERCISE 12e

1 (a) 30° (b) 70° (c) 53° (d) 18° (e) 45°
2 (a) 50° (b) 135° (c) 87° (d) 4° (e) 90°
3 (a) a and c, b and d, e and g, h and f
(b) a and e, b and f, d and h, c and g
(c) b and h, c and e (d) c and h, b and e
4 $a = 107°, b = 107°, c = 73°$
5 $d = 127°, e = 82°$ 6 $f = 107°$ 7 $g = 48°, h = 124°$
8 $i = 62°, j = 118°, k = 24°, l = 156°$ 9 $m = 59°, n = 43°$

EXERCISE 12f

1 $a = 54°, b = 72°, c = 108°$ 2 $d = 90°, e = 29°, f = 119°$
3 $g = 65°, h = 25, i = 40°$ 4 $j = 68°, k = 112°, l = 34°$
5 $m = 47°, n = 61°, p = 72°$
6 $q = 62°, r = 42°, s = 76°, t = 62°$
7 $t = 60°, u = 240°$ 8 $v = 76°, w = 104°$
9 $x = 44°$

EXERCISE 12g

You have your own accurate drawings for these questions.

EXERCISE 12h

1 93° 2 $b = 55°, c = 93°$
3 $d = 54°, e = 54°, f = 72°, g = 54°$
4 $h = 38°, i = 117°$ 5 $j = 124°$
6 $k = 82°, l = 16°$ 7 $m = 94°, n = 209°$
8 $p = 94°$ 9 $q = 95°, r = 98°, s = 106°, t = 74°$

EXERCISE 12i

1 yes 2 no 3 yes 4 yes 5 60 cm
6 4.1 m 7 15.5 m 8 52 m 9 4.8 m 10 19.4 cm
11 16.6 ft 12 6 ft 6.6 in

Multiple-choice questions 12

1 B 2 B 3 D 4 A 5 B

Self-assessment test 12

1 (a) (i) 120° (ii) 165° (iii) 360°
(b) (i) 120° (ii) 330°
2 (a) a and b (b) c and e (c) d and f
3 (a) $a = 34°, b = 146°$ (b) $c = 79°, d = 29°$
4 b and c are true, a, d and e are false
5 (a) 3 cm (b) 10 mm (c) yes
6 18.3 ft (18 ft 4 in)

EXERCISE 13a

1 32 cm^2 **2** 62 cm^2 **3** 45 cm^2 **4** 155 cm^2
5 163 cm^2 **6** 40.92 cm^2 **7** 29. 22 cm^2 **8** 41 cm^2
9 61.18 cm^2 **10** 113.4 cm^2 **11** 34.5 cm^2 **12** 80 mm^2
13 (a)

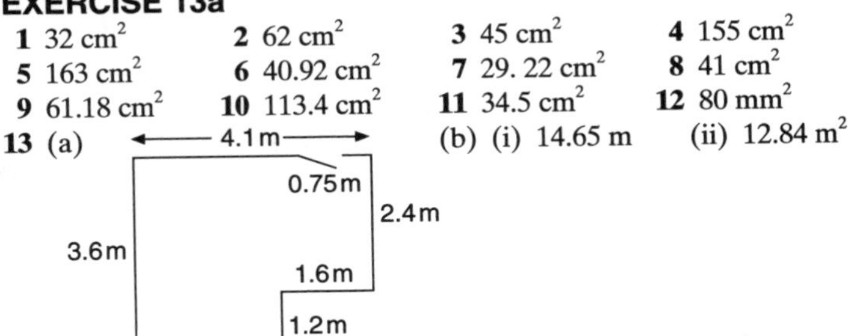

(b) (i) 14.65 m (ii) 12.84 m^2

14 (a) 392.7 cm^2 (b) 177.16 cm^2 (c) 215.54 cm^2
15 (a) 2400 cm^2 (0.24 m^2) (b) 0.98 m^2 (9800 cm^2)

EXERCISE 13b

1 16.4 cm^2 **2** 150 cm^2 **3** 132 cm^2 **4** 27.84 cm^2
5 17.6 cm^2 **6** 74.25 cm^2 **7** 11.84 cm^2 **8** 14.62 cm^2

EXERCISE 13c

1 88 cm^2 **2** 222 cm^2 **3** 1020 mm^2 **4** 1044 cm^2
5 110.4 m^2 **6** 42 m^2 **7** 21.12 cm^2
8 4.5 cm^2 (450 mm^2)

EXERCISE 13d

1 (a) 39 cm^2 (b) 12 cm^2 (c) 37.7 cm^2 (d) 19.5 cm^2
2 29.625 cm^2
3 (a) A: 24 cm^2, B: 24.5 cm^2, C: 7.5 cm^2 (b) 28 cm^2
4 1760 cm^2 **5** 65.0 m^2 (3 sf)
6 (a) 22.5 m^2 (b) 2700 **7** 94 cm^2
8 (a) 65 mm (b) 195 mm × 97.5 mm × 65 mm (c) 30

EXERCISE 13b

1 1225 cm^2 **2** 95.5 m^2 **3** 10 640 mm^2 (106.4 cm^2)
4 1140 cm^2

Multiple-choice questions 13

1 B **2** C **3** D **4** D

Self-assessment test 13

1 (a) 33 m, 42 m^2 (b) 36 cm, 54 cm^2 (c) 52 mm, 128 mm^2
(d) 80 cm, 360 cm^2
2 (a) (i) 32 cm^2 (ii) 18.27 cm^2 (b) 42.9%

EXERCISE 14a

1 (a) yes (b) no (c) yes (d) no (e) yes
(f) no

2 **3** **4**

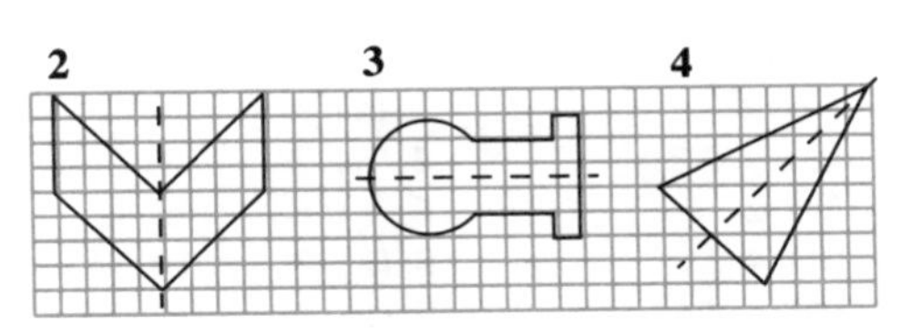

5 **6** **7**

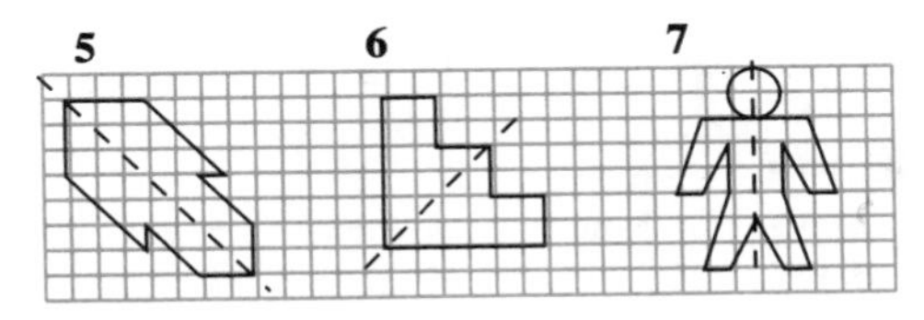

8 **9** **10**

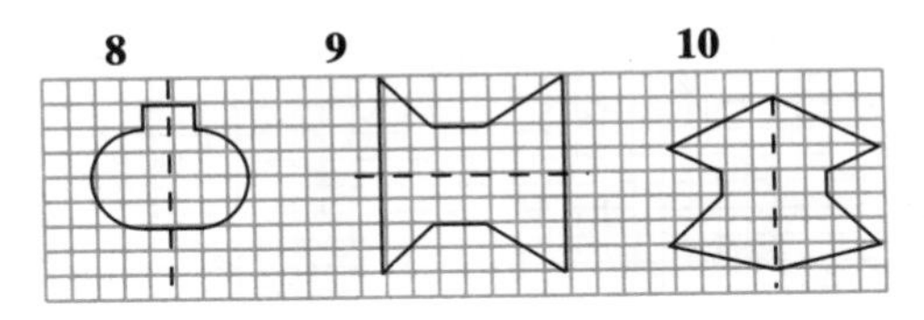

11 **12** **13**

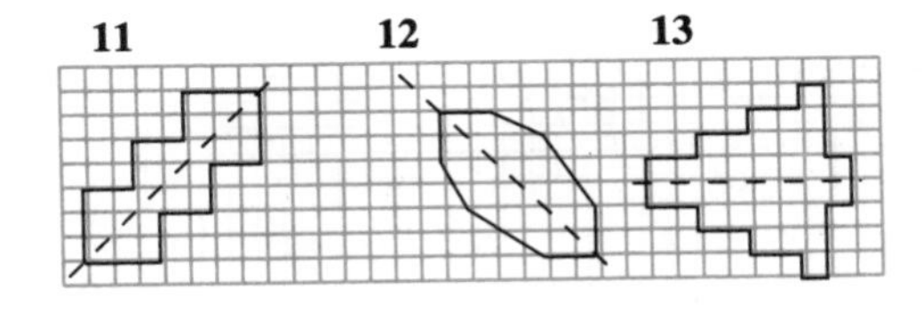

EXERCISE 14b

1 **2** **3**

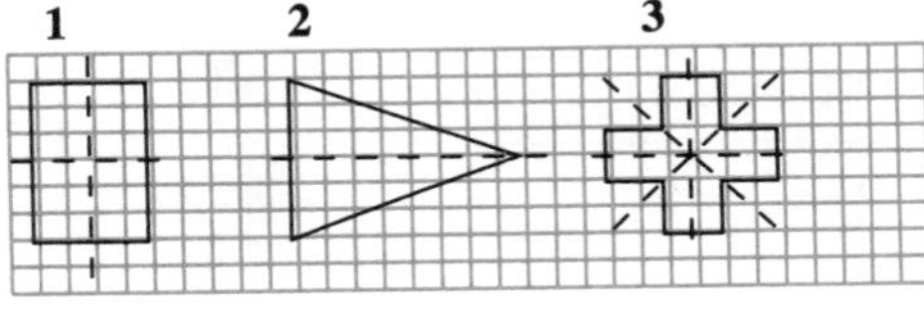

4 **5** **6**

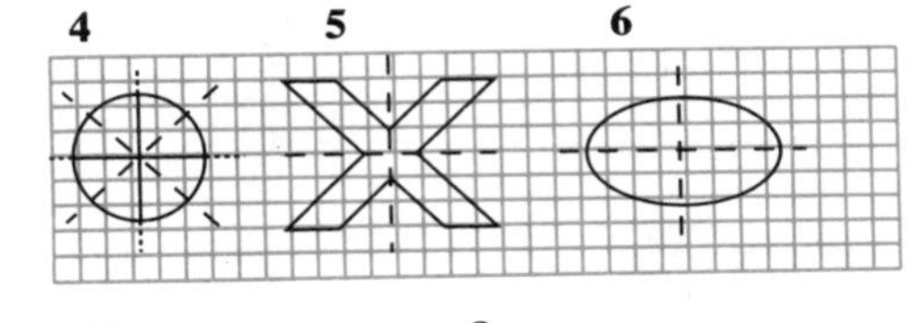

7 **8**

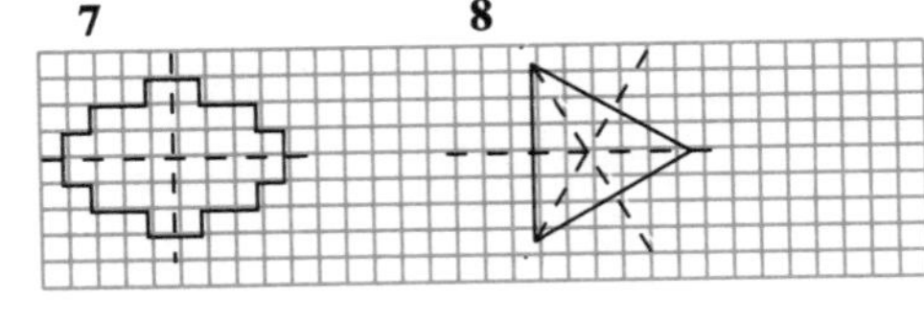

9 **10**

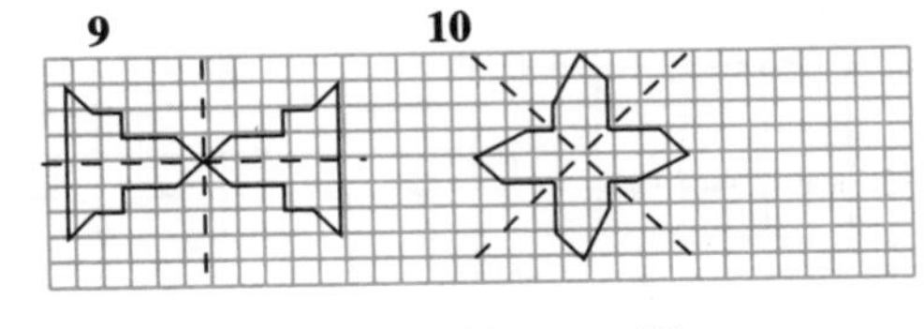

11 (a) (b) (c) (d)

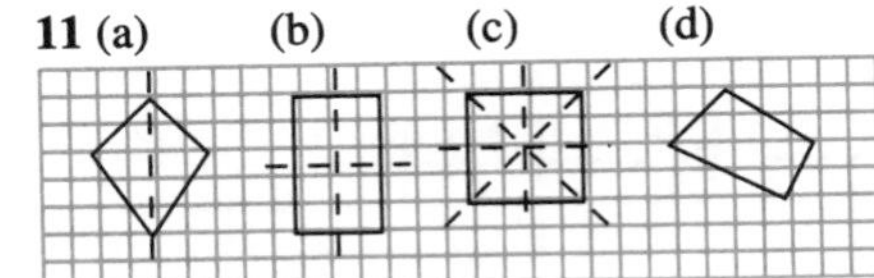

EXERCISE 14c

1 3 **2** 4 **3** 2 **4** 5 **5** 5 **6** 2
7 yes, Q1, order 2; Q3 order 4; Q4 order 4; Q5 order 2; Q6 order 2
8 You have your own answers.

EXERCISE 14d

1 (a) 2 (b) 2 **2** (a) none (b) 3
3 (a) 4 (b) 4 **4** (a) 2 (b) 2
5 (a) 0 (b) 2 **6** (a) 6 (b) 6
7 (a) 4 (b) 4 **8** (a) 2 (b) 2
9 (a) 1 (b) none **10** (a) 3 (b) 3
11 (a) 0 (b) 3 **12** (a) 0 (b) 0
13 You have your own answer. **14** (a) 6 (b) 6

EXERCISE 14e

1 yes **2** yes **3** no **4** yes **5** yes **6** no
7 yes **8** yes **9** yes **10** no **11** yes **12** yes

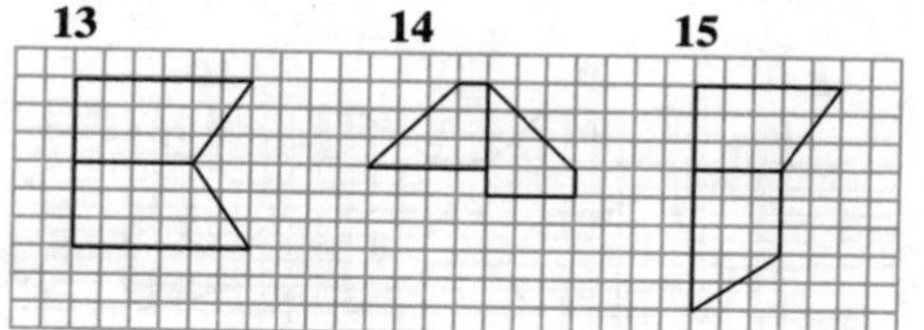

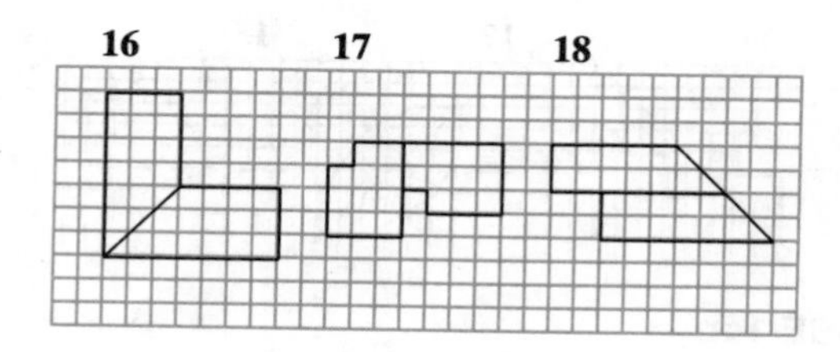

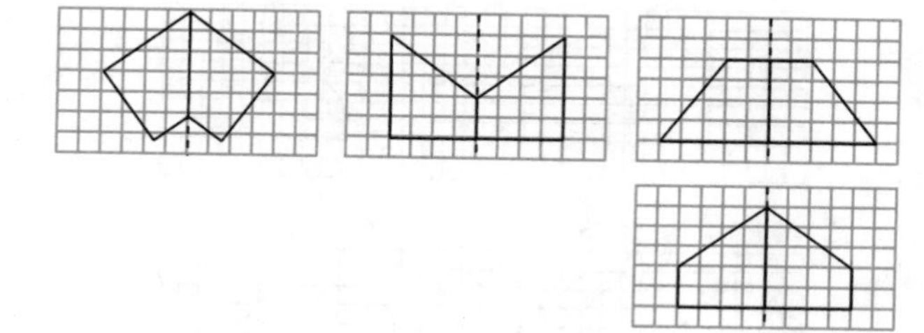

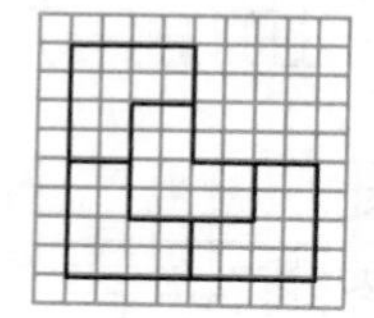

EXERCISE 14f

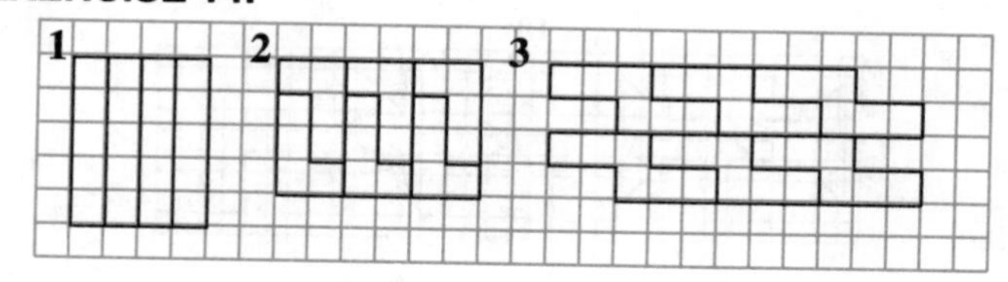

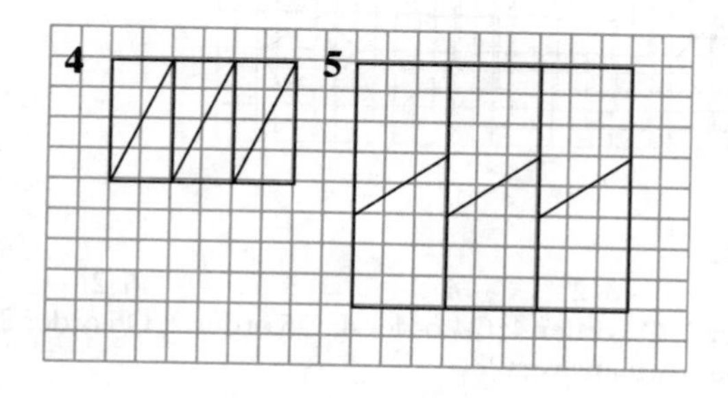

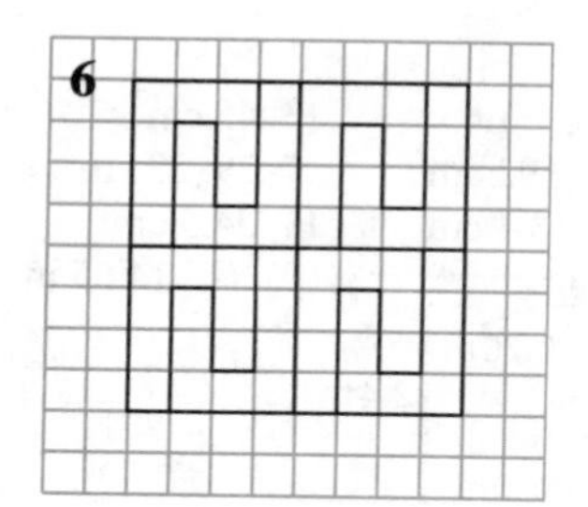

EXERCISE 14g

1 (a) yes (b) yes (c) no (d) no (e) no
(f) yes
2 (a) yes (b)

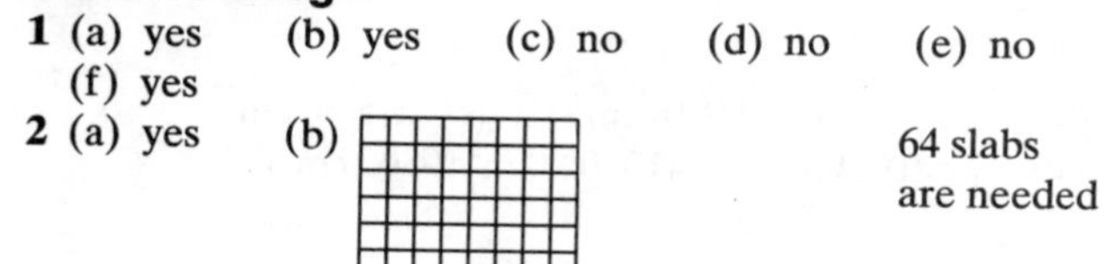

64 slabs are needed

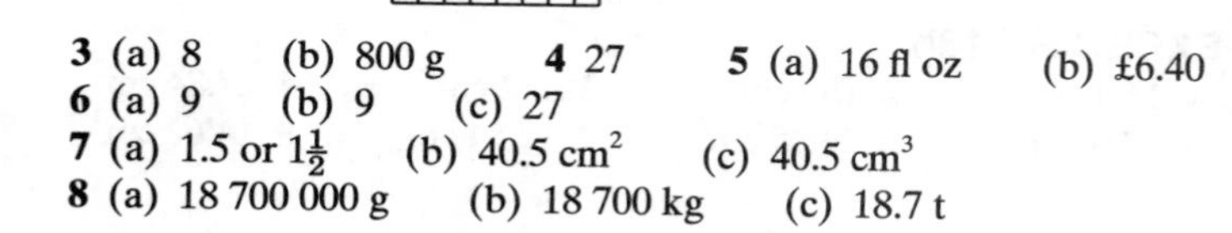

3 (a) 8 (b) 800 g **4** 27 **5** (a) 16 fl oz (b) £6.40
6 (a) 9 (b) 9 (c) 27
7 (a) 1.5 or $1\frac{1}{2}$ (b) 40.5 cm^2 (c) 40.5 cm^3
8 (a) 18 700 000 g (b) 18 700 kg (c) 18.7 t

Multiple-choice questions 14

1 C **2** D **3** B **4** D

Self-assessment test 14

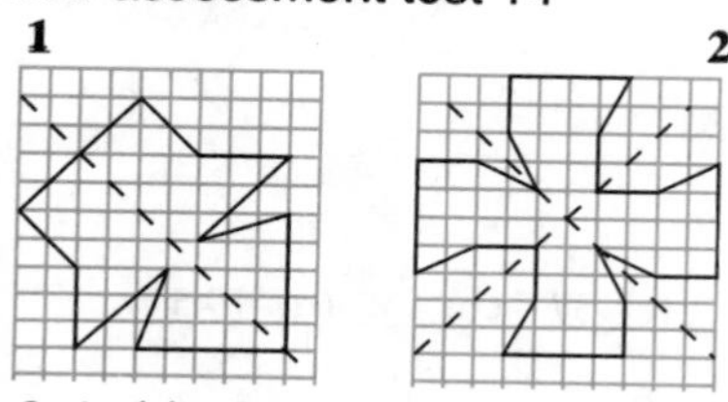

3 A (a) 2 (b) 2 **4** B, C and E **5** (a) no (b) yes
B (a) 2 (b) 2 (c) yes (d) no
C (a) 2 (b) 2

6 (a) yes: for wall $\frac{\text{length}}{\text{width}} = \frac{2}{1.5} = \frac{4}{3}$

and for tile $\frac{\text{length}}{\text{width}} = \frac{20}{15} = \frac{4}{3}$

(b) 100

7 (a) 3 (b) 3 (c) 9 (d) 27

EXERCISE 15a

1 no answers required
2 (a) 6, rectangles (b) (i) 12 (ii) 8 (c) the same

EXERCISE 15b

1 (a) a triangular prism (b) 5 (i) 3 (ii) 2
(c) (i) 9 (ii) 6
2 (a) a regular pentagon (b) a pentagonal prism
(c) (i) 7 (ii) 15 (iii) 10 (d) (i) 5 (ii) 2

EXERCISE 15c

1 (a) no answers (b) 5; 4 triangles and 1 square
(c) (i) 8 (ii) 5
2 (a)

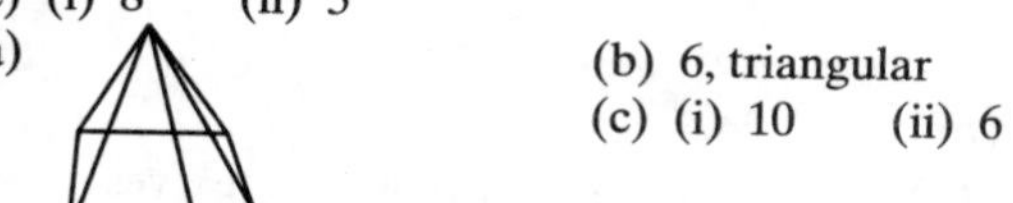

(b) 6, triangular
(c) (i) 10 (ii) 6

EXERCISE 15d

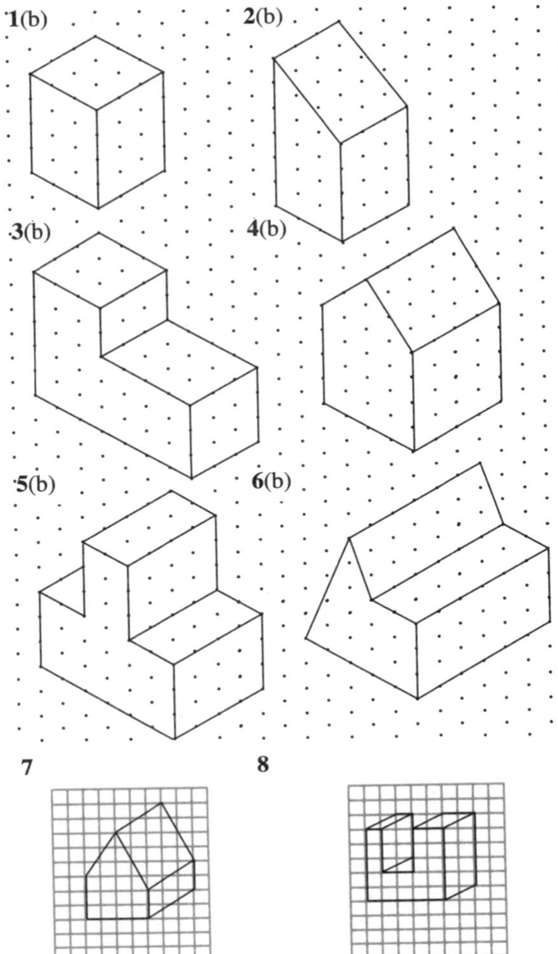

EXERCISE 15e

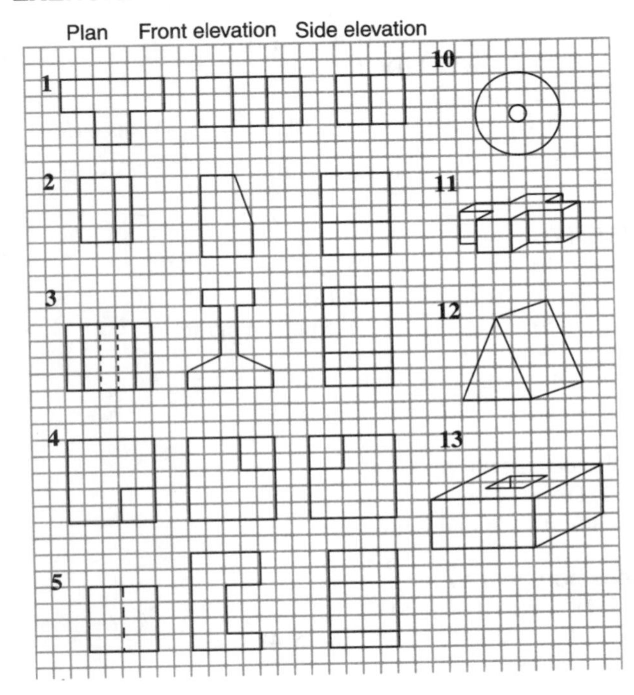

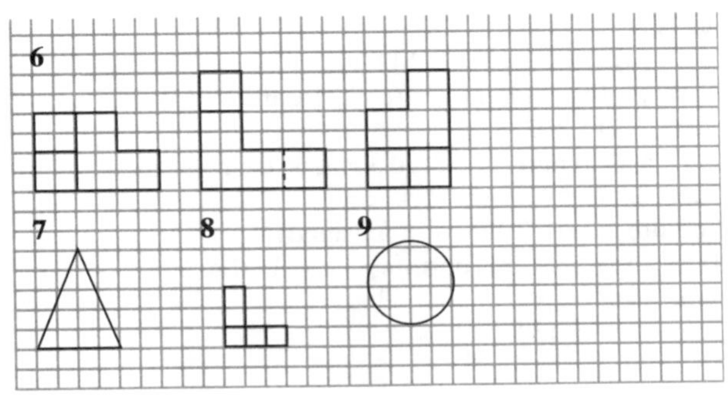

EXERCISE 15f

1 yes **2** no – it is not halfway along its length
3 yes **4** yes **5** yes **6** no
7 5 **8** 2

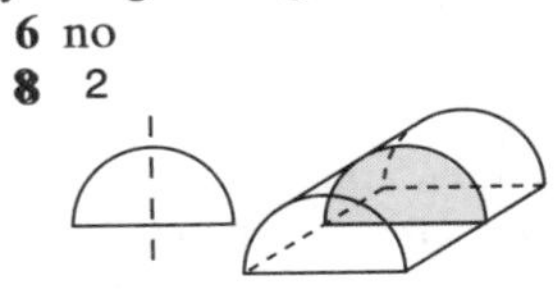

9 4 **10** 2 **11** an infinite number

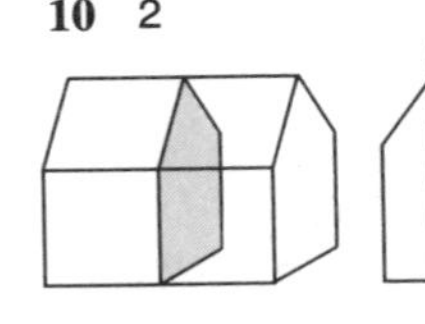

12 2

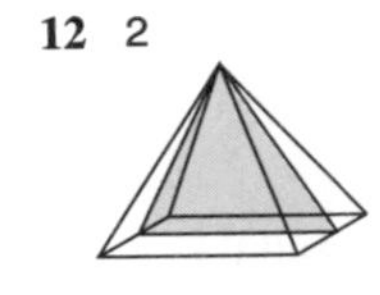

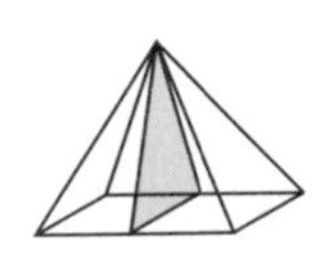

Multiple-choice questions 15

1 B **2** C **3** B **4** B

Self-assessment test 15

1 A: (a) (i) 15 (ii) 10 (b) (i) 5 (ii) 2
B: (a) (i) 24 (ii) 16 (b) (i) 8 (ii) 2
C: (a) (i) 36 (ii) 24 (b) (i) 12 (ii) 2

2

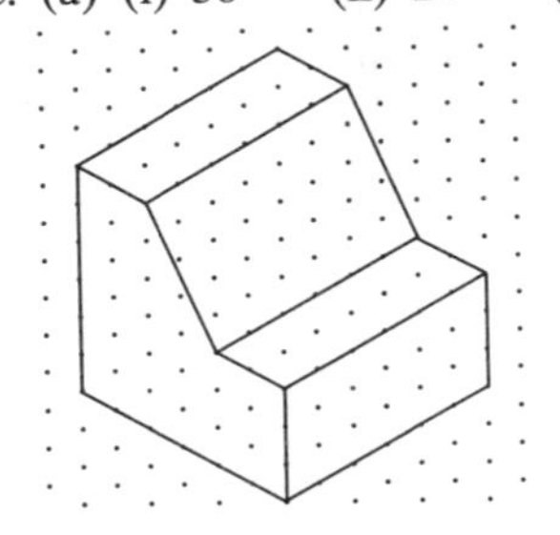

3

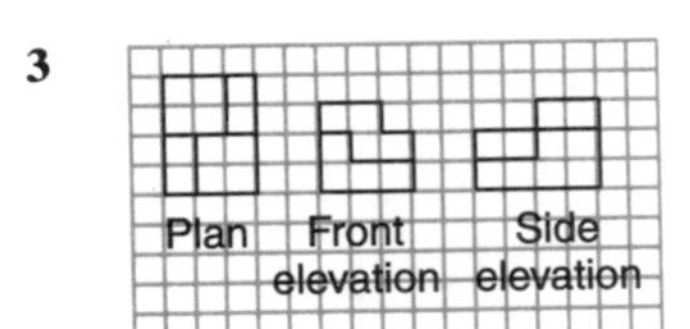

4 2

EXERCISE 16a

1, 2 You have your own answers.
3 (a) 150 cm (b) 192 cm **4** (a) 10 in (b) 30 in
5 (a) 225 cm (b) 225 cm (c) (i) 11 250 cm (ii) 110 m

EXERCISE 16b

1 (a) 3.14 (b) 3.14 (c) 3.142
2 (a) 18.8 cm (b) 26.1 cm (c) 111 mm (d) 24.5 cm
(e) 149 cm (f) 102 m
3 283 cm **4** 88.0 mm **5** 50.3 cm, 66.0 cm, 84.8 cm
6 (a) 0.35 cm (3.5 mm) (b) 1.45 cm
7 8.80 m (minute hand), 0.476 m (hour hand)
8 (a) 44.0 cm (top), 53.4 cm (bottom) (b) 97.4 cm
(c) 100 cm, 2.6 cm
9 (a) 66.0 cm (b) 150
10 603 cm
11 (a) 4.09 cm (b) 21.8 m (c) 234 mm
12 (a) 2.94 cm (b) 26.8 m (c) 51.6 mm **13** 0.764 m
14 (a) 38.2 cm (b) 33.1 cm (c) 2.55 cm
15 (a) 25.1 in (b) 87.3 yd (c) 143
16 (a) 13 (b) (i) 22 mm (ii) 16 mm
(c) (i) 17.5 mm (ii) 21 mm (iii) 17 mm
(d) yes: sizes go up in 0.5 mm steps
(e) (i) 19.75 mm (ii) 21.75 mm
17 (a) 158 cm (b) 67.2 cm (c) 532 mm (d) 308 mm
(e) 63.6 cm (f) 490 mm (49 cm)

EXERCISE 16c

1 17.6 m **2** 34.6 cm, 17.3 cm **3** 47.1 cm
4 30.4 cm **5** (a) 85 cm (b) 267 cm (c) 437 cm
6 (a) AB = AD = CD = 140 cm
(b) (i) 70 cm (ii) 220 cm (c) 640 cm
7 (a) 32 m (b) 101 m (c) 401 m (d) 8.02 km

EXERCISE 16d

1 50.3 cm^2 **2** 1520 m^2 **3** 1130 mm^2
4 9.05 cm^2 **5** 78.5 yd^2
6 (a) 4590 cm^2 (b) 4090 cm^2 (c) 12 800 cm^2
7 (a) 661 cm^2 (b) 2020 cm^2 **8** 134 cm^2
9 145 cm^2 **10** 2620 cm^2

EXERCISE 16e

1 (a) (i) 1.32 m^2 (ii) 132 m^2 (b) 606
2 3.28 m^2 **3** 239 cm^2 **4** 11.0 cm^2
5 17 700 mm^3 (17.7 cm^3) **6** 50.3 cm^3
7 1663 cm^3 **8** (a) 1.44 cm^2 (b) 0.785 cm^2 (c) 45%
9 diameter = height = 18.5 cm
10 (a) 75 000 cm^3 (b) 1360 cm^2 (c) 20.8 cm
11 78.7 mm **12** (a) 314 cm^2 (b) 79.9 cm^2
13 55 000 m^3 **14** 1290 mm^3

Multiple-choice questions 16

1 A **2** C **3** D **4** A **5** C

Self-assessment test 16

1 17.5 cm
2 (a) 122 cm (b) 3.83 m
(c) (i) 1.17 m^2 (ii) 11 700 cm^2
3 3180 cm^2
4 (a) 26.4 cm (b) 393 cm^2
(c) (i) 709 cm^3 (iii) 0.709 ℓ
5 0.0415 cm^3
6 (a) 346 mm^2 (b) 113 mm^2 (c) 233 mm^2
(d) 466 mm^3

EXERCISE 17a

1 (a) A(1, 3), B(9, 3), C(9, 9) (b) D(1, 9) (c) E(7, 3)
(d) F(7, 9) (e) (i) (5,3) (ii) (1, 6) (iii) (5, 6)
2 (a) (7, 1), (11, 1), (9, 7) (G) (b) (6, 5), (6, 8), (2, 8), (D)
(c) (0, 3), (0, 5), (3, 4)
(d) (7, 9), (6, 12), (8, 12) (B)
(e) (8, 10), (10, 8), (11, 11) (C)
3 (a), (b) and (c)

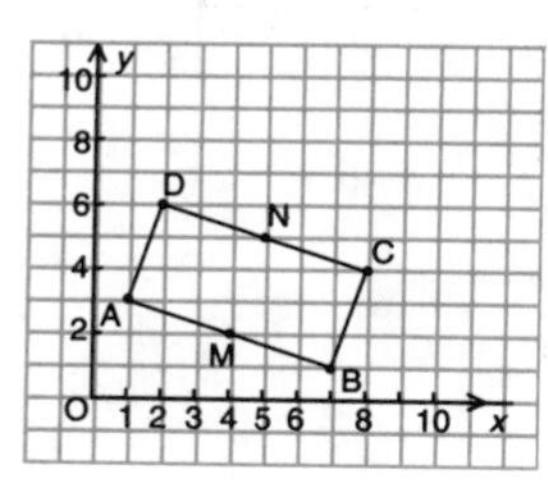

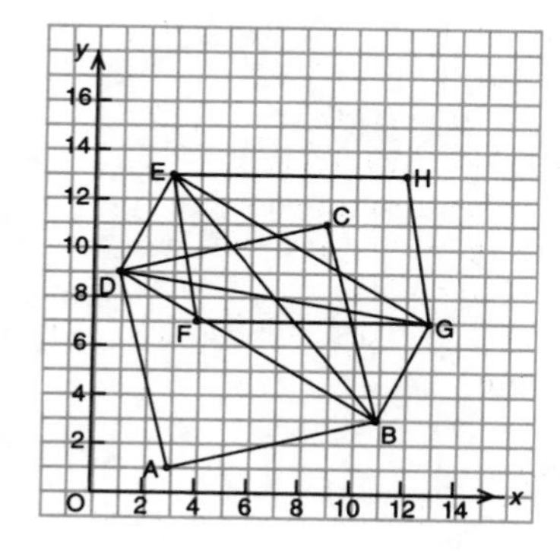

(c) D(2, 6)
(d) M(4, 2) N(5, 5)
(e) (4.5, 3.5)
4 the profile of a head
5 (a) D(1, 9) (b) H(12, 13)
(c) (i) a parallelogram; this is not a rectangle, since no angle is 90°
(ii) (7, 8)
6 (a) (i) (1, 2) (ii) (4, 8) (iii) (8, 9)
(b) (i) (7, 9) (ii) (9, 6)
(c) (i) Sandy Beach
(ii) White Ladies Peak (iii) wreck
7 (a) (i) P (ii) G (b) (i) N (ii) R
(iii) U (c) (i) WELL DONE
(ii) BRING BREAD
(d) (i) (5, 2), (5, 3), (5, 1) pause (2, 2), (5, 3), (5, 4) pause (5, 3), (1, 5), (5, 4)
(ii) (5, 4), (5, 3), (4, 3), (4, 2), (2, 2), (3, 2), (5, 4)

EXERCISE 17b

1 (a) −4 (b) −4 **2** (a) −6 (b) −3
3 (a) (4, −7) (b) (−7, 2) **4** (a) −7 (b) −3
5 (a) −1 (b) −4 **6** a parallelogram
7 (−7, 3)
8 (a) (−6, −9) (b) (−5, −1) (c) (−2, −7)
(d) (i) 6 units (ii) 6 units (e) −4

Multiple-choice questions 17

1 A **2** D **3** B
4 B and D are true, A and C are false

Self-assessment test 17

1 (a) (−4, 4) (b) (−3, −5)
2 (a) (i) (7, 4) (ii) (7, 6) (iii) (5, 4)
(b) (i) 4 (ii) 2

3

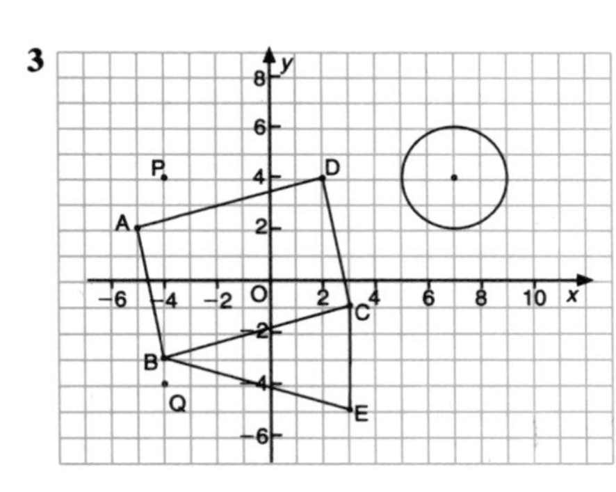

D(2, 4)

(b) 5

4 (a) E(3, −5) (b) 7

EXERCISE 18a

1 (a) 55 (b) (i) 16 (ii) 52 (iii) 43
(c) (i) 39 (ii) 3 (iii) 12 (d) 27

2 (a) (i) 6° east of true north (ii) 7° west of true north
(b) (i) 1000 AD (ii) 1800
(c) it's getting nearer to true north

3 (a) (i) 1000 rev/min (ii) 5900 rev/min
(b) 150 N m, 3000 rev/min
(c) (i) 1450 rev/min and 5200 rev/min (ii) 2150 rev/min and 4300 rev/min

EXERCISE 18b

1 (a) 10 °C (b) (i) 32 °C (ii) 68 °F (iii) 14 °F
(c) (i) 54 °F (ii) −18 °C

2 (a) (i) £10 (ii) 290 Ff (iii) £3
(b) (i) £50 = 415 Ff, so £500 = 4150 Ff (ii) 100 Ff = £12, so 1200 Ff = £144

3 (a) 110 lb (b) $11\frac{1}{2}$ kg

EXERCISE 18c

1 (a)–(e)

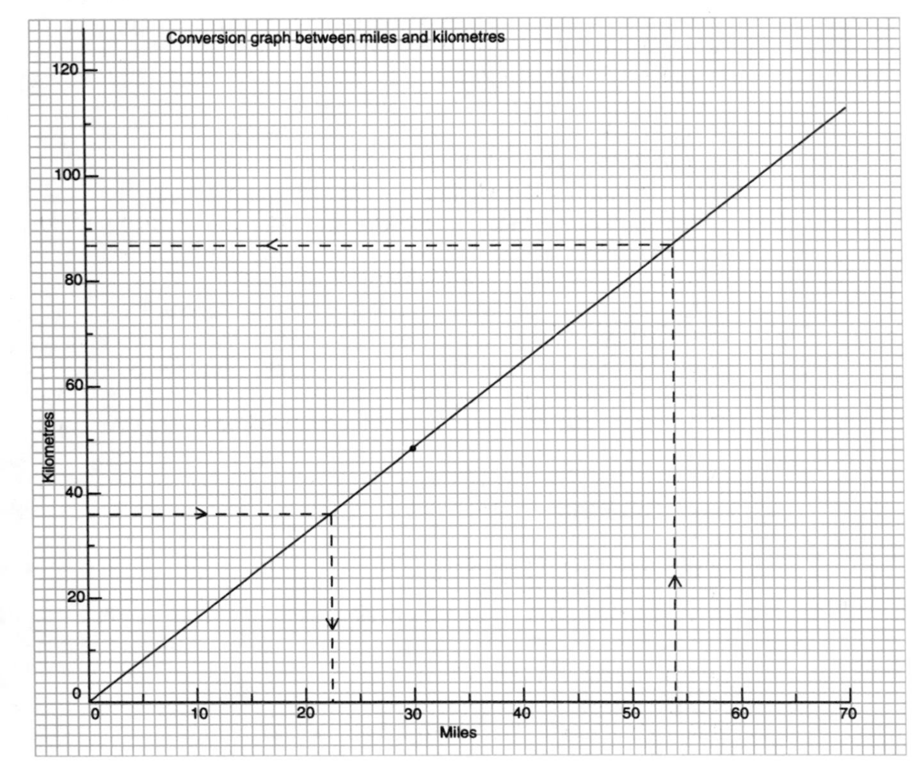

(f) (i) 87 km (ii) $22\frac{1}{2}$ miles

2 (a) your own graph (b) (i) £23 (ii) $36

3 (a) your own graph
(b) (i) 66 ha (ii) the German vineyard by 37 acres

4 (a) your own graph (b) (i) 340 ml (ii) $3\frac{1}{2}$ fl oz

EXERCISE 18d

1 (a) (i) 133 °C (ii) 69 °C (b) 3.4 min (c) 6.5 min

2 (a) your own graph (b) (i) 0.7 pints (ii) 6.75 in

3 (a) (i) 16 °C (ii) $37\frac{1}{2}$ °C (b) 8.12 a.m. and 7.57 p.m.
(c) 6 h 36 min (d) 24.1 °C
(e) 14 h (from midnight to 2 p.m.)

Self-assessment test 18

1 (a)

Conversion graph between square yards and square metres
Square metres
Square yards

(b) (i) 9.6 sq metres (ii) 16.3 sq yards (c) £42

2 (a) 6.25 litres/100 km (b) 56.5 m.p.g.

EXERCISE 19a

1 (a) 5.5 cm (b) 5.5 m (c) 4 cm (d) 4 m
2 (a) 37.5 cm (b) 6 cm (c) 5.25 cm
3 (a) (i) 6 cm (ii) 4.5 cm (b) (i) 24 ft (ii) 18 ft
(c) soccer 8 ft, rugby 10 ft (d) 30 ft
4 (a) 15 cm (b) 9.6 cm
5 (a) (i) $5\text{ m} \times 4\text{ m}$ (ii) $4\text{ m} \times 3.5\text{ m}$ (b) 2.5 m
(c) 20 m^2, £400
6 (a) (i) 236 mm (ii) 188 mm (iii) 208 mm (iv) 34 mm
(b) (i) 32 mm (ii) 26 mm
(c) yes, going $+ 2 \times$ rise $= 584$ mm (d) yes
(e) (i) 3008 mm (3.008 m) (ii) 14
(f) An area of 1995 cm^2 ($19 \times 105\text{ cm}^2$) and 2.6 cm thick. This is a volume of 5190 cm^3 (to 3 sf).

EXERCISE 19b

1 east **2** south-west **3** south **4** north-west

EXERCISE 19c

1 (a) 090° (b) 270° (c) 045° (d) 225°
2

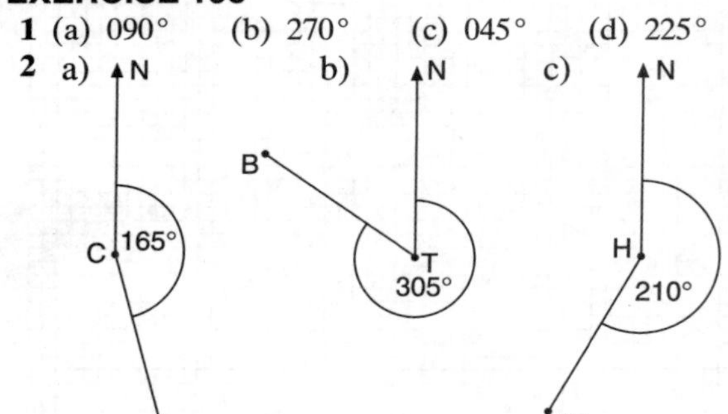

3 (a) 256° (b) 330° (c) 103°
4

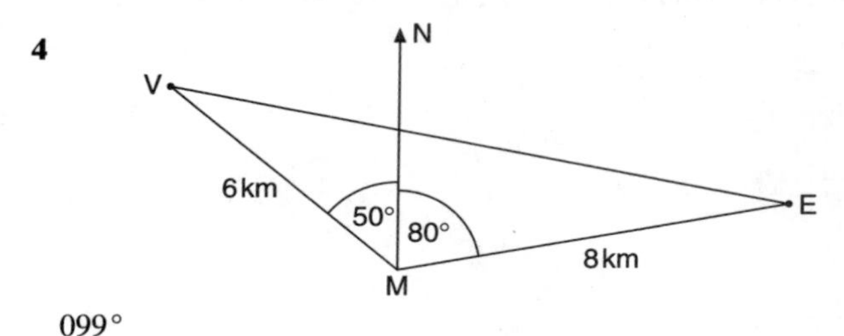

099°

EXERCISE 19d

1 the town of Cowley, Oxford **2** the village of Weston
3 Witney **4** Mortimer Common
5 the M4 motorway **6** F5
7 E6 **8** C6 **9** J2 **10** E7

EXERCISE 19e

1 Woolleigh **2** Furze Barton **3** Natty Cross **4** Dodscott
5 Little Potheridge **6** 59 13 **7** 57 12
8 52 16 **9** 53 18 **10** 53 20 **11** Cudworthy
12 Settlement **13** St Giles in the Wood Church
14 Glenmore **15** Natty Cross **16** 552 150 **17** 535 206
18 543 143 **19** 590 135 **20** 515 140

Multiple-choice questions 19

1 C **2** B **3** B **4** A and D are true, B and C are false

Self-assessment test 19

1 (a) B.T. Tower (b) the shopping centre
2 (a) church at St Mary Seaford (b) Pengam School
3 (a) 10 23 (b) 08 24 (c) 08 25
4 (a) 091 219 (b) 067 219 (c) 076 238
5 (a) 500 m (b) 2.5 km
6 (a) 090° (b) 225°

EXERCISE 20a

1 Yes **2** No; Callum is probably a much better player.
3 No; They play in different leagues. **4** Yes.
5 There are an equal number of boys and girls.

EXERCISE 20b

1 $\frac{1}{6}$ **2** $\frac{1}{2}$ **3** $\frac{1}{4}$ **4** $\frac{1}{7}$ **5** (a) $\frac{1}{6}$ (b) $\frac{1}{6}$ (c) $\frac{1}{6}$

EXERCISE 20c

1 (a) $\frac{1}{3}$ (b) $\frac{1}{12}$ (c) $\frac{19}{36}$
2 (a) yes (b) (i) $\frac{1}{4}$ (ii) $\frac{1}{26}$ (iii) $\frac{6}{13}$
3 (a) orange 5, cherries 7, lemon 6, plum 5
(b) (i) $\frac{1}{10}$ (ii) $\frac{1}{5}$ (iii) $\frac{1}{5}$
4 $\frac{7}{19}$
5 (a) 36 (b) (i) $\frac{2}{3}$ (ii) $\frac{1}{3}$ (c) (i) $\frac{2}{7}$ (ii) $\frac{4}{7}$ (iii) $\frac{3}{7}$
(d) (i) 6 (ii) 24

EXERCISE 20d

1 (a) 5 (b) 4 **2** (a) $\frac{5}{9}$ (b) $\frac{4}{9}$ **3** (a) 0 (b) $\frac{0}{9}$ i.e. 0
4 (a) $\frac{4}{9}$ (b) $\frac{5}{9}$ (c) 0 (d) 0 (e) 1
5 (a) 0 (b) 1 (c) 0 (d) 1

EXERCISE 20e

1 (a) Certain. (b) Unlikely. (c) An even chance.
(d) An even chance. (e) Certain.
(f) Only you can answer this. (g) Very unlikely.
(h) Only you can answer this.
2 (a) You have your own answers for these sentences.
(b) (i) No chance. (ii) Most unlikely. (iii) Less than even chance. (iv) Even chance. (v) Very likely.
(vi) Certain.
3 (a) 8. (b) 35. (c) 2 (either available to speak to or not).

EXERCISE 20f

1 $\frac{1}{4}$ **2** 0.992 **3** 0.28 **4** (a) $\frac{1}{20}$ (b) $\frac{19}{20}$
5 (a) $\frac{11}{31}$ (b) $\frac{9}{124}$ (c) $\frac{17}{31}$
6 (a) $\frac{15}{22}$ (b) $\frac{7}{22}$ (c) $\frac{1}{22}$ (d) $\frac{3}{11}$

EXERCISE 20g

1 $\frac{1}{6}$ (b) $\frac{1}{10}$ (c) $\frac{2}{9}$ (d) $\frac{2}{7}$ **2** $\frac{1}{16}$
3 (a) $\frac{3}{5}$ (b) £8.33 (£$3\frac{1}{3}$ + £5 stake)

EXERCISE 20h

1

		First bag				
		D	D	D	C	C
Second bag	D	D, D	D, D	D, D	C, D	C, D
	D	D, D	D, D	D, D	C, D	C, D
	D	D, D	D, D	D, D	C, D	C, D
	C	D, C	D, C	D, C	C, C	C, C
	C	D, C	D, C	D, C	C, C	C, C

2 (a)

		Lindsay's purse				
		£1	£1	£1	20p	20p
Vicki's purse	£1	£1, £1	£1, £1	£1, £1	20p, £1	20p, £1
	20p	£1, 20p	£1, 20p	£1, 20p	20p, 20p	20p, 20p

(b) 10 (c) 5 (d) 5

EXERCISE 20i

1 (a) $\frac{9}{25}$ (b) $\frac{6}{25}$ (c) $\frac{19}{25}$ **2** (a) $\frac{3}{10}$ (b) $\frac{1}{2}$ (c) $\frac{7}{10}$
3 (a) 36 (b) 7, 6 (c) (i) 3 (ii) 30
(d) (i) $\frac{1}{12}$ (ii) $\frac{5}{6}$ (iii) $\frac{13}{18}$

4

		Damien				
		D	D	D	B	B
Mel	D	D, D	D, D	D, D	B, D	B, D
	B	D, B	D, B	D, B	B, B	B, B
	B	D, B	D, B	D, B	B, B	B, B
	B	D, B	D, B	D, B	B, B	B, B
	B	D, B	D, B	D, B	B, B	B, B

(a) $\frac{3}{25}$ (b) $\frac{14}{25}$ (c) $\frac{22}{25}$

EXERCISE 20j

1 (b) 0.17 ($\frac{1}{6}$); this should agree with the value you got in part (a).
2 (b) 0.5; your value in (a) should be approximately the same.
3 (a) 0.25. (b) It should be about 0.25. (c) The value will probably get nearer to 0.25.
4 (a) can be calculated. (b), (c) and (d) must be found by experiment.

EXERCISE 20k

1 100, 60 **2** 1054 **3** (a) 1080 (b) 120 **4** 7275
5 24 **6** 390
7 (a) 0.16 (b) (i) 624 (ii) 26 (c) 1050

Multiple-choice questions 20

1 B **2** D **3** C
4 A and B are true, C and D are false **5** A

Self-assessment test 20

1 (a) $\frac{1}{13}$ (b) $\frac{3}{13}$ (c) $\frac{2}{13}$ (d) 0 **2** (a) $\frac{7}{10}$ (b) $\frac{3}{10}$
3 (a) $\frac{1}{36}$ (b) 1 (c) 1 (d) $\frac{1}{4}$
4 (a) 0.8 (b) 184

5

		Upper shelf					
		M	M	M	M	C	C
Lower shelf	M	M, M	M, M	M, M	M, M	C, M	C, M
	M	M, M	M, M	M, M	M, M	C, M	C, M
	C	M, C	M, C	M, C	M, C	C, C	C, C
	C	M, C	M, C	M, C	M, C	C, C	C, C
	C	M, C	M, C	M, C	M, C	C, C	C, C

(a) $\frac{4}{15}$ (b) $\frac{8}{15}$
6 350 **7** (a) (i) 60% (ii) 40%
(b) (i) 900 (ii) 1620 (iii) 300

EXERCISE 21a

1 2 : 1 **2** 7 : 5 **3** 2 : 3 **4** 7 : 9
5 1 : 3 **6** 3 : 2 **7** 3 : 5 **8** 5 : 9
9 6 : 9, 28 : 42, 38 : 57, 50 : 75 **10** (a) 5 : 2 (b) 2 : 5
11 64 : 81 **12** (a) 2 : 7 (b) 1 : 3 **13** 2 : 7
14 5 : 3 **15** (a) 2 : 5 (b) 5 : 2

EXERCISE 21b

1 (a) 25 lorries : 10 vans = 5 : 2
(b) 675 red posters : 540 yellow posters = 5 : 4
(c) 4344 seated spectators : 543 standing spectators = 8 : 1
2 (a) 42 pence compared with 105 pence is the same as 2 compared with 5
(b) 80 compact discs compared with 440 cassettes is the same as 2 compared with 11
(c) 357 shop-floor workers compared with 255 office workers is the same as 7 compared with 5
3 91 : 17 **4** 8 : 15 **5** 1 : 64
6 (a) 8 : 3 (b) 32 : 5 (c) 8 : 9 (d) 6 : 7 (e) 2 : 1
(f) 1 : 11 (g) 25 : 33 (h) 5 : 11
7 7 : 4 **8** (a) 7 : 19 (b) 7 : 12 (c) 12 : 7
9 (a) 3 : 11 (b) 5 : 3 (c) 17 : 8 (d) 8 : 7
10 (a) 8 : 5 (b) 15 : 4 (c) 3 : 4 (d) 11 : 14
11 (a) 1 : 2 (b) 1 : 12 (c) 7 : 12

EXERCISE 21c

1 (a) 3 (b) 4 lb (c) 28 oz **2** (a) 36 kg (b) 80 g
3 (a) 180 (b) 80 **4** (a) 300 (b) 60 (c) £30
5 (a) 50 m (b) 0.5 km ($\frac{1}{2}$ km) (d) 2.75 km
6 $\frac{3}{7}$ **7** $\frac{2}{5}$ **8** 3 : 7 **9** 7 : 2

EXERCISE 21d

1 Phil 16, Meg 20 **2** Paul £48, Amanda £36 **3** £22
4 20 acres **5** 115 kg **6** 9720

EXERCISE 21e

1 (a) 70p (b) £2.10 **2** (a) £1.10 (b) £4.40
3 £9.75 **4** 14 oz **5** 611 **6** 25 ℓ **7** £93.96
8 $15\frac{1}{2}$ ℓ **9** £774 **10** (a) 360 (b) 15 (c) 20

EXERCISE 21f

1 10 **2** 51 **3** 32 **4** (a) £308 (b) 77
5 (a) £64 600 (b) 1700

Multiple-choice questions 21

1 C **2** A **3** B
4 B and D are true, A and C are false **5** C

Self-assessment test 21

1 (a) 3 : 2 (b) 2 : 3 **2** 1 : 20
3 18 kg oranges, 36 kg sugar, 9 lemons, 9 litres water
4 166 **5** (a) 990 (b) 55

EXERCISE 22a

1 (a) 3 p.m. (b) 11 a.m. (c) 9 p.m. **2** 2376 m^2
3 (a) 40 miles per hour (b) 36 miles per hour
4 (a) 13.1 (b) 11.2
5 (a) £26 (b) £2.80 (c) £2930 (d) £84
6 (a) 35.4 (b) 25.8 (c) 19.2
7 (a)

Annual sales growth			
91–92	92–93	93–94	94–95
15.2%	13.8%	12.6%	12.1%

(b) (i) it is decreasing (ii) they are increasing more each year than in the previous year

8

Name	Mean blood pressure
Mel	100
Wendy	111
Bina	119
Hank	90

9 (a) 1997 cc (b) 3298 cc

EXERCISE 22b

1 (a) 250 (b) 255 (c) 431 (d) 83
2 (a) Number of components − 512 = 27, 539
(b) Number of components − 387 = 13, 400
(c) Number of bolts = 65 × 4 + 5, 265
(d) Number of washers = 54 × 7 + 4, 382
3 Number of components = 43 × 2 + 5, 91 components
4 1155 **5** 1083 **6** 23, 9 **7** 46

EXERCISE 22c

1 $b = 9$ **2** $a = 11$ **3** $c = 15$ **4** $p = 22$ **5** $q = 41$
6 $y = 33$ **7** $a = 68$ **8** $b = 104$ **9** $a = 37$ **10** $b = 98$
11 $c = 106$ **12** $y = 235$ **13** $a = 14$ **14** $c = 3$ **15** $y = 17$
16 $q = 9$ **17** $r = 27$ **18** $p = 23$ **19** $a = 64$ **20** $b = 30$
21 $p = 32$ **22** $q = 36$ **23** $z = 6$ **24** $y = 107$

EXERCISE 22d

1 $b = 4$ **2** $d = 15$ **3** $e = 6$ **4** $f = 9$
5 $p = 8$ **6** $p = 8$ **7** $y = 8$ **8** $z = 6$
9 $a = 9$ **10** $b = 40$ **11** $y = 78$ **12** $z = 207$
13 $w = 84$ **14** $a = 135$ **15** $b = 438$ **16** $c = 273$

EXERCISE 22e

1 $x = 7$ **2** $b = 48$ **3** $q = 22$ **4** $a = 52$
5 $c = 92$ **6** $b = 53$ **7** $b = 8$ **8** $x = 10$
9 $a = 8$ **10** $b = 17$ **11** $p = 26$ **12** $y = 12$
13 $x = 45$ **14** $y = 9$ **15** $x = 20$ **16** $p = 40$

EXERCISE 22f

1 $a = 1.5$ **2** $p = 2\frac{2}{3}$ **3** $p = 5.6$ **4** $x = 2$
5 $b = 10.6$ **6** $q = 8$ **7** $q = 9.3$ **8** $a = \frac{1}{2}$
9 $z = \frac{1}{2}$ **10** $c = 1\frac{1}{2}$ **11** $x = 71$ **12** $b = 2$
13 $w = 3\frac{1}{4}$ **14** $p = 2\frac{2}{5}$ **15** $y = 46.9$ **16** $c = 1\frac{1}{2}$

EXERCISE 22g

1 $a = 10$ **2** $q = 1$ **3** $x = 3\frac{1}{3}$ **4** $x = 3$
5 $y = 3$ **6** $z = \frac{5}{6}$ **7** $p = 4$ **8** $x = 1\frac{1}{2}$
9 $a = \frac{2}{3}$ **10** $a = 3$ **11** $b = 4$ **12** $d = 4$
13 $y = 18$ **14** $a = 15$ **15** $z = 24$ **16** $b = 80$
17 $x = 15$ **18** $c = 49$ **19** $y = 6$ **20** $a = 4\frac{4}{5}$

EXERCISE 22h

1 $3a + 6$ **2** $2b$ **3** $13c$ **4** $4y$
5 $9a$ **6** $3p + 5q$ **7** $7k$
8 cannot be simplified **9** $12a - 6$ **10** $3p$
11 $2a$ **12** $5a + 2b$ **13** $5a + 2b + 2$ **14** 0
15 $p + 6q - r$ **16** $14m - 2n - 7$ **17** $3y + z$
18 8

EXERCISE 22i

1 $a = 6$ **2** $b = 6$ **3** $c = 9$ **4** $p = 5$
5 $q = 8$ **6** $y = 9$ **7** $b = 4$ **8** $a = 4$
9 $p = 6$ **10** $q = 4.5$ **11** $y = 3.5$ **12** $x = 1$
13 $b = 2$ **14** $c = 3$ **15** $p = 1$ **16** $q = 2$
17 $x = 4$ **18** $a = 6$ **19** $b = 2$ **20** $d = 7$
21 $c = 4$ **22** $p = 7$ **23** $y = 1$ **24** $a = 5$
25 $x = 5$ **26** $z = 3$ **27** $q = 2$ **28** $y = 1$
29 $p = 7$ **30** $b = 6$

EXERCISE 22j

1 (a) 135 cm (b) 150 cm and 165 cm
2 (a) $3x$ pence (b) $8x$ pence (c) 25p (d) 50p
3 (a) 60p (b) £2.40
4 (a) 42 acres (b) 210 acres (c) 126 acres
5 £4 and £8
6 (a) 76 small, 38 medium and 19 large (b) £3135

EXERCISE 22k

1 (a) $6x$ (b) $10p$ (c) $24q$ (d) $60y$
2 (a) $12p - 16$ (b) $30 - 15b$ (c) $7p + 14$ (d) $6x + 21$
3 $a = 2$ **4** $x = 16$ **5** $p = 5$ **6** $q = 8$
7 $a = 9.5$ **8** $b = 1$ **9** $a = 5$ **10** $b = 2$
11 $c = 3$ **12** $p = 5$ **13** $y = 2$ **14** $y = 3$
15 $x = 7$ **16** $q = 0$ **17** $y = 12$ **18** $p = 3$
19 $x = 3\frac{5}{7}$ **20** $p = 1\frac{1}{3}$

EXERCISE 22l

1 $x > 14$; 15, 16 **2** $x > 13$; 14, 15
3 $x > 5$; 6, 7 **4** $x < 6$; 4, 5
5 $x < 12$; 10, 11 **6** $x > 2$; 3, 4
7 $x > 3$; 4, 5 **8** $x > 7$; 8, 9
9 $x < 4$; 2, 3 **10** $x < 7$; 5, 6
11 $x > 3$; 4, 5 **12** $x > 4$; 5, 6
13 $x < 5$; 3, 4 **14** $x < 3$; 1, 2

EXERCISE 22m

1 $a = 4, b = 3$ **2** $a = 3, b = 2$
3 $a = 5, b = 2$ **4** $a = 5, b = 3$
5 $a = 3, b = 2$ **6** $a = 1, b = 4$
7 $p = 9, q = 2$ **8** $p = 4, q = 7$
9 $a = 3, b = 8$ **10** $a = 2, b = 3$
11 $p = 4, q = 3$ **12** $x = 4, y = 1$

EXERCISE 22n

1 (a) a^4 (b) p^2 (c) q^3 (d) r^5
2 (a) $y \times y \times y$ (b) $a \times a \times a \times a \times a$ (c) $m \times m$
(d) $4 \times q \times q \times q \times q$
3 (a) 500 (b) 60 000 (c) 120 000 (d) 8300
(e) 7 210 000 (f) 49 000 000
4 (a) 9×10^2 (b) 7.5×10^3 (c) 8×10^5 (d) 6.42×10^3
(e) 3.49×10^4 (f) 1.264×10^5

EXERCISE 22p

1 5 **2** 8 **3** 10 **4** 0 **5** 3
6 2 **7** 0 **8** 10 **9** 23 **10** 7
11 7 **12** −4 **13** 45 **14** 25 **15** 29
16 88 **17** 72 **18** 62 **19** 252 **20** 54
21 3 **22** 4 **23** 2 **24** 7

EXERCISE 22q

1 26 **2** 88 **3** 28, area of rectangle **4** 102
5 (a) 60 (b) 45 (c) 90 **6** 336 **7** 240
8 283 (3 s.f.) **9** (a) 45 (b) 100 (c) 0
10 (a) 78 (b) 231 **11** 2 **12** $\frac{12}{7}$ or $1\frac{5}{7}$

13 (a) 10 (b) 5 (c) $\frac{1}{2}$ **14** 65.4 (3 s.f.)
15 1.8 or $\frac{9}{5}$

EXERCISE 22r

1 (a) 32 mm, 12in (b) 44 cm^2, 9.2 ft^2
(c) 16 m^3, 8 cm^3, 60 mm^3 (d) 2π
2 (a) Distance round edge of a door, distance from home to P.O.
(b) Amount of surface on the top of a table, region inside a circle.
(c) Space inside a room, amount of milk a jug will hold.
3 (a) m (b) m^2 (c) m^2 (d) m^3 (e) m
(f) m^3 (g) m^2
4 (b), (e) and (f) must be wrong.
5 All, except Madge, are definitely wrong.

EXERCISE 22s

1
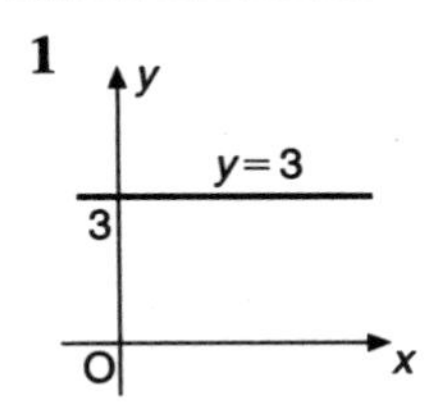

2
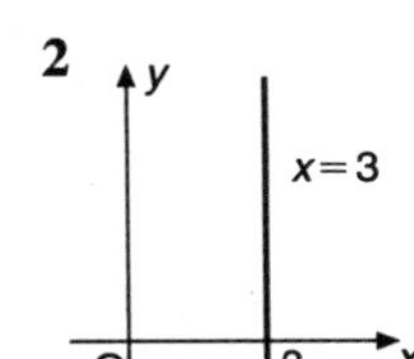

3
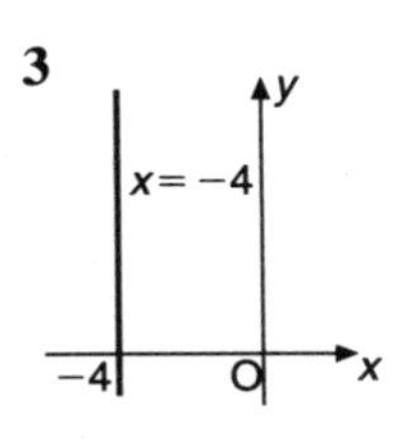

4
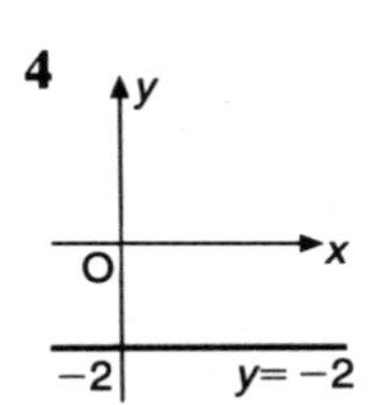

5
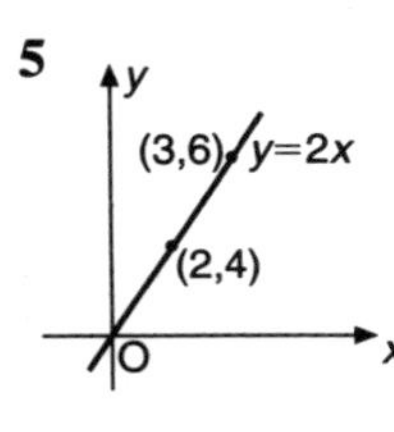

6
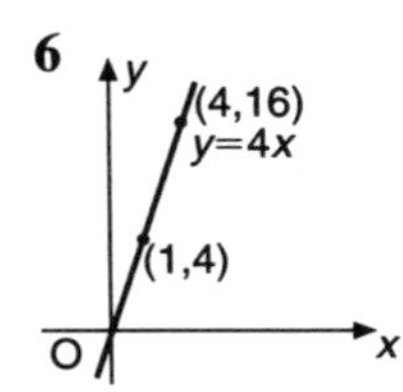

7 **8**
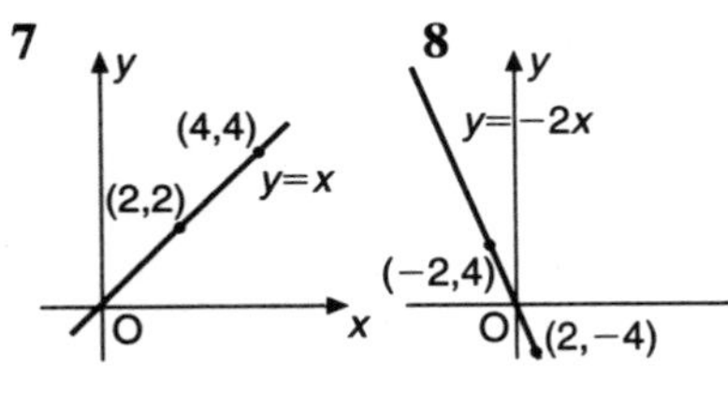

9
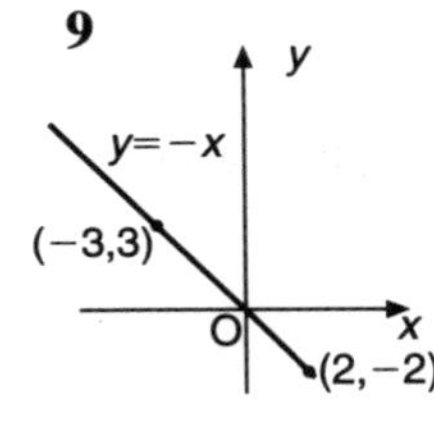

10
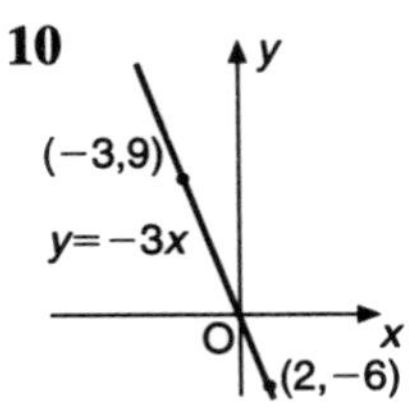

11
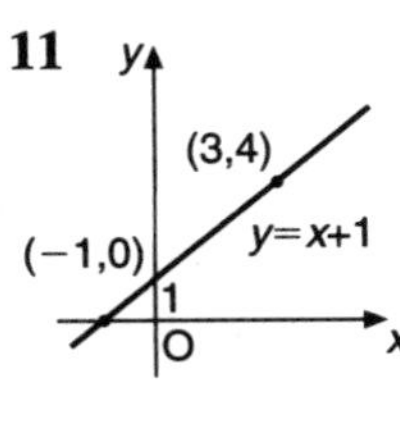

12
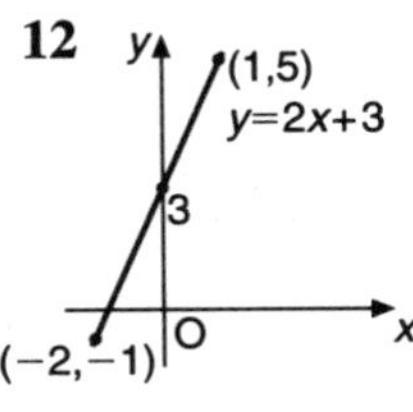

13
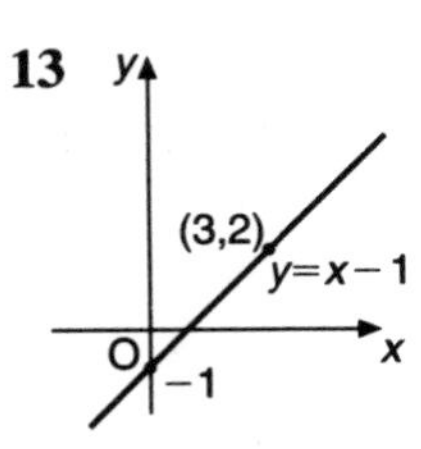

14
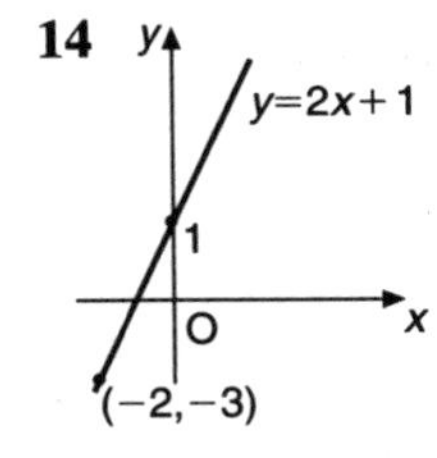

15
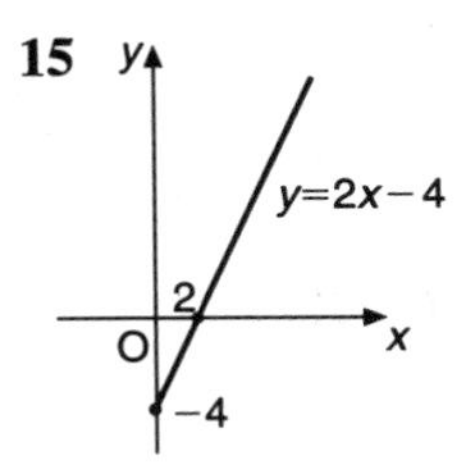

EXERCISE 22t

1
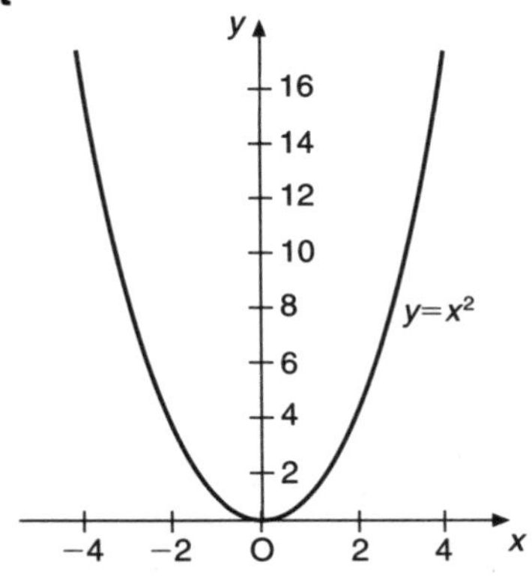

2
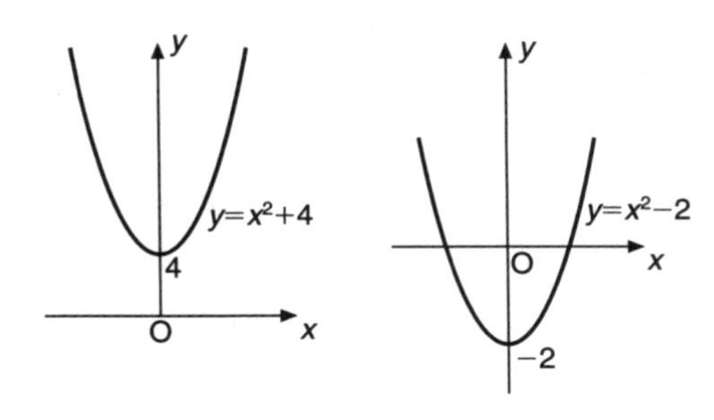

EXERCISE 22u

1 5.4 and 5.5 **2** 7.4 and 7.5 **3** 2.5 and 2.6 **4** 7.2 and 7.3
5 5.1 and 5.2 **6** 8.1 and 8.2 **7** 8.4 and 8.5 **8** 4.6 and 4.7
9 4.0 and 4.1 **10** 33.0 and 33.1

Multiple-choice questions 22

1 B **2** B **3** A **4** B
5 B and C are true, A and D are false **6** C

Self-assessment test 22

1 (a)

	BMI
Bob	28.7
Dennis	25.1
Oliver	22.5
Reg	38.8

(b) 33.4
2 794
3 (a) $a = 18$ (b) $b = 24$ (c) $c = 6$ (d) $d = 12$
4 (a) $p = 9$ (b) $q = 4\frac{1}{2}$ (c) $x = 18$ (d) $y = 3\frac{1}{4}$
5 (a) $x = 6$ (b) $y = 3$
6 (a) (i) $15p + 45$ (ii) $20q - 12$ (b) $m = 9\frac{1}{2}$
7 (a) 6 (b) 735 (c) 10
8 (a) $4x$ kg (b) 3 kg and 12 kg

EXERCISE 23a

Other suggestions could well be as good as or better than the answers given below.

1

Patient	Non-smoker	Smoker			Type of smoker		
Patient	Non-smoker	Cigarettes	Cigar	Pipe	Light	Medium	Heavy
A B C							

2

Bus stop	Number of passengers on leaving each bus stop			
	0–12	13–15	16–24	25–35
Leefold				
...				
...				
...				
Bampton				

3 Purchases from Osmond Fashions

Dress code	Number bought	Number sold		Number unsold
Size		At full price	In sales	
10				
12				
14				
16				
18				
20				

4

Variety	Cost per plant	No. of plants	Total yield	Yield/ plant	Income
A					
B					
...					

EXERCISE 23b

1 Difficult to answer this because they vary so much from one to another.
2 It is better to give different amounts, for example: less than £5, £5–£7.50, ... Otherwise some may answer a lot or very little.
3 Preferable to name the possible parties.
4 This would give the supermarket useful information. They could use it to try to improve waiting times.
5 (b) will probably be answered truthfully by everybody. The other questions could result in doubtful answers, because most people like to exaggerate their good points.
6 (a) Double negatives are not easy to understand. (b) Two questions in one.
7 (a) 1 Do you read a newspaper yes ☐ no ☐
2 If yes, which newspaper? ....
3 How many times a week do you read it?
once or twice ☐ 3 or 4 ☐ 5 or 6 ☐
every day ☐
4 On the days when you read this newspaper, how many minutes do you spend reading it?
less than 10 ☐ 10–20 ☐ 20–30 ☐
more than 30 ☐

(b) 1 Do you drink alcohol? yes ☐ no ☐
If yes please answer the following questions.
2 Where do you usually drink?
At home ☐ in a friend's house ☐ in a pub or hotel ☐ in the open air ☐ other ☐
3 On average, how many units a week do you drink?
less than 5 ☐ 5 to 10 ☐ 10 to 15 ☐
15 to 20 ☐ more than 20 ☐
(1 unit is about $\frac{1}{2}$ pint beer, 1 glass sherry or 1 measure of spirits)
4 How much do you spend a week on alcohol?
less than £5 ☐ £5 to £10 ☐ £10 to £15 ☐
£15 to £20 ☐ more than £20

EXERCISE 23c

1, **5**, **6** and **9** are discrete. **2**, **3**, **4**, **7**, **8** and **10** are continuous.
11 20–29, 30–39, 40–49
12 100–149, 150–199, 200–249
13 $160 \leqslant h < 165$, $165 \leqslant h < 170$, $170 \leqslant h < 175$
14 $8.95 \leqslant w < 9.00$, $9.00 \leqslant w < 9.05$, $9.05 \leqslant w < 9.10$,
15 (a) $0 \leqslant h < 10$ (b) $20 \leqslant h < 30$ (c) $20 \leqslant h < 30$ (d) $10 \leqslant h < 20$
16 0–79, 80–159, 160–239, 240–319, 320–400
17 $562 \leqslant v < 568$, $568 \leqslant v < 574$, $574 \leqslant v < 580$, $580 \leqslant v < 586$, $586 \leqslant h < 592$

EXERCISE 23d

1 (a)

Type of sale	Electrical (E)	Floor coverings (C)	Fabrics (F)	Bedding (B)
Tally	𝍸 𝍸 𝍸 /	𝍸 𝍸 /	𝍸 𝍸 /	𝍸 𝍸
Frequency	16	11	11	10

(b)

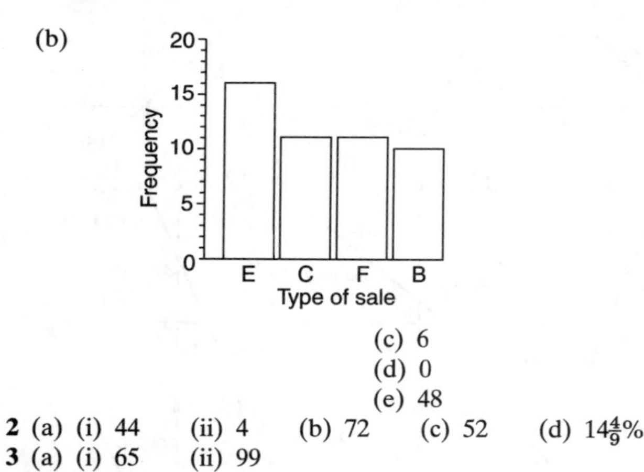

(c) 6
(d) 0
(e) 48

2 (a) (i) 44 (ii) 4 (b) 72 (c) 52 (d) $14\frac{4}{9}\%$
3 (a) (i) 65 (ii) 99

(b)

Age	65–69	70–74	75–79	80–84	85–89	90–94	95–99
Tally	𝍸 /	𝍸 𝍸 //	𝍸 𝍸 ////	𝍸 𝍸 𝍸 𝍸 𝍸 ///	𝍸 𝍸 𝍸 𝍸 //	𝍸 𝍸 ////	////
Frequency	6	12	14	28	22	14	4

(c)

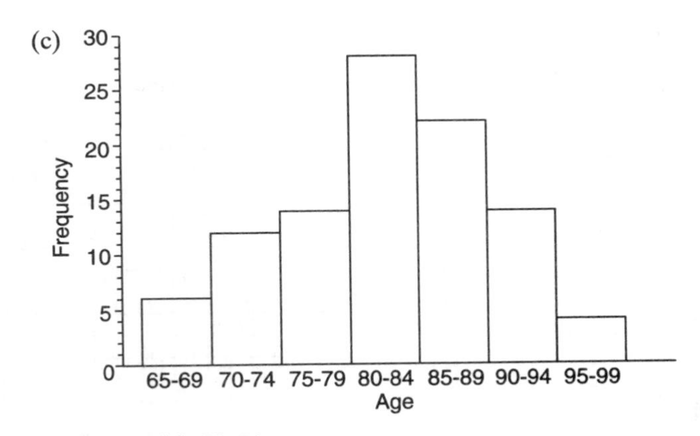

(d) 68 (e) 80–84

EXERCISE 23e

1 (a) discrete

(b)

No. of defects	Tally	Frequency
0–2	𝍸 //	7
3–5	𝍸 𝍸 /	11
6–8	𝍸 𝍸 𝍸 ////	19
9–11	𝍸 𝍸 ///	13
12–14	𝍸 /	6
15–17	////	4
18–20		0

(c) 10

(d)

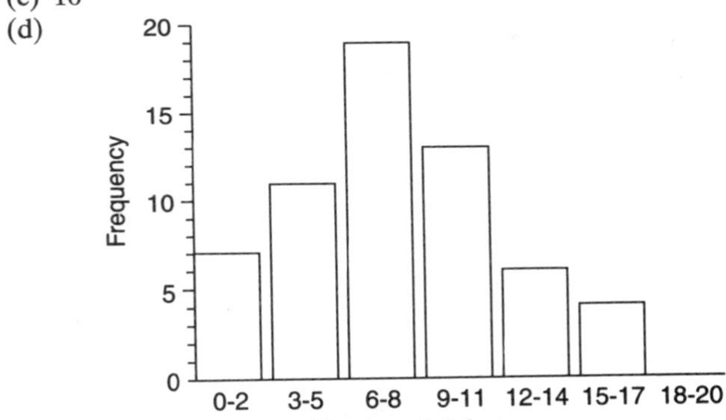

2 (a)

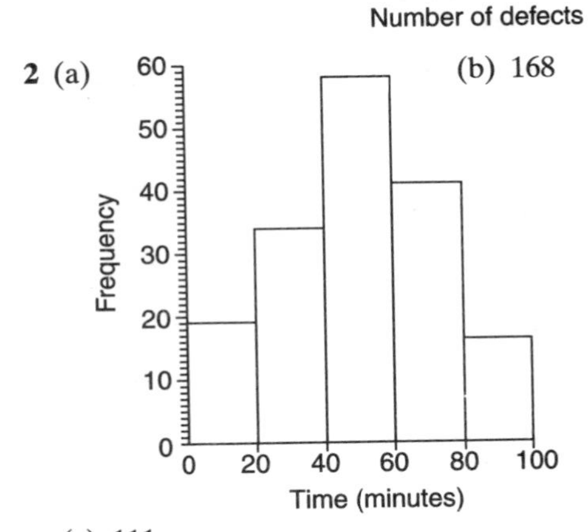

(b) 168

(c) 111

3 (a) 487 mm (b) $497.5 \leqslant v < 498.5$ where v ml is the amount

(c)

Amount (v ml)	Tally	Frequency
$484.5 \leqslant v < 489.5$	//	2
$489.5 \leqslant v < 494.5$	𝍸 //	7
$494.5 \leqslant v < 499.5$	𝍸 𝍸 𝍸 /	16
$499.5 \leqslant v < 504.5$	𝍸 𝍸 𝍸 𝍸 𝍸	25
$504.5 \leqslant v < 509.5$	𝍸 𝍸 𝍸 𝍸	20
$509.5 \leqslant v < 514.5$	𝍸 𝍸	10
$514.5 \leqslant v < 519.5$		0
		80

(d) 55

(e) Within the range $499.5 \leqslant v < 504.5$ it is impossible to say how many are more than 500 ml.

EXERCISE 23f

1 (a) (i) 5 cm (ii) 15 cm

(b) (i) 10 cm (ii) $22\frac{1}{2}$ cm ($27\frac{1}{2} - 5$)

(c) (i) the 3rd (ii) the 8th

2 (a) (i) £20 000 (ii) £35 000

(b) (i) £20 000 (ii) £30 000

(c) (i) £5000 (ii) £10 000

(d) 1992, £25 000

(e) yes, cyclical over the year; last quarter highest and first quarter lowest; yes

(g) (i) (ii)

(iii)

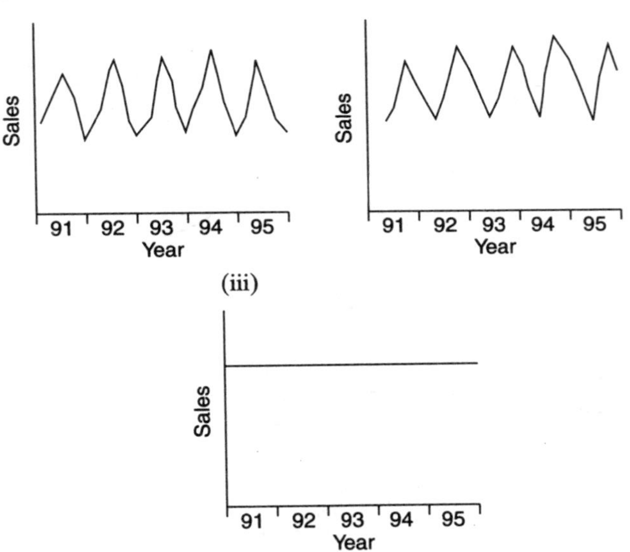

EXERCISE 23g

1 (a) (i) $\frac{1}{4}$ (ii) $\frac{5}{24}$ (b) $\frac{17}{24}$

(c) (i) 30 (ii) 20 (iii) 55

2 (a) (i) $\frac{1}{12}$ (ii) $\frac{7}{36}$ (iii) $\frac{5}{9}$

(b) (i) $16\frac{2}{3}$ (ii) 6 g (c) (i) 55.6 g (ii) 20 g

3 (a) (i) $\frac{13}{40}$ (ii) $\frac{11}{40}$ (iii) $\frac{3}{5}$

(b) (i) 189 (ii) 837 (c) (i) $27\frac{1}{2}$% (ii) 40%

EXERCISE 23h

1 (a) (i) $\frac{1}{5}$ (ii) 72° (b)

2 (a) 22p (b)

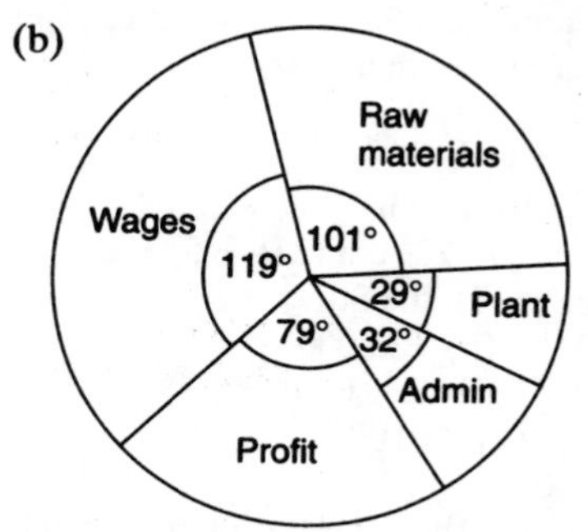

3 (a) (b)

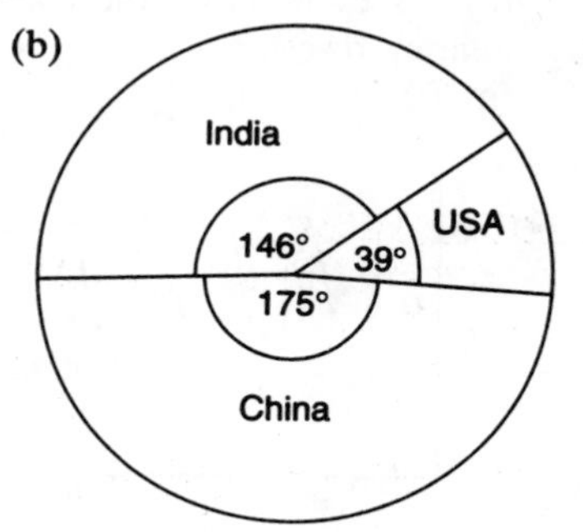

4

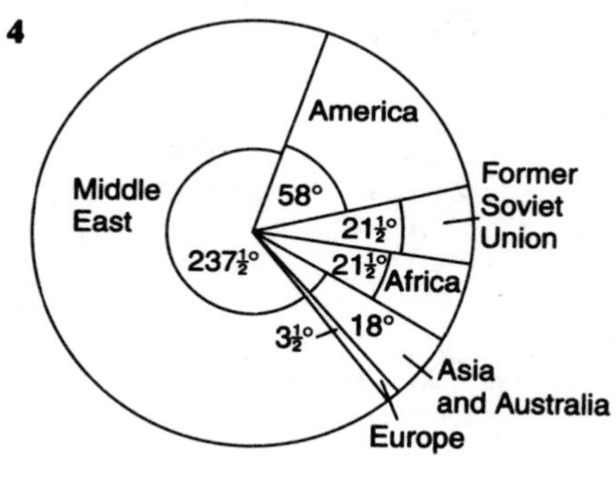

EXERCISE 23i

1 (a) 12 (b) (i) 90 kg (ii) 55 kg
(c) yes, but not a strong one

2 (a) 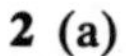

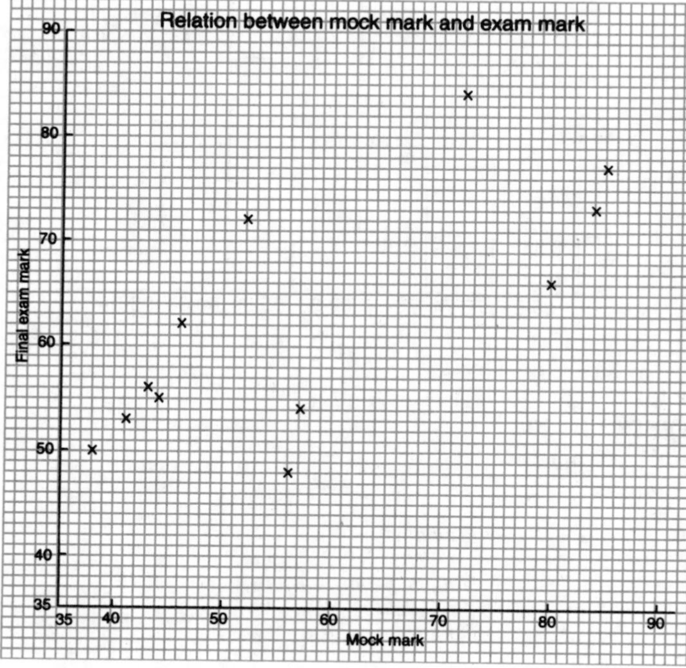

(b) They give a fair idea.
(c) About 70.

Self-assessment test 23

1 (a) B and C (b) A and D

2 (a)

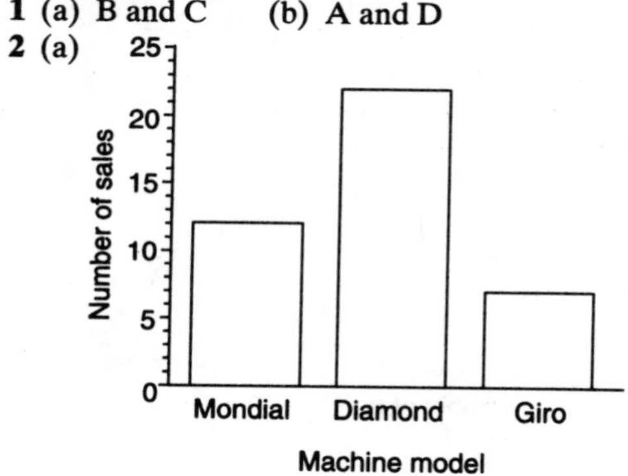

(b)

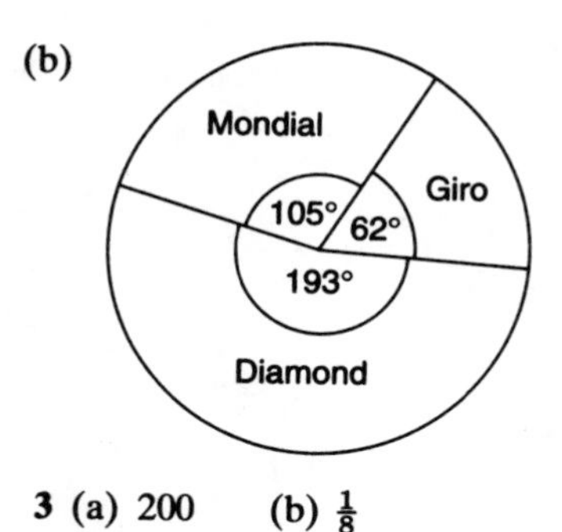

3 (a) 200 (b) $\frac{1}{8}$

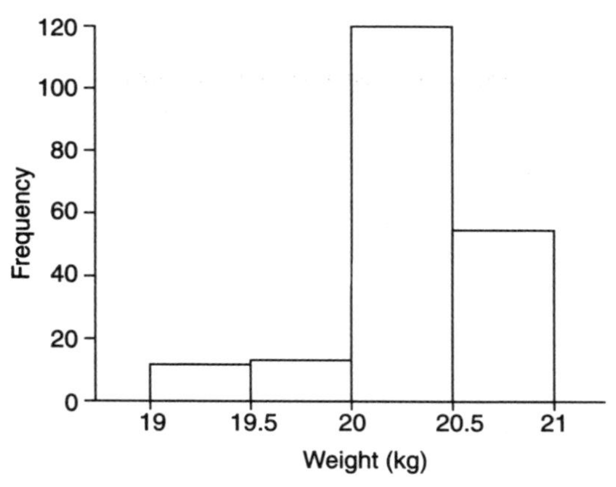

4 (a) (i) $\frac{3}{10}$ (ii) $\frac{3}{20}$ (iii) $\frac{1}{10}$ (b) 680 (ii) 510
(c) 8%

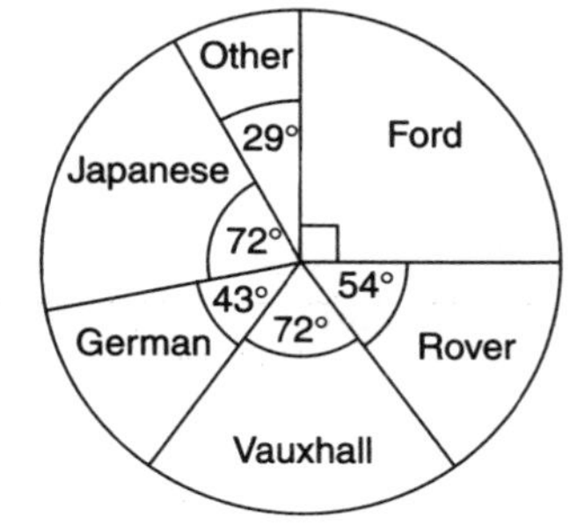

(d) (i) Vauxhall (ii) Rover, German and Japanese
(e) Ford

5 (a) (i) 22 (ii) 0 (b) (i) no (ii) no
(c) Lounge used except for mealtimes, with more use in the mornings and afternoons than in the evenings.
(d) (i) very probably (ii) unlikely

EXERCISE 24a

1 8 **2** 24 **3** 2.2 **4** 9.8 **5** 76
6 42 **7** 8.23 **8** 4.50 **9** 1.63 **10** 10.41

EXERCISE 24b

1 (a) 24 (b) 24 **2** (a) 50 and 51 (b) 53
3 (a) 23 (b) 24 **4** (a) 5 (b) 4
5 (a) 43 (b) 37.5 **6** (a) 14 and 15 (b) 14
7 (a) 2.6 (b) 2.3

EXERCISE 24c

1 42 **2** 13 **3** 4.1 **4** 6 **5** 63

EXERCISE 24d

1 mean 75, mode 70, median 71
2 (a) 20 (b) 38 (c) 1.9 (d) 1 (e) 2 (f) 4
3 (a) 160 cm (d) 160 cm (c) 160 cm (d) 10 cm
4 (a) £4.17 (b) £4.10 (c) £4.10
5 (a) 17 mm (b) 21 mm
6 (a) (i) 10 (ii) 94
(b) (i) 9.4 days (ii) 0 days (iii) 3.5 days
7 (a) 13 (b) 81 (c) 84 and 88 (d) 54%
(e) 82 (f) 31

EXERCISE 24e

1 (a) 1092 kg (b) 546 kg (c) 546 kg (d) 78 kg
2 (a) 2 h (b) 150 km (c) 230 km (d) 5 h
(e) 46 km/h
3 74
4 (a) (i) 288 (ii) 105 (iii) 393 (b) 5.95
(c) 400 (approx.)
5 (a) B on average has fewer defective components than A
(b) yes

EXERCISE 24f

1 (a) 30 (b) 62 (c) 2.07
2 (a) 42 (b) 18 (c) 0.43 (d) 0
3 (a) 12, yes (b) mean 6.92, median 7, mode 5

Multiple-choice questions 24

1 B **2** D **3** A **4** D
5 B and C are true, A and D are false

Self-assessment test 24

1 25 **2** (a) 15 (b) 16 **3** (a) 3.1 (b) 8.2
4 (a) 31 (b) mean 5.0, mode 0, median 3
5 (a) 50 (b) 195 (c) 3.9 (d) 4

Index

X	1	2	3	4	5	6	7	8	9	10
1	1	2	3	4	5	6	7	8	9	10
2	2	4	6	8	10	12	14	16	18	20
3	3	6	9	12	15	18	21	24	27	30
4	4	8	12	16	20	24	28	32	36	40
5	5	10	15	20	25	30	35	40	45	50
6	6	12	18	24	30	36	42	48	54	60
7	7	14	21	28	35	42	49	56	63	70
8	8	16	24	32	40	48	56	64	72	80
9	9	18	27	36	45	54	63	72	81	90
10	10	20	30	40	50	60	70	80	90	100